Basic Science for Aerospace Vehicles

Northrop Institute of Technology Series

Other Books in the Series

Electricity and Electronics for Aerospace Vehicles

Maintenance and Repair of Aerospace Vehicles, 3d ed.

Powerplants for Aerospace Vehicles, 3d ed.

Basic Science for Aerospace Vehicles

THIRD EDITION

Northrop Institute of Technology

James L. McKinley

Ralph D. Bent

McGRAW-HILL BOOK COMPANY

New York St. Louis San Francisco

Dallas London Toronto Sydney

Basic Science for Aerospace Vehicles

Library of Congress Catalog Card Number: 62-21243

47480

678910111213-QBQB-76543210698

Preface

"Basic Science for Aerospace Vehicles" is the first of a series of texts designed to provide the technical information needed as a foundation for work as a technician or mechanic on aerospace vehicles. It covers those subjects essential for both airframe- and powerplant-maintenance technicians and also provides background material for work in the broad field of the "aerospace" industry. The term "aerospace vehicles" refers to all vehicles which fly either through the air or in space, that is, conventional aircraft, missiles, and spacecraft.

One of the chief purposes of this "basic science" text is to present background information on subjects common to both airframes and powerplants or not limited to either area. Subjects such as physical laws, theory of flight, blueprint reading, materials, standards, structures, hydraulics, plumbing, weight and balance, and instruments are all of interest to both the airframe and the powerplant technician.

This book is not designed to teach troubleshooting or overhaul practices. It is, however, intended to teach the student "why" and "how" various principles operate and to describe many of the systems, devices, and techniques encountered in the aerospace field. The chapter on "Science Fundamentals" will help the student to understand why systems and devices operate.

Blueprint reading and drafting are explained to provide the student with knowledge which will enable him to work from various types of engineering drawings. He is shown how to prepare shop sketches according to acceptable standards so they can be interpreted easily by engineers and technicians, thus improving his ability to communicate in the engineer's language.

Elementary theory of hydraulics is explored so the student will be well prepared to study and understand the operation of complex systems used in modern aircraft and powerplant installations. These systems may apply either to aircraft or to spacecraft and their associated powerplants. The service, inspection, and repair of these systems are described in other texts in the series.

The last chapter, "A Look into Outer Space," is included because of the importance of knowledge of outer space to the technician who is assigned to work on vehicles which may travel there. The person who services, makes installations, repairs malfunctions, or otherwise contributes to the successful flight of spacecraft will have a much greater appreciation of his responsibilities if he knows something of the environment in which such vehicles must operate together with the time and distance factors involved.

RALPH D. BENT

Acknowledgments

Aluminum Company of America, Los Angeles, California
Beech Aircraft Corporation, Wichita, Kansas
Bell Helicopter Company, Division of Bell Aerospace Corporation, Fort Worth, Texas
Belmont Aviation, Long Beach, California
The Boeing Company, Transport Division, Renton, Washington
Cessna Aircraft Company, Wichita, Kansas
Convair Division, General Dynamics Corporation, San Diego, California
Douglas Aircraft Company, Long Beach, California
Federal Aviation Agency
Kollsman Instrument Corporation, Elmhurst, New York
A. Lietz Company, Los Angeles, California
Mount Wilson Observatory, Mount Wilson, California
Norair Division, Northrop Corporation, Hawthorne, California
North American Aviation Company, Los Angeles, California
Parker-Hannifin Corporation, Cleveland, Ohio
Pioneer-Central Division, Bendix Corporation
Rocketdyne Division, North American Aviation, Canoga Park, California
Sky Store, Inc., Hawthorne, California
Sperry Gyroscope Division, Sperry-Rand Corporation, Great Neck, New York
Vickers, Inc., Division of Sperry-Rand Corporation, Torrance, California
V. & E. Manufacturing Company, Pasadena, California
The Weatherhead Company, Cleveland, Ohio
Weston Instruments, Division of Daystrom, Inc., Newark, New Jersey
Weston Hydraulics, Ltd., Subsidiary of Borg-Warner Corporation, Van Nuys, California

Contents

CHAPTER 1

Science Fundamentals

In this age of technology and science the man concerned with the operation, maintenance, or design of any of the thousands of mechanical and electronic devices in regular use by mankind is constantly faced with the application of scientific law. A very simple example, applicable to almost everyone, is the driving of an automobile. If the driver of an automobile understands the physical laws governing the operation of the engine and the driving mechanisms of the car and also understands the forces in operation while the car is moving on a street or highway, he can operate his automobile more safely and in a manner which will prolong its life.

The world in which we live and work is almost completely dependent upon "modern conveniences" such as electrical appliances, automobiles, airplanes, steamships, radio, television, guided missiles, rocket ships, and others too numerous to mention in our limited space. Most of the jobs or positions at which we work involve some technical "know-how," and technical know-how involves an understanding of basic scientific law.

Since this text is designed to provide mechanics and technicians interested in aircraft and space vehicles with basic technical knowledge pertaining to these devices, it is desirable that we examine briefly many of the common laws of physics. In our study here we shall explore the areas of mechanics, heat, light, and sound. While studying these principles, the student will recognize their many applications to devices with which he is familiar.

MEASUREMENTS

In order to arrive at values of distance, weight, speed, volume, pressure, etc., it is necessary that we become familiar with the accepted methods for measuring these values and the units used to express them. Through the ages man has devised many methods for measuring; however, it would be impossible for us in this text to cover even a small part of the information accumulated for these several thousands of years. In this text we shall concern ourselves principally with the English system and the metric system, both of which are used extensively throughout the world.

Length and distance

The majority of literate persons in the English-speaking countries are familiar with such units of measurement as the **inch, foot, yard,** and **mile.** In many countries of the world the common units of distance or length are the **millimeter, centimeter, meter,** and **kilometer.** The inch, foot, yard, and mile are units of the English system. Originally these units were not exact multiples or factors of one another, but for the sake of convenience the foot was made equal to 12 in., the yard was made 3 ft, and the mile was made 5,280 ft or 1,760 yd. It is said that the inch was the width of a finger or three barleycorns laid end to end, the foot was the length of a human foot, and the yard was the distance from the tip of the nose to the tip of the thumb when the arm was extended to the side with the thumb pointing forward and the head faced forward. The **mile** was originated by the Romans and represented 1,000 paces, each pace being two steps or 5 ft. This distance was later changed to 5,280 ft, which is the present statute mile in the United States.

The nautical mile, used internationally for navigation, is based on one-sixtieth of one degree of the earth's circumference at the equator. It is approximately 6,080 ft or 1,853.2 meters (m). Many other units of length measurement have been used in various countries, some being the **rod, ell, fathom,** and **league.** All these units were established to meet particular needs in different areas. Because of the increase in travel, international commerce, and scientific exchanges, there is a need for standardization of measurements. This is taking place through the use of the **metric** system.

The basic unit of measurement in the metric system is the **meter.** The length of a meter is based on a distance equal to 1/10,000,000 of the distance from the equator to the poles measured along a meridian, the meridian being the shortest distance along the earth's surface and at right angles to the equator. Thus we see that the meter is based on a sound reference which will always be approximately the same. In order to provide an exact reference meter for scientific purposes a bar of platinum-iridium was inscribed with two lines exactly 1 m apart at the freezing point of water. This is 32° Fahrenheit or 0° centigrade. The International Meter bar is kept at the Bureau of Weights and Measures near Paris. Copies of this bar have been made and are kept in depositories in all the principal nations.

Recently a new standard for the International Meter has been established. This standard is based upon the wavelength of a certain shade of yellow light. In the metric system all the measurements of length are either multiples or subdivisions of the meter based on multiples of 10. The following table shows how the units of length are related:

10 millimeters = 1 centimeter
10 centimeters = 1 decimeter
10 decimeters = 1 meter
10 meters = 1 decameter
10 decameters = 1 hectometer
10 hectometers = 1 kilometer
10 kilometers = 1 myriameter

One meter is equal to 39.37 in. which is a little longer than the U.S. yard. Thus 1 decimeter is equal to 3.937 in., 1 centimeter is equal to 0.3937 in., and 1 millimeter equals 0.03937 in. In practice the units of length most commonly used are the millimeter, the centimeter, the meter, and the kilometer. Figure 1·1 shows a scale for 1 meter compared with a scale for 1 yard.

Area

Measurements of area are usually indicated in units which are the squares of the units of length. Hence, in the English system the units of area are the **square inch,** the **square foot,** the **square yard,** and the **square mile.** Another unit of area commonly used for measuring land is the **acre,** which is equal to 43,560 sq ft.

Area in the metric system is indicated in square metric units. These are the **square centimeter,** the **square meter,** and the **square kilometer.** Land measure in the metric system is indicated by means of the **hectare.** The hectare is equal to 10,000 square meters.

Volume and capacity

Volume and capacity are indicated in three-dimensional units or cubes of the basic linear units. The **cubic inch, cubic foot,** and **cubic yard** are the common units of volume in the English system. Other units of volume or capacity are the **gill, pint, quart,** and **gallon.** In general, when we speak of volume, we use the cubed units, and when speaking of capacity, we use the gill, pint, quart, or gallon.

The metric system employs the cubed metric units as units of volume. The most commonly expressed units are the **cubic centimeter** (cu cm) and the **cubic meter.** For capacity the **liter** and **hectoliter** are generally employed. In the metric system the liter and the hectoliter are multiples of smaller metric units. The liter, for example, is equal to 1,000 cubic centimeters, and the hectoliter is equal to 100 liters. The liter is equal to 1.056 U.S. liquid quarts.

Weight

Units of weight in the English system are no more standardized than other units of measure. Among units of weight in common use are **grain, troy ounce, avoirdupois ounce, troy pound, avoirdupois pound,** and **ton** (short ton). The following table shows the relationship among the units of weight mentioned:

7,000 grains = 1 avdp pound
5,760 grains = 1 troy pound
12 troy ounces = 1 troy pound
16 avdp ounces = 1 avdp pound
2,000 avdp pounds = 1 ton (short)

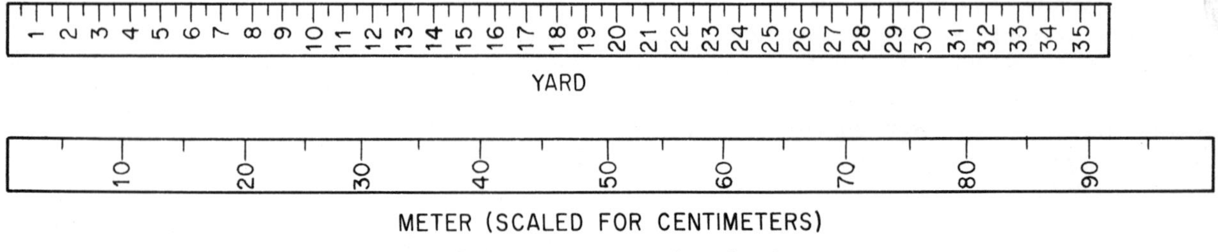

Figure 1·1 Comparison of 1 yd with 1 m.

The **grain** is the smallest unit of weight in the English system and was derived from the weight of a grain of wheat. It is used principally for the measurement of medicinal components or drugs. The **troy** ounce and pound are used for weighing precious metals such as platinum, gold, and silver. Avoirdupois weights are used for almost all materials and objects in the English-speaking countries. These are the common ounce, pound, hundredweight (cwt), and ton with which we are most familiar.

The most uniform system of weights is the metric system. The following shows the relationship among the metric units of weight:

1,000 grams = 1 kilogram
1,000 kilograms = 1 metric ton

The **gram** is the weight of 1 cubic centimeter of pure water at a temperature of 4°C or 39.2°F, which is the point of greatest density for water. The gram is equal to about 15.432 grains, and the kilogram is 2.2046 pounds avoirdupois.

It is readily seen that the metric system of weights is much less complex than the English system because the weights can be converted from one unit to another merely by moving the decimal point to the right or left. For very small measurements of weight the **milligram** (mg) is used in the metric system. The milligram is one-thousandth of a gram.

Units of measurement

It is readily understandable that units of measurement are required for many more purposes than those mentioned in the foregoing paragraphs. For example, we must be able to measure **force, density, electrical values, light intensity, sound intensity, velocity, energy,** and numerous other values. In this section we have explained only the most commonly known units of measurement; however, as we discuss other areas of physical laws and phenomena, we shall also define the units of measurement required in each area.

GRAVITY, WEIGHT, AND MASS

Gravity or **gravitation** is the universal force which all bodies exert upon one another. It is defined by the **Universal Law of Gravitation** which states, **"The attraction between particles of matter is directly proportional to the product of their masses and inversely proportional to the square of the distance between them."** This can be expressed by the equation

$$F = G\frac{m_1 m_2}{r^2}$$

where F = attractive force
r = distance between two bodies (particles)
m_1 and m_2 = masses of bodies

G is a constant whose value depends upon the values used in the equation. If F is expressed in dynes, m_1 and m_2 in grams, and r in centimeters, then G is found to have a value of 6.67×10^{-8} or 0.000000667.

Weight is the pull exerted upon a body by the gravitation of the earth. **Mass** is the amount of matter in a body and is equal to weight under standard conditions at sea level. The weight of a body may change depending upon its distance from the center of the earth. On top of a high mountain a body will weigh slightly less than at sea level. Also, at the poles of the earth a particular body will weigh slightly more than it will at sea level because the earth is flattened at the poles owing to the centrifugal force exerted at the equator because of the earth's rotation. The mass of a body will never change as long as no matter is added to or removed from it.

The units of mass and weight are the same, that is, the **pound** or the **kilogram,** depending upon whether we are employing the English system or the metric system. It must be remembered, however, that 1 pound of mass will not be exactly 1 pound of weight if the mass is not at the proper distance from the center of the earth.

Specific gravity and density

The **specific gravity** of a substance is the ratio of the density of the substance to the density of water. The **density** of a substance is its mass per unit volume.

In the centimeter-gram-second (cgs) system the density of a substance is expressed in grams per cubic centimeter. The density of water is 1, since 1 cubic centimeter of water has a mass of 1 gram. In this system the specific gravity and the density of a substance are the same.

In the British system the density is expressed in pounds per cubic foot. For water the density is therefore 62.4, since 1 cu ft of water weighs 62.4 lb. To determine the specific gravity of a substance when the density is known, we merely divide the weight of a given volume of the substance by the weight of an equal volume of water. For example, if we wish to know the specific gravity of lead and we know that the density in pounds per cubic foot is 708.24 lb, we divide 708.24 by 62.4 and obtain 11.35, which is the specific gravity.

To find the weight (mass) of a given volume of

a substance when the volume is expressed in cubic feet, we multiply the volume in cubic feet by the weight of 1 cu ft of water and then multiply this product by the specific gravity of the substance. Let us assume that we wish to find the weight of 10 cu ft of copper and we know that the specific gravity of the copper is 8.9. Then

$$10 \times 62.4 \times 8.9 = 5{,}553.6 \text{ lb}$$

If the volume of a substance is expressed in cubic centimeters we can find the weight in grams simply by multiplying the volume by the specific gravity. For example, the weight of 20 cu cm of silver is

$$20 \times 10.5 = 210 \text{ g}$$

The specific gravity and density of solids and liquids are expressed as explained in the foregoing paragraphs; however, gases require a different treatment. It is apparent that the weight of a given volume of a gas will depend upon the pressure and temperature. For this reason, the density of a gas is given according to standard pressure and temperature conditions, that is, a pressure of 76 cm of mercury and a temperature of 0°C. Under these conditions it is found that the density of dry air is 1.293 g per liter or 0.081 lb per cu ft. Since the density of air is used as a standard, the specific gravity of air is given as 1. The specific gravity of any other gas is the ratio of the mass of a given volume of the gas to an equal volume of dry air with both the gas and the air being under standard conditions.

FORCE AND MOTION

Force may be defined as a push or a pull upon an object. In the previous section a small unit of force, the **dyne,** was employed. One dyne is the force required to accelerate a mass of one gram one centimeter per second per second. This may also be expressed:

$$1 \text{ dyne} = \frac{1 \text{ g} \times 1 \text{ cm}}{\text{sec}^2}$$

The unit of force in the meter-kilogram-second (mks) system is the **newton.** The newton is the force required to accelerate a mass of one kilogram one meter per second per second. In the British system the **poundal** is the unit of force. One poundal is the force required to accelerate one pound one foot per second per second.

When we are not relating force to a particular acceleration, we often use the **pound** to express the value of the force. For example, we say that a force of 30 pounds is acting upon a hydraulic piston.

Force is required to produce motion in a body which was previously at rest, and force is also required to stop the motion of a body. The concepts of force and motion are expressed by Newton's laws of motion. Newton's First Law of Motion states: **A body at rest tends to remain at rest and a body in motion tends to remain in motion in a straight line unless forced to change its state by an external force.**

This first law of motion concerns the property of matter called **inertia.** Inertia is defined as the tendency of matter to remain at rest if at rest or to continue in motion in a straight line if in motion. Hence it is seen that Newton's First Law of Motion defines inertia. The property of inertia is demonstrated by the fact that artificial satellites will continue to orbit around the earth for months or years even though they have no means of propulsion. This is because there is no appreciable outside force in space to retard the speed of the satellite. The only substantial force acting on a satellite orbiting the earth is the force of gravity. Gravity causes the satellite to curve around the earth instead of shooting off in space.

Inertia can also be demonstrated by a simple experiment with a glass of water. If a glass of water is placed on a piece of paper on a smooth surface, the paper can be jerked from under the glass without disturbing the glass or its contents. The inertia of the glass of water causes it to remain at rest when the paper is moved.

Acceleration

Newton's Second Law of Motion explains **acceleration. Acceleration** may be defined as **the change in velocity of a body.** If the body increases in velocity, it has **positive** acceleration, and if it decreases in velocity, the acceleration is **negative.** The Second Law of Motion states: **The acceleration of a body is directly proportional to the force causing it and inversely proportional to the mass of the body.** This means that a given body will accelerate in proportion to the force applied to it. For example, if a 10-lb weight accelerates at 32.2 ft per sec^2 when a 10-lb force is applied to it, it will accelerate at 64.4 ft per sec^2 when a 20-lb force is applied to it.

If we ignore the friction of air acting on a freely falling body, we find that it will accelerate at the rate of 32.2 ft per sec^2. This is called the **acceleration of gravity** and is indicated by the letter symbol *g*. From this we know that, when a force equal to the weight or mass of a body is applied to the body, the body will accelerate at 32.2 ft per sec^2 if there is no friction or other force opposing the applied force. This knowledge is useful in developing an equation based upon Newton's second law.

$$F = \frac{Wa}{g}$$

where F = force, lb
W = weight, lb
a = acceleration, ft per sec^2
g = 32.2

With this formula, if we know the weight, we can easily determine the force required to produce the acceleration.

If we wish to know how much force is required to accelerate a 4,000-lb automobile to a speed of 60 mph in 10 sec, we must first determine the rate of acceleration. Sixty miles per hour is 88 ft per sec; hence if the automobile is accelerated from 0 to 88 ft per sec in 10 sec, the rate of acceleration is 8.8 ft per sec^2. Then, by the formula,

$$F = \frac{4{,}000 \times 8.8}{32.2} = 1093.1 \text{ lb}$$

From the above equation we know that it requires a force (push) of 1093.1 lb to accelerate the automobile from 0 to 60 mph in 10 sec.

Action and reaction

Action and reaction are explained by **Newton's Third Law of Motion: For every action there is an equal and opposite reaction.** This law indicates that no force can exist with only one body but that existence of a force requires the presence of two bodies. One body applies the force, and the other body receives the force. In other words, one body is **acting** and the other is **acted upon.** This is clear in the operation of an automobile. The wheels of an automobile exert a force against the road tending to force the road to the rear. Since the road cannot move to the rear, the automobile is forced to move forward.

There are numerous examples of action and reaction around us. When we stand on the floor, our body, through our feet, applies a force to the floor. At the same time, the floor is applying the same force to our feet. Other examples of action and reaction are the recoil of a gun, the backward force of a fire hose when the water is turned on, the thrust of a propeller, the thrust of a rocket, and the thrust of a jet engine. A modern rocket engine is shown in Fig. 1·2.

Figure 1·2 A liquid-fuel rocket engine (Rocketdyne).

CENTRIFUGAL AND CENTRIPETAL FORCE

Everyone is familiar with the fact that a weight attached to the end of a cord and twirled around as shown in Fig. 1·3 will produce a force tending to cause the weight to fly outward from the center of the circle. This outward pull is called **centrifugal force.** There is an equal and opposite force pulling the weight inward and preventing it from flying outward. This is called **centripetal force.**

From Newton's First Law of Motion we know that a body in motion tends to continue in motion in a straight line. Hence, when we cause a body to move in a circular path, a continuous force must be applied to keep the body in the circular path. This is the centripetal force mentioned in the previous paragraph.

We can use either one of two formulas for determining the magnitude of centripetal force, depending upon whether we are employing the

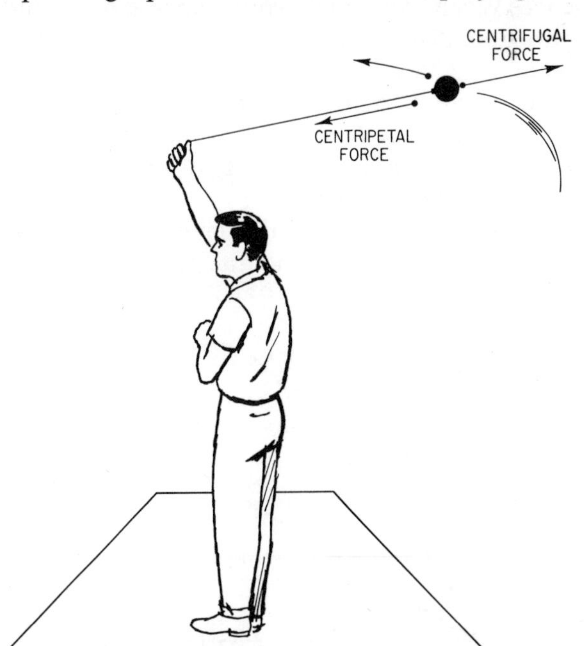

Figure 1·3 Centrifugal and centripetal forces.

metric system or the British system of measurements. In the metric system we determine the centripetal force in **dynes** by means of the formula

$$F = \frac{mv^2}{r}$$

where F = force, dynes
m = mass, g
v = speed, cm per sec
r = radius of circle, cm

To find the force in pounds we employ the formula

$$F = \frac{Wv^2}{gr}$$

where F = force, lb
W = weight, lb
v = speed, ft per sec
g = acceleration of gravity (32.2)
r = radius, ft

If we wish to determine the value of the centripetal force required to keep a 10-lb weight in a circle of 20-ft radius while moving at a speed of 60 ft per sec, we proceed as follows:

$$F = \frac{10 \times 60^2}{32.2 \times 20} = \frac{36{,}000}{644} = 55.9 \text{ lb}$$

Velocity and speed

We often hear the words **velocity** and **speed** used in the same sense, that is, to indicate how fast something is moving. The two words are similar in some respects, but there is an important difference. When we use the word velocity, we include **direction, distance in a straight line from point to point,** and the **time** required to move from one point to another. If an automobile travels from point A to point B, in Fig. 1·4, in 1 hr following the irregular path, the **velocity** of the automobile is 20 mph east-northeast.

Speed involves only the length of the path traversed by a body and the time required to traverse the path. In Fig. 1·4 the average speed of the automobile would be 35 mph because it required 1 hr to travel a distance of 35 miles.

Instantaneous speed and instantaneous velocity may be the same in magnitude; however, speed does not include direction.

Velocity may be defined as the **rate of change of position in relation to time** or the **rate of motion in a particular direction.** From the above, we can see that a body may be moving at a constant speed but it may also be accelerating by changing direction. A body moving in a circle is constantly accelerating because it is constantly changing direction. Remember that **acceleration is a change of velocity** and a **change in direction is also a change of velocity.**

Another type of velocity with which we should be familiar is **angular velocity,** which is defined as the **rate at which a body rotates about a fixed axis** or the **angle by which a body is displaced divided by the time required for the displacement.** Angular velocity is expressed in degrees per second or in **radians** per second. A **radian** is the arc of a circle equal to its radius. Since a circle is 360° and the radius of a circle is equal to the circumference divided by 2π, then 1 radian $= 360°/2\pi = 57.3°$.

COMPOSITION AND RESOLUTION OF FORCES

Vectors

A vector quantity is any quantity involving both magnitude and direction. A **vector** is a straight arrow pointing in the direction in which the quantity is acting, and the length of the arrow represents the magnitude of the quantity. For example, the arrow **OY** in Fig. 1·5 may represent a force of 40 lb acting upward, as would be the case when a man picks up a 40-lb suitcase. The arrow is marked off in segments, each representing 5 lb.

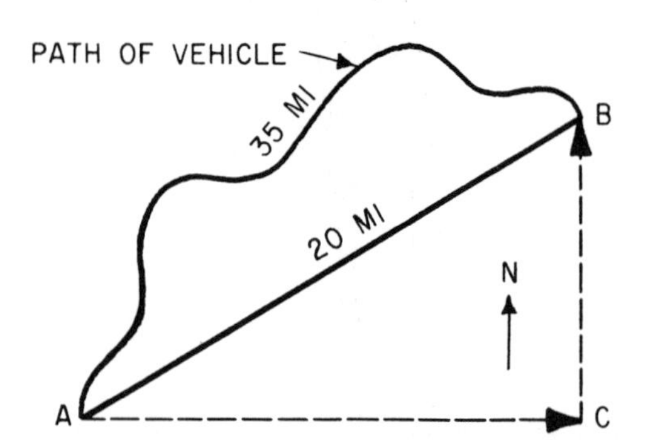

Figure 1·4 Diagram to illustrate speed and velocity.

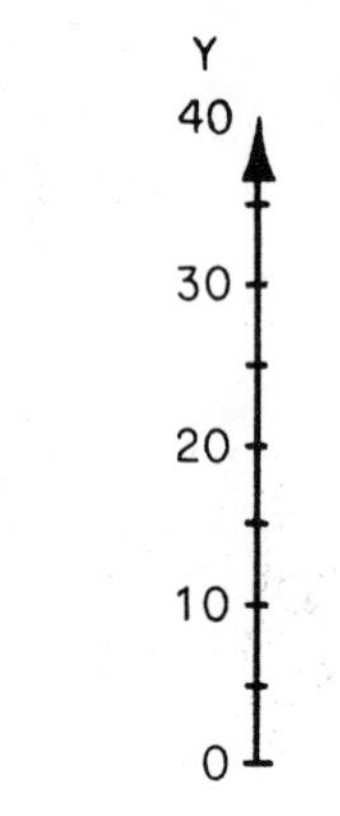

Figure 1·5 Vector representing 40 lb directed upward.

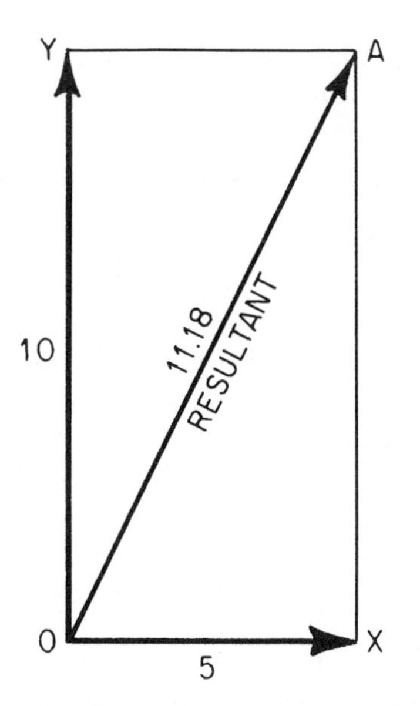

Figure 1·6 Resultant of two vectors acting from the same point.

If a force of 10 lb is acting upward from a point O and a force of 5 lb is acting to the right from the point as shown by the vectors in Fig. 1·6, we can determine the **resultant** forcc, or **resultant,** by drawing the parallelogram (rectangle in this case) $OXAY$ and then measuring the diagonal vector **OA. OA** is the resultant and by measurement is found to be approximately 11.2 lb. Since OAY is a right triangle, we can use the formula for solving right triangles as follows:

$$\mathbf{OA} = \sqrt{10^2 + 5^2} = 11.18$$

By finding the sine or tangent of the angle AOX on a table of trigonometric functions, we find the angle to be about 63°27′. The tangent of the angle is $^{10}/_5 = 2$, which is the tangent of the angle 63°27′ as shown in the tangent table. Hence we know that the direction of **OA** is 63°27′ counterclockwise from **OX.**

The method of composition of forces can also be used to determine the path of flight of an airplane flying in a crosswind. In Fig. 1·7 an airplane is flying at 150 mph on a heading of 340° and there is a crosswind of 50 mph blowing from 45°. To determine the flight path and the speed made good, we draw a triangle or parallelogram of forces. OB is drawn to a convenient scale to represent 150 mph 340° clockwise from 0°. OA is drawn from 45° through the point O and scaled to represent 50 mph. Then the parallelogram $OACB$ is drawn and the points O and C connected by the diagonal OC. This diagonal represents the direction and speed of the airplane along its actual flight path. By measurement we find that the length of the line OC represents a speed of about 137 mph and a flight path of approximately 320°.

From any one point we can combine any number of forces and obtain a resultant. In Fig. 1·8 if a force OA has a value of 20 lb, a force OB has a value of 15 lb, and a force OC has a value of 26 lb, we can easily determine the resultant force OE and find that it is about 56 lb. First we draw the parallelogram $OADB$ and then draw the diagonal OD, which is the resultant of OA and

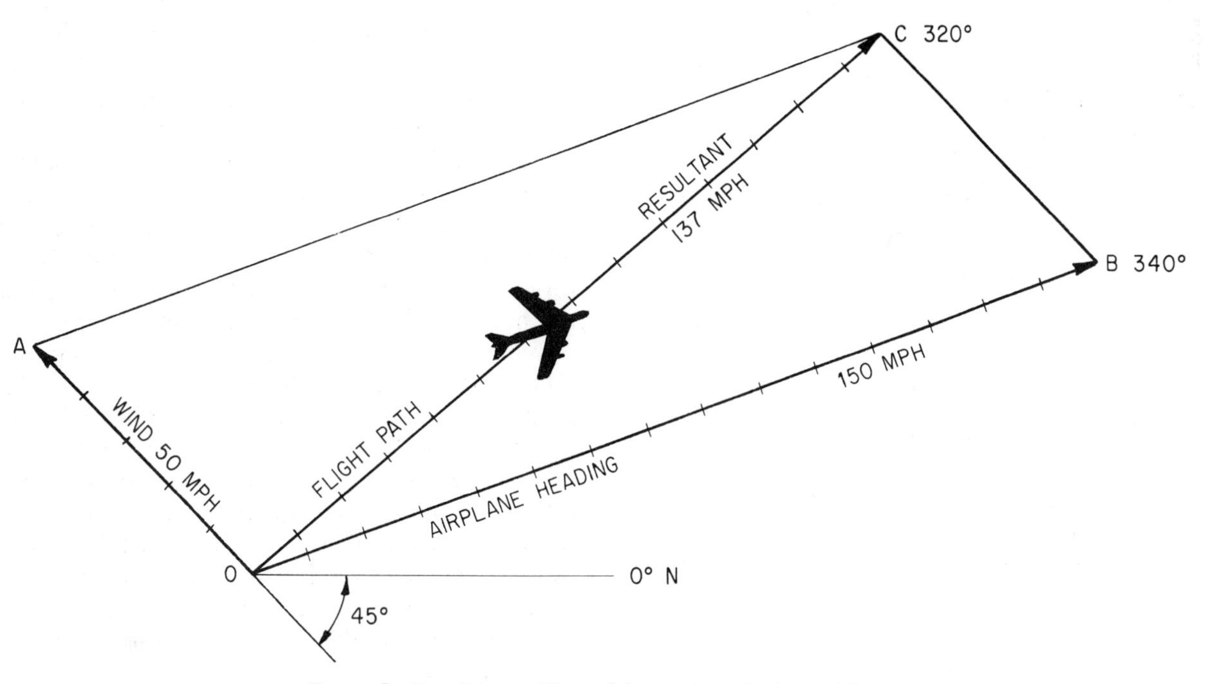

Figure 1·7 Composition of forces in a flight problem.

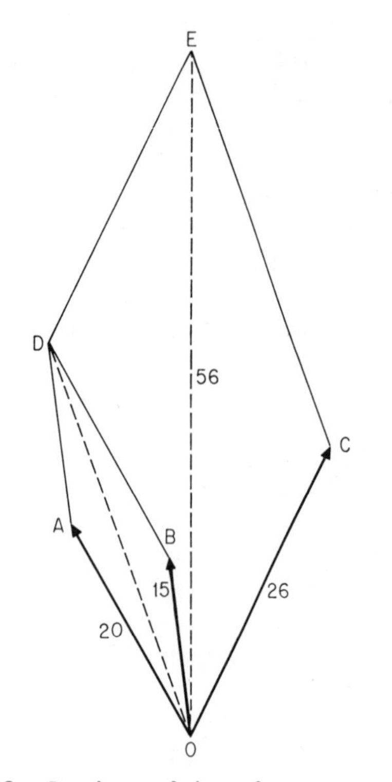

Figure 1·8 Resultant of three forces exerted at one point.

OB. Then using OD as a side, we draw the parallelogram $ODEC$. The diagonal OE is the resultant of the three forces and has a value of about 56 lb as previously stated.

A force can be **resolved** into its components if certain facts are known. For example, in Fig. 1·9 the force OA is composed of forces OB and OC whose directions are known but whose values are unknown. To determine the values of forces OB and OC it is merely necessary to draw AC' parallel to OB to the point where it intersects with OC and AB' parallel to OC to the point where it intersects with OB. If OA is 30 lb, then we find that OC' (OC) is about 24 lb and OB'

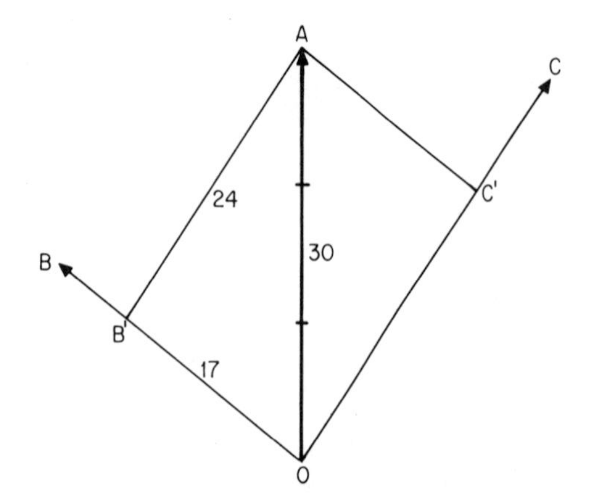

Figure 1·9 Resolution of a force into its components.

(OB) is about 17 lb. This determination of the components of a force is called **resolution of forces.**

It must be noted that the combination of vector forces, that is, forces having both magnitude and direction, requires something more than the mere addition of quantities. Vectorial addition is accomplished by means of parallelograms or triangles as demonstrated in the foregoing paragraphs. This is important in the solution of problems of alternating current, where we must combine electrical quantities having both magnitude and phase angle.

STRESS AND STRAIN

Stress may be defined as an internal force which tends to resist the deformation of a body resulting from an external load. The different types of stress are called **tension, compression, bending, torsion,** and **shear.** The five types of illustrated in Fig. 1·10. Tension tends to pull apart or stretch as shown in the illustration. Compression presses together or tends to crush; for example, the jack under an automobile is under compression when it raises the automobile. Bending actually causes two types of stress in a member. The part of the member on the outside of the bend is under tension, and the part on the inside of the bend is compressed. Torsion is a twisting force. The drive shaft and axles of an automobile are under torsion when the power is being delivered to the wheels. In the illustration a shaft is clamped solidly on one end and on the other end a pulley is mounted. A cable around the pulley is attached to a weight so the weight tends to turn the pulley. This action applies a twisting or torsion force to the shaft. Shear is most commonly developed when two pieces of material are bolted or riveted together. When force is applied such that the two plates tend to slide over each other, shear stress is applied to the bolt. If the force becomes greater than the shear strength of the bolt, it will be cut as with a pair of shears.

When a stress is applied to a piece of material, there is always some deformation of the material, even though it may be very small. This deformation is called **strain.** If the stress applied does not exceed the elastic limit of the material, the material will return to its original shape as soon as the stress is removed. The degree of stress deformation (strain) in a material is proportional to the stress as long as the elastic limit is not exceeded. This is known as **Hooke's law** after the man who discovered it.

The property of a material to return to its

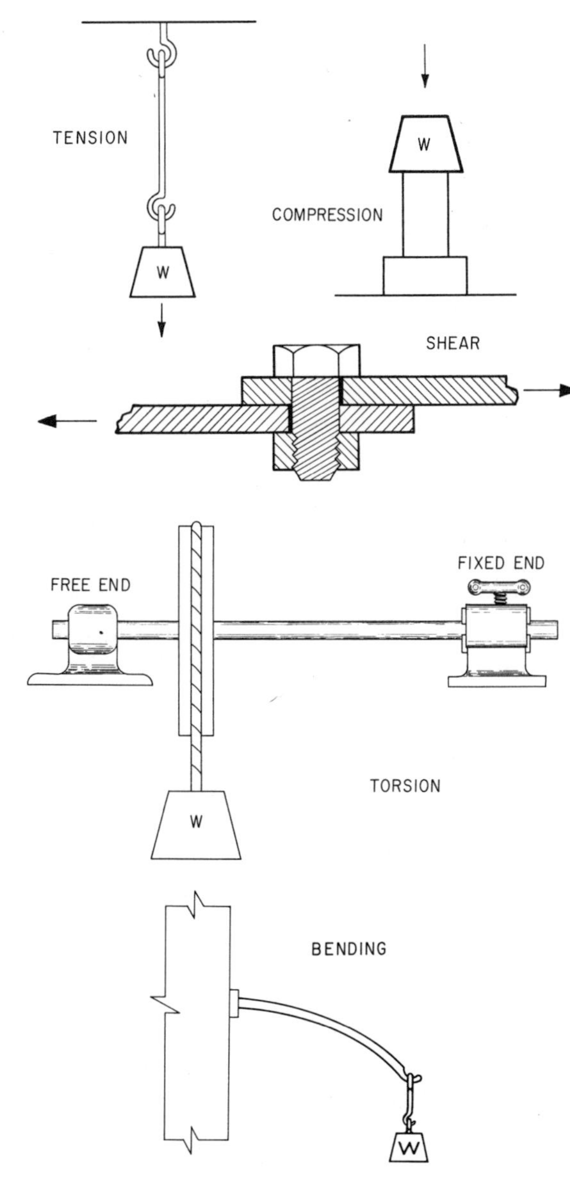

Figure 1 • 10 The five kinds of stresses.

original shape after being under stress is called **elasticity.** This property varies with the type of material. It is commonly assumed that rubber is one of the most elastic materials. This is not true because many materials will return to their original shapes after stressing more completely than will rubber. For example, glass is one of the most elastic substances in existence. If a long, straight rod of glass is bent slightly, it will become perfectly straight again when the stress is removed. This is also nearly true for spring steel and similar materials.

When a material is stressed beyond its elastic limit, it becomes permanently deformed. The point at which the permanent deformation begins to take place is called the **yield point.** If the stress is increased beyond the yield point, the **ultimate**

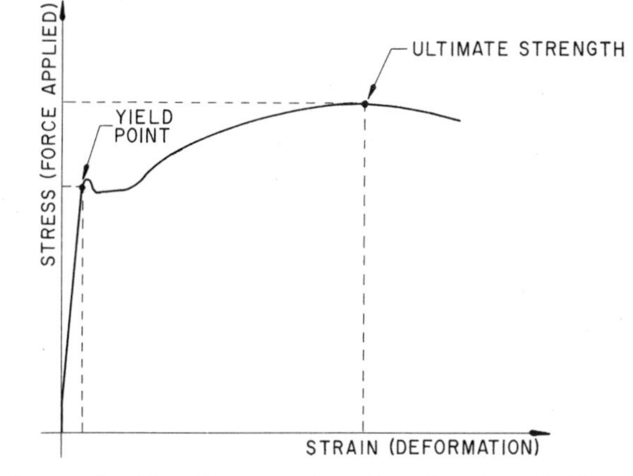

Figure 1 • 11 Stress and strain related to yield point and ultimate strength.

strength will eventually be reached and at this point the material will rupture or break. This is shown in the graph of Fig. 1 • 11.

WORK, ENERGY, AND POWER

Work, in the scientific or engineering sense, refers to the application of force to a body and the displacement of the body in the direction of the force. For example, if we apply a force of 10 lb to an object and move it 1 ft in the direction of the force, we have performed 10 foot-pounds (ft-lb) of work. This is shown by the equation

$$\text{Work} = \text{force} \times \text{distance}$$

The equation can also be expressed

$$E = Fs$$

where E represents work, F is force, and s is displacement in the direction of the force.

It is safe to say that work is performed whenever a force is applied and a movement occurs as the result of the force. If we use a lever to raise a weight, we can easily conceive how a machine performs work. In the drawing of Fig. 1 • 12 a lever is used to raise a box weighing 500 lb. The distance from the **fulcrum** f to the center of gravity of the box B is 2 ft, and the distance from the fulcrum to the applied force A is 4 ft. By measurement we shall find that to lift the box a distance of 6 in. (½ ft) we must move the opposite end A of the lever a distance of 1 ft. The work applied to the lever is then

$$250 \text{ (lb)} \times 1 \text{ (ft)} = 250 \text{ ft-lb}$$

The work done on the box is expressed by the equation

$$E = 500 \text{ (lb)} \times \tfrac{1}{2} \text{ (ft)} = 250 \text{ ft-lb}$$

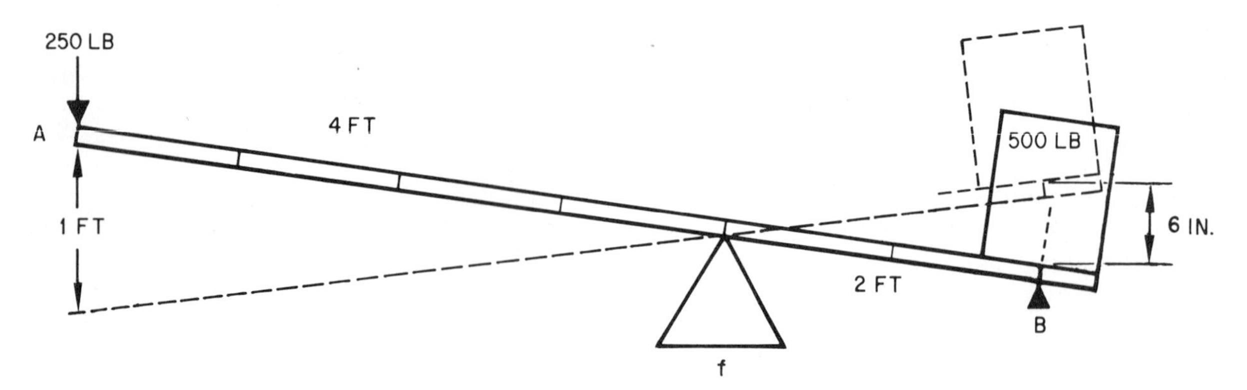

Figure **1 · 12** *Work done by means of a lever.*

Thus we see that the work applied to the lever is equal to the work done by the lever, or **output = input.** This is true for any machine which is 100 per cent efficient. There is always some loss in a machine because of friction, so the output cannot be quite as great as the input.

We can find hundreds of examples of work all about us, and new types of work are being developed constantly. A modern example is the lifting of a large rocket vehicle by means of a rocket engine. If a rocket engine lifts a 10,000-lb payload to a height of 100 miles, we can see that 5,280,000,000 or 528×10^7 ft-lb of work has been performed on the payload.

Energy

Energy may be defined as the capacity for doing work. All matter possesses energy in one form or another; however, it is not always easy to release the energy. A piece of coal has energy which can be released by burning to produce heat. Heat is one form of energy and can be converted to mechanical energy by means of heat engines. Thus we see that all fuels possess energy. When a boy throws a ball, he imparts energy to the ball. This energy is given up by the ball when the ball strikes the ground or is caught by another person.

The most spectacular form of energy produced in the modern world is nuclear energy. The tremendous forces locked in the atoms of matter are released in the form of heat when the right conditions are established. This form of energy is now being used to operate electrical powerplants, submarines, and steamships.

There are two forms of mechanical energy. These are **potential energy** and **kinetic energy.** Potential energy is the form of energy possessed by a body because of its position or configuration. For example, the water stored behind a dam possesses potential energy because of its position. When the water is released to flow by gravity through a turbine, it does work. The large hammer used in a pile driver possesses potential energy when it has been raised to the top of its tower because, when it is released, it does the work of driving a pile into the ground. A compressed or stretched spring possesses potential energy because of its **configuration.** When it is released, it can perform work.

Kinetic energy is the energy possessed by a body because of its motion. When a hammer is used to drive a nail, the kinetic energy of the hammer does the work of driving the nail. In the case of a water-driven turbine, when the water is stored, it possesses potential energy, but when it is released through the turbine, it has kinetic energy and this energy is imparted to the turbine.

The **Law of Conservation of Energy** states that energy can be neither destroyed nor created. It can only be changed in form. We can also say that the total amount of energy in the universe always remains constant. This means, of course, that the amount of energy imparted to a body is equal to the energy released by the body when the body is returned to its former state, that is, the condition of position, temperature, or configuration it was in before energy was imparted to it.

One of the principal facts to remember concerning energy is that any change in the state of a body requires either that energy be given to the body or that energy be given up by the body. If an automobile moving at a constant speed on a straight and level highway is to be accelerated, the engine must be given more fuel energy, which in turn is transmitted as mechanical energy to the wheels. If the automobile speed is to be decreased, the automobile must give up energy to the air (air friction) and to the road in the form of friction. For a more rapid decrease in speed the brakes must be applied, thus converting the kinetic energy of the automobile to heat energy at the brake drums.

Energy is expressed in the same units as those used for work. If a weight of 20 lb is raised 10 ft, the potential energy it acquires is 200 ft-lb because

$$E = Fs \qquad \text{or} \qquad E = 20 \times 10 = 200$$

In the metric system energy is expressed in dyne-centimeters (**ergs**), kilogram-meters, or gram-centimeters. In all cases the energy is the product of a force times a distance.

Kinetic energy can be expressed by the equation

$$E_k = \frac{Wv^2}{2g}$$

where W = weight
v = velocity
g = acceleration of gravity

Potential energy is expressed as

$$E_p = Fs \qquad \text{or} \qquad E_p = Wh$$

where W is the weight of a body and h is the height to which it has been raised.

Power

Power is the rate of doing work and can be expressed as

$$\frac{\text{Force} \times \text{distance}}{\text{Time}}$$

Power is expressed in several different units such as **ergs per second** or **foot-pounds per second.** The most common unit of power in general use in the United States is the **horsepower.** One horsepower (hp) is equal to 550 ft-lb per sec or 33,000 ft-lb per min. In electrical systems the unit of power is the **watt** or the kilowatt (kw). One watt is equal to $\frac{1}{746}$ hp; that is, 746 watts = 1 hp, one kilowatt is equal to 1.34 hp.

If we wish to compute the power necessary to raise an elevator containing 10 persons a distance of 100 ft in 5 sec and the loaded elevator weighs 2,500 lb, we proceed as follows:

$$\text{Power} = \frac{2{,}500 \times 100}{5 \times 550} = 90.9 \text{ hp}$$

If there were no friction, the power required would be 90.9 hp; however, there is always a substantial amount of friction to overcome, so the actual power required would be considerably greater than that indicated.

In the foregoing problem the amount of work to be done is 2,500 × 100 ft-lb. This work is to be done in 5 sec or at a rate of 50,000 ft-lb per sec. Since 1 hp equals 550 ft-lb per sec, we divide 50,000 by 550 to find the horsepower.

Let us suppose that we wish to find the horsepower required to fly a light airplane at 100 mph when we know that it requires 200 lb of thrust to overcome the drag at this speed. One hundred miles per hour is equal to 146.67 ft per sec, and 200 lb at 146.67 ft per sec equals 29,334 ft-lb per sec. We then divide 29,334 by 550 (ft-lb per sec) to obtain the horsepower, which we find to be about 53.1. In like manner we can determine that, if it requires a 32,000-lb thrust to drive a modern jet airliner at 600 mph, the power required is 51,200 hp.

VIBRATION AND OSCILLATION

Harmonic motion

Vibration is a rhythmic motion back and forth across a position of equilibrium of the particles of a fluid or of an elastic solid when its equilibrium has been disturbed. Such a state is clearly demonstrated in the plucking of a string on a musical instrument. The effects of vibration in mechanical devices create many of the problems which plague engineers in the design of such devices. It is therefore necessary in many instances to conduct vibration studies before the design of a particular machine can be approved, and even then, during operation, vibrations sometimes develop which require the redesign of the machine.

To obtain a clear picture of a simple vibratory or harmonic motion, we can use a device such as that shown in Fig. 1·13. A T-shaped bar with a slotted head is mounted so a pin on the rim of a wheel will fit into the slot in the bar. The bar is mounted in guides so its motion is limited to two directions, up and down. When the wheel is rotated at a constant speed, the movement of the bar up and down will be a harmonic motion. If we attach a marking pen P to the end of the bar so it will mark on a strip of paper moved at

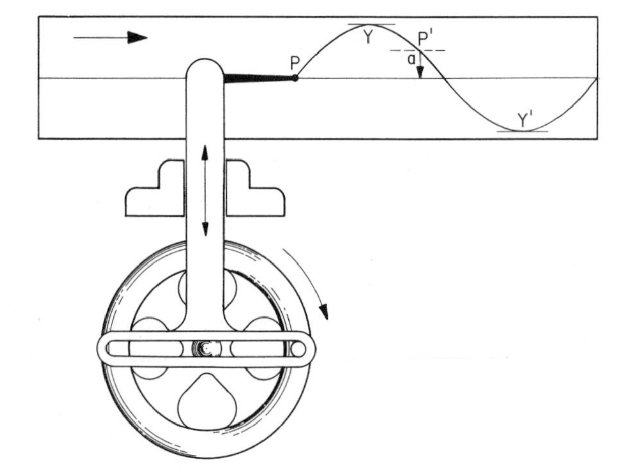

Figure 1·13 Demonstration of harmonic motion.

a uniform speed under the pen, then the pen will describe a sine curve on the paper. Thus we can see that the point P will move with a constantly changing speed, with the velocity being zero at points y and y' and maximum at the midpoint M.

Vibratory motion is **periodic** in nature and has characteristics by which it can be described. The time required for the motion to complete one cycle (one rotation of the wheel in Fig 1 · 13) is called the **period.** The number of complete cycles occurring per second is the **frequency** of the vibration. The **amplitude** of the vibration is the distance from the midpoint of the swing to the point of maximum displacement. **Displacement** is the distance of the vibrating point from the midpoint of vibration at any particular time. In Fig. 1 · 13 the displacement of the point p' is a.

If we secure a piece of spring steel solidly at one end as shown in Fig. 1 · 14, we can observe harmonic motion when we pull the open end of the strip of steel to point A and release it. On the return swing the end of the strip will spring back to point B, which is almost as far from the center point M as was point A. Without added energy to maintain the vibration, the amplitude of the swing will decrease rapidly but the frequency will remain constant. This requires that the speed of the motion also decrease. The frequency of the vibration of the steel spring in Fig. 1 · 14 depends upon the length of the strip l and the mass. If we mounted a weight on the end of the strip, we would find that frequency of vibration decreases.

The pendulum

A simple pendulum can be constructed by attaching a weight to a thin cord or thread. When the weight is suspended on the end of the thread, it will swing a certain number of times per second when displaced from the vertical position. The **period** of the pendulum is the time required to swing from vertical to one side, back to the other side, and then return to vertical. The period varies directly as the square root of the length of the suspending thread and inversely as the square root of the acceleration of gravity. The formula used to express this principle is

$$T = 2\pi \sqrt{\frac{l}{g}}$$

where T = period, sec
l = pendulum length
g = acceleration of gravity, ft per sec^2 (32.2)

The value of a pendulum lies in the fact that its period is always the same even though the displacement may vary. We can start a pendulum swinging through an arc of 4 ft and then let the arc continue to decrease over a period of time to a point where the arc is only 1 ft; however, at this time the period will be the same as it was when the arc was 4 ft. For this reason a pendulum is useful as the control for a clock escapement.

Oscillation

Oscillation means a swinging back and forth or a rhythmic movement to and fro. It is quickly seen, then, that oscillation is the same as vibration for all practical purposes. The formula for the period of oscillation of a spring, when the spring is displaced from its neutral position, is

$$T = 2\pi \sqrt{\frac{m}{k}}$$

where T = period, sec
m = mass, g
k = force, dynes per cm

LIQUIDS AND GASES

Liquids at rest

Many types of liquids are known, but the most common is water. We shall therefore consider the characteristics of water as an example of a liquid. A **liquid** is defined as a substance that flows readily but does not tend to expand indefinitely. The molecules in a liquid are free to move throughout the confining space, but they appear to have a bond one with another so that they tend to remain together.

Liquids have no appreciable elasticity and have no resistance to shear stresses. When confined, liquids resist compression and are classed as almost incompressible because the volume may be

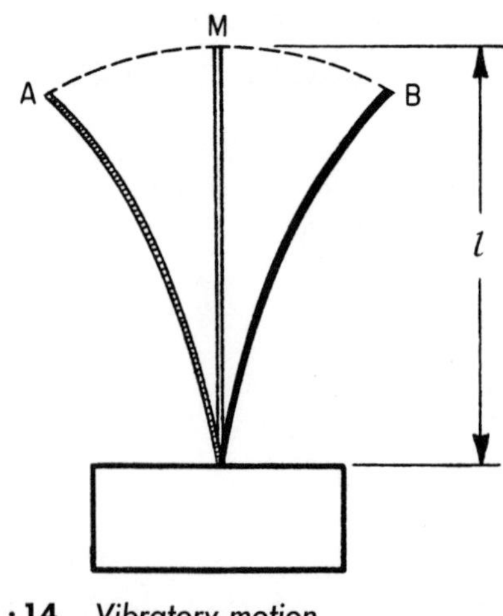

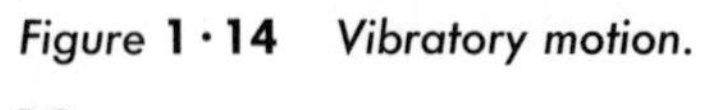
Figure 1 · 14 Vibratory motion.

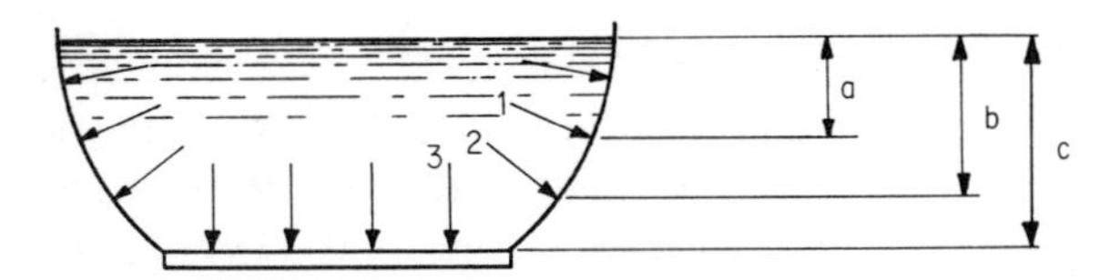

Figure 1·15 Force exerted by a liquid.

changed only very little, even under extreme pressure.

A liquid confined in a container will exert a **pressure** or force on the walls of the container. Consider the bowl of water shown in Fig. 1·15. The arrows represent the direction of force acting on the sides and bottom of the bowl. The amount of force exerted at any particular point depends upon the vertical distance from the surface of the water to the point where the force is to be measured. The force exerted at point 1 is determined by the distance *a*. Likewise, the force at 2 is determined by the distance *b* and the force on the bottom at 3 or any other point on the bottom of the bowl is determined by the distance *c*. To compute total force we must employ **force per unit area** or **pressure.** Pressure is expressed in **pounds per square inch** (psi) or in **grams per square centimeter.** In the illustration of Fig. 1·15, if the distance *c* is 4 in., the pressure *P* at the bottom of the bowl will be 0.1444 psi for water.

In the illustrations of Fig. 1·16 we see three containers of water. The areas of the bottoms of the containers are equal, and the depth of the water *h* is the same in each container. We know from these conditions that the total force on the bottom of each container is the same as that on the other two containers. We can observe, however, that the amounts of water are not the same and the weights of the containers of water cannot be the same. It seems apparent that, if the total force on the bottom of each container is equal to the total force on the bottom of each of the other containers, then the total downward force (weight) of one container would be equal to the weight of each of the other containers. We know, however, that this cannot be true, and the explanation lies in the effects of the water force on the slanting walls of the containers *B* and *C*. The force exerted against the wall of a container by a liquid is always perpendicular to the wall as shown by the arrow (vector) **ox** in the diagrams of *B* and *C*. When we construct a force diagram we find that a component of force **ox** is **oy. oy** presses upward in *B* and downward in *C*, so that the total force downward is less in *B* than it is in *A* or *C* and it is greater in *C* than it is in *A* or *B*. We can see easily that the pressure on the vertical walls of the container *A* will not exert any force upward or downward.

We are generally familiar with the pressure conditions found in great depths of water. When we dive into a swimming pool and descend to a depth of 10 ft, we can feel the effects of the pressure immediately. A deep-sea diver who descends to a depth of 150 ft must withstand a pressure of about 65 psi. Because of this he must descend very slowly to give his body a chance to develop equalizing pressures. Also, he must ascend very slowly to prevent the nitrogen in his blood from turning into a gas (such as in a bottle of soda pop when it is first opened) and causing a severe illness called "the bends." This condition is extremely painful and may be fatal if it is too severe.

Buoyancy

Buoyancy is the effect of liquid force on a body immersed or submerged in the liquid. In Fig. 1·17 a rectangular block is submerged in a container of water. Since the block is rectangular, the only upward or downward forces are those exerted on the top and the bottom of the block. If we let w equal the weight of a unit volume of the water (1 cu in. of water weighs 0.0361 lb), we know that the pressure on the top of the rectangular block will equal h_1w and the total force on the top of the block will be a_1h_1w. In like manner the

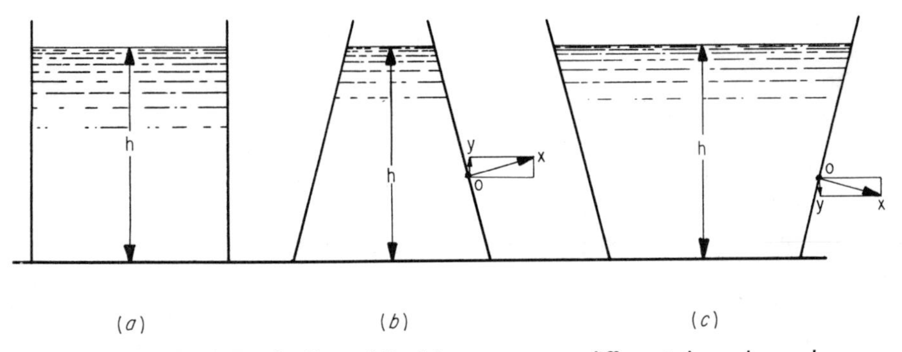

Figure 1·16 Total effect of liquid pressures on different-shaped vessels.

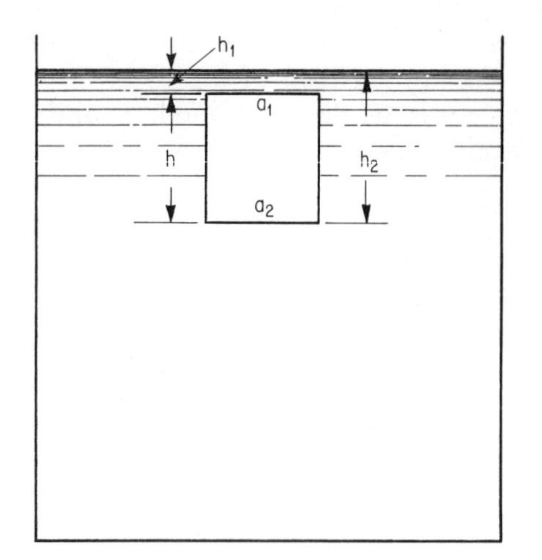

Figure 1·17 Buoyancy of a liquid.

total force on the bottom of the block will be a_2h_2w.

Since the block is rectangular, a_1 is equal to a_2 and we can represent either one of these areas by a. Then

$$ah_2w - ah_1w = aw(h_2 - h_1) = \text{buoyancy}$$

but $$h_2 - h_1 = h$$

hence $$awh = \text{buoyancy}$$

The foregoing example demonstrates Archimedes' principle, which states that **a body placed in a liquid is buoyed up by a force equal to the weight of the liquid displaced.** We can easily see from this that a floating body will displace its own weight in liquid. This can be demonstrated by placing a block of wood in a container of liquid which is filled to the overflow point as shown in Fig. 1·18. When the block is placed in the liquid, an amount of the liquid will flow out equal in weight to the weight of the block of wood. This can be proved by weighing the liquid which has flowed out of the container.

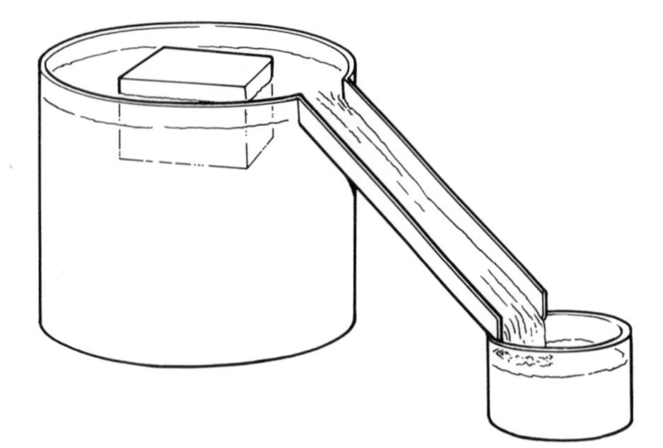

Figure 1·18 Displacement of a liquid by a floating solid.

Principles of hydraulics

Fluids, both liquids and gases, have been found to be most useful in performing work. Many of the great machines used for industrial production are hydraulically operated. Among these are hydraulic presses used for forming metal, stretch presses, stamping machines, and numerous others. We also find hydraulic power used in the familiar automobile hoist found in service stations and garages. Other uses for hydraulics include heavy construction equipment such as bulldozers, graders, loaders, and similar devices.

In aircraft and missiles hydraulic power is used to perform many functions, including the movement of controls, opening and closing of valves, operating landing gear, etc. It is also used for the motive power in automatic control systems such as those employed in guided missiles. Systems such as these are called servomechanisms.

In a hydraulic system the fluid is confined, so pressure applied to the fluid at any point is immediately transmitted to every other point touched by the fluid. Figure 1·19 illustrates Pascal's law, which states that a liquid under pressure in a closed container transmits pressure undiminished to all parts of the enclosing wall. If the 10-lb weight is acting on an area of 1 sq in., then a pressure of 10 lb is transmitted to every square inch of the enclosing wall. This principle is the key to the use of liquids or other fluids to transmit power or force from one point to another.

Figure 1·20 illustrates a simple hydraulic system used to operate a hydraulic press. When the control valve is placed in the correct position and the pump is operated, hydraulic fluid is forced through a check valve to the space under the piston of the press. The pressure of the fluid acting on the piston will cause it to rise. When the control valve is placed in the return position, the fluid can flow from the area under the piston back through the control valve to the reservoir. The check valves are placed in the lines as shown to prevent fluid from flowing in the wrong direction when the pump is operating.

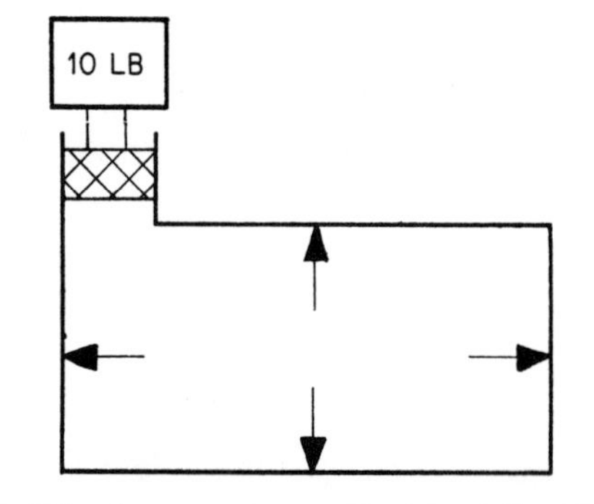

Figure 1·19 Pressure transmitted by a liquid.

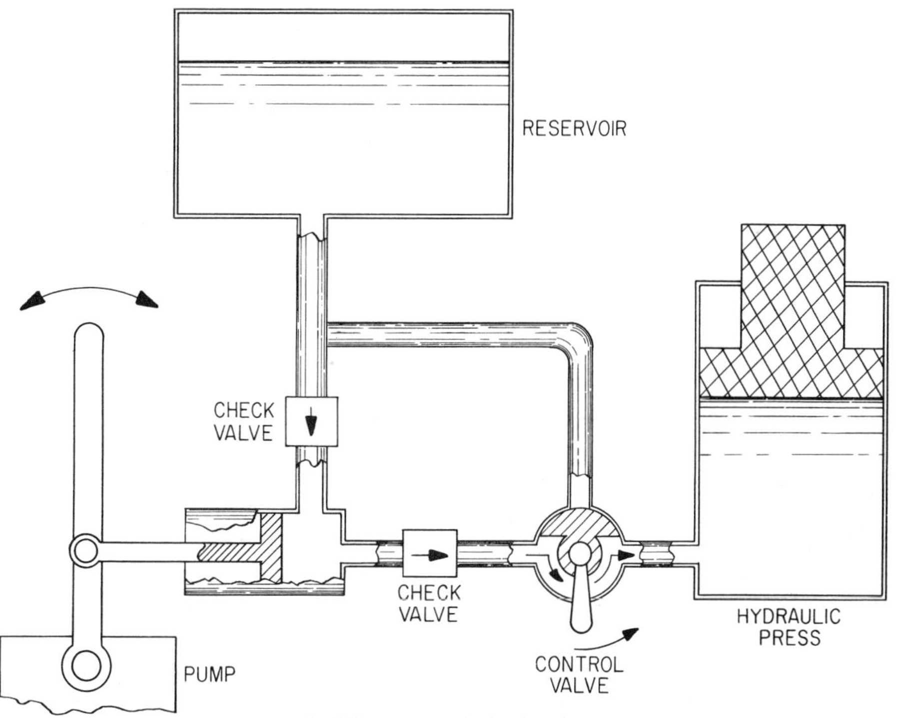

Figure 1·20 A simple hydraulic system.

Great force can be applied by means of a hydraulic system merely by selecting the size of piston to produce the desired force. The multiplication of force through the use of hydraulic pistons is illustrated in Fig. 1·21. If a force of 10 lb is applied on the small piston which has an area of 1 sq in., the pressure of the fluid becomes 10 psi. This pressure is transmitted undiminished to the large piston, which has an area of 50 sq in. Then 50 × 10 = 500 lb, which is the force exerted by the large piston.

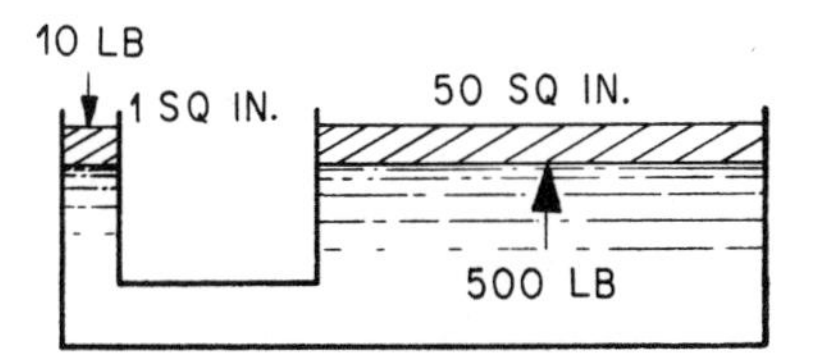

Figure 1·21 Multiplication of force by means of hydraulic pistons.

In the landing-gear actuating system for a large airplane we may find that the pressure of the system is 3,000 psi. If this pressure is applied to a piston with an area of 15 sq in., we can easily see that a force of 45,000 lb is developed to raise the landing gear. In practice this amount of force is not actually required, although the system can develop it.

Pumps

The development of pressure in a hydraulic system is accomplished by means of a pump. The most commonly used pumps for this purpose are piston pumps and gear pumps. A single-piston pump is shown in Fig. 1·22. The rotation of the

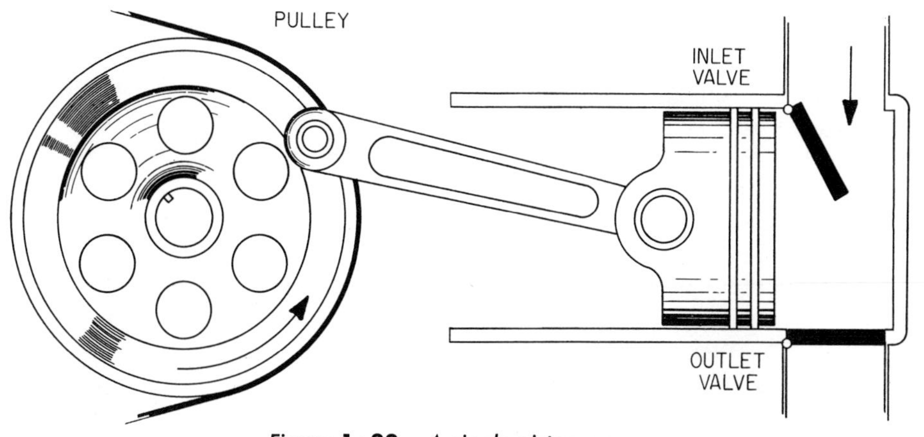

Figure 1·22 A single-piston pump.

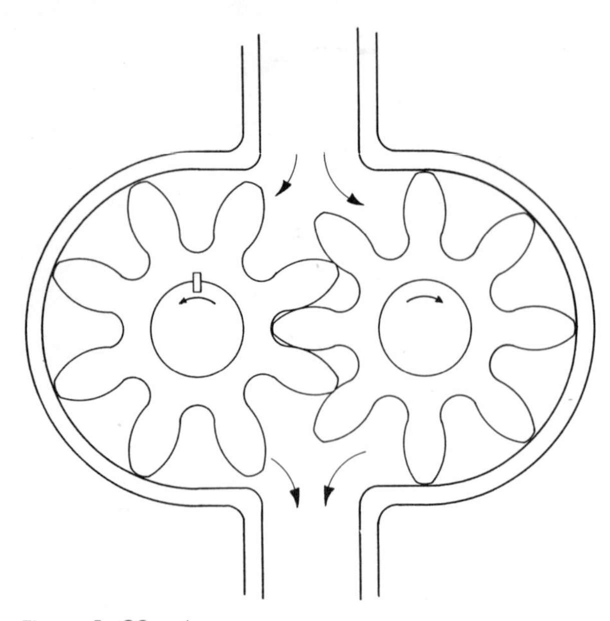

Figure **1·23** *A gear pump.*

pulley turns a crankshaft which, in turn, causes the piston to move in and out of the cylinder. As the piston moves outward, the inlet valve opens and fluid moves into the piston from a reservoir. Then when the piston moves into the cylinder, the inlet valve closes and the outlet valve opens, thus permitting the fluid to flow into the outlet line.

A gear pump is illustrated in Fig. 1·23. As the gears rotate in mesh, the fluid is carried around the gears in the spaces between the gear teeth and the wall of the case. As the gears mesh, the fluid is forced from between the teeth and therefore must flow out the outlet. This type of pump is commonly used in hydraulic systems.

The nature and laws of gases

The atmosphere surrounding the earth consists of a mixture of gases. Approximately 78 per cent of the atmosphere is composed of nitrogen and about 21 per cent is oxygen. The other 1 per cent consists of carbon dioxide and other gases.

A gas consists of a fantastically large number of very small particles called molecules. These molecules may be considered as extremely small elastic balls for the purpose of this discussion. The molecules in a gas are constantly in motion, and the velocity of the motion is dependent upon the temperature of the gas. Each molecule of a gas travels in a straight line until it strikes another molecule, and at this time both of the two colliding molecules continue their travels in different directions. The movement of molecules in a gas causes the gas to dissipate quickly when it is not confined. This can be proved easily by releasing a small amount of an odoriferous gas in one corner of a closed room and then noting how quickly the odor is detected in the opposite corner of the room. Usually this takes only a few seconds. Because of the movement of the molecules in a gas the gas will always completely fill any container in which it is placed. That is, the molecules will distribute themselves evenly throughout the space in the container.

A gas can be easily compressed, and as it is compressed, its pressure increases inversely as its volume decreases, the temperature remaining constant. This is in accordance with Boyle's law, which states that **the volume of a confined body of gas varies inversely as its absolute pressure, the temperature remaining constant.** This can be expressed by the following equation:

$$\frac{V_1}{V_2} = \frac{P_2}{P_1} \qquad \text{(temperature constant)}$$

In this equation V is the symbol for volume and P is the symbol for pressure. The subscript figures identify the first volume and pressure and the second volume and pressure.

Absolute pressure means the pressure above zero pressure, keeping in mind that the pressure of the atmosphere at sea level is approximately 14.7 psi or 29.92 inches of mercury (in. Hg). Therefore, if we have a confined gas in a cylinder with the gas at atmospheric pressure and then compress the gas to one-half its former volume, the pressure exerted by the gas will then be approximately 29.4 psi. We must assume here that the temperature remains constant, although under normal conditions, when a gas is compressed, its temperature increases.

Another characteristic of a gas is expressed by the law attributed to the French physicist Jacques A. C. Charles (1746–1823). Charles' law states that **the volume of a gas varies in direct proportion to the absolute temperature.** Absolute temperature is temperature related to absolute zero or the condition where there is a complete absence of heat. Absolute zero is $-460°$F or $-273°$C. The application of Charles' law to a gas requires that the pressure remain constant. If we confine a gas so that the volume remains constant, then we find that the pressure varies in accordance with absolute temperature. Charles' law can be expressed by the following equation:

$$\frac{V_1}{V_2} = \frac{T_1}{T_2} \qquad \text{(pressure constant)}$$

The equation relating to the pressure of a gas where the volume is constant is

$$\frac{P_1}{P_2} = \frac{T_1}{T_2} \qquad \text{(volume constant)}$$

In each of the above equations we must remember that the temperature must be expressed in absolute units, that is, in degrees above absolute zero.

In order to determine the amount of expansion in a gas as the result of an increase in temperature, we must know the **coefficient of expansion.** This value is approximately the same for all gases and is found to be $\frac{1}{273}$ or 0.00366 for each degree centigrade with the gas at 0°C.

The **general gas law** is derived by combining Boyle's law and Charles' law. It is expressed by the following equation:

$$\frac{P_1V_1}{T_1} = \frac{P_2V_2}{T_2}$$

This equation can be used to determine a change in volume, pressure, or temperature of a gas when the other conditions are changed. It must be remembered that the pressures and temperatures expressed in this equation must be stated in absolute values.

HEAT

Heat is a form of energy, and it is manifested in matter by the motion of the molecules. As heat is increased, the motion of the molecules increases. This adds to the internal energy of the material to which the heat is applied. If heat is applied to one end of a metal rod, it will be found that the other end of the rod gradually becomes warmer. This is because the molecules in the heated end of the rod increase their motion and strike other molecules along the rod with greater force. This increases the motion of the molecules progressively all along the rod. When this occurs, we say that the rod is conducting heat.

When a heated object is in contact with a cold object, the heat transfers from the hot object to the cold object. This also is brought about by the motion of the molecules in the hot object striking the molecules of the cold object, thus increasing the motion of the molecules in the cold object.

Temperature is the degree of heat or cold measurable in a body. The measurement of temperature is accomplished with a thermometer and the value is expressed in degrees of Fahrenheit (F) or centigrade (C). Absolute temperatures are expressed in degrees Kelvin or Rankine. The various temperature scales are compared in Table 1·1.

It will be noted from the following table that there is a difference of 180° Fahrenheit or Rankine between the point where water boils and ice melts. For this same range of temperature there

Table 1·1 Comparison of temperature scales

	Fahrenheit	*Centigrade*	*Rankine*	*Kelvin*
Water boils	212°	100°	672°	373°
Ice melts	32°	0°	492°	273°
Absolute zero	−460°	−273°	0°	0°

is a difference of 100° centigrade or Kelvin. From this we know that Fahrenheit and Rankine degrees have the same value and centigrade and Kelvin degrees have the same value. Furthermore, we can see that 100° in the centigrade scale are equivalent to 180° in the Fahrenheit scale. A detailed conversion table is given in the Appendix.

To convert one type of scale to the other we can use the following formulas:

$$F = \tfrac{9}{5}C + 32 \qquad C = \tfrac{5}{9}(F - 32)$$

To convert centigrade to Kelvin we merely add 273, and to convert Fahrenheit to Rankine we add 460.

Effects of heat

The effects of heat make possible many of the powerful machines which we use in our modern world. With heat we can convert water to steam and use the pressure of the steam to drive a steam engine. Also, we can burn various fuels such as gasoline to cause a great expansion of air and the gases of combustion. The expanded gases are used to move the pistons in gasoline engines thus causing the crankshaft to rotate and develop power for automobiles and other machines. In jet engines the burning of fuel with oxygen causes a great expansion of gases which drives the turbine of the engine to compress the air, and the exhausted gases cause the jet thrust. Similarly the burning of either liquid or solid fuels in a rocket causes a great expansion of gases which produces the thrust.

The energy available from a fuel is determined by the amount of heat it produces when burned. In order to measure heat energy it is necessary to employ heat units. A heat unit has been established on the basis of heating value. In the metric system the heat unit is called the **calorie** (cal). One calorie is the amount of heat required to raise the temperature of 1 gram of water through 1 degree centigrade. In the English system the unit of heat measurement is that amount of heat necessary to raise the temperature of 1 pound of water through 1 degree Fahrenheit. This quantity of heat is called the **British thermal unit (Btu).**

The amount of work which can be performed

Table 1·2

Fuel	Heat value	
	Btu/lb	Cal/g
Wood	7,000–8,000	4,000–4,500
Gasoline	20,000–20,500	11,000–11,400
Coal	13,500–15,000	7,600–8,400
Gas	9,900–11,500	5,500–6,400

by a certain amount of heat has been determined. For example, it has been found that 1 Btu can do 778 ft-lb of work. Also, 1 cal can produce 4.186 joules of work or about 3.09 ft-lb. From these values we can easily determine how much work can be obtained from a certain amount of fuel provided we know the heat value of the fuel. The heat values of a few common fuels are given in Table 1·2.

From the foregoing we can determine how much power can be developed when a certain amount of gasoline is being burned in a given time. For example, if an engine is burning 40 lb per hr of gasoline, how much power can we obtain from the engine if it is 35 per cent efficient?

40 lb of gasoline per hour would produce 800,000 Btu per hr
800,000 Btu per hr = 13,333.3 Btu per min
13,333.3 Btu per min = 10,373,307.4 ft-lb per min

Since 1 hp = 33,000 ft-lb per min,

10,373,307.4 ft-lb per min = 314 hp
$314 \times 0.35 = 110$ hp, approximately

From the foregoing example it is apparent that we can obtain approximately 110 hp from an engine burning 40 lb per hr of fuel when the engine is 35 per cent efficient.

Specific heat

The **specific heat** of a substance is the number of calories required to raise the temperature of 1 gram of the substance 1 degree centigrade or the number of Btu's required to raise 1 pound of the substance 1 degree Fahrenheit. The value is the same for each. The specific heat of water is 1, and that of other substances is usually less than 1. Table 1·3 gives the specific heats of a variety of common substances.

Table 1·3 means that only 0.22 Btu is required to raise the temperature of 1 lb of aluminum 1°F or 0.11 Btu to raise the temperature of 1 lb of iron 1°F. It is therefore obvious that the specific heat of different substances varies substantially.

Table 1·3

Substance	Specific heat
Water	1.0
Ice	0.50
Alcohol	0.59
Aluminum	0.22
Copper	0.093
Iron	0.11
Silver	0.056
Lead	0.031
Mercury	0.033
Platinum	0.032

Another interesting heat phenomenon is noted when a substance melts or when it is converted to a vapor. For example, when 1 g of water changes to ice, it gives up 80 cal. When 1 g of ice is melted, it absorbs 80 cal. This accounts for the fact that ice can be forced to melt by the application of salt, and this melting process absorbs heat and lowers the temperature of the water-salt mixture which we call brine. The home ice-cream freezer utilizes this principle in freezing the ice cream. The heat absorbed by a melting substance is called the **heat of fusion.**

The effect of heat on metals is particularly important in the design and operation of heat engines. Metals usually expand with an increase in temperature, and this expansion must be accounted for in the design of an engine. The increase in length of a metal per unit length per degree of rise in temperature is called the **coefficient of linear expansion.** For iron the coefficient of linear expansion is 0.000012 cm per cm per °C. This means that 1 cm of iron will have a length of 1.000012 cm after the temperature is increased 1°C. The coefficient of expansion for aluminum is twice that of iron. The modern alloys used in jet engines often expand much more than ordinary iron or steel. For this reason a jet engine must be designed to "grow" as its temperature increases. A large engine may increase in length more than an inch at operating temperature. This is one of the reasons the mechanic must be careful to allow correct clearances when assembling a jet engine. This same precaution must be taken in assembling any device which is subject to large changes in temperature during operation.

MECHANICAL ADVANTAGE

The lever

The lever is one of the simplest machines which enables man to exert greater force than his direct effort can produce. In Fig. 1·24 is shown a lever

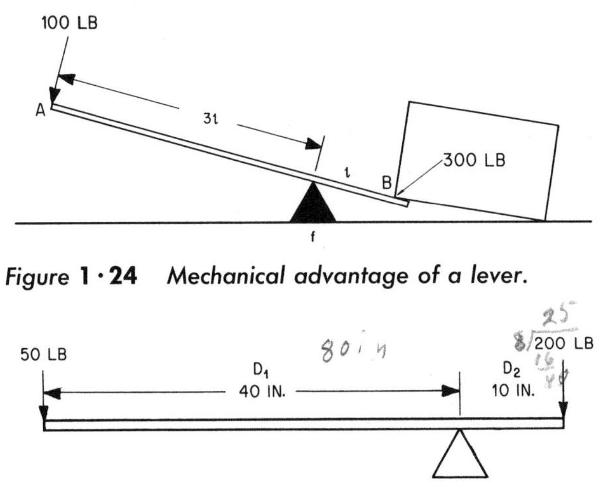

Figure **1·24** *Mechanical advantage of a lever.*

Figure **1·25** *Balancing a lever.*

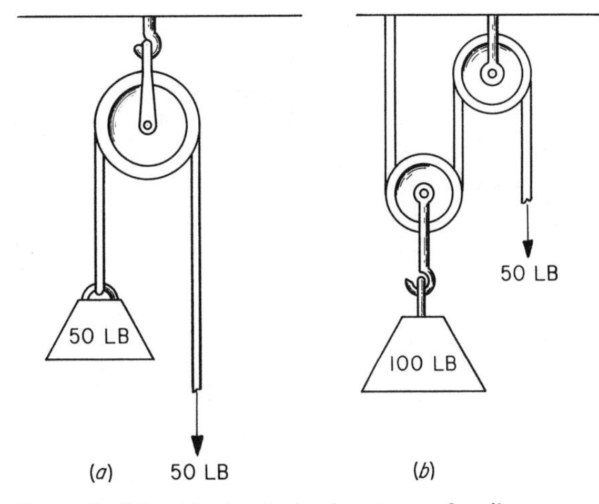

Figure **1·26** *Mechanical advantage of pulleys.*

being used to raise one end of a heavy box. The distance from the fulcrum *f* to the point *A* is three times the distance from *f* to *B*. Under these conditions a 100-lb force at *A* will balance a 300-lb force at *B*. This principle is used by railroad yardmen in moving freight cars short distances by means of a specially constructed lever. The principle of the lever is illustrated in Fig. 1·25. When the lever is balanced, it will be found that

$$F_1D_1 = F_2D_2$$

In the illustration $50 \times 40 = 200 \times 10$. The product of the force times the distance is called a **moment.** The distance from the reference point (in this case *f*) is called the **arm.** In a balance problem the force is usually a weight, so we can say that the **moment is equal to the weight times the arm.** This principle is utilized in determining the weight and balance conditions of an airplane.

Pulleys

Pulleys, also called **sheaves,** are often used to provide a mechanical advantage. In Fig. 1·26 a single pulley is shown at *A* with a rope to support a weight of 50 lb. In order to raise the weight, at least 50 lb must be applied downward on the end of the rope. In *B* are shown two pulleys with a rope to provide a 2:1 advantage. Observe here that the weight is being supported by two sections of rope; hence one section of rope only must support one-half the total weight. It is therefore possible to apply 50 lb at the end of the rope and raise 100 lb with the pulley. (In *B* we are not considering the weight of the lifting pulley.) In any arrangement of pulleys (block and tackle) the number of ropes actually supporting the weight determines the mechanical advantage of pulley combination. In Fig. 1·27 is shown a set of double pulleys. It will be noted that there are four sections of rope supporting the weight of 80 lb. This means that each rope is required to support only 20 lb, disregarding the weight of the pulleys. It is necessary to apply only slightly over 20 lb to the traction rope to raise the 80-lb weight. The mechanical advantage is therefore 4:1, since the weight is four times as great as the effort required to raise it.

Gears also are employed to provide a mechanical advantage. If one gear having a diameter of 2 in. is meshed with a gear having a diameter of 4 in., as shown in Fig. 1·28, the mechanical advantage is 2:1. The small gear must turn two

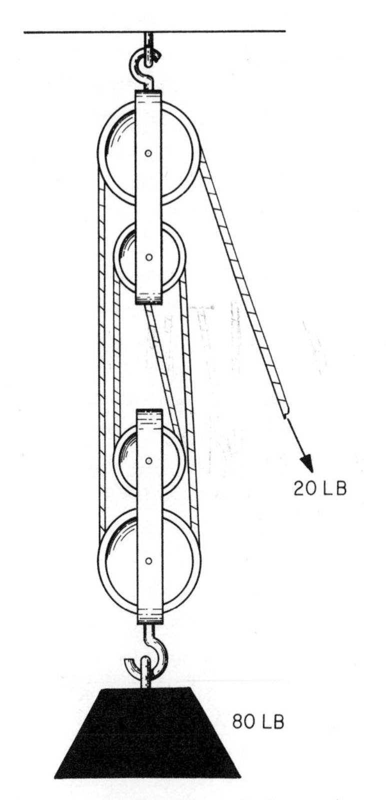

Figure **1·27** *Multiplication of force by means of pulleys.*

Figure 1·28 Mechanical advantage produced by gears.

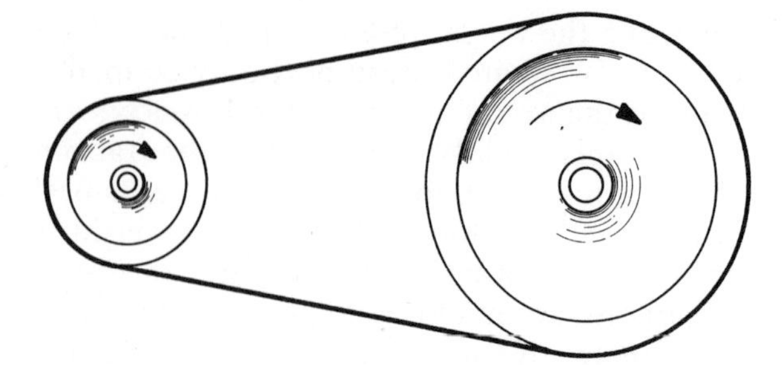

Figure 1·29 Mechanical advantage with pulleys.

revolutions in order to rotate the large gear one revolution. The turning force applied to the small gear need be only one-half the force applied to the large gear by the driven load. The turning force is called **torque** or **twisting moment.** A train of many gears can be used to provide an extreme mechanical advantage. However, if the number of gears is too great, the friction will eventually become so large that the mechanical advantage is lost.

When a machine is driven by a belt, mechanical advantage can be obtained by driving a large pulley with a small pulley as shown in Fig. 1·29. The diameter of the large pulley is twice that of the smaller pulley; hence the mechanical advantage is 2:1. The large pulley will turn one-half the speed of the small pulley, but the torque required on the small pulley shaft will be only one-half the torque of the large pulley shaft.

Inclined plane

The **inclined plane** offers a simple example of mechanical advantage which is used in many devices. Figure 1·30 illustrates the principle of the inclined plane. Assume that B is a 120-lb barrel of flour and it must be raised 1 ft. The work to be done is 120 ft-lb. If the barrel is moved a distance of 6 ft to do the work, then the force

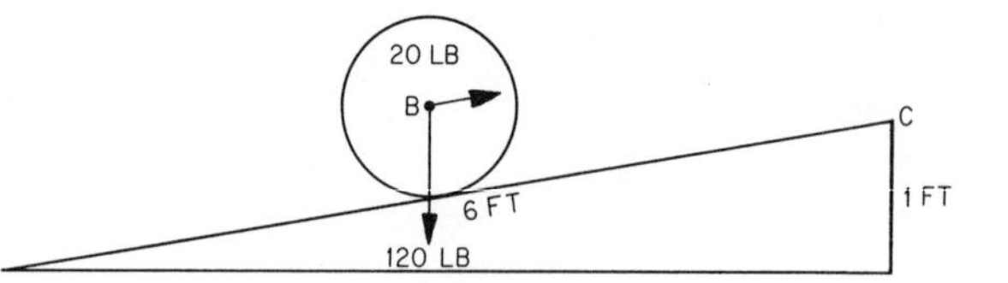

Figure 1·30 Principle of the inclined plane.

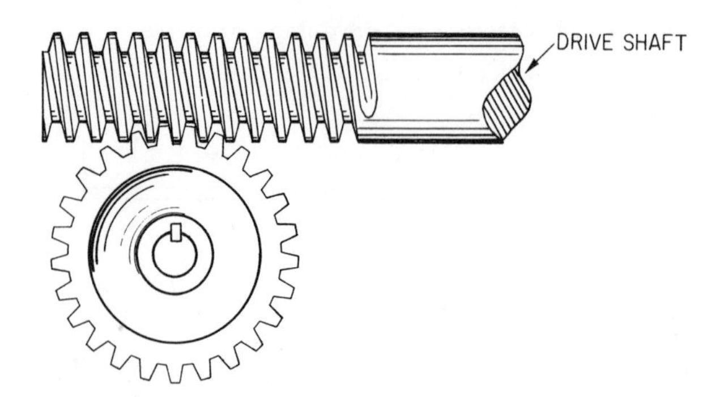

Figure 1·31 Worm-gear drive to develop mechanical advantage.

need be only 20 lb, because $6 \times 20 = 120$. Therefore, the ratio of the length of the inclined plane to the vertical distance is the mechanical advantage, disregarding friction.

The screw is actually an adaptation of the inclined-plane principle. A screw jack can be used to raise buildings through human power by providing a large multiplication of the human effort. There is considerable friction in a screw arrangement, but even with the friction the screw makes possible a great multiplication of force.

A combination of the screw and a gear, called a "worm-gear" arrangement, is often used in machines to provide a large mechanical advantage. A worm-gear drive is shown in Fig. 1·31. One revolution of the drive shaft will move the rim of of the driven gear the distance of 1 tooth. The mechanical advantage is therefore equal to the number of teeth on the driven gear. If the gear has 20 teeth, the mechanical advantage is 20:1.

SOUND

Wave motion

To understand sound it is first necessary to examine **wave motion,** because sound travels in waves. The nature of the sound determines the kind of wave by which the sound is transmitted.

Almost everyone has seen waves in water resulting from a disturbance in or on the water. The effects of sound in the atmosphere are similar to disturbances in water, but the difference in the compressibility of the two media also makes a difference in the nature of the waves. Figure

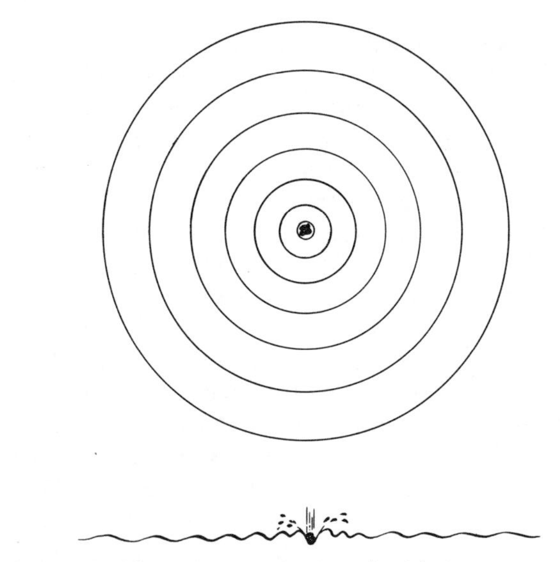

Figure 1·32 Wave motion in a liquid.

Figure 1·33 Wave motion demonstrated with a rope.

1·32 shows how waves emanate from a point in water where an object such as a small stone has been dropped. The illustration below the series of circles shows how a cross section of the water surface will appear when an object is dropped into the water.

Waves occur as two different kinds of motion. Wave movements are therefore described as **transverse** and **longitudinal.** If you tie one end of a rope to a stationary point and then, after stretching the rope to its full length, move the free end up and down rapidly with uniform motion, **transverse** waves will be produced in the rope. This is illustrated in Fig. 1·33. From this it will be seen that a transverse wave is one in which the material moves back and forth sideways or up and down from a zero reference line. The surface waves on water are of the transverse type.

One of the simplest methods for illustrating a **longitudinal** wave is to use a long coil spring stretched between two stationary points. After the spring is stretched, if one end is compressed and then released, a longitudinal wave will travel the length of the spring. The longitudinal wave is formed by a series of alternately compressed and expanded coils of the spring as illustrated in Fig. 1·34.

The molecules of the air are compressed and expanded in waves when sound is traveling through the air. Figure 1·35 illustrates this principle with small circles representing molecules and a row of vertical lines illustrating expansion and contraction.

Figure 1·34 Wave motion in a coiled spring.

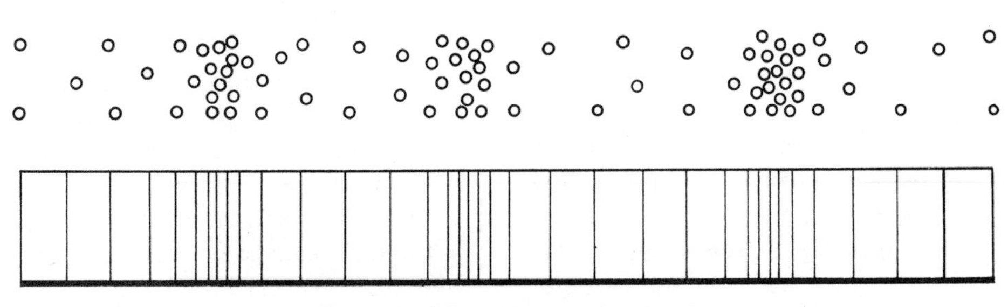

Figure 1·35 Wave motion in air.

The nature of sound

Sound may be defined in a number of ways, but the simplest definition is **that which can be heard.** Some have argued that sound can exist only when there is an ear in the vicinity to hear it, while others claim that a sound exists whether anyone hears it or not. Since sound is actually a vibration of a substance, solid, liquid, or gas, we can say that a sound can exist even though there may be no human ear in the vicinity to hear it. From this we can also understand that sound cannot travel in a vacuum. Our interest at this time is not the hearing of a sound but the nature of the vibration that causes the sensation of sound in the ear. In Fig. 1·35 we have indicated that sound is a series of expansions and compressions in the molecules of the air. It is also of a similar nature when passing through a liquid or a solid; however, the velocity will be different. The velocity of sound through a substance depends upon both the density and the elasticity of the substance which is conducting the sound. Table 1·4 gives the speed of sound through several common substances at the indicated temperatures.

Table 1·4

Medium	*Temperature, °C*	*Speed, ft/sec*
Air	0	1,087
Hydrogen	0	4,220
Oxygen	0	1,040
Aluminum	0	16,700
Copper	0	13,000
Glass	0	17,000
Iron, cast	0	14,200
Lead	0	4,040
Steel	0	16,000
Water	15	4,760

In Table 1·4 it will be noted that sound travels about 1,087 ft per sec in air when the temperature is 0°C. As temperature increases, the speed of sound increases about 2 ft per sec for each degree centigrade rise in temperature. From this we know that at very high altitudes where the temperature is many degrees below zero, the speed of sound is much lower than it is at sea level.

Doppler effect

Today we often encounter the term **Doppler effect** in discussions of electronic navigation and control systems as well as in discussions of sound. This is possible because electromagnetic energy and sound both travel in waves. The Doppler effect is observed in sound when the source of a sound wave changes its direction with respect to the hearer of the sound so the number of sound waves per second reaching the ear is changed. Let us assume that a whistle is emitting a sound with a frequency of 1,100 cycles per second (cps) and that the whistle is mounted on an automobile approaching the listener at a speed of 100 ft per sec. Assume also that the temperature is such that the speed of sound is 1,100 ft per sec. Then with the frequency at 1,100 cps and the speed of sound 1,100 ft per sec, we know that there will be one sound wave (cycle) for each foot of distance from the sound source. Since the sound source is approaching the listener at 100 ft per sec, the listener will hear 1,100 + 100 or 1,200 cps. That is, the sound will have a higher pitch than that at which it is emitted. When the sound source reaches and then goes away from the listener, the pitch will suddenly change, so the listener will hear a pitch of 1,000 cps. This apparent change in pitch is called the **Doppler effect.**

The formula for determining the change in frequency as a result of the Doppler effect is

$$p = f\frac{V}{V - S}$$ source moving toward listener

$$p = f\frac{V}{V + S}$$ source moving away from listener

where p = apparent frequency of sound heard by listener
f = frequency of sound at source
V = speed of sound
S = speed of source

The Doppler effect principle is used in electronic indicating systems because electronic signals are transmitted by means of waves, and the apparent frequency of a signal from an approaching signal source will be higher than the frequency of a signal from a signal source which is moving away from the receiver. One of the principal applications of the Doppler effect in electronics is in navigation radar equipment.

REVIEW QUESTIONS

1. How many feet are there in 100 m?
2. What is the weight in pounds of 1 metric ton?
3. State the Universal Law of Gravitation.
4. Explain *specific gravity* and *density*.
5. Explain the difference between *weight* and *mass.*
6. Define *dyne.*
7. State Newton's three laws of motion.
8. Explain *centrifugal* and *centripetal* forces.
9. Explain *velocity* and *speed.*
10. What is a *vector?*

11. What do we mean by resolution of forces?
12. Name five types of stresses.
13. Explain the term *strain.*
14. What do we mean by *elasticity?*
15. Give the formula for work. For power.
16. What is the difference between *kinetic* energy and *potential* energy?
17. How many horsepower must be applied to raise 2 tons a distance of 100 ft in 1 min?
18. With respect to vibratory motion explain *period* and *frequency.*
19. Compare *oscillation* and *vibration.*
20. If the liquid pressure on a surface is 8 psi, what is the total force if the surface area is 150 sq in.?
21. If a seaplane weighs 2,000 lb and the floats have a total volume of 64 cu ft, approximately how much of the floats must be submerged to support the seaplane?
22. State Pascal's law.
23. How much force can be applied by a pressure of 80 psi on a piston 8 in. in diameter? (Compute the area of the piston first.)
24. Explain how force can be multiplied by means of a hydraulic system.
25. State Boyle's law.
26. What is the formula for the *general gas law?*
27. How is *heat* manifested in matter?
28. What causes conduction of heat through a metal rod?
29. If a thermometer reads 30°C, what would a Fahrenheit thermometer indicate in the same location?
30. What is the temperature reading for absolute zero Fahrenheit?
31. What amount of work (in foot-pounds) can be done by the heat energy of 1 Btu?
32. If all the heat energy in 1 lb of gasoline could be used, how much work (in foot-pounds) could be done?
33. Explain *specific heat* of a substance.
34. Name two common devices by which mechanical advantage can be obtained.
35. What mechanical advantage can be obtained when a drive gear has 30 teeth and a driven gear has 120 teeth?
36. Explain the difference between *transverse* waves and *longitudinal* waves.
37. What is the approximate speed of sound at sea level, 0°C?
38. What is meant by *Doppler effect?*

CHAPTER 

Elements of Aerodynamics

INTRODUCTION

Aerodynamics as explained in this chapter may also be termed "theory of flight" because the flight of any aircraft or any object moving through the air depends upon the laws of acrodynamics. **Aero** means "pertaining to air, aircraft, aviation, or aeronautics." **Dynamics** is that branch of physics which considers bodies in motion and the forces that produce or change such motion. **Aero** is derived from the Greek word meaning air and **dynamics** comes from the Greek word **dynamis** meaning power. When **aero** is combined with **dynamics,** we have **aerodynamics,** meaning "the science relating to the effects produced by air or other gases in motion."

Aerodynamics may also be defined as that branch of dynamics which treats of the motion of air and other gaseous fluids and the forces acting in motion relative to such fluids.

An advanced treatment of aerodynamics is based upon the supposition that the student has previously completed extensive studies in mathematics and physics. On the other hand, the treatment in this chapter presents the basic principles of aerodynamics and flight without requiring the use of advanced mathematics and in such a manner that the subject can be easily understood by mechanics and pilots.

PHYSICAL PROPERTIES OF THE AIR

The atmosphere

Air is a mixture of several gases. For practical purposes it is sufficient to say that air is a mixture of one-fifth oxygen and four-fifths nitrogen. **Pure, dry air contains about 78 per cent (by volume) nitrogen, 21 per cent oxygen, and almost 1 per cent argon.** In addition, it contains about 0.03 per cent carbon dioxide and traces of several other gases such as hydrogen, helium, neon, etc. The distribution of gases in the air is indicated by Fig. 2 · 1.

The **atmosphere** is the whole mass of air extending upward for hundreds of miles. It may be compared with a pile of blankets. Air in the higher altitudes, like the top blanket of the pile, is under much less pressure than the air at the lower altitudes. The air at the earth's surface may be compared with the bottom blanket in a pile because it supports the weight of all the layers above it.

Air has weight and can be weighed. If an unsealed glass jar is weighed, it is heavier than it will be after the air has been exhausted with a vacuum pump. This experiment is illustrated in Fig. 2 · 2. The difference in weight is the weight of the air which was in the unsealed jar. Perfectly dry air weighs 0.07651 lb per cu ft at sea level when the temperature is 59°F (15°C), at 40° latitude, with a barometric pressure of 14.69 psi (29.92 inches of mercury). Figure 2 · 3 represents the cross section of an open container. The arrows show that the air everywhere exerts a uniform pressure in every direction. If the inside pressure against the bottom were greater than the outside pressure, the container would tend to bulge out

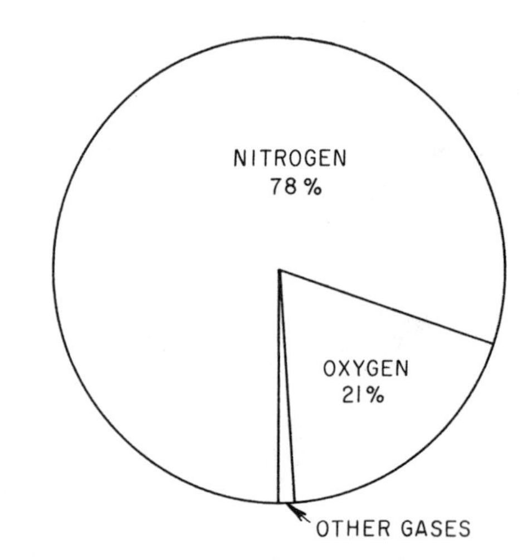

Figure **2 · 1** *Distribution of gases in the air.*

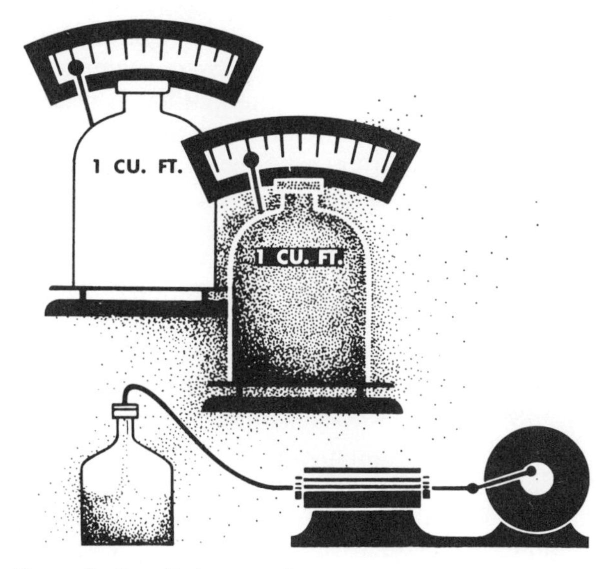

Figure **2·2** *Air has weight.*

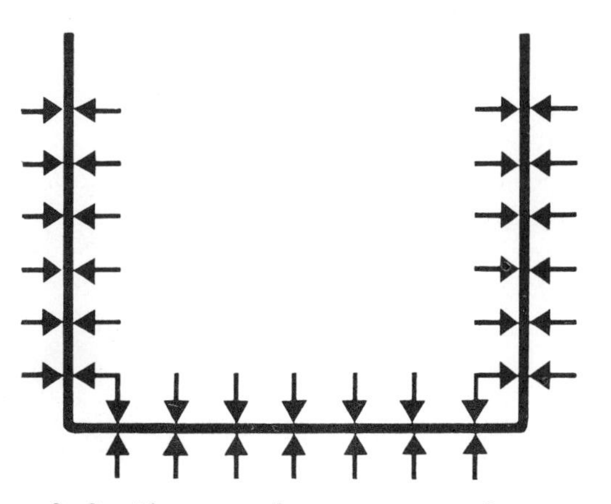

Figure **2·3** *The atmosphere exerts equal pressure in all directions.*

at the bottom. Likewise, if the inside pressure against the bottom were less than the outside pressure, the bottom would tend to bend upward.

Pressure

Pressure may be defined as force acting upon a unit area. For example, if a force of 5 lb is acting against an area of 1 sq in., we say that there is a pressure of 5 psi. Also, if a force of 20 lb is acting against an area of 2 sq in., the pressure is 10 psi. This has been explained in the previous chapter, but it is repeated here for emphasis.

We have seen that air is always pressed down by the weight of the air above it. The atmospheric pressure at any place is equal to the weight of the column of air above it and may be represented by a column of water or mercury of equal weight. If the cube-shaped box shown in Fig. 2·4 has dimensions of 1 sq in. on all sides and is filled with mercury, the weight of the mercury will be 0.491 lb and a force of 0.491 lb will be acting on the square inch at the bottom of the box. This means that there will be a pressure of 0.491 psi on the bottom of the box. If the height of the box were extended to 4 in. with the cross-sectional area remaining at 1 sq in., the pressure at the bottom would be 4 × 0.491 psi, or 1.964 psi. The pressure exerted by a column of mercury does not change with the area of the cross section. If a 1-in. column of mercury has a cross-sectional area of 10 sq in., the pressure will still be 0.491 psi even though the total volume of mercury weighs 4.91 lb. Likewise, if the 1-in. column of mercury has a cross-sectional area of ¼ sq in., the pressure will still be 0.491 psi.

It has been explained that atmospheric pressure at sea level under standard conditions is 29.92 in. Hg or 14.69 psi. When we remember that 1 in. of mercury produces a pressure of 0.491 psi, we can easily see that 29.92 in. Hg will produce a pressure of 14.69 psi ($0.491 \times 29.92 = 14.69$).

In Fig. 2·4 a tube of mercury is shown with the open end in a container of mercury. This illustrates the fact that normal atmospheric pressure at sea level will support a column of mercury 29.92 in. in height. If a glass tube having a length of 36 in. is sealed at one end and is filled with mercury and then the open end of the tube is placed in a container of mercury and raised to a vertical position, the mercury will fall until its height is 29.92 in. above the level of the mercury in the container. This will hold true only at sea level under standard conditions.

The space above the mercury in the vertical tube of Fig. 2·4 is a vacuum because no air can enter, and the pressure is therefore 0 psi. Atmos-

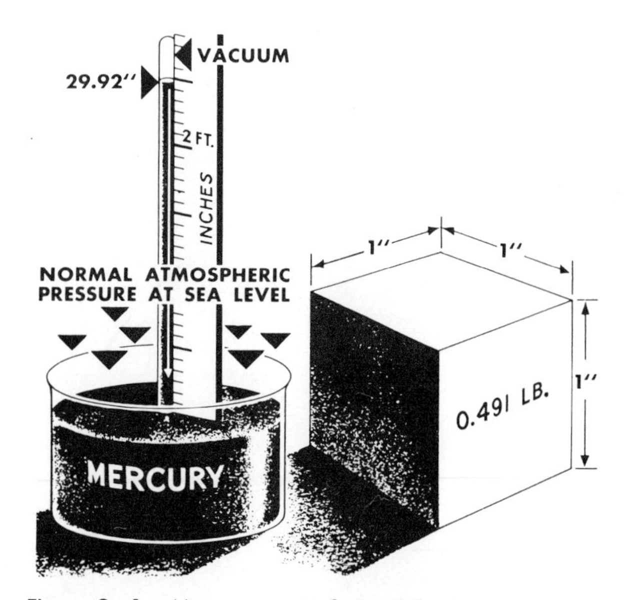

Figure **2·4** *Measurement of atmospheric pressure.*

pheric pressure acting on the surface of the mercury in the container presses down and forces the mercury up into the tube until the weight of the mercury in the tube creates a pressure equal to the atmospheric pressure. A mercury barometer is essentially a mercury-filled tube such as that illustrated, with a scale to show the height of the mercury column. Atmospheric pressure is commonly given in inches of mercury (in. Hg) for flight purposes. On weather maps and some other applications a unit called the **millibar** is used to indicate the atmospheric pressure. Sea-level pressure under standard conditions is approximately 1,013 millibars; 1 in. Hg = 37.2 millibars (approximately).

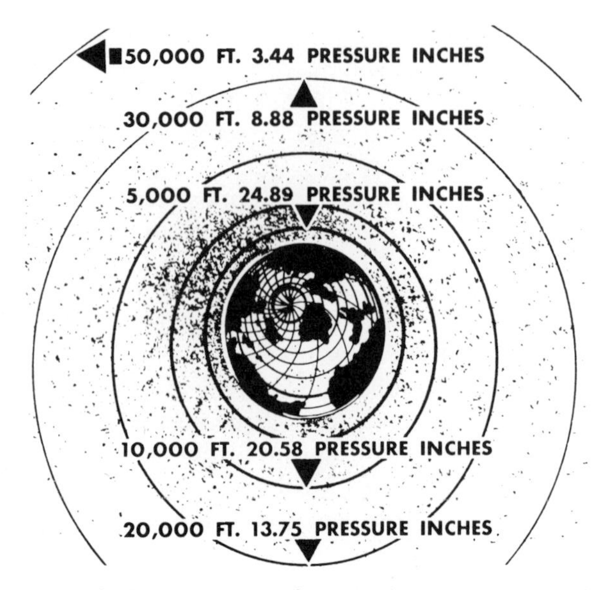

Figure **2·5** *Variation of atmospheric pressure with altitude.*

For the convenience of aeronautical engineers, a "standard" atmosphere was adopted by the National Advisory Committee for Aeronautics (now National Aeronautics and Space Administration or NASA). This standard atmosphere is entirely arbitrary, but it provides a reference and standard of comparison and should be known by all persons engaged in work involving atmospheric conditions. As previously explained, standard atmosphere at sea level is a pressure of 29.92 in. Hg with a temperature of 59°F (15°C) when the air is perfectly dry. This is supposed to be the average condition prevailing at lat. 40°N, although on different days or at different times during a day, the temperature and pressure at lat. 40°N might be much different.

Since air has weight, it is easy to recognize that the pressure of the atmosphere will vary with altitude. This is illustrated in Fig. 2·5. Notice that at 20,000 ft the pressure is less than half sea-level pressure. This means, of course, that more than half the atmosphere lies below the

Table 2·1 ICAO standard atmosphere

Altitude, ft	t		P		$\rho \times 10^3$, slugs/cu ft	c_s, ft/sec
	F	C	In. Hg	Psi		
−2,000	66.1	18.9	32.1	2,273.7	2.52	1,124.54
0	59.0	15.0	29.92	2,116.2	2.38	1,116.89
1,000	55.4	13.0	28.86	2,040.8	2.31	1,113.05
2,000	51.9	11.0	27.82	1,967.7	2.24	1,109.19
3,000	48.3	9.1	26.82	1,896.6	2.18	1,105.31
4,000	44.7	7.1	25.84	1,827.7	2.11	1,101.43
5,000	41.2	5.1	24.90	1,760.8	2.05	1,097.53
10,000	23.3	−4.8	20.58	1,455.3	1.76	1,077.81
15,000	5.5	−14.7	16.89	1,194.3	1.50	1,057.73
20,000	−12.3	−24.6	13.75	972.5	1.27	1,037.26
25,000	−30.2	−34.5	11.10	785.3	1.07	1,016.38
30,000	−48.0	−44.4	8.89	628.4	0.89	995.06
36,089	−69.7	−56.5	6.68	472.7	0.71	968.46
40,000	−69.7	−56.5	5.54	391.7	0.585	968.46
50,000	−69.7	−56.5	3.425	242.2	0.362	968.46
60,000	−69.7	−56.5	2.118	149.8	0.224	968.46
70,000	−69.7	−56.5	1.322	93.52	0.1388	968.46

t Standard temperature
P Pressure, lb/sq ft or in. Hg
ρ Density
c_s Standard speed of sound

altitude of 20,000 ft even though the "outer" half extends hundreds of miles above the earth. Table 2·1 shows the pressures at various altitudes above the earth. This table is based upon standard conditions established by the International Civil Aviation Organization (ICAO).

Air temperature

Under standard conditions, temperature decreases at approximately 1.98°C for each increase of 1,000 ft of altitude until an altitude of 38,000 ft is reached. Above this altitude the temperature remains at approximately −57°C.

Textbooks on meteorology often state that the temperature normally decreases with altitude at a rate of approximately 0.5°C per 100 m or about 1°F per 300 ft. This amounts to a decrease of about 1.52°C for each increase of 1,000 ft, which is obviously different from the decrease under standard conditions at lat. 40°N. It must be remembered that the textbooks using the foregoing values are discussing **average** conditions rather than standard conditions. This explanation is given to clear up any confusion which might exist in the mind of a student who has received previous instruction in this subject.

Density

Density has been defined previously; however, additional discussion is given here to relate density to the study of aerodynamics. Air is compressible, as illustrated in Fig. 2·6. As the air is compressed, it becomes more dense because the same quantity of air occupies less space. Density varies directly with pressure, with the temperature remaining constant. In the illustration of Fig. 2·6 the air in cylinder B has twice the density of the air in cylinder A.

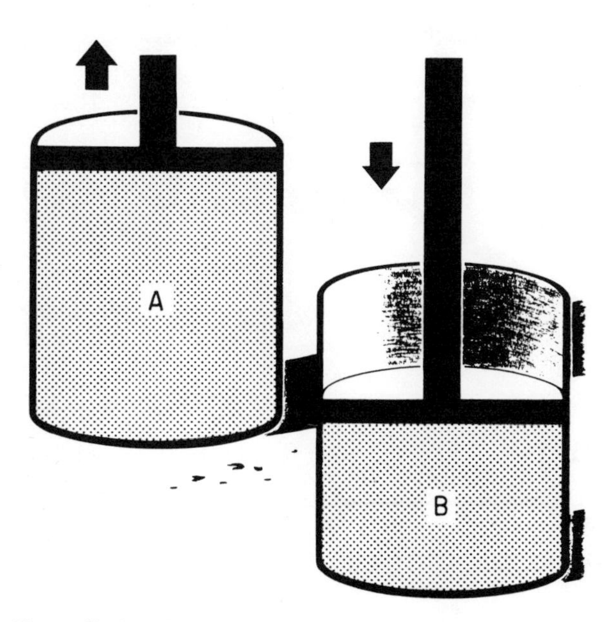

Figure 2·6 Compression and expansion of air.

Air under pressure can perform useful work. As an example, two structural-steel workers are installing steel rivets in a steel girder. The air-operated rivet hammer (pneumatic hammer) is used by one man who is called the "rivet driver," and the setting up of the rivet shank is done by his partner who is called the "rivet bucker."

Air can also be very destructive. A tornado, which is a circular whirl of great intensity and small horizontal extent with a great velocity, can lift a house, the people in it, and even animals into the air and carry them for a long distance. The horizontal diameter of a tornado varies from a few feet up to several hundred feet, and the velocity of the air may reach more than 200 mph. The pressure in the center of a tornado is very low and may be called a partial vacuum. The forces thus produced by a tornado become extremely destructive.

Since the air has less density at high altitudes, it is often described as being "thinner." In a like manner, air at low altitudes, having more density, is often described as being "thicker." Of course, these are not scientific terms, but they help a beginner to understand the meaning of density.

Changes in air density affect the flight of an airplane. With the same thrust the airplane can fly faster at a high altitude, where the density is low, than it can at a low altitude, where the density is greater. This is because the air offers less resistance to the airplane when it contains a smaller number of particles of air per unit volume. This is illustrated in Fig. 2·7.

Air expands as it is heated, and thus it tends to occupy more space. In a hot desert country an automobile tire may be properly inflated early in the morning while the air is comparatively cool, but as the sun rises and the atmosphere becomes warmer, the pressure in the tire increases. If the automobile is driven at high speeds along the hot pavement, the air in the tire becomes greatly heated and the expansion may eventually cause a "blowout," especially if the tire wall is weak. For this reason, motorists driving in desert areas usually watch their tire pressures very carefully.

The density of air is of particular importance to pilots. If the climate is cold and the altitude is low, the air will be dense and an airplane will take off at a much lower speed than it will when the air is warm or at high altitudes. In the dense air more power will be required to fly at a particular speed than when the air is less dense. For this reason a pilot must be aware of the effects of

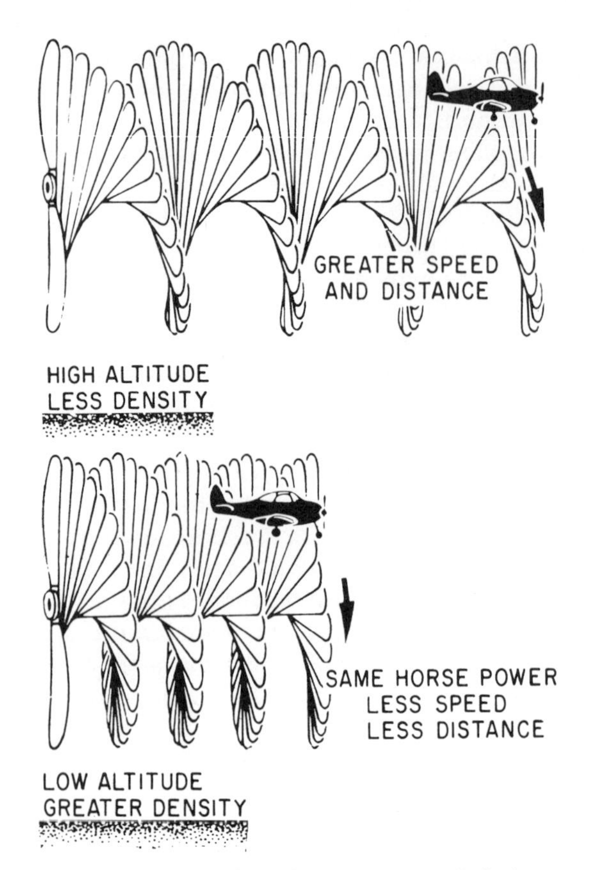

Figure 2·7 Effect of air density on aircraft flight.

density, especially if he plans to take off from a short runway.

The air may be perfectly still in one place for a short period of the time, but most of the time it is in motion. The differences in temperature between the poles and the equator and between the lower and upper atmosphere are important sources of energy which cause air motion. Furthermore, the rotation of the earth and the force of gravity affect the movement of air. As a result of the more or less constant motion of air, masses of warm air may be encountered at fairly high altitudes and masses of cold air may be found where there would be every reason to expect warm air. Nothing is so changeable as the atmosphere.

Humidity

Humidity is a condition of moisture or dampness. The maximum amount of water vapor that the air can hold depends entirely on the temperature; the higher the temperature of the air, the more water vapor it can absorb. By itself, water vapor weighs approximately five-eighths as much as an equal volume of perfectly dry air. Therefore, when air contains 5 parts of water vapor and 95 parts of perfectly dry air, it is not so heavy as air containing no moisture. This is because water is

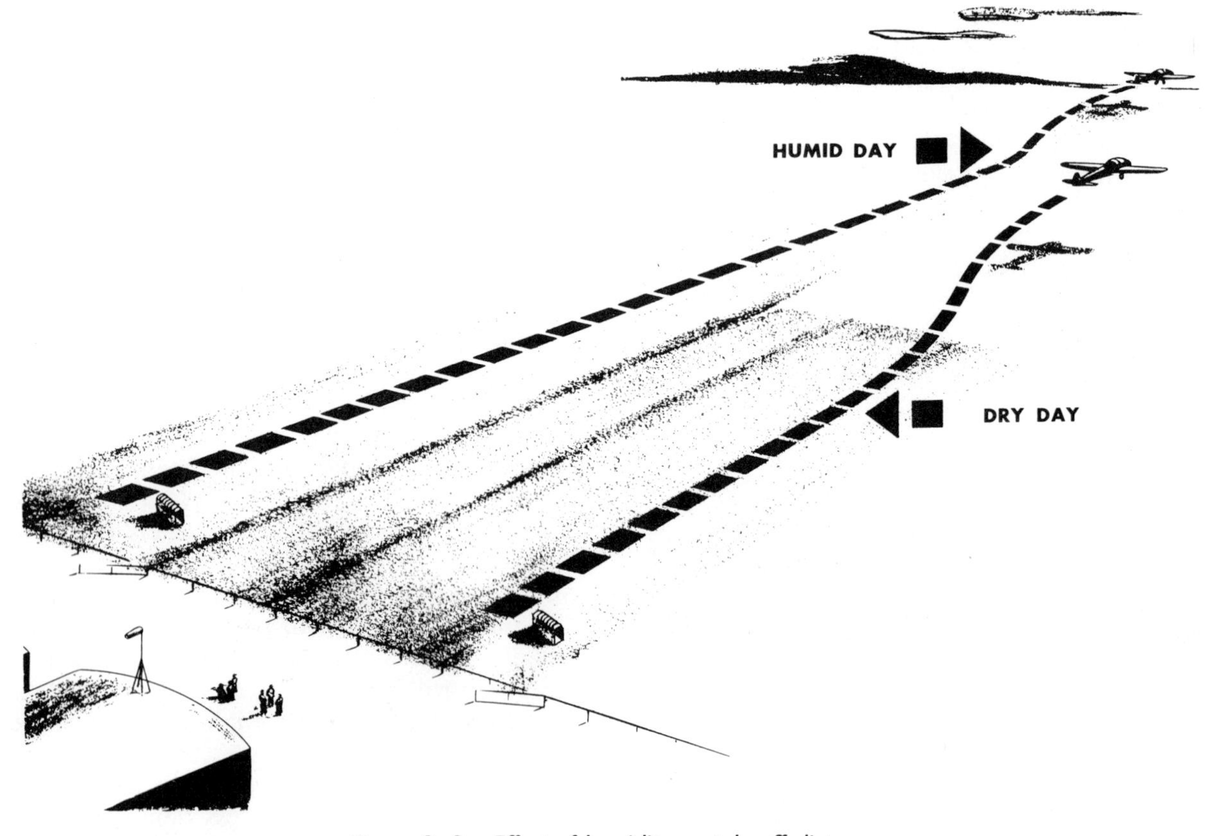

Figure 2·8 Effect of humidity on takeoff distance.

composed of hydrogen, an extremely light gas, and oxygen. Air is composed principally of nitrogen, which is almost as heavy as oxygen.

Assuming that the temperature and pressure remain the same, the density of the air varies with the humidity. On damp days the density is less than it is on dry days. For this reason an airplane requires a longer runway for takeoff on a damp (humid) day than it does on a dry day. This is illustrated in Fig. 2·8.

Air Currents

Air currents are movements of the air with respect to the earth. If the air is rising from the earth, it is called a **vertical current** or **thermal.** These currents are also called convection currents, and they often occur over sandy beaches and freshly plowed fields, in desert areas, and in other places where the air is unstable. In the past, rising or falling air currents have often been called "air pockets" or "bumps," but these terms are misnomers. The ability of rising air currents to lift an airplane is utilized by glider pilots, who are often able to keep a glider in the air for many hours merely by keeping the glider in the rising currents. Figure 2·9 illustrates how a vertical current can lift an airplane.

Relative Motion

Motion is movement. If an object changes its position, it is in motion. Any object can be located by its distance from adjacent objects; hence an object which has moved has changed its position with respect to some other object which has a fixed position, and relative motion has taken place. Picture a skater leaping through the air. There is relative motion between the skater and the ground, and there is also relative motion between the air and the skater's body. Even if the air were perfectly still with respect to the earth when the skater moved forward, there would be relative motion between the skater and the air. If we could imagine the skater poised for a moment in the air without moving, there would be no relative motion if the air were still, but if a wind were blowing, there would be relative motion.

To fix the position of an object it is necessary that three **axes** be established. On the surface of the earth one axis could be a straight line running from east to west, the second axis could be a line running from north to south and crossing the first axis, and the third axis would be a vertical straight line extending upward from the intersection of the first two axes. This is illustrated in Fig. 2·10. By using the three axes we can accurately locate the point P with respect to the intersection of the

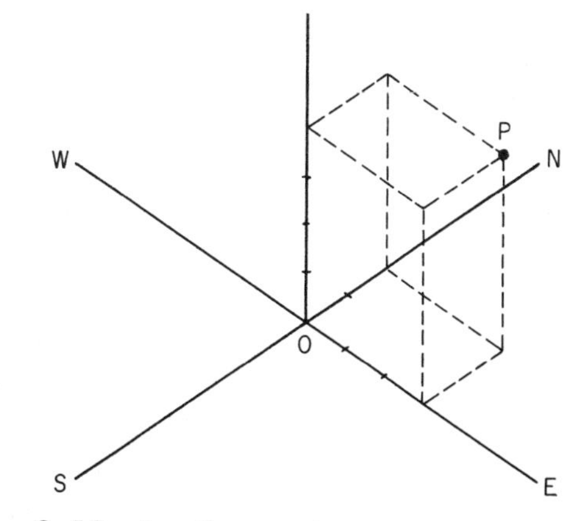

Figure **2·10** *Locating a point.*

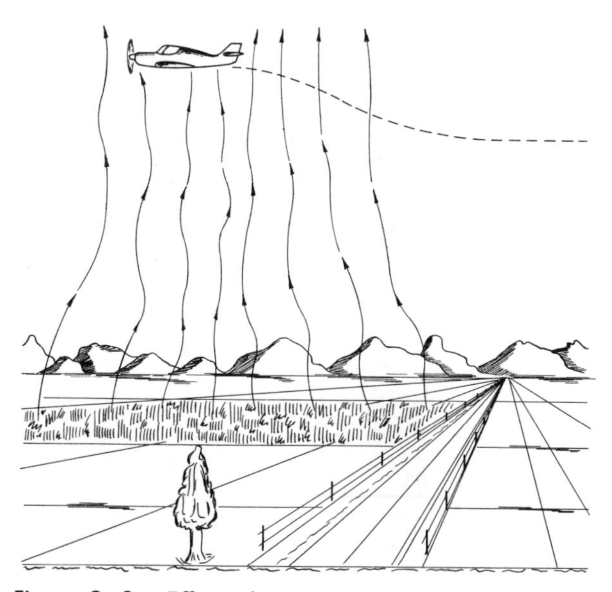
Figure **2·9** *Effect of a rising air current on airplane flight.*

Figure **2·11** *Relative motion between wind and windsock.*

three axes at O. If we use the foot as a unit of measurement in the illustration, we see that the point P is 3 ft east of the north-south axis, 2 ft north of the east-west axis, and 4 ft above the plane of the north-south and east-west axes. If the point P should move, one or more of the values would change.

To determine the degree of relative motion between two objects accurately, it is necessary to establish axes (references) from which to measure. In Fig. 2·11 a relative motion exists between the wind and all objects fixed to the earth. The windsock is fixed with respect to the earth, and relative motion exists between the wind and the windsock. In this case the reference is the earth.

A person riding in an airplane may be sitting still even though the airplane is traveling 500 mph. In this case there is no relative motion between the person and the airplane but there is relative motion between the airplane and the air.

When the air is calm, a free balloon will maintain a fixed position over its point of departure from the ground. If the wind begins to blow, the balloon will be carried away from the point of departure at the same speed as that of the wind; hence there will be no relative motion between the wind and the balloon (assuming that the balloon maintains a constant altitude), but there will be relative motion between the balloon and the earth.

An airplane must have relative motion between itself and the air in order to fly. The velocity of this motion is called the **true airspeed.** If an airplane is flying at a speed of 75 mph and there is no wind, the ground speed of the airplane will be 75 mph; that is, the relative motion between the airplane and the ground will have a velocity of 75 mph. If the airplane is flying at 75 mph and is heading directly into a 75-mph wind, the airplane will remain stationary with respect to the ground. If an airplane is flying at 75-mph airspeed against a 25-mph wind, it will have a speed of 75 mph with respect to the air and a speed of 50 mph with respect to the ground.

Thus we see that velocity is relative, because all motion is relative and velocity is the time rate of motion. **True airspeed,** represented by the symbol V_t, is the velocity of the airplane along its flight path with respect to the body of air through which the airplane is moving.

Application of Bernoulli's principle

Figure 2·12 shows an atomizer such as might be used in the home for spraying a liquid. When the rubber bulb is squeezed, air is forced through a horizontal tube which is wide where it joins the

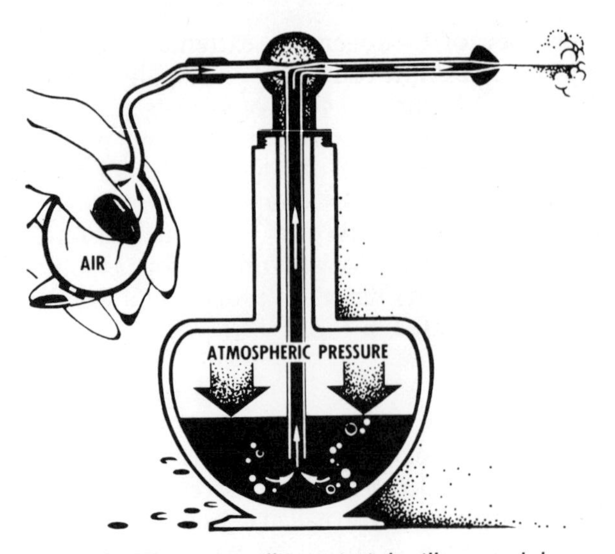

Figure **2·12** *Bernoulli's principle illustrated by an atomizer.*

bulb, narrow in the middle, and wide again where it approaches the nozzle. The narrow, middle portion is called the throat and is also called a **venturi** because of its shape. A vertical tube, called the vertical riser, extends from the lower portion of the throat into the liquid. The motion of air passing through the throat is accompanied by a reduction of pressure, so the pressure on the liquid in the riser becomes less than the atmospheric pressure on the surface of the liquid. The difference in pressure forces the liquid to ascend in the riser to join with the stream of air and be expelled through the nozzle.

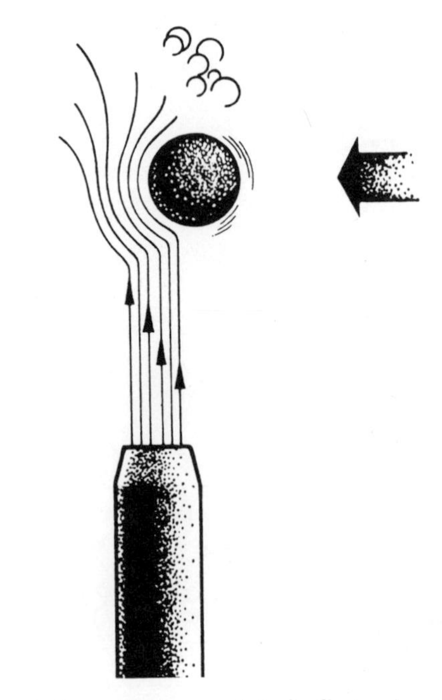

Figure **2·13** *Air jet and ball illustrating Bernoulli's principle.*

Figure 2·13 shows a ball balanced in a stream of air rising from a vertical tube at a comparatively high velocity. This simple phenomenon has been used many times in store windows to attract attention by its apparently mysterious action. Actually the principle is easily explained. The velocity of the air coming from the jet is greater than that of the surrounding air, but its pressure is less. When the ball starts to move horizontally out of the airstream, the atmospheric pressure, which is greater, forces it back into the balanced position.

A simple experiment can be performed with a small strip of lightweight paper. Hold one end by the thumb and forefinger just below the lower lip and blow. The paper will rise when you begin to blow and will fall when you stop blowing. The velocity of the air above the paper creates a region of reduced pressure which is less than the atmospheric pressure acting on the lower surface. The difference of pressure between the upper and lower surfaces causes "lift."

Another experiment to demonstrate Bernoulli's principle is illustrated in Fig. 2·14. When two sheets of paper are held by the edges in such a manner that there is a space between them as shown and a stream of air is blown through the space, the two sheets will immediately come together. The atmospheric pressure above the top sheet and below the lower sheet is greater than the air pressure between the sheets. The difference of pressure then forces the sheets together.

An amazing demonstration of the same principle is shown in Fig. 2·15. The equipment consists

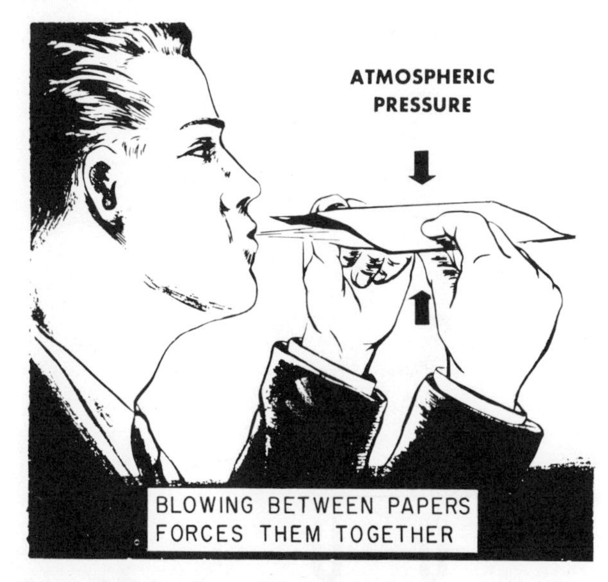

Figure **2·14** *Bernoulli's principle demonstrated by blowing between two sheets of paper.*

Figure **2·15** *Card and spool used to demonstrate Bernoulli's principle.*

of an ordinary sewing-thread spool, a small piece of cardboard, and a pin. The pin is inserted through the center of the cardboard and into the hole in the spool. This is to prevent the cardboard from slipping down away from the spool. Now, if you hold the card so it fits snugly against the end of the spool and blow through the spool, you can let go of the card and it will cling to the end of the spool. When you stop blowing, the card will fall away. The reason for this phenomenon is that the velocity of the air escaping between the card and the spool is high and its pressure is therefore low. The atmospheric pressure on the other side of the card is greater than the pressure of the air escaping between the card and the spool; hence the card is held against the end of the spool by the atmospheric pressure.

The experiments described in the foregoing paragraphs are all based upon **Bernoulli's principle.** This principle states that **as the air velocity increases, the pressure decreases; and as the velocity decreases, the pressure increases.** Actually, in technical language, Bernoulli's principle states that **the total energy of a particle in motion is constant at all points on its path in a steady flow.** From this formal statement is derived the simple principle given above. However, it is sufficient for the pilot or the technician to remember merely the fact that pressure decreases as velocity increases, and vice versa, in order to grasp the fundamentals of aerodynamics.

Pressure and force differential

The difference between **pressure** and **force** must be kept in mind when their respective effects are considered. A pressure of 5 psi acting on an area of 20 sq in. will exert more force than a pressure of 10 psi acting on an area of 5 sq in. This is illustrated in Fig. 2·16. In this case the 5 psi pressure will move the pistons against the 10 psi pressure because the 5 psi produces a force of 100 lb and the 10 psi produces a force of only 50 lb.

The direction in which the pressure is acting is also important. The pressure of a gas always exerts a force perpendicular to the surface upon which it is acting. In the illustration of Fig. 2·17 is shown a hemisphere (one-half sphere). Obviously the spherical side has more area than the flat side. It would appear from this that the force acting on the spherical side would be greater than the force acting on the flat side when the pressure is equal on all sides. It is true that the total force acting on the spherical side is greater than the force acting on the flat side; however, the directions of the forces acting on the spherical side vary as much as 180°. The resultant total force, indicated by the arrow *A*, is exactly equal to the total force acting on the flat side as indicated by arrow *B*.

The movement of an airplane wing through the air creates both differential of pressure and differential of force between the top and the bottom of the wing. The air flowing over the curved top surface increases in velocity with respect to the air flowing across the flat bottom of the wing because the air over the top has a greater distance to travel. This results in a lowering of pressure on

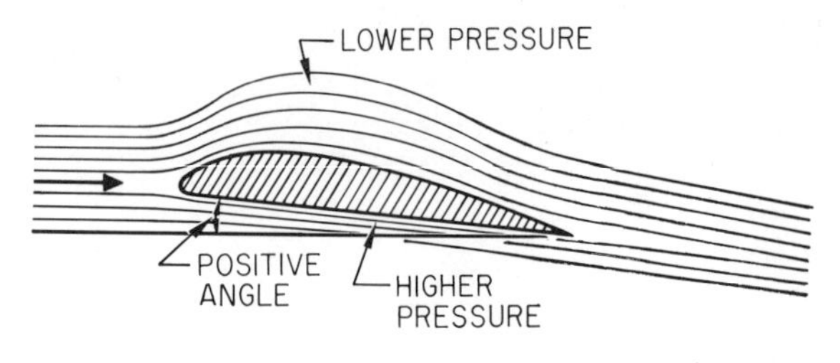

Figure **2·18** *Pressure differential created by a wing in flight.*

the top of the wing; hence lift is developed. This is illustrated in Fig. 2·18.

The venturi tube

The operation of a **venturi tube** provides a good illustration of Bernoulli's principle. The upper drawing of Fig. 2·19 shows a venturi tube or meter used originally for the measurement of the flow of water in pipes. The device consists of a conical nozzlelike reducer through which air or water can enter, a narrow section called the throat, and a conical enlargement for the outlet which attains the same size as the inlet but more gradually. The quantity of air drawn through the inlet will be discharged through the same-sized opening at the outlet. The velocity of the air must therefore increase as it passes through the inlet cone, must attain a maximum value in the throat, and thereafter gradually slows down to its initial value at the outlet. The pressure in the throat is consequently less than at the entrance.

The lower drawing of Fig. 2·19 shows a venturi tube with manometers, which are gages for measuring pressure. Bernoulli's principle states that the total energy of a particle in motion is constant at all points on its path in a steady

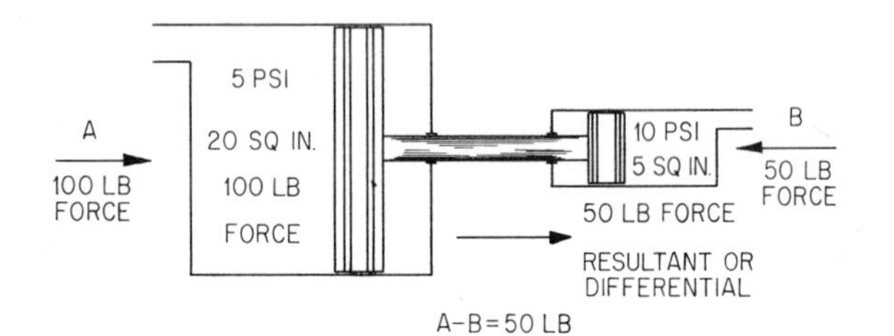

Figure **2·16** *Force differential.*

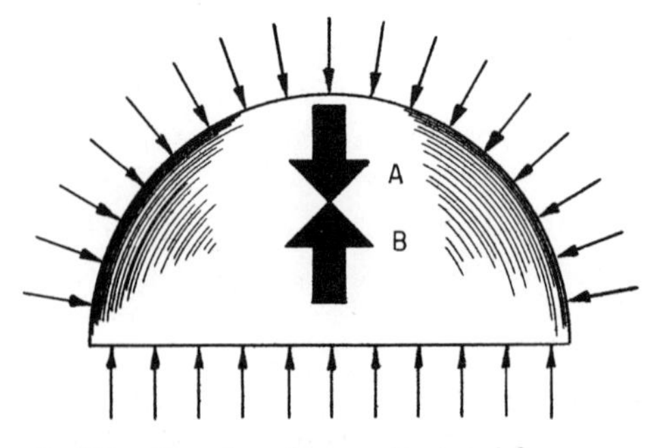

Figure **2·17** *Equal and opposite total forces.*

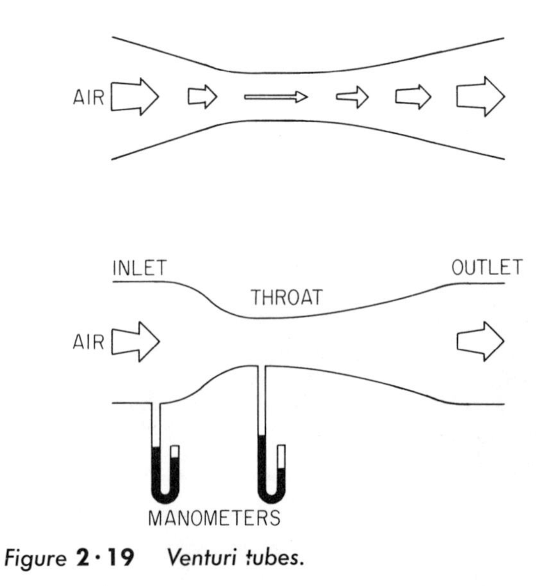

Figure **2·19** *Venturi tubes.*

flow. The pressure in the throat of the venturi tube is less than the pressure in any other part because of increased velocity. This is explained by the fact that the same amount of air passes all points in the tube in a given time. That is, the air must come out of one end of the tube as fast as it enters the other end. Since the throat is smaller, the air must travel faster through the throat for the same amount of air to pass through the throat as passes through the inlet and outlet.

The total energy remains constant in any system. In the venturi tube the energy of motion has increased in the throat; hence it is necessary for the energy of pressure to decrease. The reduction of pressure in the throat as compared with the pressure in the inlet is shown by the height of the mercury or other liquid in the manometers.

Figure 2·20 shows the method for measuring air pressure on various parts of the wing. Such measurements can be taken in flight or on the ground. Tests made a number of years ago showed that for a typical wing of that period, having a flat lower surface, when this lower surface was parallel to the direction of motion of the wing through the air, all the lift was due to the pressure on the upper surface of the wing being less than atmospheric. When the leading edge of the wing was raised so that the lower surface made an angle to the direction of motion, part of the lifting force came from the pressure on the lower surface being greater than atmospheric. Most of the lift, however, still came from the lower pressure on the upper surface of the wing.

Reaction of air on a flat plate

The effect produced by a flat plate moving through the air is illustrated in Fig. 2·21. When the air strikes the leading edge of the flat plate, the passage of the air is obstructed and its velocity is reduced. Some of the particles of air flow over the upper surface and some flow under the lower surface, but all particles of air must reach

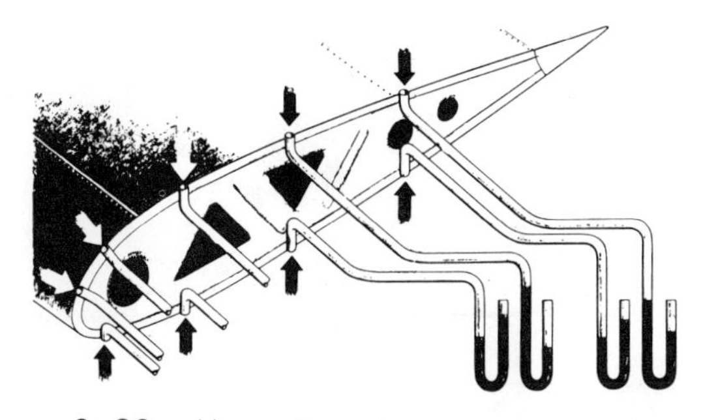

Figure **2·20** *Measuring air pressure on a wing test section.*

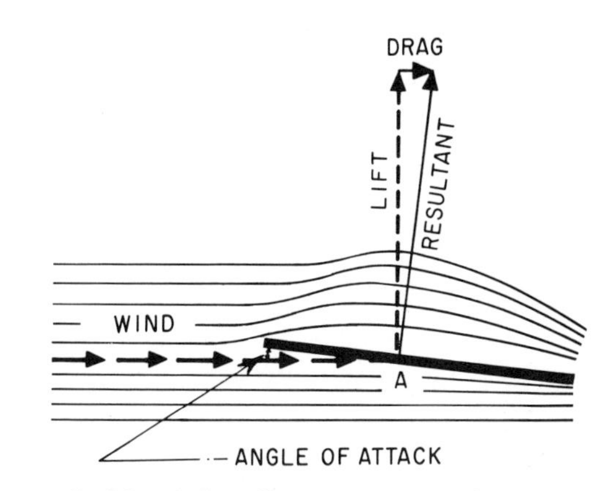

Figure **2·21** *A flat plate in a stream of air.*

the trailing edge of the plate at the same time. Those particles which pass over the upper surface have farther to go and therefore must move faster than those passing under the lower edge. In accordance with Bernoulli's principle, the increased velocity above the plate results in a lower pressure than that existing below the plate. Since there is a difference of pressure, the greater must prevail, and there is an upward force exerted on the plate. This force is called **lift.**

If the region of very low pressure immediately above the plate is too large, the particles of air do not flow smoothly downward to the rear but they drop into this region and behave wildly, causing turbulence and eddy currents. The loss of velocity causes an increase of pressure above the plate and a loss of lift. If the turbulence is not too great, there is still enough difference between the pressure above and below the plate to sustain lift.

The angle between the plate and the airstream in Fig. 2·21 is the **angle of attack.** The formal definition is rather technical and will be explained later in this text. When the angle of attack changes, the lift and the resistance to the forward movement of the plate, called **drag,** change. If the flat plate is placed in the airstream in such a position that it does not materially change the direction of the streamlines, there is no lift because there is no difference between the velocity of the air flowing over the upper surface and that flowing under the lower surface. Under these conditions there is no difference in pressure between the upper and the lower surfaces of the plate. As we have already observed, however, when the plate is inclined at a small angle of attack, lift and drag become important. As we increase the angle of attack, the airstream must change direction more and there is more differential and more lift through a range of several degrees.

The dynamic development of lift can be understood by considering Newton's Third Law of Motion: **For every action there is an equal and opposite reaction.** When there is an angle between the flat plate and the direction of the airstream, the air is forced to change direction. If the flat plate is tilted upward against the airstream, the air flowing under the plate is forced downward. The plate therefore applies a downward force to the air, and the air applies an equal and opposite upward force to the flat plate. This is **lift.** The same principle applies to a water skier. When the skis are moving along the surface of the water, they are applying a downward force to the water and causing some of the water to change position. The water applies a force to the skis sufficient to support the weight of the skier.

The angle through which an airstream is deflected by any lifting surface is called the **downwash angle.** It is especially important when control surfaces are studied because they are normally placed to the rear of the wings where they are influenced by the downward deflected airstream known as the **downwash.**

Drag does not behave like lift. Lift increases as the angle of attack increases, and this increase in lift is roughly proportional to the increase in the angle of attack. Drag also increases as the angle of attack increases, but it increases much more rapidly than lift. Therefore, when the angle of attack reaches a certain magnitude, the drag may be greater than the lift.

Center of pressure

The **center of pressure** (CP) is shown at *A* in Fig. 2·21. The CP is the point at which the chord of an airfoil section intersects the line of action of the resultant aerodynamic forces and about which the pressures balance. The CP of an airfoil must not be confused with the **aerodynamic center.** The aerodynamic center is defined as a point in a cross section of an airfoil or other aerodynamic body or combination of bodies about which the pitching moment remains practically constant with nearly all changes in angle of attack. The CP moves when the angle of attack changes.

In Fig. 2·21, the arrow pointing vertically upward from the CP represents the lift because the force of lift tends to raise the flat plate. The arrow pointing horizontally to the rear at the top of the diagram represents drag, because that force tends to resist any forward movement of the flat plate. If the flat plate were a kite, we could say that the drag is the force which represents the tendency of the wind to blow the kite to the rear. However, a kite is held by a string which counteracts the tendency of the wind to blow the kite to the rear and permits the force of lift to raise the kite. If the string breaks, the kite is no longer maintained at the proper angle and it is carried away by the airstream. Since lift has disappeared, the kite eventually falls to the ground.

If there is no wind, a kite can be raised by holding the string and running. This creates an artificial wind, or in technical terms, there is relative motion between the kite and the air. We have already learned that, if the string breaks, whether we run with the kite in still air or stand motionless and hold the string while the wind opposes the kite, the kite will fall; returning to the flat plate, the same fact holds true. There must be relative motion between the plate and the air to cause a pressure differential and create lift.

Lift and drag components

The effects of lift and drag can be determined by employing force vectors as shown in Fig. 2·22. If the lift vector is represented by the line **AB** and the drag vector by the line **AD,** then the resultant of the two forces is **AC.** As previously explained, lift is always vertical and drag is always horizontal when the airplane is flying straight and level. The lengths of the arrows **AB, AC,** and **AD** are in proportion to the magnitudes of the forces they represent. For example, if lift is four times as great as drag, the arrow representing lift must be drawn four times as long as the arrow representing drag.

The resultant of lift and drag shows the direction and magnitude of the force created by the

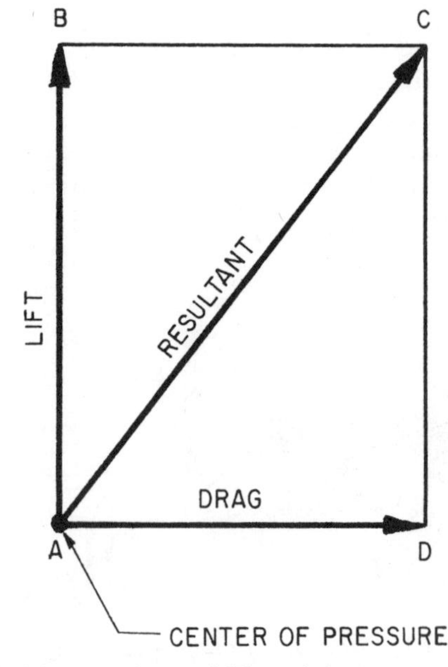

Figure **2·22** *Resultant of lift and drag.*

difference in pressure between the top surface and the bottom surface of a flat surface. Lift and drag vectors applied to a flat plate are shown in Fig. 2·23. If the plate represents a kite, then the kite string will take a direction the same as the resultant of lift and drag except for a small difference caused by gravity.

If the direction and magnitude (length) of the resultant are both known but the magnitudes of the lift and drag are not known, they can be found. Simply draw a horizontal line to the left from the arrowhead on the resultant and draw a vertical line upward from the CP. The two lines will intersect and establish the point from which the magnitudes of the lift and drag can be determined. These lift and drag arrows (vectors) are called **components** because the forces which they represent are component parts of the force represented by the resultant.

Lift-drag ratio

The angle of attack in the drawing of Fig. 2·23 is greater than that shown in Fig. 2·21; hence both the lift and the drag are greater, but the drag has increased in proportion more than the lift. The ratio of the lift to the drag at any angle of attack is a measure of the "effectiveness" because lift is a beneficial force and drag is a detrimental force. However, drag must be accepted as a necessary evil to produce lift. The drag developed to produce lift is called **induced drag.** The ratio of lift to drag is called the **lift-drag ratio** and is commonly referred to as the **L/D ratio.** However, when any L/D ratio is given, the corresponding angle of attack should also be given because the L/D ratio has no meaning by itself.

The L/D ratio is a fraction with the lift for the numerator and the drag for the denominator. It is a perfectly simple principle of mathematics that, if the numerator remains the same and the denominator increases, the value of the fraction decreases. For example, one-half is obviously greater than one-fourth. Likewise, if the denominator is small and the numerator large, the value of the fraction is greater. If the L/D ratio is 21:1 at a certain angle of attack, the value of the fraction, and hence the effectiveness, is greater than when the L/D ratio is 14:1.

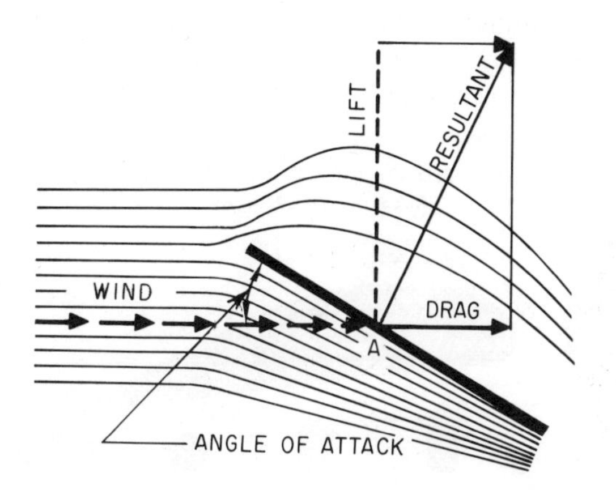

Figure 2·23 Lift and drag applied to the flat plate.

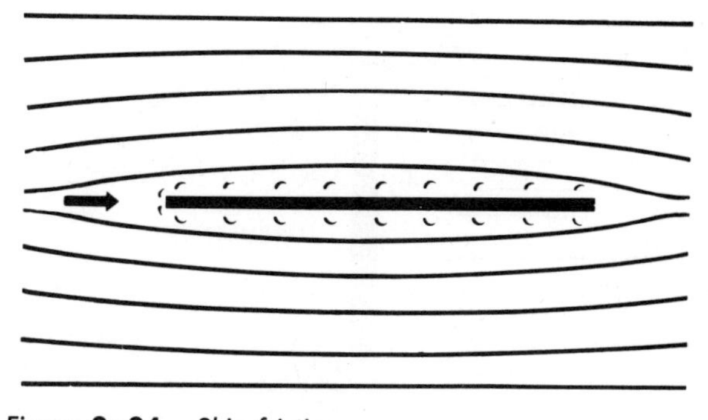

Figure 2·24 Skin friction.

Skin friction

Skin friction is illustrated in Fig. 2·24. A thin, flat plate is held edgewise to an airstream. The particles of air separate at the leading edge and flow smoothly over the upper surface and under the lower surface, reuniting behind the trailing edge. The resistance of skin friction is caused by the particles of air tending to cling to the surface of the plate. There are two reasons for the air clinging to the surfaces of the plate. First, the plate has a certain amount of roughness, relatively speaking. Regardless of how much we attempt to smooth a surface, it is impossible to make it perfectly smooth. This can be proved quickly by observing a polished surface through a high-powered microscope. To eliminate skin friction altogether it would be necessary to have all the molecules of the material in perfect alignment on the surface of the material.

The second reason why air tends to cling to the surface of the plate is because of the **viscosity** of the air. Even though it is not always apparent, air does have "thickness" like oil or sirup. Technically, viscosity is the resistance offered by a fluid (gas or liquid) to the relative motion of its particles, but in the common use of the term it means the adhesive or sticky characteristics of a fluid.

Streamline and turbulent flow

A **streamline flow** may be defined as a smooth, nonturbulent flow. A **turbulent flow** is defined as a flow characterized by turbulence, that is, a flow in which the velocity varies erratically in both

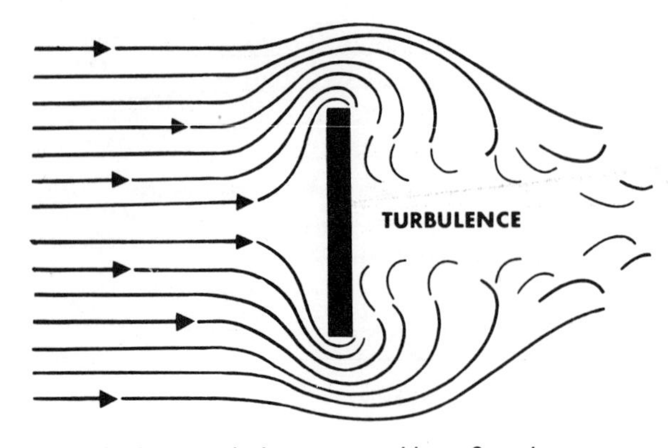

Figure **2·25** *Turbulence caused by a flat plate perpendicular to airstream.*

magnitude and direction with time. Figure 2·25 illustrates the turbulence which is created when a flat plate is held perpendicular to (normal to) the direction of an airstream. The air striking the plate must change its velocity and direction to pass around the plate. The abrupt change in direction of the airflow around the edges of the plate creates the turbulence which can be seen on the side of the plate opposite to that from which the air is approaching.

It must be understood that a streamline flow may occur with certain shapes other than that of a thin, flat plate held edgewise to an airstream. A typical streamline form, for example, may be shaped like a teardrop. Later in this text we shall discuss the flow of air around different-shaped sections.

When a flat plate is at a low angle of attack, as in the lower part of Fig. 2·26, there is a slight increase of pressure over the upper surface, caused by turbulence, with a resulting loss of lift, but when the flat plate is at a higher angle of attack, as in the upper part of Fig. 2·26, the turbulence

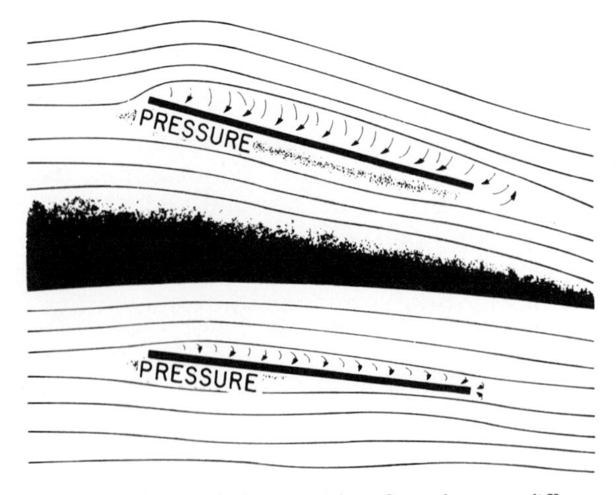

Figure **2·26** *Turbulence with a flat plate at different angles of attack.*

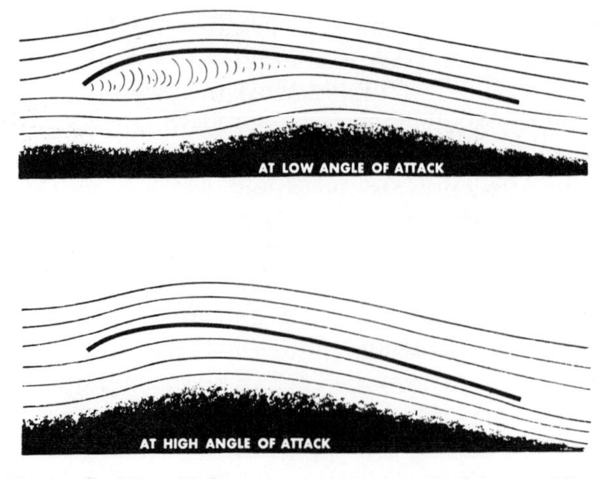

Figure **2·27** *Airflow around a curved plate at different angles of attack.*

is greater and the reduction of lift is more pronounced.

The study of a flat plate in an airstream makes it easy to understand the elementary principles of lift and drag, but the wing of an airplane is not a flat plate. Instead, it is a curved plate, somewhat resembling the wing of a bird; hence the next step is to observe the performance of curved plates in airstreams.

The upper part of Fig. 2·27 shows the airflow about a curved plate at a low angle of attack. The particles of air which reach the upper surface flow smoothly to the rear, but the particles which strike the lower surface must abruptly change direction to follow the shape of the plate. This sudden change of direction causes a turbulent region behind the leading edge and increases the drag at a low angle of attack where the drag should be low.

The lower part of Fig. 2·27 shows the airflow about a curved plate at a slightly higher angle of attack. The airstreams flow much more smoothly to the rear than they do when the curved plate is at a low angle of attack or when a flat plate is at a high angle of attack. It is apparent that a curved is better than a flat plate for high angles of attack but inferior to a flat plate at low angles of attack.

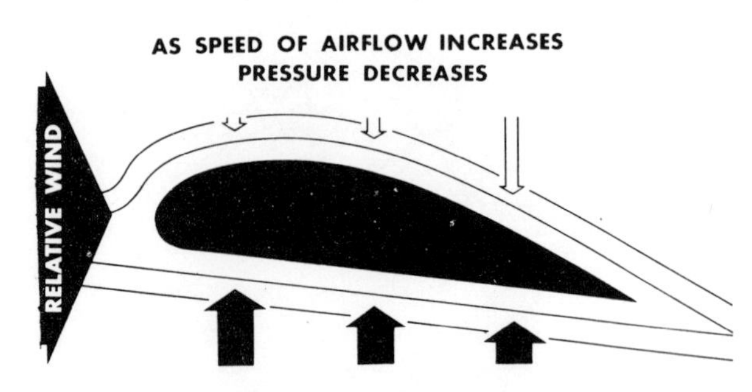

Figure **2·28** *Airfoil in an airstream.*

Furthermore, a simple curved plate lacks the thickness necessary to contain the wing structure. The problem of drag caused by turbulence behind the leading edge of a curved plate at a low angle of attack and the problem of housing the wing structure can be solved by using a form like that shown in Fig. 2·28, which shows the silhouette of an airfoil, called an airfoil section.

Laminar flow

The word **laminar** is derived from the Latin word **lamina** meaning a thin plate of metal or some other material. **Laminar flow** employs the concept that air is flowing in thin sheets or layers close to the surface of a wing with no disturbance between the layers of air. That is, there is no cross flow of air particles from one layer of air to another. Also, there is no sideways movement of air particles with respect to the direction of airflow.

Laminar flow is most likely to occur where the surface is extremely smooth and especially near the leading edge of an airfoil. Under these conditions the boundary layer will be very thin. The **boundary layer** is that layer of air adjacent to the airfoil surface. The air velocity in this layer varies from zero on the surface of the airfoil to the velocity of the airstream at the outer edge of the boundary layer. The cause of the boundary layer is the friction between the surface of the wing and the air.

Ordinarily the airflow at the leading edge of a smooth-surfaced wing will be laminar, but as the air moves toward the trailing edge of the wing, the boundary layer becomes thicker and laminar flow diminishes. This is illustrated in Fig. 2·29. Many experiments have been carried out in an effort to control the boundary layer and increase laminar flow. One of the methods used for boundary-layer control is illustrated in Fig. 2·30.

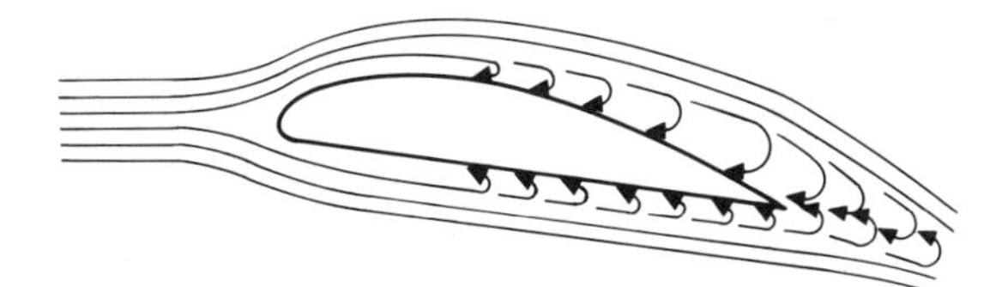

*Figure **2·29** Development of boundary layer as a result of skin friction.*

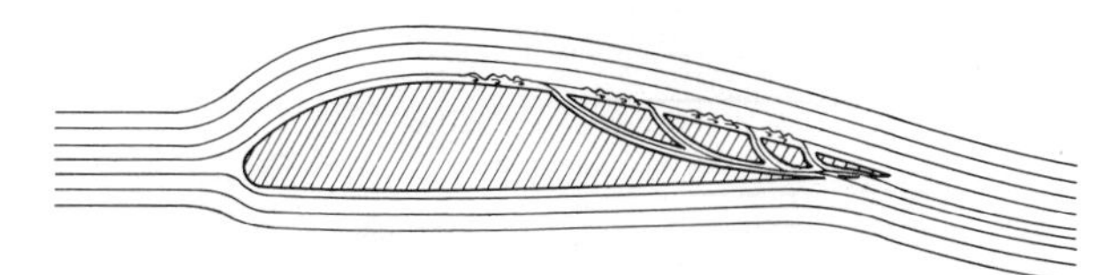

*Figure **2·30** One method for boundary-layer control.*

Small holes are placed in the upper surface of the wing, and the boundary-layer air is drawn through these holes by means of a high-volume, low-pressure air pump and ejected through holes under the trailing edge of the wing. The effect is to keep the boundary layer thin and permit laminar flow to continue.

Low-drag boundary-layer control

One of the most interesting methods used to overcome the effects of turbulence in the boundary layer has been developed by the Norair Division of the Northrop Corporation and is called **low-drag boundary-layer control.** Wind-tunnel tests were used to study the nature of boundary-layer turbulence, and the results of one of these tests is shown in Fig. 2·31. This illustration shows smooth flow near the leading edge of the wing and turbulence developing as the air flows to the rear. A mixture of lampblack and kerosene is used to make the turbulence visible.

The principle of low-drag boundary-layer control involves maintaining the speed of the boundary layer by sucking part of it through thin slots extending along the wing surfaces from the fuselage to the wing tip. A diagram illustrating this principle is shown in Fig. 2·32. When the turbulent air is drawn through the slots in the

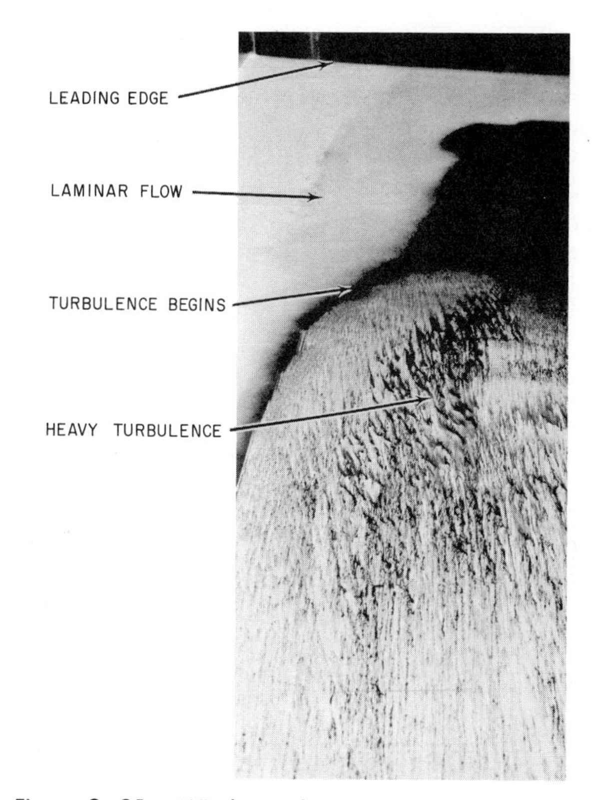

*Figure **2·31** Wind-tunnel experiment showing turbulence over a wing.*

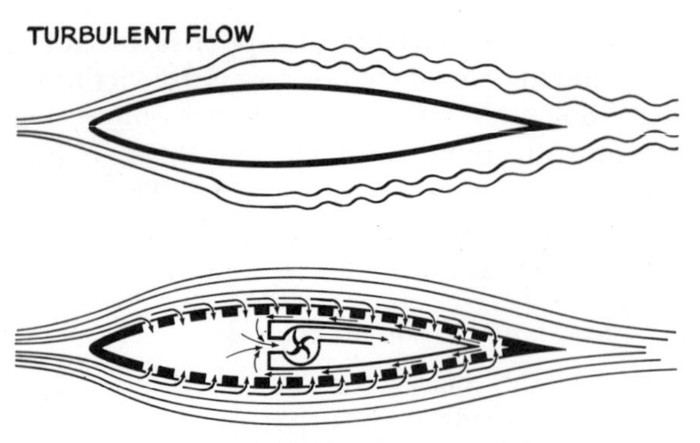

Figure **2·32** *Diagrams showing principle of low-drag boundary-layer control.*

wing, a smooth flow can continue to the trailing edge of the wing. The air drawn into the wing may be discharged at the trailing edge of the wing, or it may be ducted into the fuselage and discharged through the tail of the fuselage.

A cutaway cross section of a wing designed for low-drag boundary-layer control is shown in Fig. 2·33. The upper surface of the wing is made with two sheets of aluminum alloy separated by I sections to produce plenum chambers extending along the wing from the fuselage to the wing tip. In the top surface, small slots, extending the full length of the wing, are cut. Small holes are drilled from the slots into the plenum chambers to permit the air to enter the chambers.

The construction of the slotted wing surface is accomplished by using two sheets of aluminum alloy. The thicker of the two sheets is approximately 3/32 in. in thickness, and into this sheet are cut rectangular grooves about 3/16 in. in width and 0.030 in. in depth. In the bottom of these grooves holes are drilled as shown in the illustration. After this preparation a very thin sheet of aluminum alloy is bonded to the top of the thick

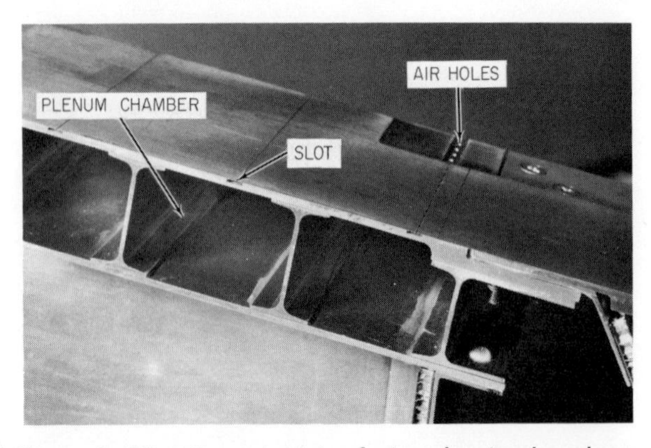

Figure **2·33** *Cross section of wing showing low-drag–boundary-layer-control construction.*

sheet. Following this, slots about 0.004 in. in width are cut in the top skin along the grooves in the thick sheet. This construction provides continuous slots along the surface and still retains a large percentage of the strength of the wing skin.

One of the essential features of the construction described above is a mirror-smooth surface. This is important because ripples or other surface irregularities would greatly reduce the effectiveness of the slots.

The effect of low-drag boundary-layer control is to reduce the friction drag of the wing by as much as 80 per cent. This, of course, will greatly reduce fuel consumption for a given flight distance, thus increasing the range proportionately. The airplane will therefore fly farther, carry larger payloads, and operate at a reduced ton-per-mile cost.

Airfoils

An **airfoil** is technically defined as any surface, such as an airplane aileron, elevator, rudder, or wing, designed to obtain reaction from the air through which it moves. An airfoil section is a cross section of an airfoil which can be drawn as a silhouette as illustrated in Fig. 2·28. If the wing of an airplane were sawed through from the leading edge to the trailing edge, the side view of the section through the wing at that point would be its airfoil section. An **airfoil profile** is merely the outline or shape of an airfoil section. It is a common practice among aircraft people to use the word "airfoil" when "airfoil section" or perhaps "airfoil profile" is meant.

The previous discussion of streamline flow, laminar flow, turbulence, and the reaction of forces between the airstream and an object in its path is essential to any explanation of airfoils. A flat plate perpendicular to an airsteam obtains reaction from the air through which it moves, but it is not useful as an airfoil because there is no lift and turbulence is excessive. When an airfoil is at an acute angle (less than a right angle) to the airstream, it is an airfoil because there is lift. The flat plate is not an efficient airfoil, however, because of the excessive resistance resulting from the turbulence which accompanies the disturbed airflow. Likewise, a curved plate is not an efficient airfoil because of turbulence at a low angle of attack.

As already mentioned, an efficient airfoil must have both curvature and thickness. Curvature directs the airflow downward and reduces the turbulence at the leading edge when the airfoil is at a high angle of attack. Thickness eliminates the turbulence occurring behind the leading edge of the simple curved plate and provides the thickness necessary for the internal bracing used in a modern airplane wing. Of course, the wing could be externally braced, but this would create turbulence and cause drag.

Referring to Fig. 2·28, it will be observed that the particles of air flow over and under the airfoil and, in accordance with Bernoulli's principle, the pressure decreases as the speed of the airflow increases. The arrowhead at the left in Fig. 2·28 represents the **relative wind.** Technically speaking, the relative wind is the velocity of the air with respect to a body in it. It is usually determined from measurements made at such a distance from the body that the disturbing effect of the body upon the air is negligible. In other words, the relative wind refers to the velocity of the air before it strikes the leading edge of the airfoil and divides the flow around it. In calm, still air, the direction of the relative wind is opposite to the flight path of the airplane with reference to the ground. When the wind blows, the path of the airplane referred to the ground usually is not the same as the path referred to the moving air. The aerodynamic forces on the airplane are always considered as a function of the relative wind and not of the ground wind.

Figure 2·34 illustrates four airfoil profiles of different shapes together with their chords. A **chord** may be defined as **the reference line from which the upper and lower contours of an airfoil are measured.** A chord is also defined as **a straight line directly across an airfoil from the leading edge to the trailing edge.** In Fig. 2·34, profile *A* has a double convex shape. The chord is simply the straight line from the leading edge to the trailing edge. Profile *B* has a convex upper curvature and a concave lower curvature. The chord is the straight line connecting the imaginary perpendiculars erected at the leading and trailing edges. Profile *C* has a flat lower surface; hence the chord is the straight line connecting the leading and trailing edges. Profile *D* resembles profile *B*, and again the chord is the straight line connecting imaginary perpendiculars erected at the leading and trailing edges.

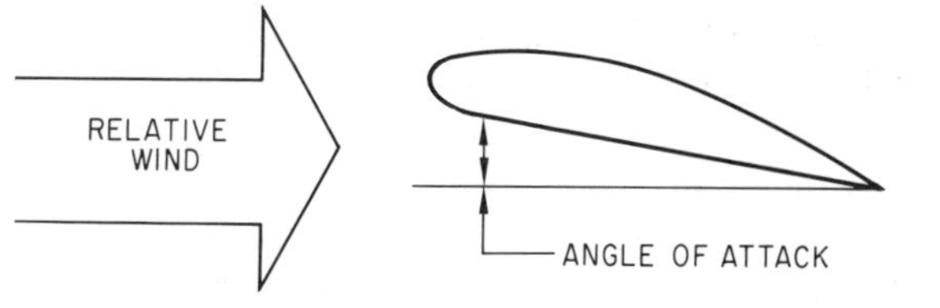

Figure **2·35** *Angle of attack.*

The **angle of attack** is the acute angle between a reference line in a body and the line of the relative wind direction, as shown in Fig. 2·35. The angle of attack can be defined more simply as **the acute angle between the chord of an airfoil and the relative wind.** In the National Aeronautics and Space Administration Aeronautical Dictionary the definition of angle of attack is: **The angle at which a body, such as an airfoil or fuselage, or a system of bodies, such as a helicopter rotor, meets a flow, ordinarily measured between a reference line in the body and a line in the direction of the flow or in the direction of movement of the body.** The airfoil profile in Fig. 2·35 has a flat lower surface, like *C* in Fig. 2·34; hence its chord is simply the straight line along its lower surface. The angle of attack is the acute angle between the lower surface of the air-

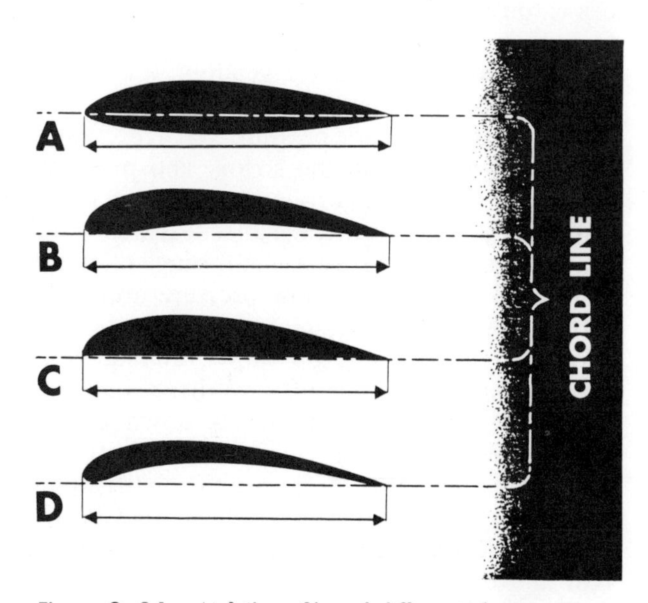

Figure **2·34** *Airfoil profiles of different shapes.*

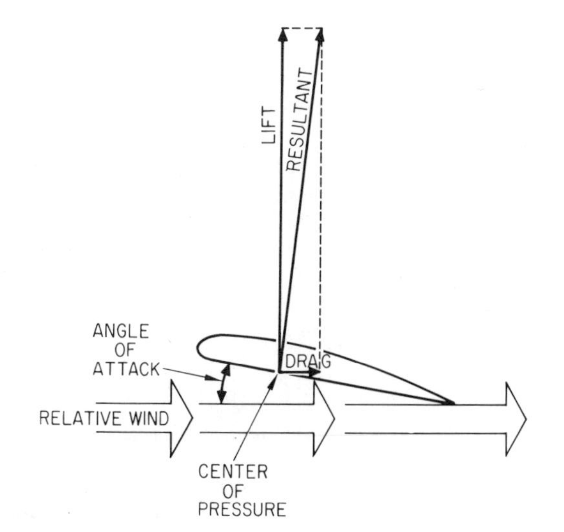

Figure **2·36** *Forces acting on an airfoil in an airstream.*

foil and the line parallel to the direction of the relative wind.

Figure 2·36 shows the forces acting on an airfoil in an airstream. The relative wind, angle of attack, lift, drag, resultant, and CP are emphasized. The point at which the aerodynamic forces may be considered concentrated is called the **center of pressure.** Its abbreviation is CP and it is assumed to be on the chord. From the CP are drawn vectors (arrows of magnitude and direction) representing the lift, drag, and resultant force. The location of the CP and the direction in which the resultant will point depend upon the center of the airfoil section and the angle of attack.

The CP can be located for each angle of attack by installing parallel rows of small static pressure tubes at right angles to the leading edge of a wing flush with the upper and lower surfaces as illustrated in Fig. 2·37. These tubes are connected by means of rubber tubing to manometers located outside the experimental chamber of the wind tunnel in the case of a model test or to manometers located in the cockpit of the airplane in a flight test. For any angle of attack, manometer readings indicate the pressure at each point where there is a static pressure tube. These readings can be used to develop diagrams such as those shown in Fig. 2·38 which illustrate the pressure distribution on a certain airfoil surface at −5, +10, and +20° angles of attack. The solid black areas represent regions of positive pressure, and the gray areas represent regions of negative pressure.

When these diagrams were prepared, the airfoil profiles were drawn first and then points were drawn on the profile which represented the inlets for the manometer tubes. At each point, the corresponding manometer reading was represented by a line drawn to scale. Pressures below the normal atmospheric pressure were represented by arrows away from the airfoil, and pressures above the normal atmospheric scale were represented by arrows toward the airfoil. It was found that over most of the usual flight range of angles of attack, the relatively low pressure above the airfoil constituted from 60 to 80 per cent of the lifting force. Figure 2·38 shows, among other things, that at an angle of −5° there is an area of positive pressure which acts down on the leading edge, while the remaining distribution of pressure is such that the resultant for the upper and lower surfaces produce a **down** load on the front section of the wing and an **up** load on the rear of the wing.

The middle diagram of Fig. 2·38, illustrating

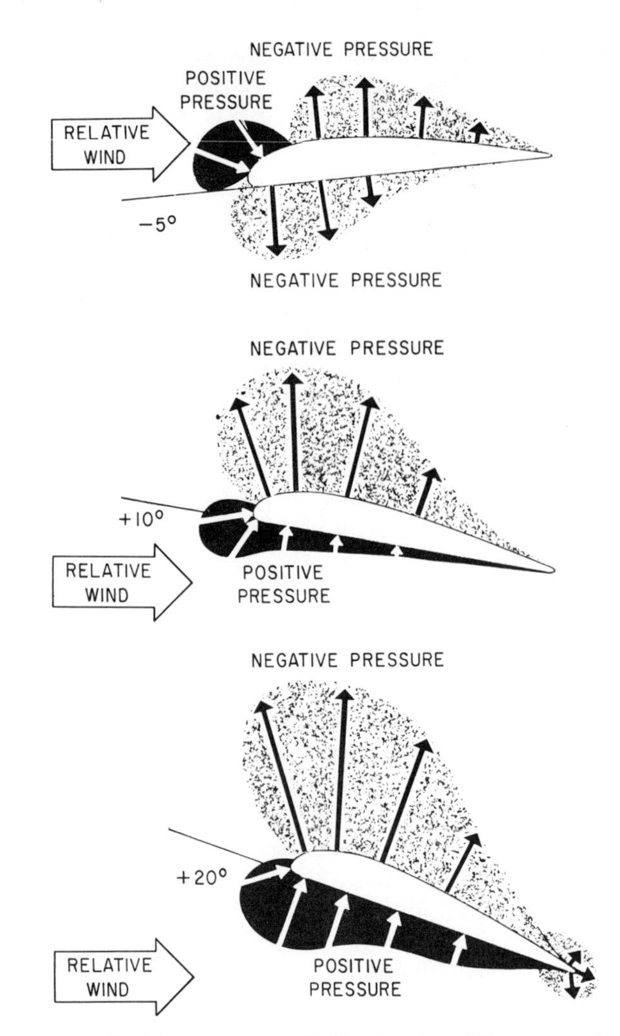

Figure **2·38** *Pressure distribution for different angles of attack.*

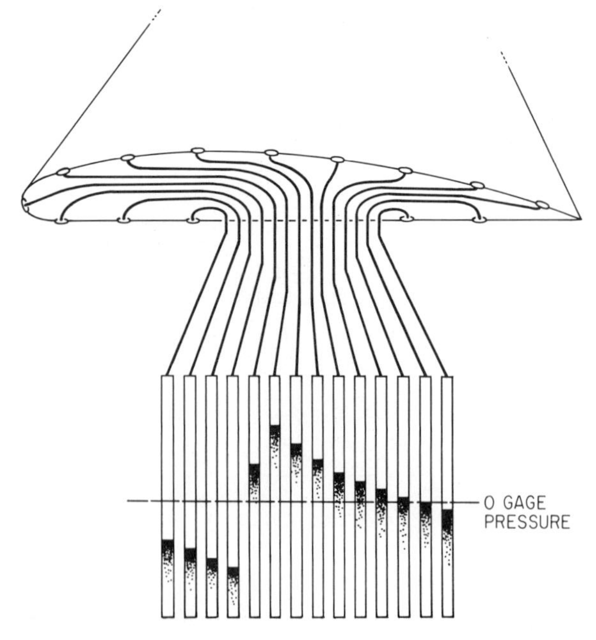

Figure **2·37** *Manometers used for locating CP.*

the pressure distribution at an angle of attack of $+10°$, shows that the negative-pressure region is greater than the positive-pressure region, in accordance with the principles already discussed. The lower diagram, illustrating the pressure distribution at an angle of attack of $+20°$, shows that both the positive- and the negative-pressure areas have increased and that there is an area of negative pressure both above and below the wing at the trailing edge.

Certain general conclusions can be drawn from a study of Fig. 2·38. First, the pressure is not uniformly distributed either above or below the airfoil. Second, the greatest pressures, both positive and negative, are near the leading edge. Third, the pressures, both positive and negative, generally decrease toward the trailing edge.

Regions of different pressures tend to merge with one another. At the leading edge, this is almost impossible because the direction of flow is to the rear. If particles of air tried to reverse their course and mix with particles going in another direction, they would be opposed by onrushing multitudes of other air particles sweeping above and below the airfoil. Near the trailing edge, most particles of air are rushing to the rear; hence they can mix with one another at the trailing edge without much opposition. The result is that there is sometimes no difference between the pressure above and below the trailing edge; hence there is no lift at this point.

Figure 2·39 shows the airflow about a certain airfoil from a 4° angle of attack to and including a 20° angle of attack. At the 4° angle of attack, the airflow is described as **streamline** and there is no appreciable turbulence. At angles of attack of 8 and 10°, the streamlines above the leading edge begin to crowd together more than they did at a lower angle of attack. This causes an increase of velocity above the upper surface and consequently a reduction of pressure; hence lift is increasing. At each successive increase of the angle of attack, the point at which the airflow breaks away from the upper surfaces moves forward, and this increases the amount of burbling or turbulence. We have already seen that where burbling occurs on a surface, the pressure cannot drop below atmospheric, and the failure to have a region of pressure differential destroys lift in that region. At a very high angle of attack, burbling is so excessive that the drag may be even greater than the lift.

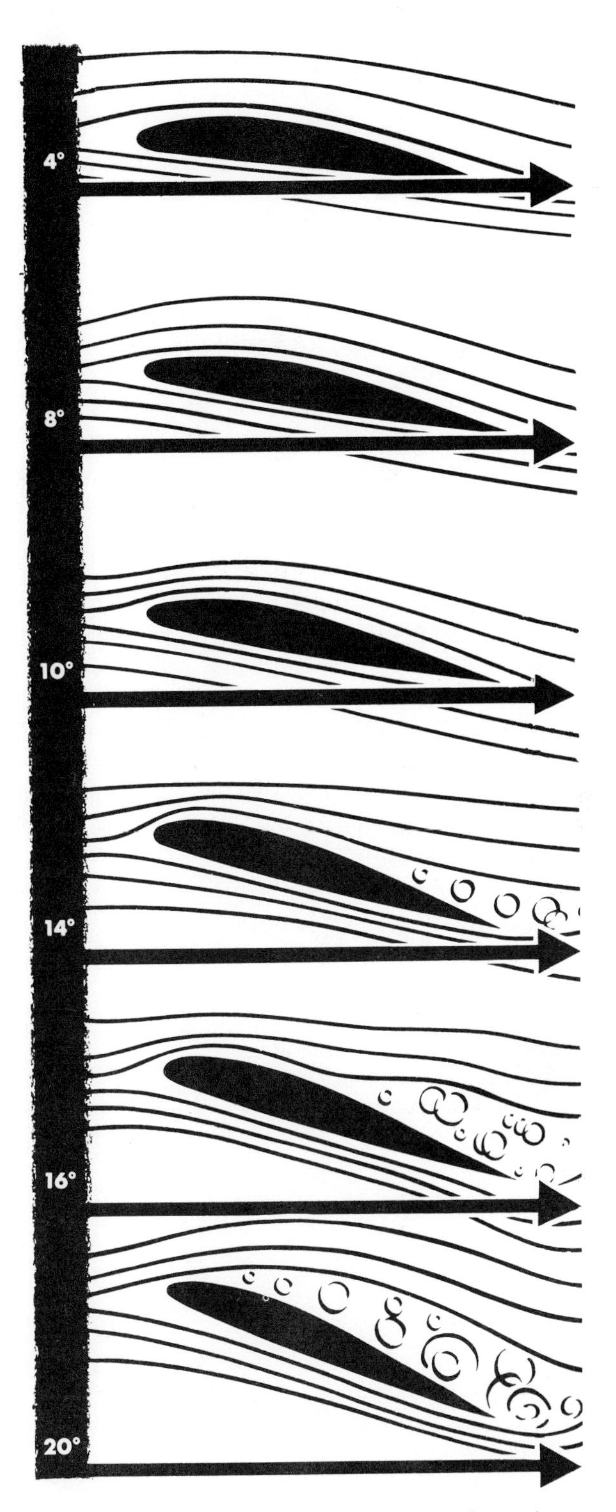

Figure **2·39** *Airflow at different angles of attack.*

Center-of-pressure travel

We have previously said that the CP is on the chord and that its location and the direction in which the resultant will point depend upon the shape of the airfoil section and the angle at which it is set to the airstream. Throughout most of the flight range, that is, at the usual angles of attack, the CP moves forward as the angle of attack increases and moves backward as the angle of attack decreases. The most forward position is usually about 0.3 of the chord back from the leading edge for most airfoil sections, although this is by no means an infallible statement. If the airplane wing has a chord of 63 in., for example, the most forward position of the CP may be 0.3 × 63 or 18.9 in. behind the leading edge.

The farthest position to the rear that the CP may reach on some airfoil sections is 0.4 of the chord back from the leading edge. If the chord is 63 in. long, for example, the CP in this case may be 0.4 × 63 or 25.2 in. behind the leading edge. Therefore, in the example mentioned, the CP, at the usual angles of attack, will be somewhere between 18.9 and 25.2 in. behind the leading edge on the chord. Notice carefully that we have said that these may be the positions at the **usual** angles of attack, but the CP can still travel forward or backward from these usual positions. For example, at a low angle of attack, the CP may run off the trailing edge and disappear because there is no more lift.

Figure 2·40 shows the travel of the CP along the chord at various angles of attack, as well as changes in the magnitude, direction, and location of the resultant. In actual flight, there is a different airspeed for different angles of attack, but in a wind-tunnel test, the velocity of the airstream can be constant while the angle of attack changes, as is the case in Fig. 2·40. At small angles of attack, shown at top of Fig. 2·40, the CP is quite a distance from the leading edge, the resultant is comparatively small, and it points upward and to the rear of the vertical. At medium angles of attack, center Fig. 2·40, the CP has moved toward the leading edge, the resultant is greater, and its direction more nearly approaches right angles to the chord. At high angles of attack, bottom Fig. 2·40, the CP has moved to its farthest forward position and the resultant is still greater.

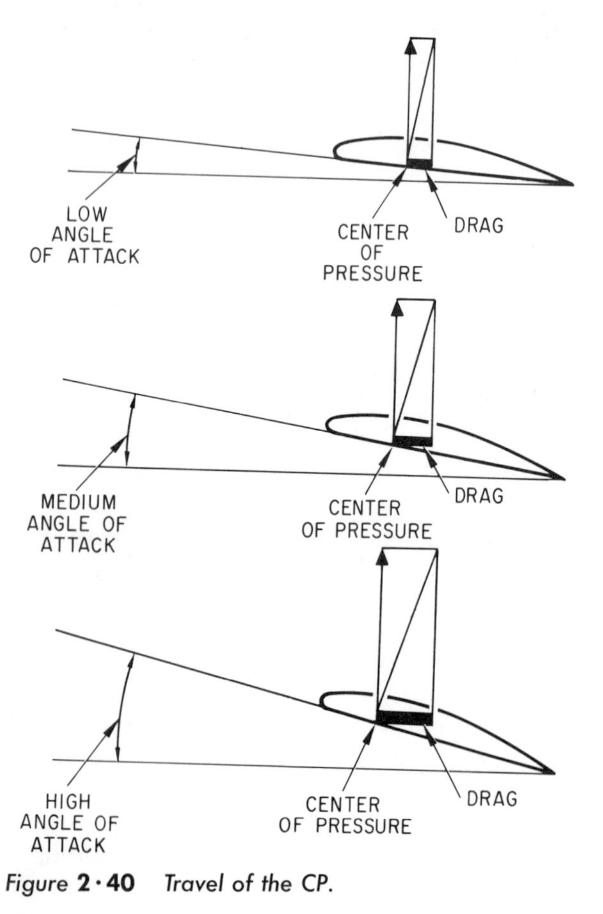

Figure **2·40** *Travel of the CP.*

Before proceeding further in the discussion of Fig. 2·40, it is necessary to introduce some new terms. The **critical angle of attack** is the angle of attack at which the flow about an airfoil changes abruptly as shown by corresponding abrupt changes in the lift and drag. We have already shown that **burble** is a breakdown of streamline airflow about a body. The **burble point** is the angle of attack at which the streamline flow about a body begins to break down. In Fig. 2·40, the high angles of attack, represented by *C*, approach the burble point, the CP either remains in the same position or moves back slightly, the resultant decreases in magnitude, and its departure from the vertical toward the rear becomes greater.

The CP behaves differently on a flat plate. There the CP moves backward as the angle of attack increases and forward as it decreases. It is possible to design an airfoil section which will behave in this manner, and it is well worth considering. For example, if a rising column of air strikes the leading edge of an airplane wing with an airfoil section of this type, the angle of attack is increased. This causes the CP to move to the rear. Therefore, the lift is at the rear of the wing, where it raises the wing and decreases the angle of attack, which was unexpectedly raised by the column of air. This type of airfoil section is described as **stable** because forces are developed that tend to restore the airfoil to its original state. The question naturally arises as to the reason for not using airfoil sections having the CP travel characteristics of a flat plate. A full explanation will be given later. For the present, it is sufficient to say that the characteristic of stability produced by the direction of CP travel is less important than certain other features; hence most airfoil sections are designed so that the CP travels forward as the angle of attack increases and backward as it decreases. These usual airfoil sections are described as unstable because, after a disturbance, the forces tend to move the airfoil farther away from its original state.

One of the reasons for studying the CP travel

is that the CP is the point at which the aerodynamic forces can be considered to be concentrated; hence the airplane designer must make provisions for the CP travel by preparing a wing structure which will meet any stress imposed upon it. Pilots, technicians, and inspectors cannot change the design, but they can perform their duties better if they know the characteristics and limitations of an airplane.

Area and lift

It has already been explained that the lift force depends upon the angle of attack. Also, our discussion of airflow has demonstrated the fact that the shape of the airfoil section affects the amount of lift obtained from any airfoil. For example, we found that an airfoil section approaching a teardrop shape is better than either a flat plate or a curved plate.

Still another factor in the total lift of an airfoil is the area of the surface exposed to the airstream. If the area is small, the region of pressure differential is small and there is little lift. On the other hand, if the area is great, the region of pressure differential is great and there is a large amount of lift. Later in this text, we shall explain why more lift can be obtained from a long, narrow wing than from one in which the width more closely approaches the length (span), but for the present it is sufficient to remember one simple statement: **Lift varies directly as the area, other things being equal.** In practice, the areas of wings are measured in square feet.

Earlier in the text it was shown that, if a person blew into a spool against a card held by a pin at the opposite end of the spool, the harder he blew, the more tightly the card adhered to the spool. This is in accordance with Bernoulli's principle that, as the velocity of the air increases, the pressure decreases.

We have seen that the same principle applies to the airflow around an airfoil. If the air flows slowly around the airfoil, a certain amount of lift is generated. If the velocity of the airstream increases, the pressure differential increases and the lift increases. It would be easy to remember that lift varies directly as the air velocity, but this would not be correct. Actually, the lift varies as the square of the velocity. When we use the word "velocity" in this sense, we mean the airspeed with respect to the airfoil.

Remember that two conditions are essential for lift: relative motion and pressure differential. It does not matter whether a stream of air is blowing against a flat plate or the flat plate moves through still air. In either case there is relative motion. These facts are repeated because they are so very simple that they are easily overlooked, and yet they are so important that no discussion of the theory of flight or aerodynamics can overlook them even for a moment.

Air density and lift

We have seen that lift depends upon the shape of the airfoil, on the angle of attack, on the area of the surface exposed to the airstream, and on the square of the airspeed. One more factor of lift remains, the air density. On hot days the density of the air is less than on cold days. On wet days, the density is less than on dry days. Also, density decreases with altitude. When the density is low, the lift will also be comparatively lower.

If an airplane flies at a certain angle of attack at sea level and flies at the same angle of attack at a higher altitude, where density is less, the airplane must be flown faster. On hot days, when the density is less, the airplane must be flown faster for the same angle of attack than on cold days, when the density is greater. On wet days, the density is less; hence the airplane must be flown faster for the same angle of attack than on dry days. Therefore greater airspeed is required for a particular airplane when the density is lower. To express the same idea in different words, the airspeed must increase as the density decreases in order to maintain the airplane at the same angle of attack in level flight.

Angle of maximum lift and minimum speed

Beginning with small angles of attack, the lift increases as the angle of attack increases until an angle of attack is reached where the lift has a maximum value. This angle corresponds to the burble point and is the angle of attack at which the streamline flow begins to break down over the upper surface of the wing and burbling begins at the trailing edge. This angle of attack is called the **stalling angle.** At angles greater than the angle of maximum lift, the lift decreases rapidly and the drag increases rapidly.

For each angle of attack there is a corresponding airspeed, assuming that other conditions, such as wing area, air density, etc., remain constant. As the angle of attack increases, this airspeed decreases; hence the least possible airspeed exists at the angle of maximum lift (stalling angle). Therefore we can say that another name for the angle of maximum lift is the **angle of minimum speed.** We also point out that the **stalling speed** of an airplane is the minimum speed at which the wing will maintain lift under a certain set of conditions.

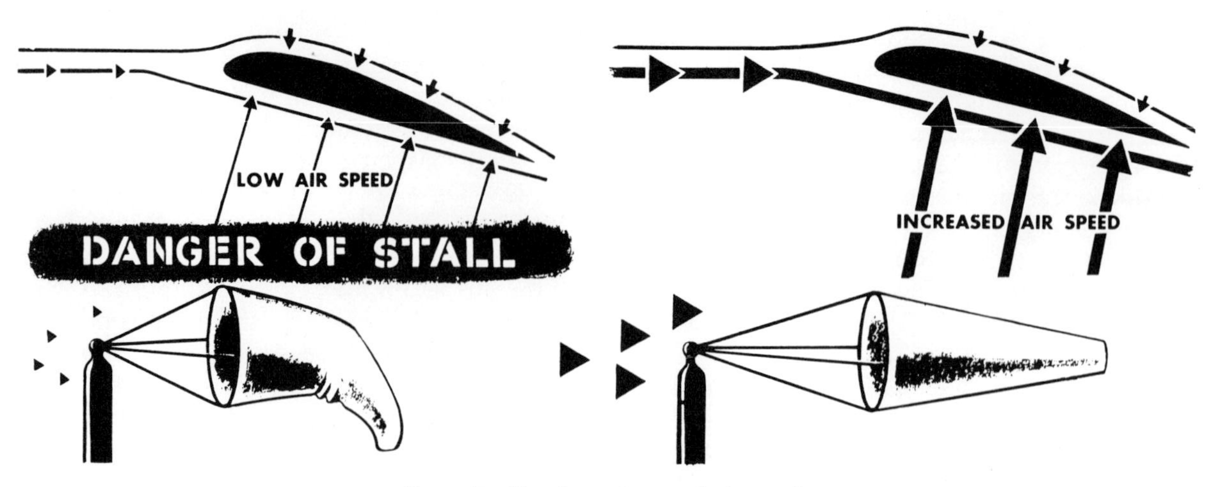

Figure **2·41** *Importance of airspeed.*

Figure 2·41 illustrates the importance of airspeed. If the pilot is not careful to maintain adequate airspeed, there is danger of a stall. In the drawing, the increased airspeed is shown by means of a windsock.

The reason for stalling at low airspeeds, even though an airplane is held in the horizontal position, can be understood by examining the illustrations of Fig. 2·42. As long as the wing is developing sufficient lift to hold level flight, there will be no stall. If the speed is reduced until the total lift is less than the weight of the airplane, the airplane will begin to descend. This causes the angle of attack to increase if the airplane is held in a horizontal position. If the angle of attack does not become as great as the stalling angle, the wing will not stall and the airplane will "mush" as shown in *b* of Fig. 2·42. In the drawing, the wing is actually stalling. When the wing completely stalls, the nose of the airplane will drop rapidly, the airspeed will increase, and the airplane will be recovered from the stall.

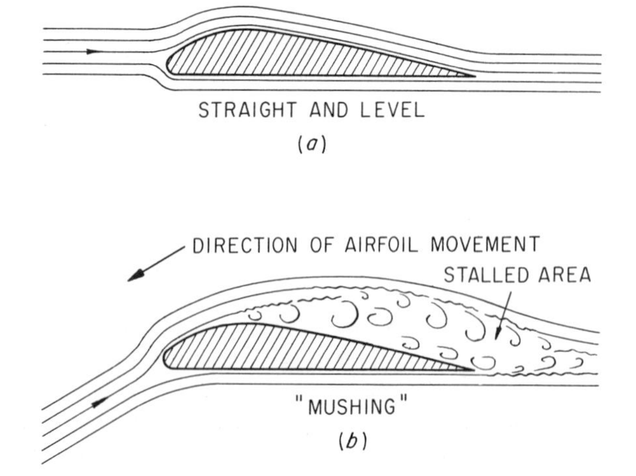

Figure **2·42** *How a stall develops in horizontal flight. (a) Airspeed sufficient to maintain level flight; (b) airspeed too low—wing stalls.*

When an airplane approaches the ground to land, the air between the wing and the ground is slightly compressed before it can flow backward under the trailing edge of the wing. This is especially true in the case of low-wing monoplanes but less true of midwing and high-wing monoplanes. Compression increases air density and decreases the velocity. The effect of the increased density and the air reaction between the wing and the ground causes the airplane to "float" for a time before settling to the ground. This condition is called **ground effect.** The nature of ground effect depends upon the design of the wing, so it is important for the pilot to know the design specifications relative to stalling and landing speeds. This information is provided in the airplane flight manual approved by the Federal Aviation Agency (FAA).

Lift and weight

The forces acting on an airplane in flight are lift, weight, drag, and thrust. The weight acts vertically downward from the center of gravity (CG) of the airplane. The lift acts in a direction perpendicular to the direction of the relative wind from the CP. In straight and level flight the lift and weight must be equal.

When the airplane is flying at a constant speed, the thrust must equal the drag. Thrust, of course, is provided by the engine and propeller or by high-velocity gases ejected from the tail pipe of a jet engine.

Figure 2·43 illustrates the forces acting on an airplane in straight and level flight at a constant speed. In this case all the forces are in balance.

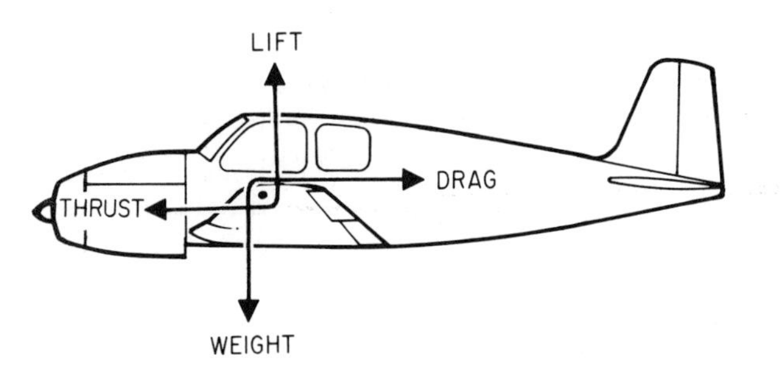

Figure **2·43** *Forces on an airplane in level flight.*

Drag and thrust

The **thrust line** is an imaginary line passing through the center of the propeller hub, perpendicular to the plane of the propeller rotation, as illustrated in Fig. 2·43. In the case of a jet-propelled airplane the thrust line is parallel to the path of the ejected gases from the jet engine.

Propeller thrust is technically defined as the component of the total air force on the propeller which is parallel to the direction of advance. In simple terms, thrust is merely the force which drives the airplane forward. In a propeller-driven airplane, thrust acts from the hub of the propeller along the thrust line.

Thrust is also defined as the forward-directed pushing or pulling force developed by an aircraft engine. This includes reciprocating engines, turbojet engines, turboprop engines, or rocket engines.

Drag, in general terms, is the force which opposes the forward motion of the airplane. Specifically, drag is a retarding force acting upon a body in motion through a fluid, parallel to the direction of motion of the body.

Previously, when we discussed drag, we referred only to the drag of the wing, but in the broad sense, the total drag of the airplane includes not only the wing drag but also a number of other forms of drag, including that caused by the fuselage, the landing gear, and other parts of the airplane. The total drag of the airplane is in opposition to thrust, as illustrated in Fig. 2·43.

Assuming that the airplane is flying straight and level in calm air, the drag acts parallel to the direction of the relative wind. As long as thrust and drag are equal, the airplane flies at a constant speed. If the engine power is reduced, the thrust is decreased and the speed of the airplane is reduced. If the thrust is lower than the drag, the speed of the airplane becomes less and less until it finally is lower than the speed required to maintain level flight, and the airplane will descend.

On the other hand, if the power of the engine is increased, the thrust is increased and the airplane gains speed or, in technical terms, it **accelerates.** While the airplane accelerates, the drag increases until it eventually equals the thrust. Then the airplane flies at a constant speed.

These facts can be summarized by saying that in straight and level flight at a constant speed, the lift and weight are equal and the thrust and drag are equal. These four forces—lift, weight, thrust, and drag—are then in balance. In technical language, the sum of the components of the forces acting on an airplane in straight and level flight at a constant velocity equals zero.

HIGH-SPEED FLIGHT

Thus far we have discussed airflow and aerodynamic principles with respect to subsonic airspeeds only. The behavior of an airfoil under subsonic conditions is easily predictable. However, when we consider operations at transonic and supersonic speeds, we find the reaction of an airfoil altogether different from that which is found at subsonic speeds. The reason for this is the reaction of the air itself.

When discussing high-speed aerodynamics, we constantly refer to the speed of sound. This can be understood when we consider that great changes take place in the forces caused by the air flowing over an aircraft as the aircraft approaches the speed of sound. We must remember that sound waves are pressure changes and that an aircraft in flight produces pressure changes.

Speed of sound

The speed at which sound travels in air under standard sea-level conditions is 1,116 ft per sec (761 mph or 661 knots). The speed of sound is not affected by a change in atmospheric pressure because the density also changes. However, a change in the temperature of the atmosphere changes the density without appreciably affecting the pressure; hence, the speed of sound changes with a change in temperature. The speed of sound can be calculated with the equation

$$a = 49.022\sqrt{T}$$

where a = speed of sound, ft per sec
T = absolute temperature, °F

The temperature of the air decreases with an increase in altitude up to an altitude of about 37,000 ft, and it is then constant to an altitude of more than 100,000 ft. Therefore the speed of sound decreases with altitude to about 37,000 ft and then remains constant to more than 100,000 ft. For example, at 30,000 ft the temperature of standard air is -48°F and the speed of sound is 994 ft per sec or 588 knots.

Mach number

Although we discuss Mach number elsewhere in this text, we must mention it briefly here to clarify this portion of our discussion. Because of the relationship between the effect of the air forces at high speed and the speed of sound and because the speed of sound varies with altitude, it is the ratio of the speed of the aircraft to the speed of sound that is important rather than the speed of the aircraft with respect to the air. This ratio, called the **Mach number,** is the true airspeed of the aircraft divided by the speed of sound in the air through which the aircraft is flying at the time. Thus, Mach 0.5 at sea level under standard conditions is 558 ft per sec; however, Mach 0.5 at 30,000 ft is only 497 ft per sec (294 knots).

Types of high-speed flight

The speed of the air flowing over a particular part of the aircraft is called the local speed. The local speed may be higher than the speed of the aircraft, for example, the speed of the air across the upper portion of the wing. If the local speed is everywhere less than the speed of sound, the speed of the aircraft is referred to as **subsonic.** If all local speeds are greater than the speed of sound, the aircraft speed is **supersonic.** The speed at which some local speeds are less than the speed of sound and some are greater than the speed of sound is called **transonic.**

Subsonic flight

At speeds less than 300 mph the airflow around an aircraft behaves as though the air were incompressible. Pressure disturbances, or pressure pulses, form ahead of the parts of the aircraft such as the leading edge of the wing. These pressure pulses travel through the air at the speed of sound and, in effect, serve as a warning to the air of the approach of the wing. As a result of this warning, the air begins to move out of the way. As the speed increases, the time between the warning of the approach of the wing and the arrival of the wing decreases, because the time between the warning received by the air and the arrival of the wing is dependent upon the difference between the speed of the aircraft and the speed of sound.

At speeds above 300 mph the fact that air is compressible becomes a factor—the lift coefficient increases slightly with increasing speed, while the drag coefficient is relatively unaffected. This increase in the lift coefficient continues until the speed of the aircraft is such that the local speed across the upper portion of the wing reaches Mach 1. When a local speed has reached Mach 1, the aircraft speed is at the **critical Mach number.** This speed varies with the airfoil shape and even the angle of attack, but it is usually between Mach 0.7 and 0.8. At the critical Mach number a disturbance, referred to as a shock wave, takes place in the airflow over the wing. When this occurs, there is a great reduction in lift and a still greater increase in drag.

Transonic flight

During transonic flight a shock wave forms on both the top and the bottom surfaces of the wing. The magnitude and location of these shock waves are constantly changing, and at the present time there appears to be no theory to predict these changes accurately. The forces and turbulence that accompany transonic flight may cause the pilot to lose control, especially if the airplane is not designed to operate under transonic conditions. When the speed becomes supersonic, the shock waves move back and become attached to the trailing edge of the wing. When this takes place, control conditions become predictable and orderly again.

Supersonic flight

When a wing is moving at a speed greater than the speed of sound, there can be no warning pressure changes because the wing is traveling faster than the pressure changes can travel. Thus, the sudden arrival of the aircraft finds the air stationary and the movement necessary to allow the aircraft to pass takes place violently, forming another shock wave. This shock wave forms ahead of the leading edge of the wing, and as speed increases, it moves closer to the leading edge. If the leading edge is sharp, the shock wave becomes attached as shown in Fig. 2·44.

The shock waves formed at supersonic speeds are not imaginary or theoretical, and in a suitably arranged high-speed wind tunnel they can be photographed. Figure 2·45 is an unretouched photograph showing shock waves formed on a wind-tunnel model at low supersonic speed.

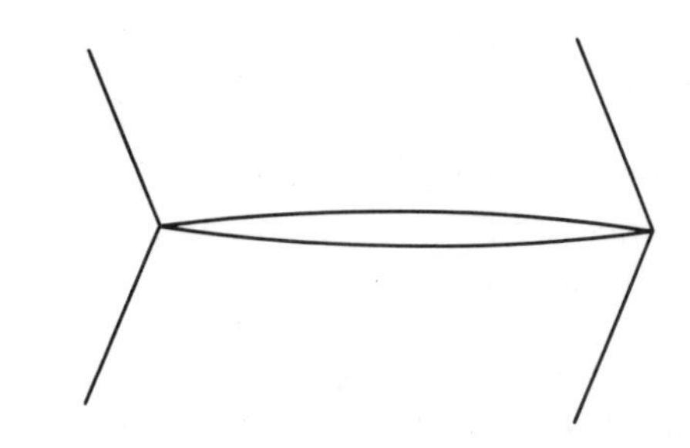

Figure **2·44** *Shock waves at the edges of an airfoil.*

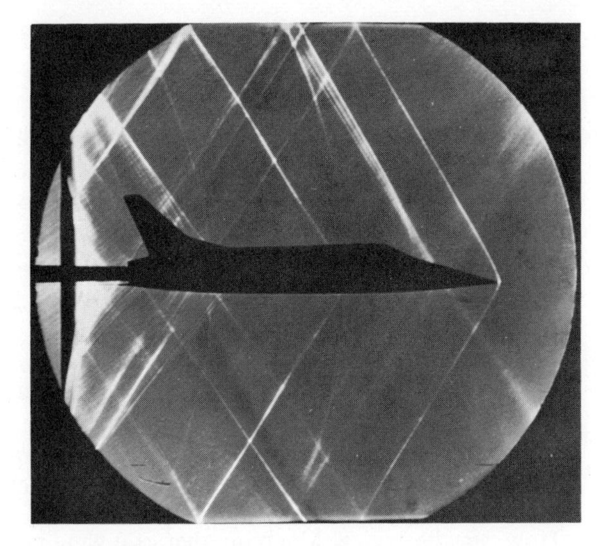

Figure **2·45** *Photograph of shock waves.*

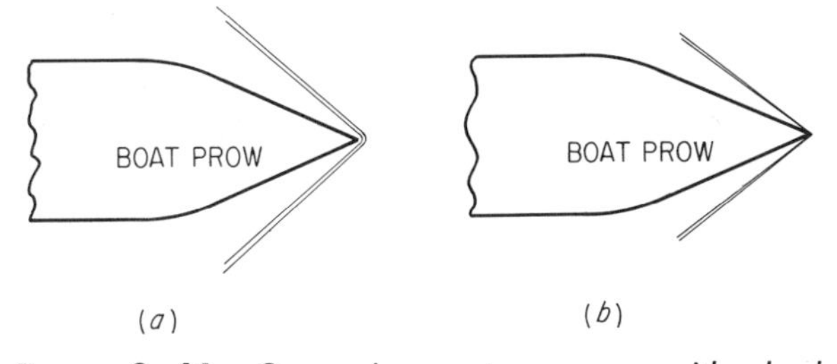

Figure **2·46** *Comparing water waves with shock waves.*

The nature of supersonic flight can be illustrated by the passage of a boat through water. If the boat is moving slowly, a bow wave will move ahead ot the prow as shown in Fig. 2·46*a*. When the speed of the boat is increased sufficiently, the water does not have time to form the bow wave ahead of the prow and the prow cuts directly into still water. This is shown in Fig. 2·46*b*.

Shapes for high-speed flight

Because of the complex nature of supersonic phenomena, aircraft and missile designers have been required to resort to designs which at first seem rather unconventional. Many of these designs are decidedly inferior to the more familiar aircraft forms at subsonic flight speeds. When we consider the airflow across a wing, it becomes obvious that, as a wing becomes thicker, the increase in local speed across the curved areas will become greater. If we wish to obtain an increase in critical Mach number, we must utilize wings as thin as possible. This presents difficulties, however, because a very thin wing does not have great strength and its lift is poor at low speeds.

Another method for increasing the critical Mach number is to sweep back the wing. This will improve the critical Mach number, but it will also present a problem in stability. If an aircraft with a pronounced sweepback changes heading as a result of rudder movement or a disturbance in the air, the wing that moves forward will have much greater lift than the other wing and the airplane will have a tendency to roll. At supersonic speed and higher, the advantage of the swept-back wing begins to decrease, and at Mach 2, the straight wing is superior.

Another method for increasing the critical Mach number is to reduce the aspect ratio. This is not a completely satisfactory solution because a low aspect ratio adversely affects flight at low speeds.

REVIEW QUESTIONS

1. What are the approximate percentages of the principal gases in our atmosphere?
2. What is the weight of dry air at sea-level standard conditions?
3. What is the atmospheric pressure at sea-level standard conditions in pounds per square inch and inches of mercury?
4. How does the density of the air affect the take-off speed of an airplane?
5. What effect has humidity on the density of the air?
6. Explain *relative motion.*
7. In simple terms, explain Bernoulli's principle.
8. Describe a venturi tube, and explain how it affects the pressure and rate of flow of a moving fluid.
9. Why is lift generated when a flat plate is moved through the air with the leading edge slightly higher than the trailing edge?
10. What is the cause of skin friction on a surface moving through the air?
11. What is meant by a *streamline* flow of air?
12. What is the effect of turbulence over the top of a wing?
13. Describe *laminar flow.*
14. What is the *boundary layer?*
15. Describe methods for controlling the boundary layer to permit continuation of laminar flow.
16. Define *airfoil.*
17. What are the basic requirements of an efficient airfoil?
18. Define *chord* for an airfoil.
19. Explain *angle of attack.*
20. At what point on an airfoil do we consider the aerodynamic forces to be concentrated?
21. Name the four principal forces associated with an airfoil in flight.

22. Approximately how much of the lifting force of a wing is produced at the top of the wing?
23. At what point on a wing are the greatest forces developed?
24. Explain the development of lift by a wing moving through the air.
25. How does angle of attack affect the CP on a wing?
26. Compare the lift characteristics of a long narrow wing and a short wide wing when the wing areas are equal.
27. What two conditions are essential for the development of lift by an airfoil?
28. Discuss the effect of air density with respect to lift.
29. Explain *angle of maximum lift.*
30. What is meant by *stall* of a wing?
31. Explain *stalling speed.*
32. What is the difference between lift and weight when an airplane is flying straight and level?
33. What is the *thrust line?*
34. If the thrust of an airplane is greater than the drag, what is the effect on velocity?
35. What is the speed of sound when the air temperature is $-30°F$?
36. If an airplane is flying at Mach 0.9 and the air temperature is $-40°F$, what is the speed of the airplane in miles per hour?
37. Explain transonic flight as compared with supersonic flight.
38. What is a shock wave?
39. What airfoil shapes are best for supersonic flight?
40. How can the critical Mach number of a wing be improved?

CHAPTER 3

Airfoils

PERFORMANCE OF AIRFOILS

Airfoil characteristics

A particular airfoil, that is, one having certain definite dimensions, has specific lift, drag, and CP position characteristics during flight. These features are collectively known as airfoil characteristics and they are classified as follows:

1. Lift coefficient.
2. Drag coefficient.
3. Lift/drag ratio.
4. Center-of-pressure position. In place of the CP position, highly technical publications may use some equivalent characteristic, such as the moment of aerodynamic force about the leading edge or the aerodynamic center, but it is sufficient for the mechanic or pilot to consider only the CP position.

Fundamental equation for lift

The lift of an airfoil can be determined mathematically by using given known values in the fundamental equation for lift. This formula is given as follows:

$$L = C_L \frac{\rho}{2} V^2 S$$

where L = lift, lb
C_L = lift coefficient
ρ = mass density, slugs per cu ft
V = velocity of wind relative to the body, ft per sec
S = airfoil area, sq ft

Coefficient

A **coefficient,** according to any dictionary, is a number, a symbol, or a group of symbols placed before another number, symbol, or group of symbols as a multiplier. For example, let us imagine that someone has selected the furniture for a bedroom and wants to order enough for three bedrooms. If the items needed for one bedroom consist of 1 bed, 1 dresser, 1 rug, and 3 chairs, these pieces of furniture can be listed within parentheses, thus: (1 bed, 1 dresser, 1 rug, 3 chairs). The quantity needed for three bedrooms can then be expressed thus: 3(1 bed, 1 dresser, 1 rug, 3 chairs). Obviously the 3 in front of the first parenthesis sign is the coefficient. In simple words, a coefficient can be regarded as a number used as a multiplier.

Coefficient of lift

The fundamental equation of lift can be used to determine the coefficient of lift by rewriting it as follows:

$$C_L = \frac{L}{\frac{1}{2}\rho V^2 S}$$

The coefficient for lift is a function of the airfoil shape and the angle of attack. For a given shape, the coefficient of lift varies with the angle of attack; hence, when the fundamental equation for lift is used, the angle of attack must be specified to make the computation meaningful. A certain airfoil has a C_L of 0.4 at a 4° angle of attack and a C_L of 1.2 at a 16° angle of attack. It is clear, then, that the angle of attack must be known before the answer to the equation has a usable value.

Let us assume that we now wish to know the amount of lift which can be obtained from an airplane wing having an area of 180 sq ft, at a velocity of 120 mph, at an altitude of 1,000 ft, with a C_L of 0.4 at a 4° angle of attack. First the velocity is converted into feet per second. A velocity of 120 mph is equal to 176 ft per sec. Next, by reference to the NASA standard atmosphere tables, it is found that the value of ρ (density) is 0.002309. Substituting values in the fundamental equation for lift, we have

$$L = 0.4 \times \frac{0.002309 \times (176)^2 \times 180}{2}$$

or $L = 2574.85$ lb

Fundamental equation for drag

The fundamental equation for drag is found to be almost identical with the equation for lift except that we use drag and the coefficient of drag in the place of the values for lift. The equation for drag is then

$$D = C_D \frac{\rho}{2} V^2 S$$

The symbol meanings are the same as those stated previously in the equation for lift except for D (drag) and C_D (coefficient of drag).

The equation for drag can be rewritten to obtain the coefficient of drag as follows:

$$C_D = \frac{D}{\frac{1}{2}\rho V^2 S}$$

Like the coefficient of lift, the coefficient of drag is a function of the airfoil shape and the angle of attack. For a given shape the coefficient of drag varies with the angle of attack. For example, a certain airfoil has a C_D of 0.11 at a 4° angle of attack but at a 16° angle of attack it has a C_D of 0.24.

The fundamental equation for drag is used in the same manner as the equation for lift by substituting known values for the symbols.

Slugs

In solving lift-drag problems, ρ is the symbol for mass density in slugs per cubic foot. ρ is the Greek letter rho, corresponding to the English letter R, although it looks something like the English letter P.

The **slug** is a unit of mass with a value of 31.1739 lb under standard conditions of gravity. As previously explained, the word **mass** designates the pull in standard gravitational units exerted by the earth upon a piece of matter. Generally speaking, mass is approximately the same as weight. Since the slug is used to indicate the density of air, it is sufficient for the pilot or technician to know that the value of ρ can be found in standard atmosphere tables. The density of air in motion is one of the principal factors governing the dynamic pressure exerted by the air. **Dynamic pressure** is the pressure resulting from the motion of the air and is equal to one-half the density times the velocity squared ($P_d = \frac{1}{2}\rho V^2$). Dynamic pressure is developed whenever the velocity of the molecules in the air is changed.

Lift/Drag ratio

The **lift/drag ratio,** abbreviated L/D, is the ratio of the lift to the drag of any body in flight and is a measure of the effectiveness of an airfoil because the lift is the force required to support the weight while the drag is a necessary nuisance which must be accepted to obtain lift. For any angle of attack, the C_L divided by the C_D will give the L/D ratio.

The maximum value of L/D ratio for the wing is always more than the maximum value of L/D ratio for the complete airplane because the drag for the complete airplane includes not only the drag of the wing but also the drag contributed by the rest of the airplane. This is based upon the assumption that all the lift of a conventional airplane is obtained from the wing. It can be represented in a formula, thus:

$$\text{Airplane } L/D = \frac{\text{lift from wing}}{\text{wing drag} + \text{other drag}}$$

Center-of-pressure coefficient

It has been explained that the **center of pressure** of an airfoil is the point in the chord of the airfoil, prolonged if necessary, which is at the intersection of the chord and the line of action of the resultant air force. The **center-of-pressure** coefficient is the ratio of the distance of the CP from the leading edge to the chord length. In other words, the CP is given by stating that it is a certain percentage of the chord length behind the leading edge. For example, if the chord is 6 ft long and the CP is 30 per cent of the chord length behind the leading edge, then it is 30 per cent of 6 ft, or 1.8 ft, behind the leading edge at the particular angle of attack. Since the pressure distribution varies along the chord with changes in the angle of attack, the CP, which is the point of application of the resultant, moves accordingly. We have previously explained that the CP generally moves forward as the angle of attack increases and moves backward as it decreases, although there are exceptions to all rules, including this one.

Characteristic curves

At the beginning of this section we explained that the lift coefficient, drag coefficient, lift/drag ratio, and CP position are collectively known as airfoil characteristics. **Characteristic curves** are graphical representations of airfoil characteristics for various angles of attack. It is important to understand that the values of all the airfoil characteristics vary with the angle of attack and that they are different for different airfoil sections.

Figure 3·1 is a **coefficient-of-lift diagram** for the NACA2421 airfoil. The angle of attack is plotted horizontally, and the value of the lift coefficient is plotted vertically. Notice that a horizontal line is drawn and along this line are located points which correspond to the various

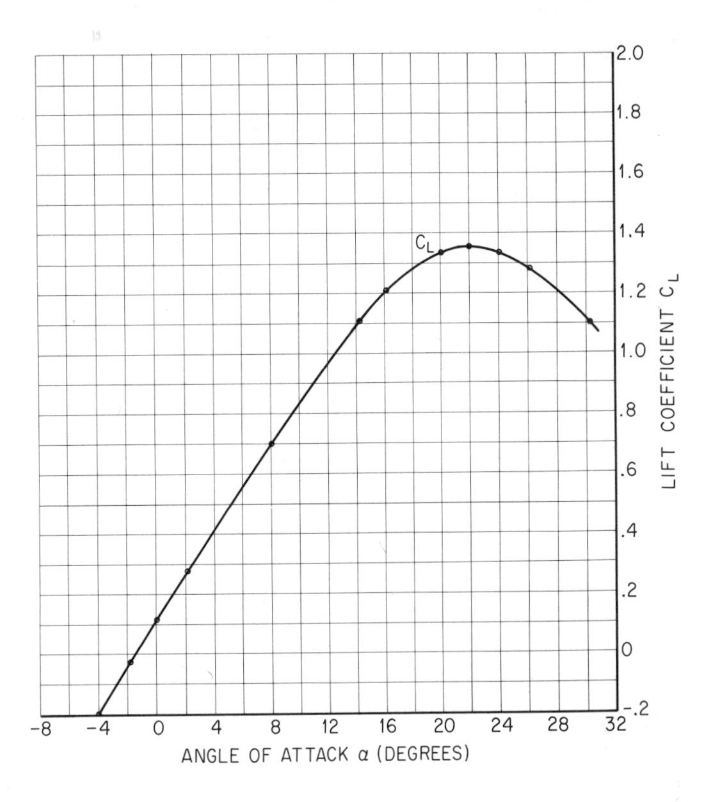

Figure **3·1** *A coefficient-of-lift curve.*

angles of attack from minus 8 to plus 32°. These points are marked with the angles represented. At each of these points the person preparing the illustration measures vertically upward a distance which represents to any suitable scale the coefficient of lift for that particular angle of attack and makes a dot or draws a tiny circle. A smooth curve is then drawn through the points located in this manner. This curve is technically called the **lift-coefficient curve** or simply the **lift curve** for the particular airfoil being represented. In this case it is the NACA2421 airfoil. We have repeated

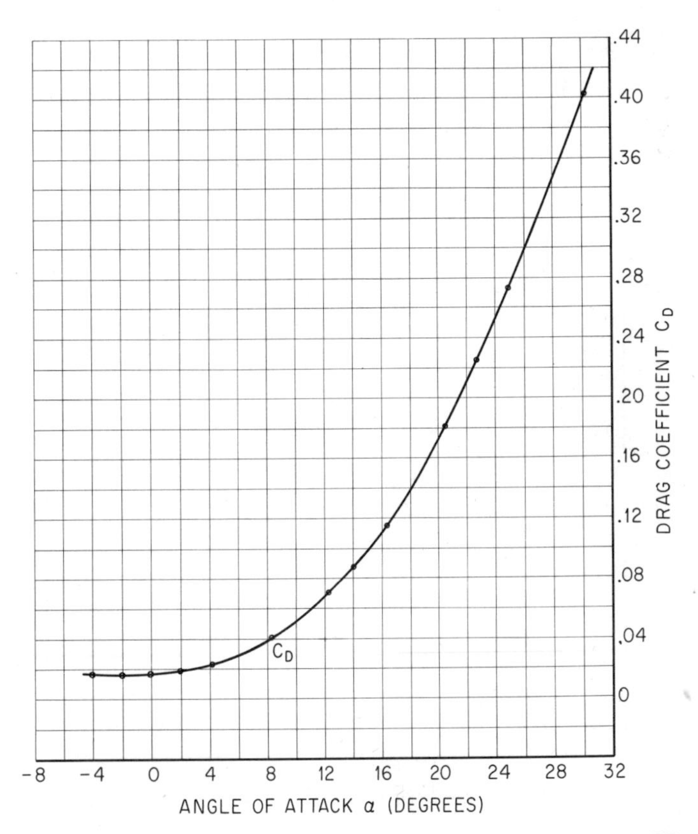

Figure **3·2** *A coefficient-of-drag curve.*

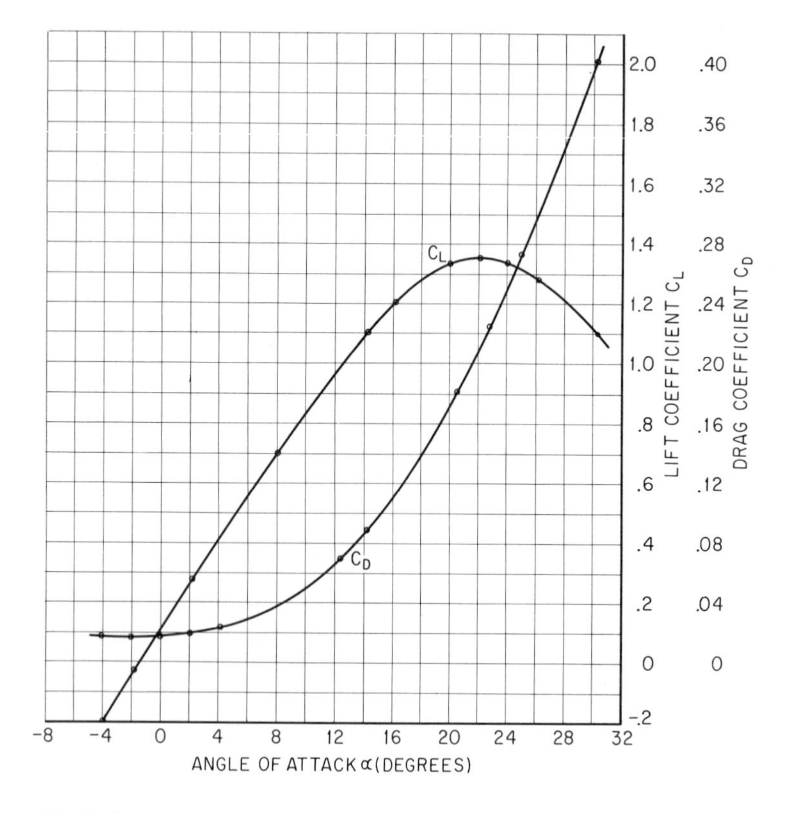

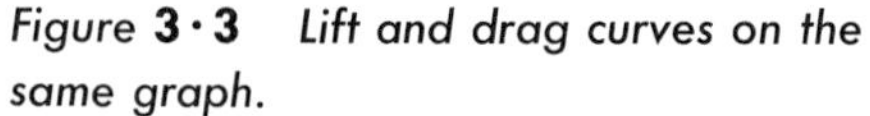

Figure **3·3** *Lift and drag curves on the same graph.*

this information because it is vitally important to know that a curve for one airfoil will not illustrate the characteristics of another airfoil.

Figure 3·2 is a **coefficient-of-drag** diagram for the NACA2421 airfoil. The angle of attack is again plotted horizontally, and the drag coefficient is plotted vertically for each angle of attack. The resulting curve is technically called the **coefficient-of-drag curve** or simply the **drag curve** for the airfoil.

Figure 3·3 shows the lift and drag curves for the NACA2421 airfoil drawn on the same diagram. This is common practice because it presents two types of information on one drawing. The

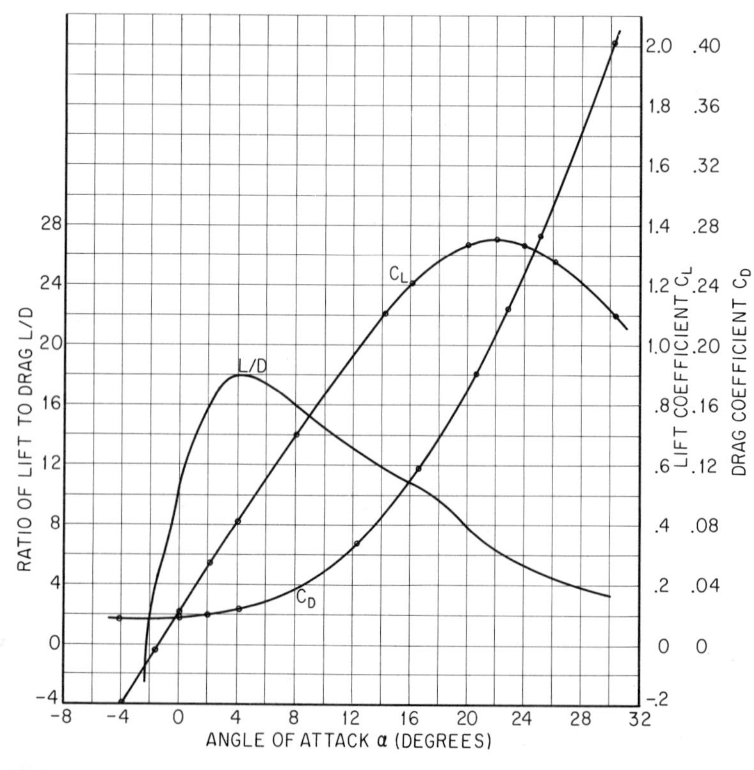

Figure **3·4** *The lift/drag ratio curve.*

coefficient-of-lift and coefficient-of-drag curves were shown on separate drawings in the previous illustrations to make it easier to understand their construction.

Figure 3·4 shows the lift/drag ratio curve drawn on the same diagram with the lift and drag curves. For each angle of attack the corresponding coefficient of lift is divided by the corresponding coefficient of the drag to obtain the L/D ratio for that particular angle of attack. A distance is measured vertically upward to represent the L/D ratio value, and a dot or circle is drawn. The dots or circles found in this manner are connected by a smooth line to represent the L/D ratio curve on the diagram.

So that we can see how the L/D ratio curve is obtained from the C_L and C_D curves on the diagram of Fig. 3·4, let us consider a specific instance. If the airfoil is at an angle of attack of 12°, the coefficient of lift C_L is approximately 0.95 and the drag coefficient C_D is approximately 0.07. Then the L/D ratio equals $C_L/C_D = 0.95/0.07 = 13$. Thus we see that the lift/drag or L/D ratio is equal to 13. If we observe the L/D ratio curve on the diagram of Fig. 3·4, we note that at 12° angle of attack this curve has a value of 13. Figure 3·5 shows the curve representing the position of the CP, drawn on the same diagram with the lift, drag, and L/D ratio curves. For each of the angles of attack represented on the horizontal line, the location of the corresponding CP is plotted vertically upward in terms of the percentage of chord from the leading edge, and the points so found are connected by a smooth line to provide the curve.

Airfoil dimensions

We have previously discussed airfoil dimensions, but they should be reviewed thoroughly because airfoil characteristics depend upon the proportions of the plan form (determined by its span,

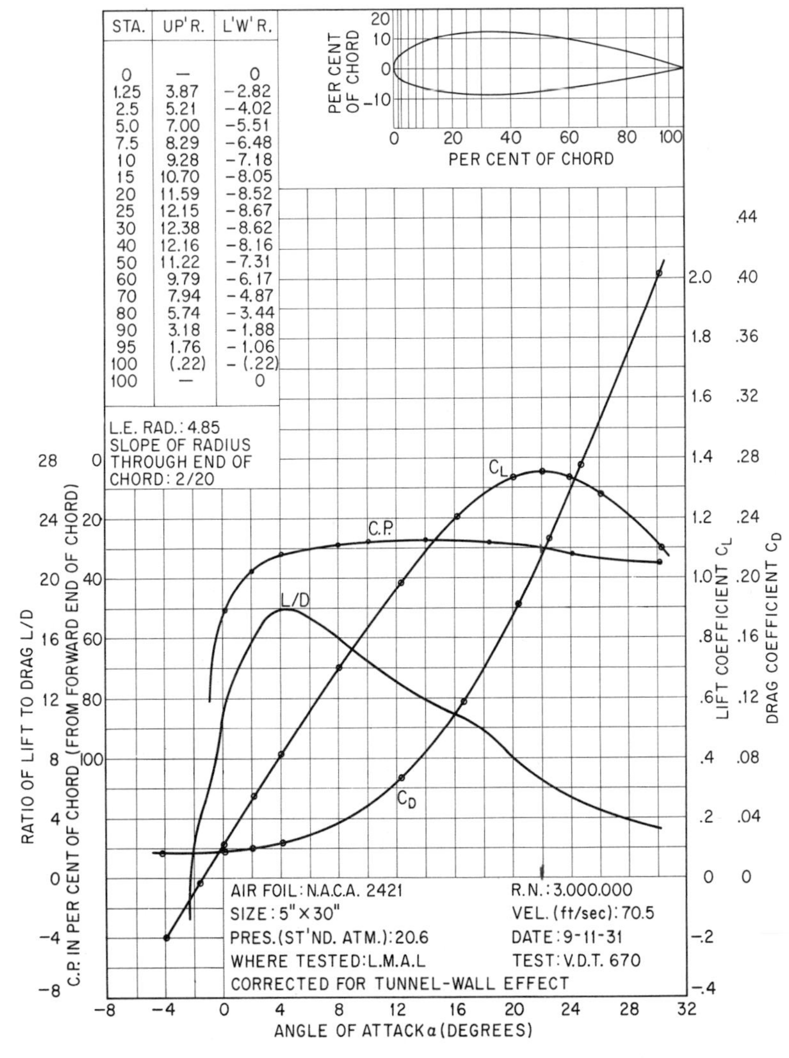

STA.	UP'R.	L'W'R.
0	—	0
1.25	3.87	−2.82
2.5	5.21	−4.02
5.0	7.00	−5.51
7.5	8.29	−6.48
10	9.28	−7.18
15	10.70	−8.05
20	11.59	−8.52
25	12.15	−8.67
30	12.38	−8.62
40	12.16	−8.16
50	11.22	−7.31
60	9.79	−6.17
70	7.94	−4.87
80	5.74	−3.44
90	3.18	−1.88
95	1.76	−1.06
100	(.22)	−(.22)
100	—	0

Figure 3·5 Center-of-pressure curve.

chord length, contour of wing tips, and aspect ratio) and also the amount of curvature of the airfoil section. The **span** is the distance between the wing tips, including ailerons. It is technically defined as the maximum distance, measured parallel to the lateral axis from tip to tip of an airfoil, of an airplane wing inclusive of ailerons or of a stabilizer inclusive of the elevator. The chord has been explained in great detail earlier in this text, but it will be discussed again where necessary for emphasis or clarity.

The **aspect ratio** may be defined as the ratio of the square of the span of an airfoil to the total airfoil area or the ratio of the airfoil span to its mean chord. Thus a high-aspect-ratio wing is comparatively long and slender while the low-aspect-ratio wing appears short and stubby.

Camber is defined as the curvature of the mean line of an airfoil or an airfoil section from the leading edge to the trailing edge. The degree or amount of camber is expressed as the ratio of the maximum departure of the curve from the chord to the chord length. Figure 3·6 shows an airfoil having a double convex curvature, which means that it has camber above and below the chord line. **Upper camber** refers to the curve on the upper surface of an airfoil, and **lower camber** refers to the curve of the lower surface. **Mean camber** is the curvature of the mean line of an airfoil profile from the chord. Camber is positive when the departure from the straight line is upward and negative when it is downward.

In Fig. 3·7 the leading edge and trailing edge of the airfoil section are indicated by arrows. The chord of this particular section is the straight line between the leading and trailing edges. The mean line, sometimes called a median line, is an intermediate line between the upper and lower contours. Any point on this mean line should be the same distance from the upper and lower lines. The distance from the chord to the upper surface is the upper camber, indicated by the arrow marked *AC*. The distance from the chord to the lower surface is the lower camber, indicated by the arrow marked *BC*. If a line were drawn from the chord to the mean line at any point, the length of the line would represent the mean camber. The distance obtained by adding together the lengths of the upper camber and the lower camber is called the **profile thickness.** For example, the profile thickness where arrows *AC* and *BC* are drawn is just what the phrase indicates. It is the thickness at that point on the chord.

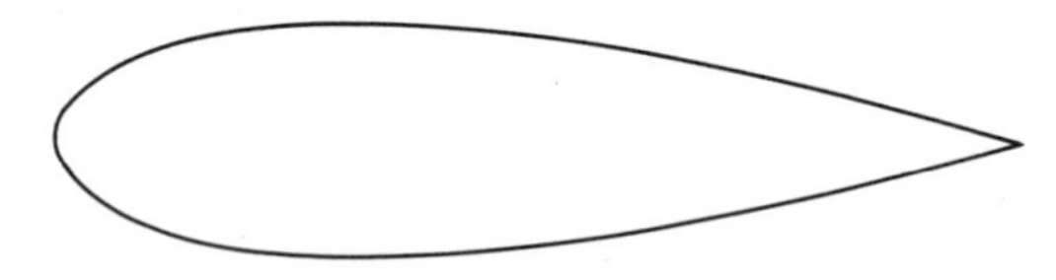

Figure 3·6 Airfoil with double convex curvature.

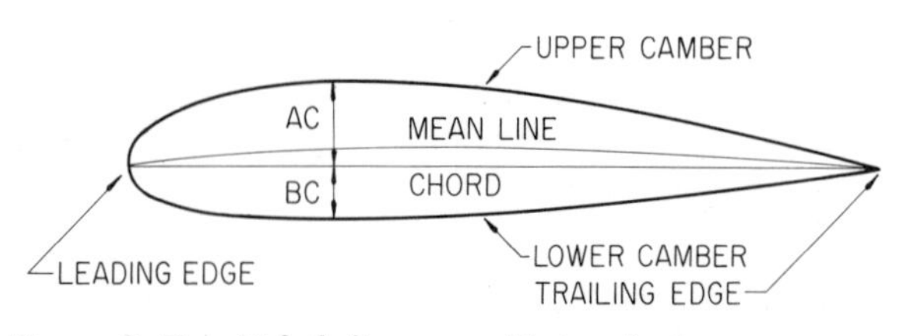

Figure 3·7 Airfoil diagram with terminology.

Airfoil profiles

An **airfoil profile** is the outline of an airfoil section. An **airfoil section** is a cross section of an airfoil parallel to the plane of symmetry or to a specified reference plane. An **airfoil** is any surface, such as an airplane wing, aileron, or rudder, designed to obtain reaction from the air through which it moves. This definition was given previously, but it is repeated here for emphasis. If we imagine that Fig. 3·8 is a cross section of an actual airplane wing, it is correct to call it an airfoil section, but if it is merely the outline, it should be called an airfoil profile. As a matter of fact, the three terms are used interchangeably in conversation, even by people who know the technical distinctions. Airfoil profiles can be considered as made up of certain profile thickness forms disposed about certain mean lines. The major shape variables then become two, the thickness form and the mean-line form. The thickness form is of particular importance from a structural standpoint. On the other hand, the form of the mean line determines almost independently some of the most important aerodynamic properties of the airfoil section.

Early textbooks on the theory of flight use the Clark *Y* airfoil to illustrate various statements, and this practice has been continued by authors who simply rewrote the existing material. However, the airfoil profiles developed by the National Advisory Committee for Aeronautics (now the National Aeronautics and Space Administration) were described in detail in NACA Report 460, published November, 1933, entitled "The Characteristics of Seventy-eight Related Airfoil Sec-

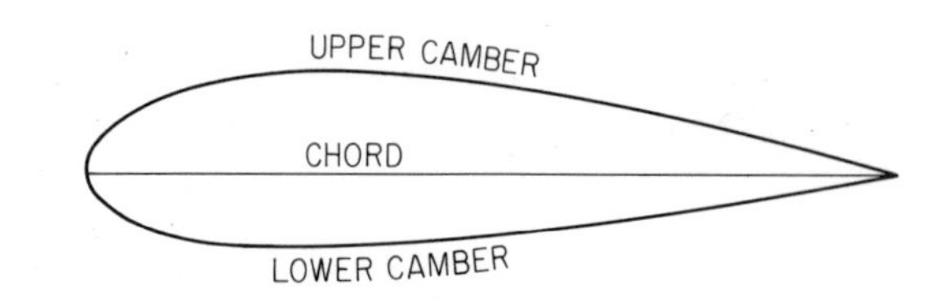

Figure 3·8 Diagram of wing cross section.

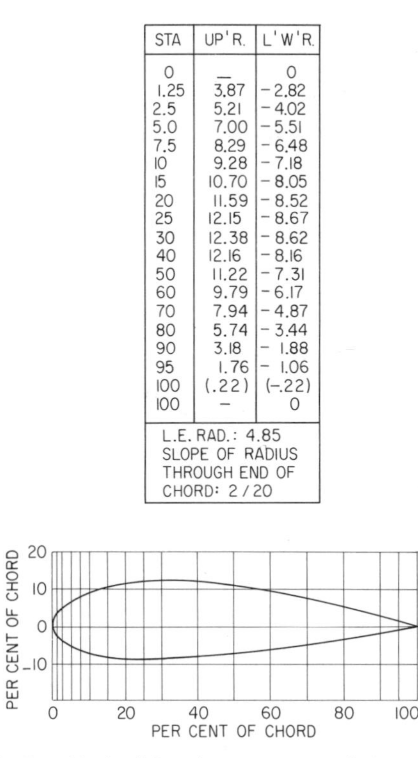

STA	UP'R.	L'W'R.
0	—	0
1.25	3.87	−2.82
2.5	5.21	−4.02
5.0	7.00	−5.51
7.5	8.29	−6.48
10	9.28	−7.18
15	10.70	−8.05
20	11.59	−8.52
25	12.15	−8.67
30	12.38	−8.62
40	12.16	−8.16
50	11.22	−7.31
60	9.79	−6.17
70	7.94	−4.87
80	5.74	−3.44
90	3.18	−1.88
95	1.76	−1.06
100	(.22)	(−.22)
100	—	0

L.E. RAD.: 4.85
SLOPE OF RADIUS THROUGH END OF CHORD: 2/20

Figure **3·9** *Method for drawing an airfoil profile.*

tions from Tests in the Variable Density Wind Tunnel." This report was obtainable from the Superintendent of Documents, Government Printing Office, Washington, D.C.; however, it has been superseded by Reports 669 and 824. The reports on airfoils do not contain information which a pilot or technician needs to pass an examination in addition to the facts given in this text, but they are of interest to those who wish to widen their knowledge of aerodynamics. NACA airfoil profiles are designated by a number consisting of four digits and also by numbers with five or more digits. In the four-digit numbers, the first digit indicates the camber of the mean line in percentage of chord, the second digit shows the position of the maximum camber of the mean line in tenths of the chord from the leading edge, and the last two digits indicate the maximum thickness in percentage of the chord. Thus the NACA2315 profile has a maximum mean camber of 2 per cent of the chord at a position 0.3 of the chord from the leading edge and a maximum thickness of 15 per cent of the chord. Likewise the NACA0012 airfoil is a symmetrical airfoil having a maximum thickness of 12 per cent of the chord. The NACA2421 airfoil, which was used to obtain the characteristic curves shown in Figs. 3·1 to 3·5, has a maximum mean camber of 2 per cent of the chord at a position 0.4 of the chord from the leading edge and has a maximum thickness of 21 per cent of the chord.

Figure 3·9 shows how to draw the NACA2421 profile. First, draw a base line and call it the chord; second, divide the chord into 20 equal divisions. Each division will represent 5 per cent of the chord. Draw vertical lines of indefinite length at the beginning of each of these divisions and number them, starting with 0 at the leading edge and ending with 100 at the trailing edge. These lines are called stations. Then draw vertical lines at the other stations shown on the table. For this particular airfoil the additional stations are 1.25, 2.5, and 7.5 per cent of the chord behind the leading edge. Third, lay out the points for the upper and lower contour lines from the ordinates given in the second and third columns of the table shown in the figure. Notice that those in the second column are positive ordinates and those in the third column are negative ordinates. Positive ordinates are measured upward from the chord at their stations and negative ordinates are measured downward from the chord at their stations in percentage of chord. Fourth, using a spline or French curve, connect all these points with a smooth line. This provides the airfoil section except that the nose requires more work.

Notice that the bottom of the table says: "L.E. rad.:4.85. Slope of radius through end of chord: 2/20." Refer to Fig. 3·10, which shows how to draw the nose. Through the 0 per cent station of the chord, that is, the leading edge, construct the line *OC* at an angle which will have a slope of 2:20. This is the same as a slope of 1:10, which means that for every 10 units of horizontal distance there will be a rise of 1 unit of vertical distance. You can establish this slope by measuring 10 in. along the chord, erecting a perpendicular 1 in. above the chord, and connecting the top of that perpendicular with the leading edge.

On the line *OC*, locate the center of the leading-edge radius by measuring 4.85 per cent of the chord length from zero, the leading edge. Set a compass for 4.85 per cent of the chord length, place the point of the compass at the point found to be the center of the leading-edge radius, and inscribe an arc which passes through the leading edge. This provides the nose. Now, with a spline or French curve, connect the leading-edge curve

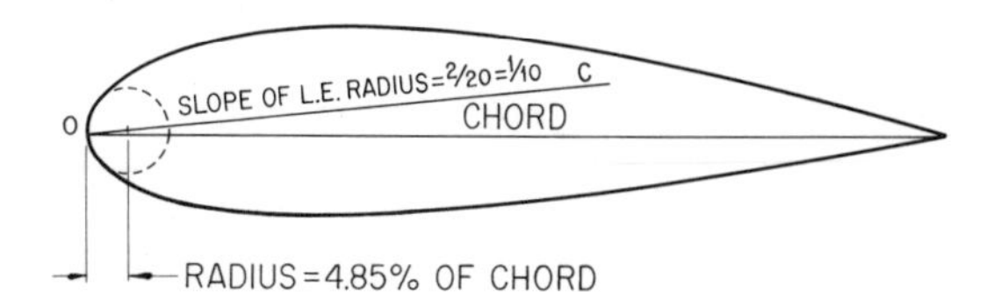

Figure **3·10** *How to draw the nose of an airfoil profile.*

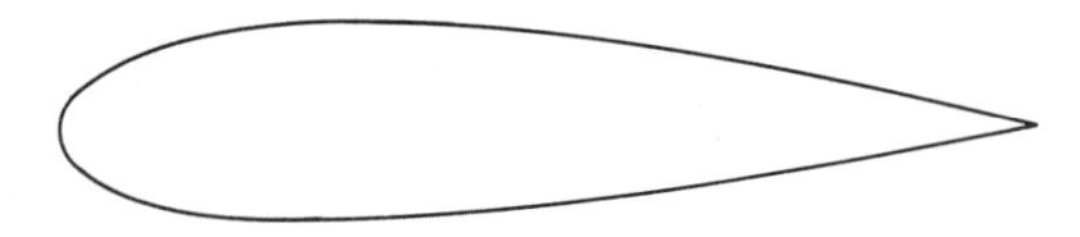

Figure 3·11 NACA23019 profile.

so that it blends smoothly into the curve previously constructed.

In practice, the nose is usually drawn before the ends of the ordinates are connected, but this part of the instruction was postponed so that the principal work could be explained before discussing the details.

In addition to the NACA airfoils of the four-digit series there are also airfoils of a five-digit series. An example of this is the NACA23019, shown in Fig. 3·11. The first digit, 2, is the camber designation; that is, it shows that the maximum ordinate of the mean line is 2 per cent of the chord. The next digit, 3, gives the maximum camber location times 0.20, which, in this case, makes the maximum camber location 15 per cent of the chord. The zero after the figure 3 indicates the nature of the mean line from the point of maximum ordinate to the trailing edge. The last two digits, 19, give the maximum overall thickness of the airfoil profile, which is 19 per cent of the chord in this case. Airfoil numbers with more than five digits can now be found in the NACA and NASA reports.

Aspect ratio

The **aspect ratio** of an airfoil of rectangular shape is the ratio of the span to the chord. Thus, airfoil A in Fig. 3·12 has a span of 24 ft and a chord of 6 ft, and the aspect ratio is 4. Likewise, airfoil B of the same figure has a span of 36 ft and a chord of 4 ft; hence the aspect ratio is 9. The formula for aspect ratio can be written thus:

$$\text{AR} = \frac{\text{span}}{\text{chord}}$$

However, for aerodynamic reasons, airfoils are hardly ever designed with a rectangular planform. The aspect ratio for nonrectangular airfoils is defined as the span squared divided by area. If we represent the chord by the letter a and the span by the letter b, the formula for nonrectangular airfoils can be expressed thus:

$$\text{AR} = \frac{b^2}{S}$$

where S represents the area.

The formula for the aspect ratio of a nonrectangular airfoil could be applied to a rectangular airfoil if any such object were in existence. Since S, the area, is a product of the width a and the length b, we can write the formula thus:

$$\text{AR} = \frac{bb}{ab}$$

By canceling where there is the same value above and below the division line, we have

$$\text{AR} = \frac{b}{a}$$

Since b represents the length, or span, and a represents the width, or chord, we are back where we started.

Wing-tip vortices

Air flows over and under the wing of an airplane, as shown in Fig. 3·13. This produces a region of relatively low pressure above the wing and a region of relatively high pressure under the wing. If the airfoil were of infinite span, that is, if it had no ends, the airflow would be direct from

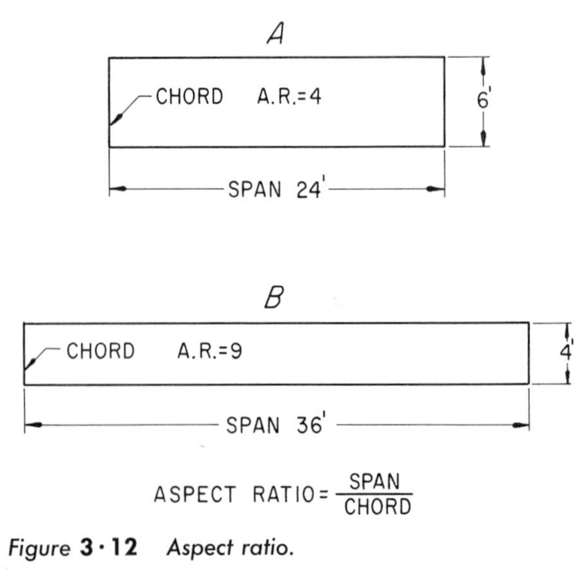

Figure 3·12 Aspect ratio.

Figure 3·13 Airflow over and under the wing.

Figure **3·14** *Air spilling over wing tips.*

the leading edge to the trailing edge, as shown in Fig. 3·13, because there would be no way for the air in the region of high pressure below the wing to flow into the region of low pressure above the wing. However, it is obvious that the airfoil is of finite area and span; that is, it has ends. Hence the air under the wing will seek the region of low pressure above the wing by "spilling over" the tips as shown in Fig. 3·14. Eddies, or regions of turbulence, are formed in this manner at the tips, causing the streamlines to form **vortices** which are like little whirlpools such as those illustrated in Fig. 3·15.

The streamlines below the wing bend toward the tips, and those above the wing bend toward the center. The turbulence thus produced absorbs energy and increases the drag. At the same time, the lift is reduced by destroying the force of the airstream near the tips.

Wing-tip vortices are unavoidable, but their effect can be reduced by increasing the aspect ratio. Since wing-tip vortices exert their influence for a distance inboard from the tips in any given airfoil, it is apparent that the percentage of area so affected is less for a long, narrow airfoil than it is for a short, wide airfoil. This is shown in

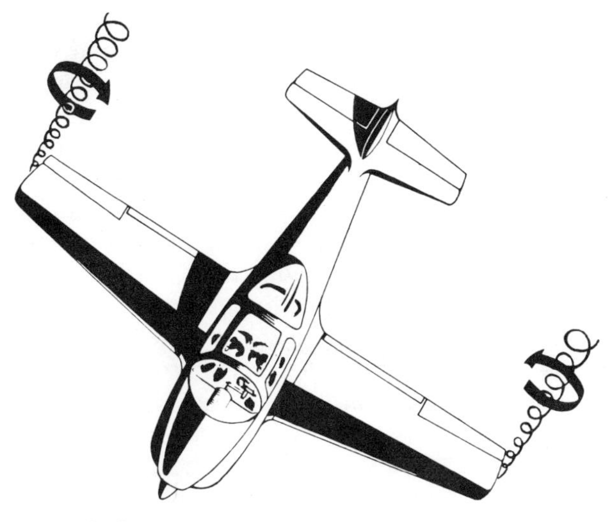

Figure **3·15** *Wing-tip vortices.*

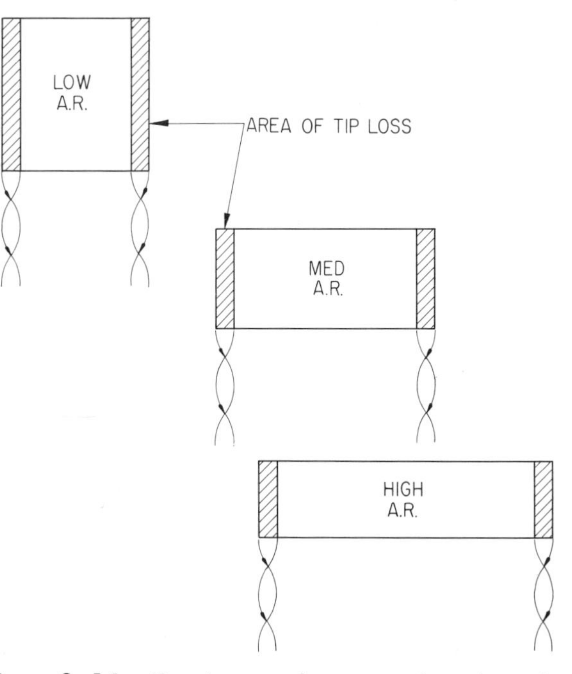

Figure **3·16** *How increased aspect ratio reduces the effect of wing-tip vortices.*

Fig. 3·16, which illustrates the area affected by wing-tip vortices. The shape in the upper left-hand corner of Fig. 3·16 is short and wide. The center shape is long and relatively narrow. The lower right shape is still longer and narrower. Although the area affected by wing-tip vortices remains the same for all these shapes, a smaller proportion of the total area is affected when the airfoil is long and narrow, which is merely another way of saying that increasing the aspect ratio reduces the effect of the wing-tip vortices.

Effects of aspect ratio

The effect of increasing aspect ratio is principally to reduce inducted drag for any given coefficient of lift. This, of course, improves the L/D ratio. **Induced drag** is that part of the drag caused by lift; that is, this drag is caused by the change in direction of airflow. The effect, then, of a higher aspect ratio is to increase the range of an aircraft because there is less drag to overcome. Subject to certain limitations, the most efficient airfoil has the greatest aspect ratio.

A true cantilever wing has no external bracing. If it has a high aspect ratio, it is long and narrow. It is obvious that, when the length is increased too much, the wing will droop from its own weight. Furthermore, the root section (where it joins the fuselage) must be of heavy construction, and this added weight may in itself offset some or all of the gain in lift.

When a wing reaches a certain length, it requires

external bracing, which adds to the weight and causes increased drag. Also, if the wing is too long, a change from cantilever to semicantilever (externally braced) construction will not permit an extremely high aspect ratio because the angle which the struts make between the wing and the fuselage becomes so flat that they do not provide the proper support.

An increase in aspect ratio means a shorter chord; hence the internal fore-and-aft bracing of the wing is relatively shorter. If weight must be added to give the required strength, some of the gain in lift is lost here.

As the span increases, it becomes necessary to have either a longer fuselage or a higher vertical stablizer to place the tail in a position to provide directional stability and control. This adds to the weight of the airplane, and again there is a possibility that this additional weight may offset the advantages gained from increasing the aspect ratio.

When the aspect ratio is increased, the slope of the lift curve is steeper. This proves that there are greater changes of lift with changes in the angle of attack and that the burble point is reached at a lower angle of attack than it would be with an airfoil having a lower aspect ratio.

All the foregoing considerations lead to the conclusion that there is a limit to the practical increase of the aspect ratio. One of the textbooks on the theory of flight states that it is seldom wise to have a value greater than 9 in conventional airplanes, but shortly after the book was printed, an airplane was developed that proved very successful in all respects although it had an aspect ratio of 11.5:1. There is a limit on low aspect ratios as well as high aspect ratios. Some racing airplanes and fast, low-wing fighting airplanes have been built with an aspect ratio of 5, and there have been airplanes with an aspect ratio as low as 4. A low aspect ratio permits better control in landing because the stall is less abrupt. Also, at low angles of attack (at high speed), a low aspect ratio does not result in an important increase of drag because the air pressure acting on the wing is more uniform, and although it decreases toward the trailing edge, the difference between pressure near the leading edge and that near the trailing edge is less than it is at high angles of attack. Consequently, it is not important to have a large proportion of the wing area near the leading edge under these circumstances.

It is interesting to observe that the NACA Report 460, previously mentioned, presents the results for infinite aspect ratio and for an aspect ratio of 6. Some of the most widely used modern light airplanes have an aspect ratio which is close to 7. It is impossible to make any sweeping statement about aspect ratios which will apply to airplanes in general because the selection of aspect ratio depends upon so many other factors.

Taper

The **root section** of an airfoil is the inboard section. In the case of a wing, it is either the section at the center line of the airplane or the section at the fuselage, depending upon how the wing is attached. The **tip section** of an airfoil is the outboard section. An airfoil is tapered when one or more of its dimensions gradually decreases from the root to the tip. If the thickness and chord remain the same from the root to the tip, there is no taper.

When there is a gradual change (usually a decrease) in the chord length along the wing span from the root to the tip, with the wing sections remaining geometrically similar, the airfoil is said to have **taper in plan only,** as shown in the upper right drawing of Fig. 3 · 17.

When there is a gradual change in the thickness ratio along the wing span with the chord remaining constant, the airfoil is said to have **taper in thickness ratio only,** as shown in the middle drawing of Fig. 3 · 17.

There is a fourth form of taper which is seldom mentioned in texts on the theory of flight. In this form, the section at any point along the span has no simple, direct relation to the root section. In other words, there is a constant change in the shape of the airfoil from the root to the tip. Examinations given to technicians and pilots usually require a knowledge of only the first three kinds of taper, but it is well also to know of the fourth kind.

When a wing is tapered in thickness in such a manner that the thickness near the tip is 60 per cent of the thickness at the root and it is compared with an airfoil of constant section (not tapered) equal to the mean (average) section of the tapered wing, the following characteristics are observed on certain airfoils: (1) The CP moves less for changes in angle of attack; (2) the maximum C_L is greater and the peak of the characteristic curve is flatter because all the wing does not attain the maximum C_L at the same time, that is, each section reaches its maximum C_L at a different angle of attack from any other section; (3) the C_D values are lower, the most noticeable decrease being at the low angle of attack; and (4) the maximum L/D ratio is greater and values of L/D ratio are larger at small angles of attack. It is interesting to note that a tapered wing may also

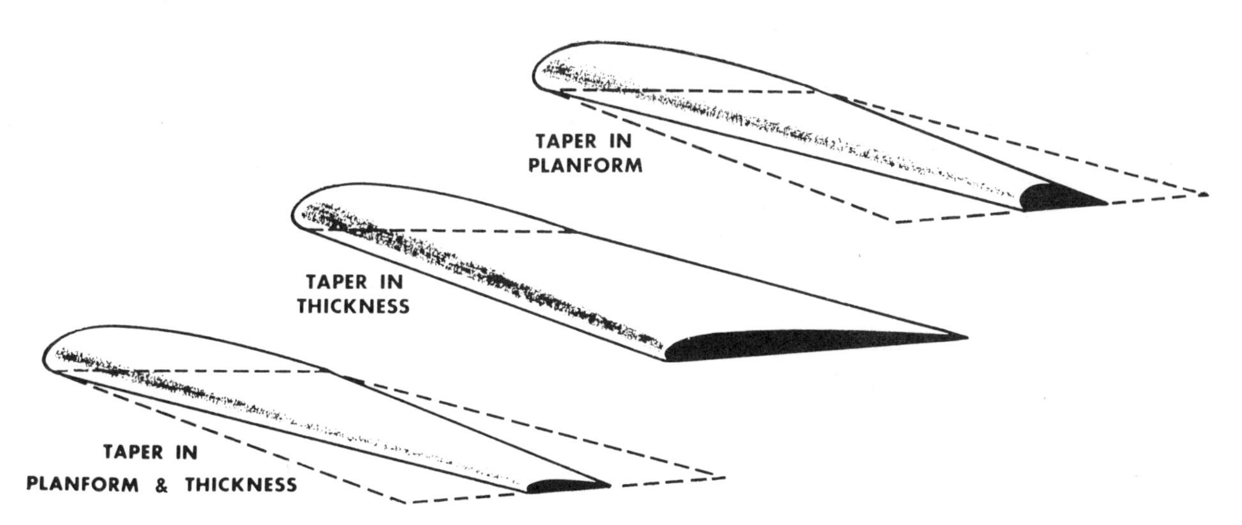

Figure **3·17** *Taper in aircraft wings.*

have a constantly changing airfoil section from the root of the wing to the tip.

When a wing is tapered in planform and is compared with a rectangular airfoil having an equivalent aspect ratio, the following characteristics are observed on certain airfoils: (1) The CP moves more for changes in angle of attack; (2) there is a greater maximum C_L; (3) there are lower values of C_D, especially at low angles of attack; and (4) the L/D ratio is greater throughout the flight range, especially at the higher angles of attack. When a wing or any airfoil is tapered in both thickness and planform, it is possible to take advantage of the best aerodynamic features of the airfoil tapered in thickness only and the airfoil tapered in planform only.

When the distribution of the area of a tapered wing places the resultant force near the center line, it may be possible to build a wing of relatively light weight, having the thicker, heavier, and stronger portions near the root, where the greatest stresses normally occur. On the other hand, in a tapered airfoil, the spars must be tapered and different jigs must be used for building the ribs. For this reason the construction of the wing tapered in both planform and thickness becomes considerably more costly than the construction of other types of wings.

Airfoil selection

The selection of the best airfoil for an airplane requires a careful consideration of the many factors which may conflict with one another, with the result that the final decision is usually a compromise. Some of the more important factors to be considered in airfoil selection are (1) airfoil characteristics, (2) airfoil dimensions, (3) facility of airflow about the airfoil, (4) the speed at which the aircraft is designed to operate, and (5) flight operating limitations.

Biplane pressure interference

Even though it is recognized that the biplane type of airplane is not used so extensively today as it has been in the past, still there are many such airplanes in operation, and it is important for the mechanic and technician to understand some of the details of construction and the aerodynamic characteristics of such aircraft. For this reason we shall discuss the aerodynamic characteristics of biplanes and point out some of their special features.

When the air flows over and under the wing of a monoplane, there is decreased pressure above the wing and increased pressure below. The region of high pressure seeks the region of low pressure, but these two regions can merge only at the tips and at the trailing edge. If the upper and lower wings of a biplane were far enough apart, the airflow would be the same for each of the two wings of the biplane as it would be for the wings of the monoplane, disregarding the effect of the struts connecting the wings of the biplane.

In actual practice, however, the wings of the biplane are so close together that the interference of the streamlines reduces the comparatively low pressure on the upper surface of the lower wing because air always attempts to flow from a region of high pressure to a region of low pressure. The lift of both wings is therefore reduced, but the lower wing loses more lift than the upper wing, and the loss is so great that a biplane is usually less efficient than a monoplane having an equivalent wing area.

In general, the greater the distance between the wings of a biplane, the smaller is the loss of lift due to interplane interference. The opposite is also true; that is, the closer the wings are together, the greater will be the interplane interference. The gap/chord ratio, stagger, and decalage are all involved in interplane interference.

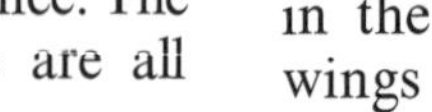

Gap/chord ratio

Gap is the distance between the leading edges of the upper and lower wings of a biplane as shown in Fig. 3·18 and is measured perpendicular to the longitudinal axis of the airplane. Gap is sometimes defined as the distance separating two adjacent wings of a multiplane. These definitions mean the same thing.

The **chord** has been defined and explained before in this text. In addition to other definitions it may be defined as the straight line tangent to the lower surface of the airfoil at two points or as the straight line between the trailing edge and the imaginary perpendicular line at the leading edge. The chord is indicated in Fig. 3·18. Instead of the gap of a biplane, it is customary to give the **gap/chord ratio.** If the gap/chord ratio is 1, it means that the gap and the chord have the same length. In practice the gap/chord ratio is usually close to 1. The principal determining factor for the gap/chord ratio is the **interplane interference.** The upper and lower wing should be as near to each other as possible and still far enough apart so that interplane interference is kept at a minimum.

Gap/Span ratio

Some textbooks on aerodynamics mention the **gap/span ratio.** This is the ratio of the gap to the span, but the gap is always much less than the span; hence the ratio is always less than 1. Gap/span ratio is also defined as the ratio of the gap between two superposed surfaces to the span of the surfaces.

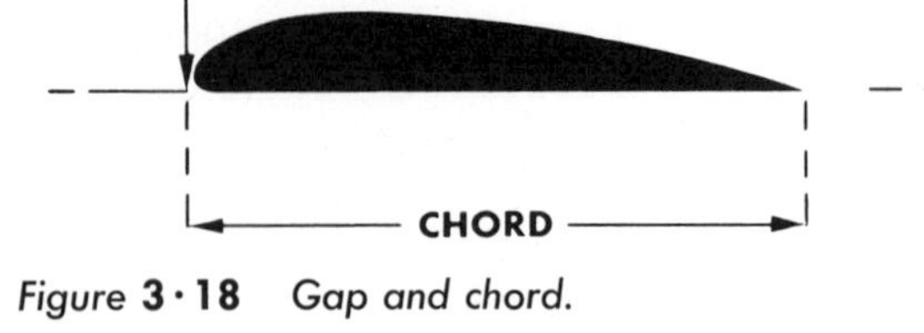

Figure **3·18** *Gap and chord.*

Stagger

Stagger is technically defined as the difference in the longitudinal position of the axes of two wings of an airplane. In simple words, **stagger** is the amount which the leading edge of one wing of a biplane is ahead of the leading edge of the other wing. Stagger is also used to define the distance of one compressor stator blade ahead of another and also the distance of one rotor of a tandem rotor helicopter ahead of the other.

The upper biplane of Fig. 3·19 has **positive stagger** because the leading edge of the upper wing is ahead of the leading edge of the lower wing. The lower biplane of Fig. 3·19 has a **negative stagger** because the leading edge of the upper wing is **behind** the leading edge of the lower wing. Stagger is expressed in inches, in percentage of chord length, or degrees.

When stagger is expressed in degrees, a line is drawn between the leading edges, and the angle that this line makes with a line drawn perpendicular to the chord of the upper wing is the **angle of stagger.** For example, in Fig. 3·20 the angle

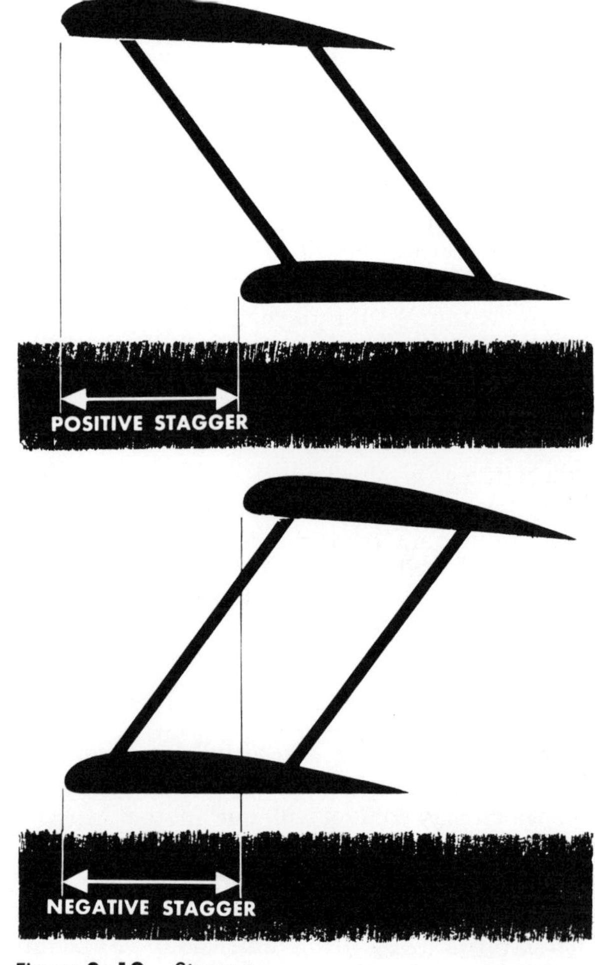

Figure **3·19** *Stagger.*

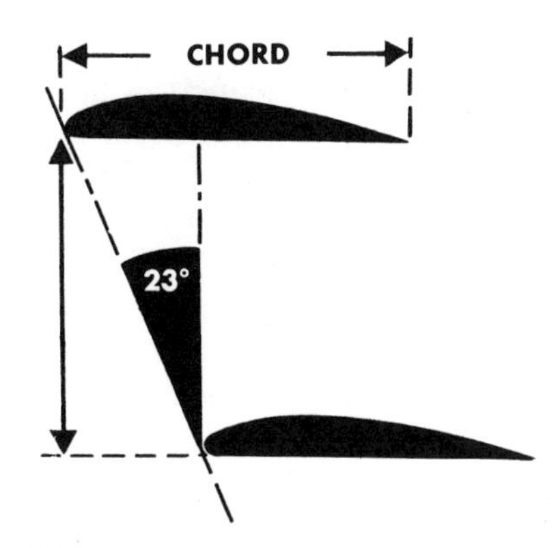

Figure **3·20** *Stagger expressed in degrees.*

formed by a line connecting the leading edges of the wings and a line drawn perpendicular to the chord of the upper wing is 23°. Since the leading edge of the upper wing is ahead of the leading edge of the lower wing, we can say that there is 23° positive stagger.

The aerodynamic advantages of stagger are small. A biplane may have stagger to improve the vision of the pilot, to provide better access to the cockpits, or to provide better angles of fire for machine guns. Since biplancs are no longer used for combat, the last reason is historical rather than practical today. In some types of biplanes, when the positive stagger is increased, the pilot can see better forward and downward.

Decalage

Decalage is the angular difference between the mean aerodynamic chords of the wings of a biplane. The **angle of wing setting** or chord angle is the same thing as the **angle of incidence.** Therefore, we can say that decalage is the difference between the angles of incidence of the wings of a biplane.

The **angle of incidence** is defined as the acute angle between the plane of the wing chord and the longitudinal axis of the airplane. Figure 3·21 shows the angle of incidence of a low-wing monoplane.

The decalage is measured by the angle (less than a right angle) between the chords in a plane parallel to the plane of symmetry. The decalage is considered positive if the upper wing of a biplane is set at the larger angle of incidence. In

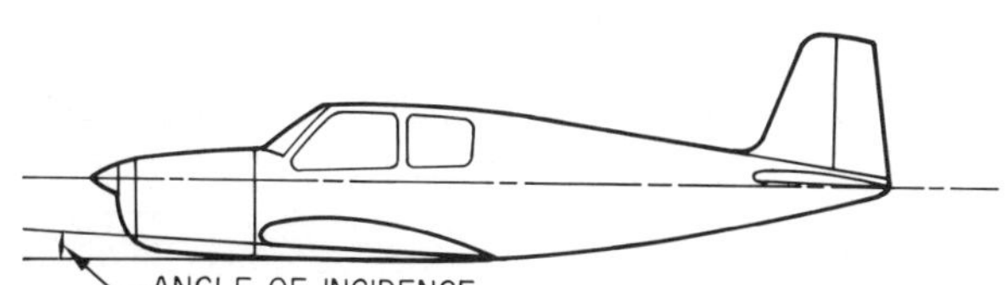

Figure **3·21** *Angle of incidence.*

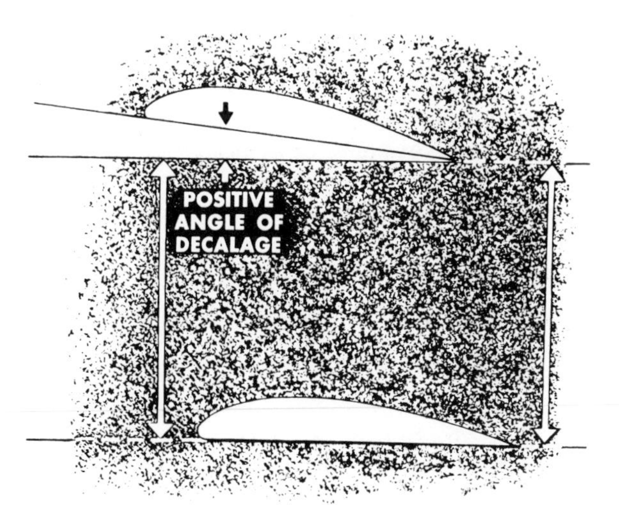

Figure **3·22** *Positive decalage.*

Fig. 3·22 there is an angle of incidence for the upper wing but none for the lower wing; hence there is a positive angle of decalage which, in this particular case, happens to be the same as the angle of incidence of the upper wing.

In Fig. 3·23, the lower wing has an angle of incidence but the upper wing has none; hence there is a negative angle of decalage. In this particular case, the angle of incidence of the lower wing is the angle of decalage.

If the upper wing were set at an angle of incidence of 3° and the lower wing were set at an angle of incidence of 2°, there would be a positive angle of decalage of $3° - 2° = 1°$.

If the chords of the upper and lower wings of a biplane are parallel, the downwash of the upper wing has the effect of decreasing the angle of attack of the lower wing. Setting the lower wing at a greater angle of incidence will more properly distribute the lift between the two wings. Since the upper and lower wings then have different angles of incidence, they have different angles of

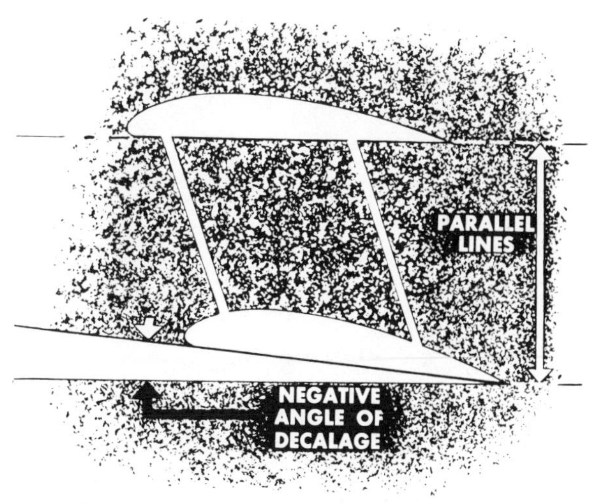

Figure **3·23** *Negative decalage.*

attack in flight, and there will be a difference of pressure distribution between them. Positive decalage gives the upper wing an increase in load percentage, especially at high speed. Negative decalage gives the lower wing an increase in load percentage. Each of the wings will reach its burble point at a different angle of attack, with a result that a stall will be less abrupt. On lift curves, this condition is shown by a flatter peak.

Mean aerodynamic chord

The **mean aerodynamic chord (MAC)** is the chord of an imaginary rectangular airfoil that would have pitching moments or force vectors throughout the flight range identical with those of an actual wing or combination of wings under consideration.

The MAC must not be confused with the mean chord of a wing, which is merely the quotient obtained by dividing the wing area by the span.

When the MAC of a nontapered monoplane wing is not known, it can be assumed to be the same as the actual chord, and the leading edge of the wing can be regarded as the leading edge of the MAC. Figure 3·24 represents a biplane with wings of unequal chords. One line is drawn connecting the leading edges, and another line connects the trailing edges of the airfoils. If the upper wing is known to carry two-thirds of the load carried by the entire combination, the MAC is located at a vertical distance of one-third the gap distance from the chord of the upper wing. Its trailing edge is on the line connecting the trailing edges of the upper and lower wings, and its leading edge is on the line connecting the leading edges of the wings. Also, if a line is drawn

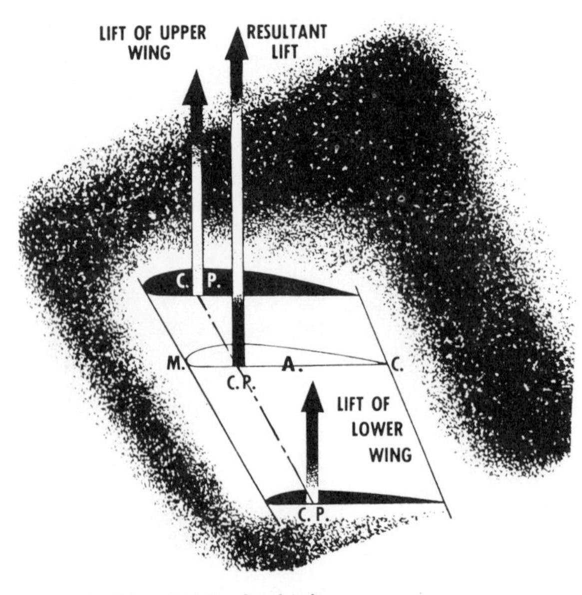

Figure **3·24** *MAC of a biplane.*

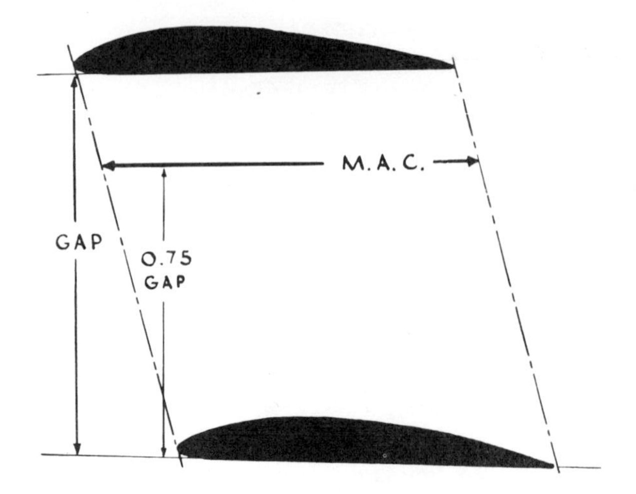

Figure **3·25** *MAC of biplane with rectangular or moderately staggered arrangement of nontapered wings.*

connecting the CP of the two wings, the CP of the imaginary airfoil drawn around the MAC is on the same line.

Notice that in Fig. 3·24 the lift of the upper wing is represented by an arrow and the lift of the lower wing is also represented by an arrow, both arrows originating in the CP of their respective airfoils. An arrow drawn upward from the CP of the imaginary airfoil based upon the MAC will represent the resultant lift, that is, the lift obtained by the combination of the two airfoils. The MAC having been found, certain corrections are made to the figures, and then the combination of the two airfoils can be regarded as the single airfoil of a monoplane.

It must be understood that this discussion of Fig. 3·24 is given only as an attempt to simplify what is, in reality, a very complicated and highly technical subject. The figures applying to Fig. 3·24 would hold true only under certain conditions, and they cannot be used as a rule-of-thumb procedure in every case.

The MAC of a biplane with a rectangular or moderately staggered arrangement on nontapered wings can be determined approximately according to the method illustrated in Fig. 3·25, where the MAC is located 25 per cent of the gap distance below the chord of the upper wing. Obviously, it is also 75 per cent of the gap distance above the chord of the lower wing. The position of the MAC having been found, its length can be measured.

The position of the CG of an airplane is often expressed as a percentage of the MAC. For example, the specifications for a certain airplane may show that the CG must lie between 28 per cent and 34 per cent of the MAC. This means that the forward limit for the CG is 28 per cent of the MAC and the rearward limit is 34 per cent of the MAC. If the technician is working a problem to determine the location of the CG, it is obvious that he must know the location of the MAC.

Monoplane compared with biplane

The early airplane designers and builders reasoned that a biplane would provide more lifting surface than a monoplane of the same span, but they soon found that drag was caused by interplane interference and also by the struts and wires. Many designers were aware that a cantilever (unbraced) monoplane with tapered wings was superior on a basis of aerodynamic performance, but they had not yet developed a deep airfoil section which would eliminate the need for external bracing. Furthermore, they lacked materials which would provide the necessary structural strength and rigidity for an unbraced wing.

The early biplane designers also argued that, even if they had a deep airfoil section and the proper materials for building cantilever wings, the biplane was structurally more efficient, it provided more visibility, and it was more maneuverable. There were other arguments which were extremely important, although they were seldom mentioned. One was that those making biplanes had a vast amount of money invested in their equipment. Another was that the engineers and mechanics were reluctant to change from familiar procedures to untried methods. For all these reasons, the conversion from biplanes to monoplanes was a slow process. However, today the monoplane is the accepted type of aircraft and no new biplanes are being regularly produced, even though many are still in use, especially as agricultural aircraft.

Wing flaps

The purpose of wing flaps on an airplane is to reduce the landing speed and make it possible for the airplane to land on a shorter runway than it would otherwise require. The effect of a wing flap is to vary the effective camber of the wing, although it is usually accomplished with a substantial increase in drag. A flap hinged to the trailing edge of the wing acts as an air brake when it is deflected sufficiently. This makes it possible for the airplane to have a steeper angle of descent for the landing without increasing the airspeed. Figure 3·26 shows the advantage of using flaps to enter a small field over an obstruction.

A wing flap is defined by the NASA as a hinged, pivoted, or sliding airfoil, usually near the trailing edge of the wing. It is designed to increase the lift, drag, or both when deflected and is used principally for landing, although some large airplanes use partial flap deflection for takeoff. When the flaps are placed at 30°, there is a substantial increase in lift and very little increase in drag.

Some of the basic types of flap design are illustrated in Fig. 3·27. A basic airfoil without a flap is shown at the top of the illustration. The next drawing is a **plain flap.** This flap resembles an aileron in configuration. However, it is linked with the flap on the opposite wing so that both flaps move down and up together instead of moving in opposite directions as the ailerons do. Normally, flaps are installed inboard of the ailerons on a monoplane, although, in some cases, they may be placed both inboard and outboard of the ailerons.

The **split-edge flap** is usually housed flush with the lower surface of the wing, immediately forward of the trailing edge. This flap is illustrated in the middle drawing of Fig. 3·27. The split-edge flap is usually nothing more than a flat metal plate hinged along its forward edge.

The **Zap flap,** similar in design to one called the **Alfaro flap** and shown in the drawing next to the bottom in Fig. 3·27, is roughly similar to the plain split flap when it is fully retracted, but as the flap is opened, the hinge axis moves rearward to keep the trailing edges of the wing and the

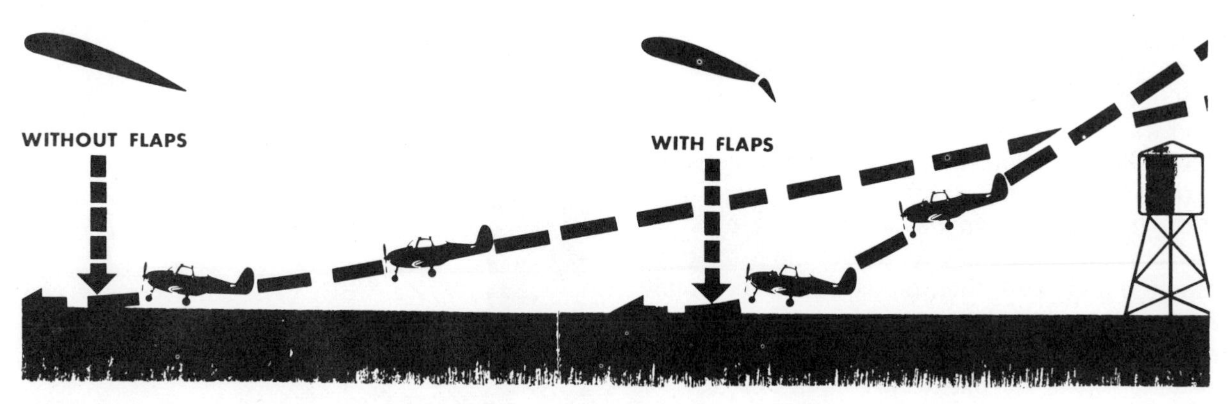

Figure **3·26** *Advantage of flaps in landing.*

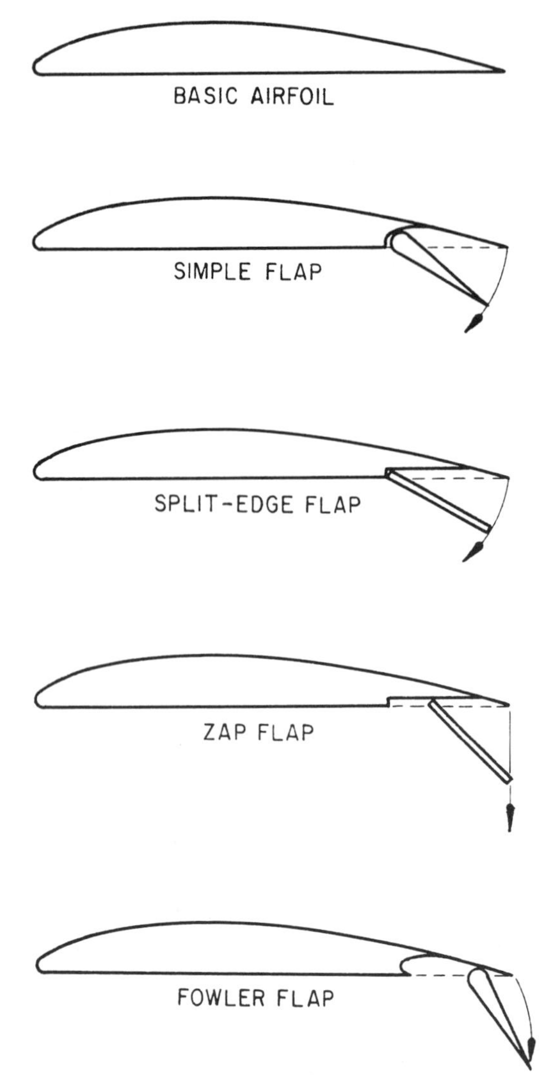

Figure **3 · 27** *Basic types of flaps.*

flap on a line perpendicular to the chord of the wing.

The **Fowler flap,** shown in the bottom picture of Fig. 3 · 27, is constructed so that the lower part of the trailing edge of the wing rolls back on a track, thus increasing the effective area of the wing and at the same time lowering the trailing edge. The flap itself is a small airfoil which fits neatly into the trailing edge of the main wing when closed. As shown in Fig. 3 · 28, when the flap opens, the small airfoil slides downward and backward on tracks until it reaches the position desired by the pilot, thus providing a wing with a variable coefficient of lift and a variable area. With the Fowler flap the wing area can be increased and at the same time both the lift and the drag are increased, the exact amount of increase of each depending upon the angle to which the flap is lowered. The Fowler flap is one of the designs which are particularly well adapted for use at takeoff as well as landing.

Figure **3 · 28** *Operation of the Fowler flap.*

At normal flying speeds, when flaps are fully retracted, that is, they are all the way up, they have no effect on the lift characteristics of the wing. On the other hand, when they are lowered for landing, there is increased lift for similar angles of attack of the basic airfoil, and the maximum lift coefficient is greatly increased, often as much as 70 per cent, the exact amount of increase depending upon the type of flap installed. The curves of Fig. 3 · 29 illustrate the lift characteristics of a wing with flaps and without flaps. With the increase of lift comes a decrease in landing speed, but there is also an increase of drag when the flap is down, and this requires a steeper glide to maintain the approach speed. The increase of

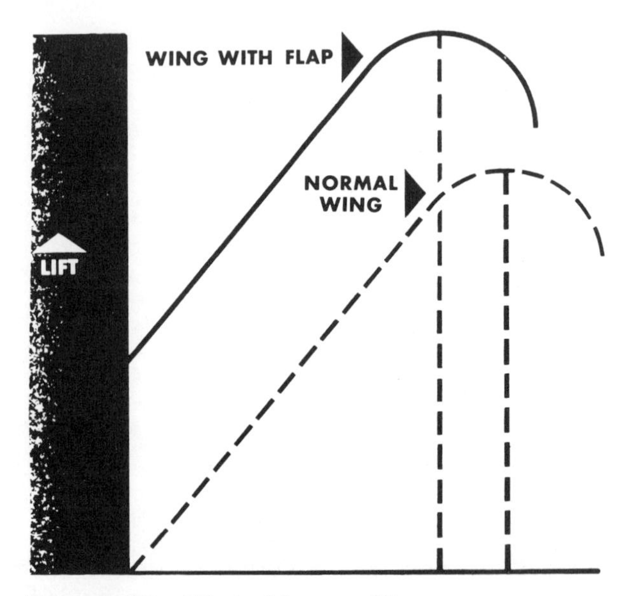

Figure **3 · 29** *Effect of flaps on lift.*

drag also acts as a brake when the airplane is rolling to a stop on the landing strip.

The person who flies an airplane equipped with flaps for the first time may experience some difficulties. The obvious remedy for any dangers that may accompany the use flaps is careful pilot training. The advantages and disadvantages of using flaps listed here are the general ones usually presented to pilots and technicians. Like all such statements, they are subject to exceptions.

1. The higher lift coefficient obtained from the use of flaps permits a lower landing speed.
2. When air brakes are used, flaps permit a shorter run on the ground in stopping the airplane.
3. The use of flaps makes it possible to have a steeper gliding angle without increasing the speed, thus permitting the airplane to clear obstacles in landing and also make easier spot landings.

Flaps on an airplane also have certain disadvantages. These disadvantages should be understood by the pilot and the technician so that they can operate and maintain the aircraft properly and safely. Disadvantages are as follows:

1. The use of flaps requires training and skill on the part of the pilot.
2. The flap is not automatic in operation; hence its control requires additional time and thought from the pilot. This disadvantage is actually part of the one given above.
3. Flaps add to the weight of an airplane and increase the possibility of mechanical failure.
4. Since the flaps normally extend along the trailing edge of the wing between the ailerons, when fully extended it is possible that they may have some effect on the lateral control of the airplane. The amount of effect depends upon the size and type of flaps as well as the design of the airfoil.

Slots

A **slot** is a nozzle-shaped passage through a wing designed to improve the airflow conditions at high angles of attack. It is normally placed veıy near the leading edge and is formed by a main and an auxiliary airfoil or **slat.**

A slat is a movable auxiliary airfoil, attached to the leading edge of the wing, which when closed falls within the original contour of the wing and which when opened forms a slot. Slots are illustrated in Figs. 3·30 and 3·31.

There are two general types of slots, the fixed and the automatic. When the fixed type is used, the airflow depends on the angle of attack. As the angle of attack of the wing increases, more of the air is deflected through the slot, thus maintaining a streamline flow around the wing. The automatic slot consists of an auxiliary airfoil nested into the leading edge of the wing while the wing is at low angles of attack but free to move forward a definite distance from the leading edge at high angles of attack to form a flat nozzle (slot) through which a portion of the airstream flows to be deflected along the upper surface of the wing. Figure 3·30 shows the effect of the airstream diverted by a slot and the advantage gained by its use. The center picture shows the airfoil with a slot closed at a high angle of attack. The airfoil is shown in a stalling position because the burbling of the air reaches almost to the leading edge of the wing. The top drawing shows the airfoil at a medium angle of attack. It is apparent that the airflow depends not only upon the presence or the absence of the slot but also upon the design of the basic airfoil; hence a different airfoil would have a different pattern of airflow.

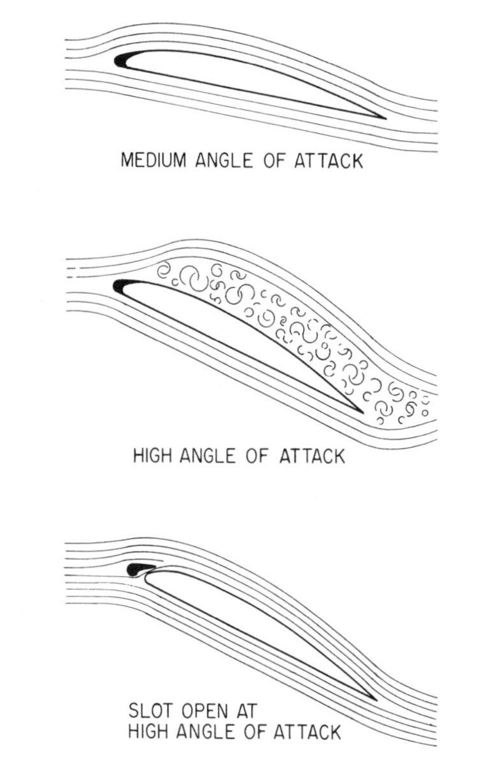

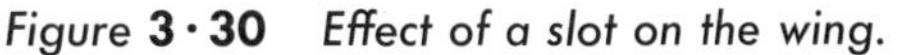

Figure **3·30** *Effect of a slot on the wing.*

The auxiliary airfoil section is a highly cambered airfoil normally mounted on the leading edge of a wing. When this airfoil is nested against the leading edge of the wing, the airfoil will be as shown in the top two drawings of Fig. 3·30. However, it is free to move on a system of linkages which can be supported by the front spar of the wing.

When the auxiliary airfoil is moved forward of the wing leading edge at a high angle of attack to form the slot, the air flows through the slot from

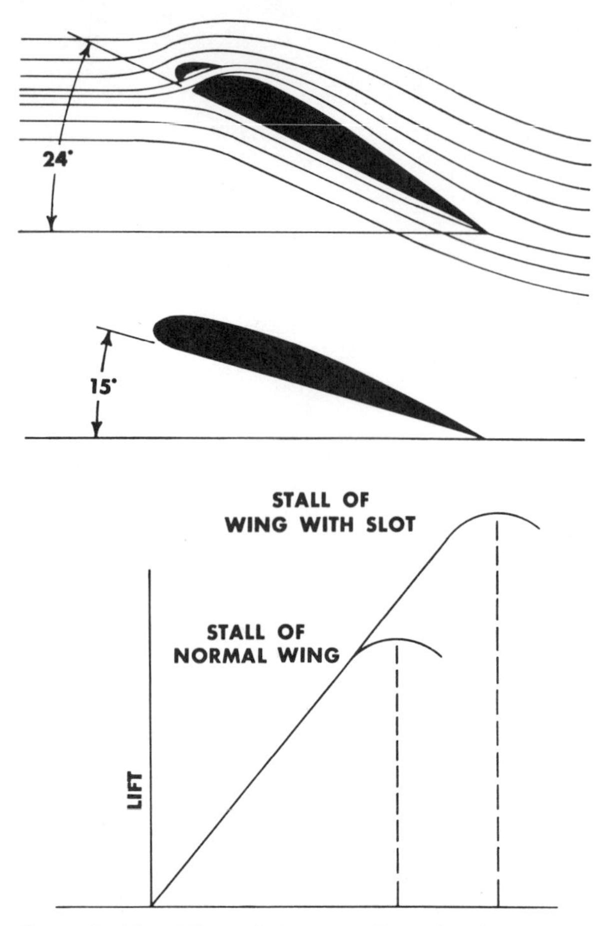

Figure **3·31** *Effect of slot on stalling speed.*

the high-pressure region below the wing to the low-pressure area above the wing as shown in the bottom drawing of Fig. 3·30. The air which has come from the high-pressure region below the wing is now deflected along the upper surface of the wing by the shape of the slot, and this flow of air postpones the breakdown of streamline flow which accompanies an increase in the angle of attack. If the slot is well designed, and if it is working properly, the burble point will not be reached until the angle of attack is very much greater than that of a normal stall. In some cases, the burble point will not be reached until the angle of attack is almost twice that of a normal stall, but it must be understood that a general statement cannot be made which will apply to all circumstances. Figure 3·31 illustrates the effect of the slot on the lift coefficient. Notice that at angles where the slot is opened, the lift is greater and the maximum C_L occurs at a much higher angle of attack, which indicates that an airplane with a slotted wing has a lower stalling speed than one without slots, other things being equal.

Earlier in this text it was shown that the pressure distribution changes with the angle of attack. The automatic operation of the slot depends upon this fact. There is a down load on the leading edge of the wing at low angles of attack. As long as this condition continues, the slot remains closed, but as the pressure is reduced over the auxiliary airfoil, the resultant of all forces acting on it finally attains a value and direction sufficient to move the auxiliary airfoil forward.

The automatic slot has disadvantages as well as advantages. The number of moving parts and the weight of the wing are increased. In the past, weight was also added because it was necessary, in the case of some airplanes, to have longer landing-gear struts to eliminate tail skid landings brought about by the increased angle of attack at the stall. The slots must be installed properly and operate equally well on both wing tips or they are useless. If a slot on one wing should open before the slot on the opposite wing opened, disasterous results could occur. The usual location of slots is such that they are subjected to ice formation, and in spite of any anti-icing or deicing equipment they may fail to function. If any of these factors cause a lack of balance, the airplane may accidently spin and lateral control is impaired. For these reasons, a device is usually provided for locking slots in a closed position if they do not function properly or if the pilot wishes to perform violent maneuvers. A locking device is normally controlled from the cockpit.

Figure 3·32 illustrates the effect of having a combination of slots and flaps. With this arrangement, it is possible to have a much lower landing speed, better control of the flight path, and at least a partial elimination of the nose heaviness which may result from the use of flaps alone. It should be understood that Fig. 3·32 is

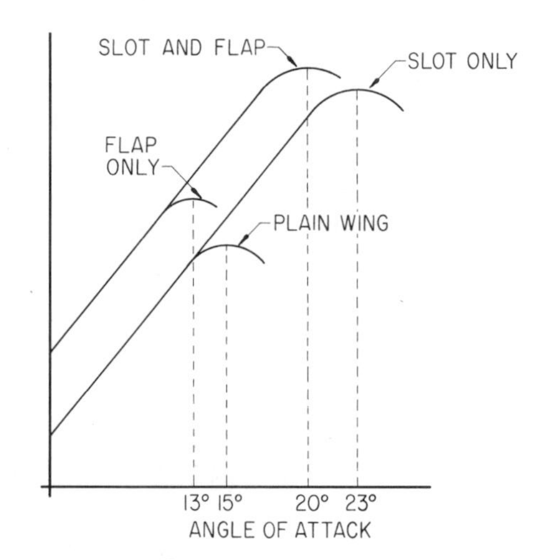

Figure **3·32** *Effect of the combination of slots and flaps.*

based upon a particular set of conditions and does not illustrate the effect produced by various airfoils and combinations of different flaps and slots. Other types of flaps and combinations with slots will produce values differing from those shown in the drawing.

Reynolds number

Osborne Reynolds studied the flow of liquids in pipes and found that at a low speed the flow is smooth but at a high speed the flow is turbulent. By experimenting with pipes of various sizes and different liquids, he found a value which he called the critical Reynolds number (RN). The flow was laminar (smooth) for values below the critical RN and turbulent for the values above the critical RN. This value worked well for the flow of liquids inside circular tubes, but it had to be handled differently when it was applied to the flow of air around objects which were unconfined, such as airfoils.

It was found by experiments that the airflow around an unconfined object changed when the velocity changed and that the airflow also changed when the size of the object was changed. It was also discovered that, if the size of the object and the velocity of the air remained the same but the air density increased, the flow would change. Furthermore research showed that decreasing the coefficient of viscosity has the same effect as increasing either the velocity or the density of the air.

With this information, the aeronautical engineers were ready to make a practical application of their knowledge of viscosity and Reynolds numbers. They found that, if the RN of a model airplane is the same as the RN of the full-scale airplane, wind-tunnel tests of models of full-sized airplanes will indicate the actual performance of full-sized airplanes, and the same principle applies to wind-tunnel tests of wings or other parts of an airplane. However, the models are much smaller than the full-scale objects; hence either the velocity or the density of the air in the wind tunnel must be greater than it would be in actual flight. That is the reason that some wind tunnels are described as variable-density wind tunnels.

In finding the Reynolds number, the velocity V must be in feet per second and the linear dimensions L (sometimes written as lower case l) of the object to be tested must be in feet. When wings are being tested, the length of the chord is usually chosen for L. If the test is conducted under standard atmospheric conditions (15°C and 760 mm or 29.92 in. Hg pressure), the density of the air ρ is 0.002378 slug per cu ft and the coefficient of viscosity μ is 0.000000373 slug per ft-sec. If standard atmospheric conditions are not used, corrections must be made for density and viscosity. The formula for the Reynolds number is $RN = \rho v(L/\mu)$, where ρ is air density, V is velocity, L is the dimension (usually the chord), and μ is the coefficient of viscosity.

If the Reynolds number for a model wing having a chord of 6 in. is desired, and if the test is to be conducted at standard atmospheric conditions and at a velocity of 100 mph, the chord dimension is changed to feet, giving 0.5 ft, and the velocity of 100 mph is changed to its equivalent of 146.7 ft per sec. We then have $RN = 0.002378 \times 146.7 \times 0.5/0.000000373 = 467{,}630.9$.

A term frequently used in discussing airplane design is **scale effect.** This is the change in any force coefficient, such as a drag coefficient, due to a change in the value of a Reynolds number.

Vortex generators

Even though modern jet airliners do not fly at the speed of sound (Mach 1), there are certain areas on the airplane where the airflow velocity will be greater than Mach 1. This is particularly true at the upper surface of parts of the wing where, because of the curvature of the wing, the air velocity must increase substantially above the airspeed of the airplane. This is illustrated in Fig. 3·33, which shows an airfoil profile moving through the air at high subsonic speed. A short distance back from the leading edge of the wing above the top surface, the air reaches supersonic speed. At the rear part of the supersonic area where the airflow returns to subsonic speed, a shock wave is formed. To the rear of this shock wave the air is very turbulent, and this area of the wing is, in effect, partially stalled. This, of course, causes a substantial increase in drag, which increases as airspeed increases.

In order to reduce the drag caused by supersonic flow over portions of the wing, small airfoils

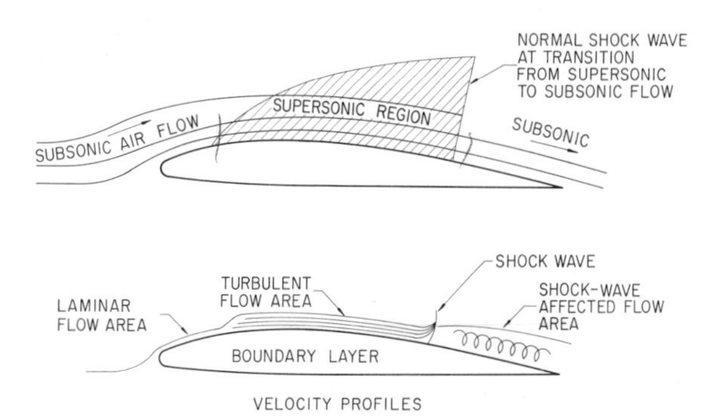

Figure 3·33 Development of supersonic airflow over a subsonic wing.

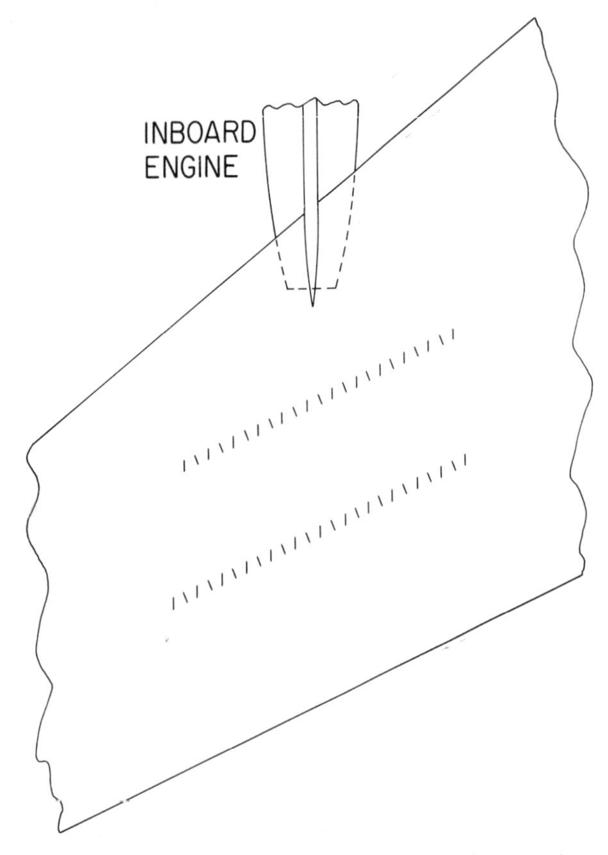

Figure **3·34** *Vortex generators mounted on airplane wing.*

called **vortex generators** are installed perpendicular to the surface of the wing. On the Boeing 720 airplane a total of 96 vortex generators are mounted in two rows as shown in Fig. 3·34. There are 23 generators in the forward row and 25 in the aft row. The two rows are parallel and centered spanwise aft of the inboard nacelles, with the aft row extending slightly more inboard than the forward row.

The vortex generators are mounted in complementary pairs as shown in the drawing of Fig. 3·35. This causes the vortices being developed to add to one another, thus increasing the effect.

Because of the low aspect ratio of the vortex generators, they develop a strong tip vortex. The

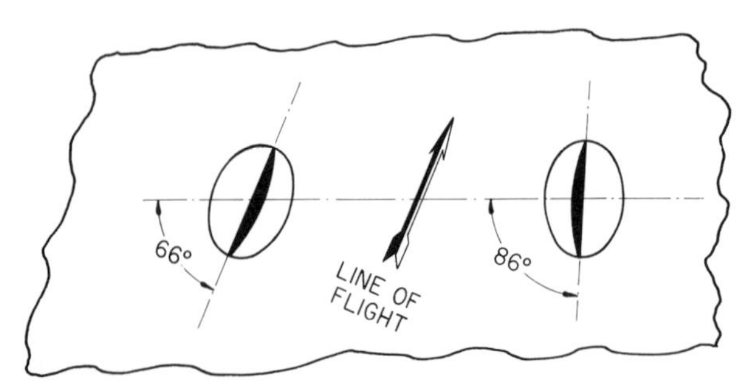

Figure **3·35** *Vortex generators arranged in pairs.*

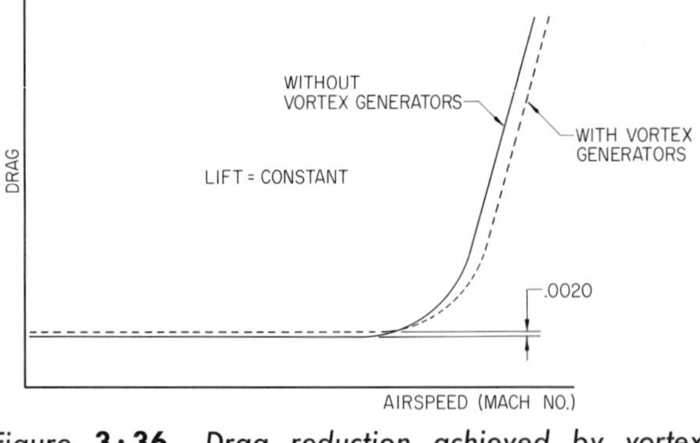

Figure **3·36** *Drag reduction achieved by vortex generators.*

tip vortex causes air to flow upward and inward in a circular path around the ends of the airfoil. The vortex generated has the effect of drawing high-energy air from outside the boundary layer into the slower-moving air close to the skin. The strength of the vortex is proportional to the lift developed by the generator. To operate effectively, the generators are mounted forward of the point where separation begins.

Drag reduction achieved by the addition of vortex generators can be seen in the drag-rise curve. Since the generators effectively reduce the shock-induced drag associated with the sharp rise in the curve at speeds approaching Mach 1.0, the curve is pushed to the right as shown in Fig. 3·36.

Addition of the vortex generators actually increases overall drag very slightly at lower speeds. However, the gains at cruise speeds more than balance out the losses at lower speeds. Since the airplane spends most of its flight time at cruise speeds, the net gain is significant.

REVIEW QUESTIONS

1. Name four airfoil characteristics.
2. What is the fundamental equation for lift?
3. What is meant by the lift/drag ratio?
4. Define *slug.*
5. In general, how does the center of pressure of an airfoil behave as the angle of attack changes?
6. What is meant by the *span* of an airplane?
7. Define *aspect ratio.*
8. In what terms is *camber* expressed?
9. What is the difference between *airfoil profile* and *airfoil section?*
10. Explain the meaning of the digits in the NACA airfoil number.
11. What is the cause of wing-tip vortices?
12. What is the effect of increasing aspect ratio?

13. Give some of the limitations for increase of aspect ratio.
14. List design factors which must be considered in selecting an airfoil design.
15. Explain *gap/chord* and *gap/span* ratio.
16. Define *decalage.*
17. Compare *angle of incidence* and *angle of attack.*
18. What is meant by *mean aerodynamic chord?*
19. What advantage is provided by flaps in the landing of an airplane?
20. What is the advantage of the Fowler flap?
21. What is the value of a slot at the leading edge of a wing?
22. What is the significance of the Reynolds number?
23. Why are vortex generators used on some high-speed aircraft?

CHAPTER 

Aircraft in Flight

INTRODUCTION

Any person associated with aviation should have some understanding of the actual processes of flight. An individual who is responsible for the design, construction, and operation or maintenance of aircraft and other flying vehicles must be thoroughly familiar with the forces acting on an airplane in flight, the components of the airplane which control the flight forces, the reactions of the airplane to its control, and the atmospheric conditions which affect flight. It is therefore appropriate that we study the factors involved with the flight of an airplane and how these factors are related to our own activities in aviation.

Proper maintenance of an airplane requires that the person responsible for such maintenance have a knowledge of the forces acting on the airplane in flight so he knows what repairs and adjustments will accomplish the desired result. It is obvious that any repair to an airplane should be just as strong as the original part. If the maintenance technician knows what stresses will be applied to a given part of the aircraft in flight, he will be in a better position to judge the suitability of a particular repair. For example, on a high-wing monoplane the wing struts are subjected to high tensile stresses during flight, especially if the air is gusty and the airplane is flying at or near maximum speed. These same struts are subjected to compression stresses when the airplane lands. The maintenance technician must therefore make sure that the struts, attachment fittings, and adjacent structure are maintained in such a manner that full strength is preserved.

The parts of an airplane are classed in two principal categories relating to strength. These are **structural** members and **nonstructural** members. The structural members are subjected to major stresses in flight and landing, while the nonstructural members have to sustain comparatively small loads. A detailed consideration of aircraft structures is covered in the chapter concerned with this subject.

AIRCRAFT CONTROL

Nomenclature

An airplane is equipped with certain fixed and movable surfaces or airfoils which provide for stability and control during flight. These are illustrated in the drawing of Fig. 4·1. Each of the named airfoils is designed to perform a specific function in the flight of the airplane. The fixed airfoils are the **wings,** the **vertical stabilizer,** and the **horizontal stabilizer.** The movable airfoils, called control surfaces, are the **ailerons, elevators, rudder,** and **flaps.** The ailerons, elevators, and rudder are used to "steer" the airplane in flight to make it go where the pilot wishes it to go and to cause it to execute certain maneuvers. The flaps are normally used only during landings and sometimes for takeoff.

Axes of the airplane

An airplane has three axes of rotation, namely, the **longitudinal axis,** the **vertical axis,** and the **lateral axis.** These are illustrated in Fig. 4·2 and can be remembered by relating them to their names. **Longitudinal** can be remembered by think-

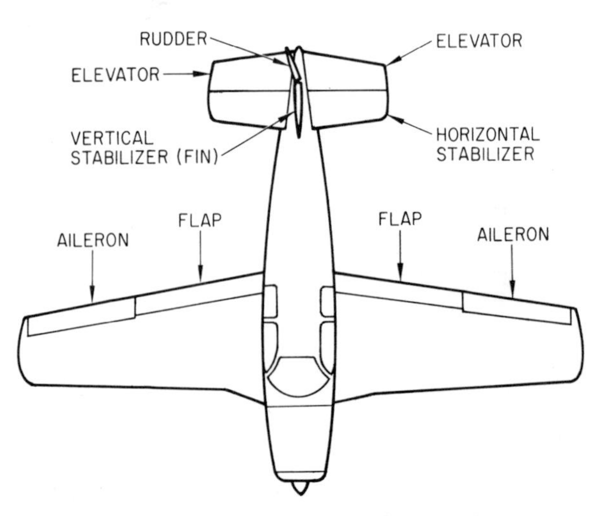

Figure 4·1 The control surfaces of an airplane.

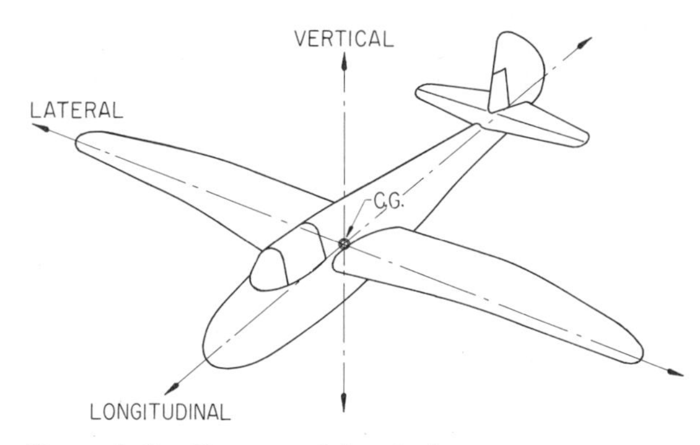

Figure 4·2 The axes of the airplane.

ing of the word "longways." That is, the longitudinal axis goes "longways" with the fuselage of the airplane. It may be considered to enter at the propeller hub or nose of the airplane and to pass through the fuselage, going out at the tail. **Vertical** may be defined as "up and down" in this case, so we can think of the vertical axis as an imaginary line going up and down through the center of gravity of the airplane. For our purpose here **lateral** means "sideways," so the lateral axis is an imaginary line passing sideways through the center of gravity of the airplane. We can also think of it as a line going from wing tip to wing tip.

In considering the axes of the airplane it is important to note that all three axes pass through the CG. This is one of the reasons why the CG must be located within certain limits if the airplane is to fly satisfactorily. In our study of weight and balance we shall see how the CG location is affected by loading.

Ailerons

Aileron may be defined as a movable control surface attached to the trailing edge of a wing to control an airplane in **roll,** that is, rotation about the longitudinal axis. The conventional monoplane has two ailerons, one attached to each wing. They are rigged so that, when one is applying an upward force to one wing, the other is applying a downward force to the opposite wing.

The ailerons are moved by means of a control stick or a wheel in the cockpit. If it is desired to roll the airplane to the right, the stick is moved to the right or the wheel is turned to the right. After the desired degree of bank is obtained, the stick or wheel is returned to neutral to stop the roll. During normal turns of an airplane the movement of the ailerons is coordinated with movements of the rudder and elevators to provide a banked horizontal turn without "slip" or "skid."

The correct rigging of the ailerons is of primary importance. After an airplane has been over-

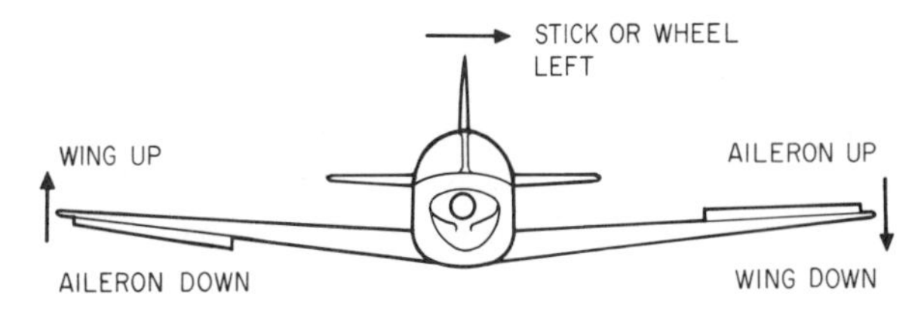

Figure 4·3 Effect of ailerons in flight.

hauled and during preflight inspections, the direction of aileron movement with respect to control-stick movement must be carefully noted. If the stick or wheel is moved to the right, the right aileron must move up and the left aileron must move down. Reverse movement of the control should then cause a reverse of the position of the ailerons.

During flight of the airplane, a down movement of the aileron causes an increase in lift for the wing and the wing rises. At the same time the opposite aileron moves up and causes a decrease in lift for the opposite wing and this wing moves down. This action is illustrated in Fig. 4·3.

It was mentioned in this section that conventional monoplanes are equipped with two ailerons, one being attached to the trailing edge of each wing. This does not apply to modern jet airliners. These high-speed airplanes usually employ at least two sets of ailerons. At low speeds all the ailerons are used, but at high speeds only one small pair of ailerons is required because the effectiveness of aileron control increases with speed and because **spoilers** are used with the ailerons for effective control at high speeds. A spoiler is a flaplike device used to destroy lift and increase drag.

Elevators

An **elevator** is defined as a horizontal, hinged control surface, usually attached to the trailing edge of the horizontal stabilizer of an airplane, designed to apply a **pitching moment** to the airplane. A pitching moment is a force tending to rotate the airplane about the lateral axis, that is, "nose up" or "nose down." When the control stick or wheel in the airplane is pulled back, the elevators are raised. The force of the relative wind

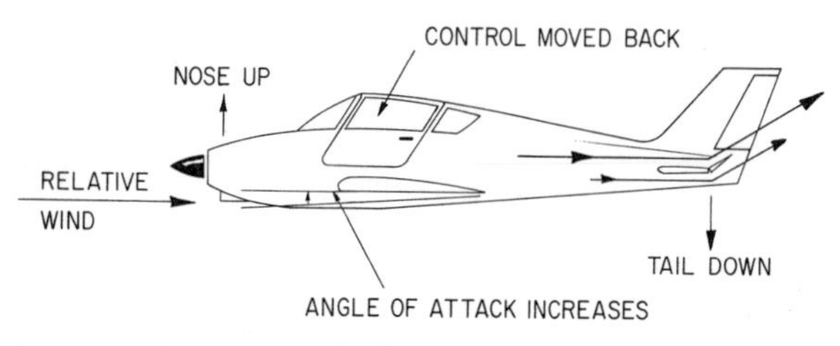

Figure 4·4 Action of elevators.

on the elevator surfaces tends to press the tail down, thus causing the nose to pitch up and the angle of attack of the wings to increase. The reverse action takes place when the control stick or wheel is pushed forward. The action of the elevators is illustrated in Fig. 4•4.

During flight of an airplane the operation of the elevators is quite critical, especially at low speeds. When power is off and the airplane is gliding, the position of the elevators will determine whether the airplane dives, glides at the correct angle, or stalls. The pilot must know the stalling speed of the aircraft and keep the elevators in a position which will enable the airplane to maintain flying speed. A safe gliding speed must be well above stalling speed, otherwise a gust or quick shift in wind velocity could cause the airplane to stall.

During the handling of the elevator control it is necessary for the pilot to remember that an airplane will not necessarily climb when the control is pulled back. It is the power developed by the engine that determines the rate of climb of an airplane rather than the position of the elevators. As a matter of fact, if the elevators are held in a fixed position, the throttle alone can be used to make the airplane climb, dive, or maintain level flight. The position of the elevator is important, however, to establish the most efficient rate of climb and to establish a good gliding angle when power is off. It is also most essential for proper control when "breaking the glide" and holding the airplane in landing position.

Rudder

A **rudder** is a vertical control surface usually hinged to the tail post aft of the vertical stabilizer and designed to apply **yawing** moments to the airplane, that is, to make it turn to the right or left about the vertical axis. The movement of the rudder is controlled by pedals or a "rudder bar" operated by the feet of the pilot. When the right pedal is pressed, the rudder swings to the right, thus bringing an increase of dynamic air pressure on its right side. This increased pressure causes the tail of the airplane to swing to the left and the nose to turn to the right. The operation of a rudder is shown in Fig. 4•5.

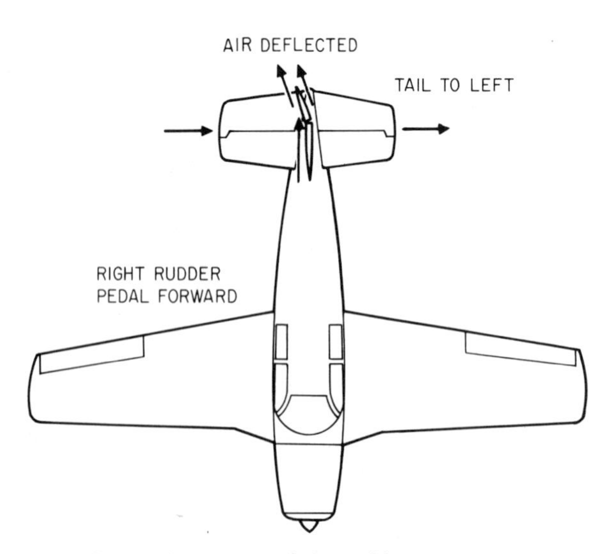

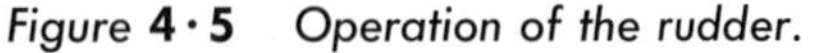
Figure **4•5** *Operation of the rudder.*

Although it appears that the rudder causes the airplane to turn, it must be pointed out that the rudder by itself cannot cause the airplane to make a good turn. We remember from Newton's First Law of Motion that a moving body tends to continue moving in a straight line unless some outside force changes its direction. When rudder is applied to an airplane in flight, the airplane will turn but it will continue to travel in the same direction as before unless a correcting force is applied. Thus, with rudder only, we find that the airplane **skids.** In order to prevent this skid in a turn, we use the ailerons to **bank** the airplane. Anyone who drives a car will know that a banked turn is much easier to negotiate at comparatively high speeds in a car than a flat turn. It is the same with an airplane. To prevent skidding in a turn, the airplane must be banked.

Too much of a bank without sufficient rudder in a turn will cause **slipping.** That is, the airplane will slide down toward the inside of the turn. It is therefore necessary that the proper amount of rudder and aileron be applied when entering a turn in order to produce what is termed a **coordinated** turn. Usually, after the airplane is placed in a turn, the rudder pressure is almost neutralized to hold the turn. Likewise it is necessary to reduce the amount of aileron used to place the airplane in the turn.

Another factor to note concerning turns is that the steeper the turn, the more the **elevator** will have to be used. Picture an airplane in a 45° bank. The tail control surfaces form an X, and the nose of the airplane must be held up with **up elevator.** Thus we see that a properly executed turn requires the use of all three of the primary controls.

Unusual controls

Some airplanes have been designed with special types of control surfaces that do not fit into the descriptions of the conventional controls. One such control is called the **ruddervator.** The ruddervator is used on airplanes with "butterfly" tails, and the surfaces serve both as rudders and as elevators. When it is desired to increase the

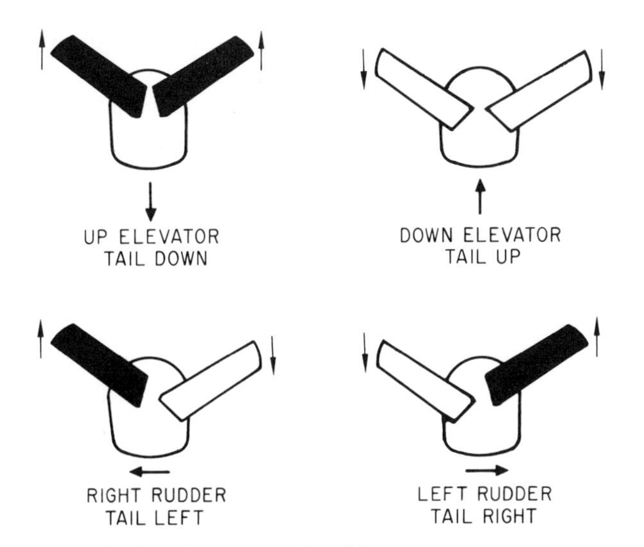

Figure 4·6 Operation of ruddervators.

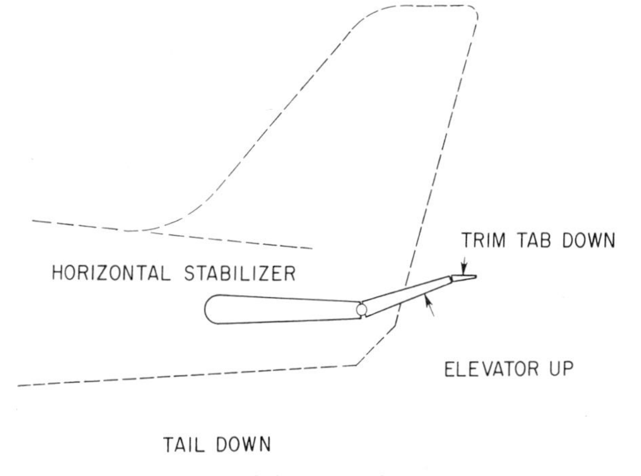

Figure 4·7 Action of the trim tab.

angle of attack, the control wheel is pulled back and both ruddervators move upward and inward as shown in Fig. 4·6. When the wheel is pushed forward, the ruddervators move down and outward as illustrated.

If it is desired to turn an airplane with ruddervators and right rudder is applied, the right ruddervator will move down and outward while the left ruddervator will move up and inward. These movements will be in response to the movement of the rudder pedals and will provide the forces necessary to rotate the airplane about the vertical axis. The turning action of the ruddervators is also illustrated in Fig. 4·6.

Another somewhat unconventional control is the **elevon.** Elevons are combination elevators and ailerons used on the outer tips of some delta wings. When used as elevators, they both move in the same direction, and when used as ailerons, they move in opposite directions. Elevons are especially needed for all-wing airplanes or "flying wings."

Trim tabs

Trim tabs are essentially small auxiliary control surfaces, usually hinged to the trailing edges of the main surfaces. **Controllable** trim tabs are used by the pilot in flight to adjust the control surfaces so the airplane will fly as desired without holding pressure on the main controls. If it were necessary to apply continuous pressure to the flight controls over a period of extended flight, it would be very tiring to the pilot. By adjusting the trim tabs for the conditions of flight, the pilot need only apply a slight corrective pressure occasionally to keep the airplane on the proper course.

The operation of a trim tab is illustrated in Fig. 4·7. When the elevator trim tab is moved down by means of the cockpit control, the airstream develops a force tending to push the tab up. This force is transmitted to the elevator and moves the elevator up, and this change, in turn, causes the tail of the airplane to move down and the nose to go up. The elevator-trim-tab control in the cockpit is usually a small wheel or knob arranged so its plane of rotation is vertical and longitudinal with respect to the airplane. When it is desired to raise the nose of the airplane, the top of the wheel is moved rearward. If it is desired to lower the nose, the top of the wheel is moved forward.

The trim control for the ailerons is a knob or wheel with its plane of rotation vertical and lateral. If it is desired to lower the right wing of the airplane and raise the left, the top of the knob or wheel is moved to the right. The reverse direction is used to lower the left wing.

Adjustable trim tabs are attached in a manner similar to controllable tabs; however, they are adjusted only when the airplane is on the ground. If the pilot reports that the airplane is nose-heavy, tail-heavy, or wing-heavy, the tab can be adjusted to correct the condition. It is only possible to adjust tabs of this type so the airplane will fly satisfactorily under one set of conditions. These conditions would usually be those established for normal cruising power and speed.

Balancing tab

A balancing tab is linked to the airplane in such a manner that a movement of the main control surface will give an opposite movement to the tab. Thus the balancing tab will assist in moving the main control surface. Balancing tabs are particularly useful in reducing the effort required to move the control surfaces of a large airplane.

Servo tab

A servo tab is one which is directly operated by the primary controls of the airplane. The control moves the tab, and the tab, in turn, develops forces which move the main control surface. This system is also used to reduce the effort required to move the controls on a large airplane.

Wing flaps

Wing flaps are hinged or sliding surfaces mounted at the trailing edges of wings and designed to increase the camber of the wings. The effect is to increase the lift of the wing at a particular speed and angle of attack and also to increase the drag. Wing flaps are particularly useful in the approach to a landing to increase the gliding angle and decrease the landing speed. Hence, with wing flaps in use an airplane can land safely on a shorter runway than would otherwise be possible.

There is a variety of designs for wing flaps including the Fowler flap, the split flap, and the plain flap. These are illustrated in Fig. 4·8. Note that the Fowler flap slides outward from the wing, thereby increasing the wing area and camber at the same time. This flap is useful for both takeoff and landing. The split flap increases lift but also increases drag very substantially. It is therefore useful for landing but should not be used in takeoff. The plain flap adds somewhat to lift and drag, but if it makes a large angle with the chord of the wing, air separation probably will occur at the hinge line and the lift of the flap will be greatly reduced. For this reason it cannot be used for high lift.

During cruising flight, flaps are streamlined with the wing to offer a minimum of drag. On small airplanes equipped with flaps, the flaps are used most often for landing and the landing approach. In some cases, however, the flaps can be used for takeoff.

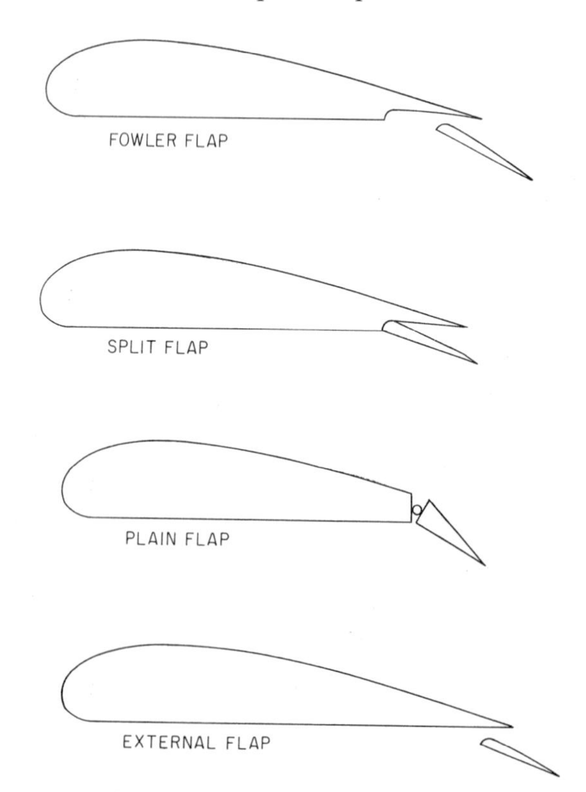

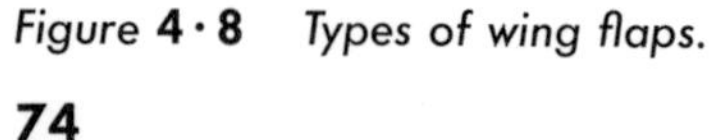

Figure 4·8 Types of wing flaps.

FORCES ON THE AIRPLANE IN FLIGHT

Impact and drag

As explained in the chapter on theory of flight the forces which tend to hold an airplane back during flight are summed up in the word "drag." When thrust and drag are equal, the airplane flies at a constant speed. Drag is created by air impact forces, skin friction, and displacement of the air.

In designing or repairing an airplane, one must consider the drag forces exerted on the structure of the airplane. As the airplane flies through the air, the effect is as if millions of tiny particles were striking against the forward parts of the airplane. If the total force of these particles becomes too great for the strength of the structure, damage will result. It is therefore necessary to make sure that the leading edges of the wings, the leading edges of the stabilizers, and the forward parts of the engine cowling are constructed of material with sufficient strength to withstand the maximum impact forces that will ever be imposed upon them. Furthermore, the devices by which the parts are attached to the main structure must have sufficient strength to withstand maximum forces.

In addition to the impact forces imposed upon the flight surfaces of an airplane, the effects on landing gear, struts, and other parts exposed to the direct force of the air must be considered. To reduce the effects of such drag forces high-speed airplanes are usually constructed with retracting landing gear, and in the case of many modern airplanes the struts have been eliminated. Parts exposed to the direct impact of the air are often covered with streamlined fairings to reduce the effects of air impact and other forms of drag.

Level flight

During level flight the forces exerted on an airplane are at a minimum; however, they still exist. The drawings of Fig. 4·9 show the forces acting on an airplane in level flight. It will be

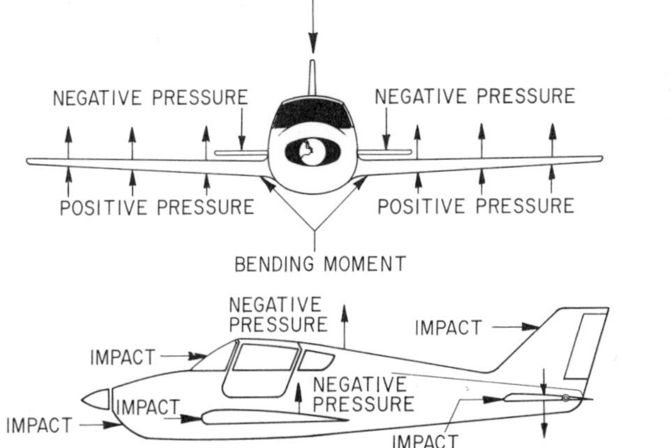

Figure **4·9** *Forces on an airplane in flight.*

noted that impact pressures exist at all points where the air strikes the surfaces from a forward direction. Negative pressures exist above and to the rear of the cabin, above the wings, and below the horizontal stabilizer. The total upward force exerted on the airplane is equal to the weight of the airplane; hence the airplane flies in a level flight path.

The internal structure of the airplane wing shown in Fig. 4·9 must be such that it can withstand the severe bending moments imposed by the combination of weight and lift. The wing shown is called a **cantilever** wing because it is supported at only one end and has no external bracing. Such wings are constructed with sturdy internal members and a stressed skin to support the flight and landing loads.

A biplane is constructed with external bracing between the wings to support a large part of the loads that occur during flight and landing. These external supporting members are shown in Fig. 4·10. During flight the **flying wires** are under a high-tension stress and the wing struts are subjected to compression stress. Upon landing, the **landing wires** are under tension and the wing struts are still under compression. The cabane struts are always under compression, and the cabane wires are under tension.

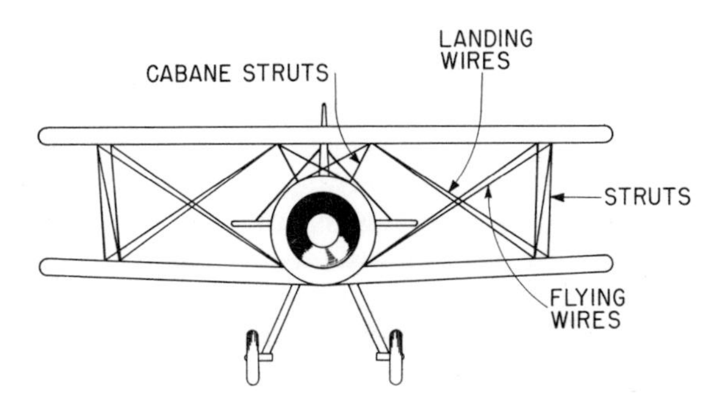

Figure **4·10** *Load-bearing members in a biplane.*

Loads in turns

During maneuvers an airplane in flight is subjected to much more than the normal flight loads. An airplane in straight and level flight in calm air is subjected to a load of 1 *g*, or 1 gravity unit. The wings are supporting only the actual weight of the airplane.

When an airplane is dived and then pulled out of the dive, the load factor increases substantially. If the dive is steep and the pullout is abrupt, the "*g* load" may be several times as great as normal. That is, the wings must support several times the weight of the airplane. If the airplane is placed in a climb and then turned rapidly back toward the earth, the load factor may become less than zero *g* and loose objects in the airplane will fly upward. A carefully controlled maneuver such as this is used to create a condition of weightlessness to determine how a human being will react in space flight where bodies become weightless.

In turns, the load factors on an airplane are similar to those experienced in pulling out of a dive. The reason for increased wing loading in a turn is illustrated in Fig. 4·11. In this diagram the airplane is in a turn with a 45° bank. Under these conditions the gravity will still be pulling the airplane down with a force of 1 *g* and the centrifugal force will be pulling the airplane horizontally with a force of 1 *g*. When these forces are resolved, a resultant of 1.41 *g*'s is found. This means, of course, that the wing is required to carry 1.41 times the weight of the airplane. In a 60° bank the load factor is 2, in a 70° bank the load factor is nearly 3, and in an 80° bank it is about 5.

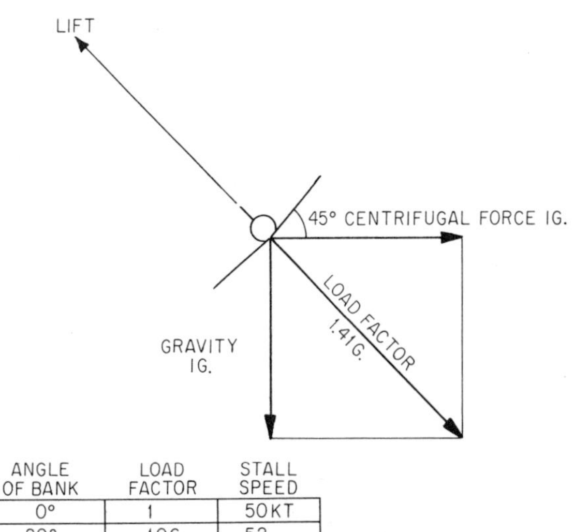

ANGLE OF BANK	LOAD FACTOR	STALL SPEED
0°	1	50 KT
20°	1.06	52
30°	1.15	54
45°	1.41	59
60°	2.0	71
80°	5.75	120

Figure **4·11** *Load factor in a turn.*

It is obvious that an airplane should not be turned with a bank so steep that the safe load factor of the airplane is exceeded. For example, if an airplane has a maximum safe load factor of 4, it should never be turned with a bank of more than about 76°. Because of the possibility of exceeding the safe load factor and stalling, airplanes are "placarded" to show the limits of approved maneuvers. Airplanes designed for normal flight purposes are limited to normal maneuvers and are not permitted to perform acrobatics.

In order to avoid placing undue stress on any part of an airplane, movements of the controls should be made smoothly and gradually. Sudden movements can easily overstress portions of the structure to the extent that failure will occur.

STALLS AND THEIR EFFECTS

Conditions leading to a stall

In our chapter on the theory of flight it was pointed out that a stall occurs when the angle of attack becomes so great that the laminar airflow separates from the surface of an airfoil, leaving an area of burbling which destroys the low-pressure area normally existing at the upper surface of a wing in flight. Figure 4·12 illustrates this condition, which also represents the maximum coefficient of lift.

When an airplane is in flight, there are a number of flight conditions which may lead to a stall. First, if an airplane is pulled up sharply until its forward speed diminishes to a point where lift is less than gravity, the airplane will begin to lose altitude. The angle of attack increases, and when it reaches the stalling value (about 20°), the wing stalls and the airplane stops flying. If the stall is balanced on both sides of the airplane, it will pitch forward and may soon regain flying speed. In this case, the pilot will usually move the control stick or wheel forward to keep the airplane in a nose-down position until flying speed is regained. On most airplanes the approach to a stall is recognized by tail buffeting or a stall-warning device, and the stall can be avoided by releasing pressure on the stick.

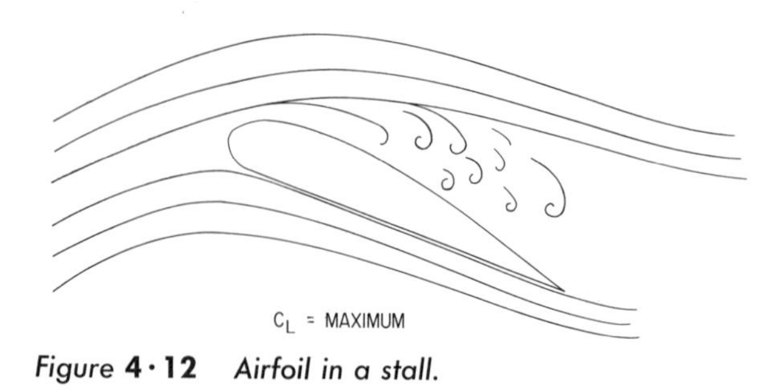

Figure **4·12** *Airfoil in a stall.*

Stalls may also occur at high speeds. Stalls occurring under these conditions are called **high-speed stalls,** and they occur when an airplane is pulled up so abruptly that the angle of attack exceeds the stall angle. This stall is not often encountered because under ordinary conditions it is not necessary to pull an airplane up sharply enough to cause a stall.

Stalls are more likely to occur during turns than in level flight. This is because greater lift is required to maintain level flight in a turn. A pilot must therefore be more alert for stalls in a turn than in level flight. Many accidents have occurred shortly after takeoff because the pilot turned the airplane while it was climbing at near stalling speed.

Spins

On early airplanes, one of the immediate effects of a stall was a spin. If one of the wings stalled slightly before the other, the stalled wing lost lift and the airplane fell off on that side. In a spin, the unstalled wing continues to develop lift and the airplane starts to spin with the stalled wing inside the path of rotation and the "flying" wing on the outside. With early airplanes the spin was greatly feared because the design of airplanes was such that a spin was often difficult to neutralize. More recent designs include antispin characteristics, so it actually requires considerable effort to make the airplane spin. Once the airplane is made to spin, it can be brought out quickly by releasing the controls and allowing them to return to neutral.

Stall warning

Under ordinary conditions of flight, when the pilot is reasonably familiar with the airplane, there is no reason for the airplane to stall. The only time that the airplane approaches the stalling speed is when it is about to land. Sometimes, however, a pilot may not be particularly familiar with the airplane or the load conditions of the airplane are not normal. Then a pilot might allow the airplane to approach a stalling condition. For this reason many airplanes are equipped with stall-warning devices. Typical of such devices is a small vane mounted near the leading edge of the wing and arranged so it will actuate a switch when it rises as a result of an excessive angle of attack. The switch causes a warning horn to sound when the angle of attack approaches maximum, usually about 5 to 10 knots above stalling speed.

The experienced pilot can usually sense when a stall is about to happen because of the "feel" of the airplane controls and the reactions of the airplane. Often the airplane will start to shake or buffet because of the flow separation on the wing and the turbulent air buffeting the tail surfaces. The controls become "sloppy" and do not have the solid feel of normal flight.

The effect of flaps on stalling speed must be recognized. When flaps are down, the stalling speed of a wing is decreased. If an airplane has a normal stalling speed of 50 mph and a stalling speed of 35 mph with the flaps down, the flaps must not be raised while flying under 50 mph. In such a case the pilot must know the conditions of stalling with flaps either up or down. If flaps are used for takeoff, the pilot must make sure that flying speed is sufficiently high before raising the flaps.

Stalls have caused many accidents, usually because the pilot did not exercise sufficient caution or was unfamiliar with the airplane. A good rule to follow is **always fly the airplane at speeds well above stalling speed.**

LOAD FACTORS AND SAFETY

Load factors have already been discussed in relation to the forces exerted on an airplane in flight. A **load factor** may be defined as the ratio between two loads. In the cases discussed the load factor was given as the ratio between a normal load (1 *g*) and higher loads developed as a result of maneuvers. The safe load factor for an airplane is designed into it by the design engineers. For example, an airplane may have a design safe load factor of 4, meaning that the structure has sufficient strength to carry loads four times greater than would be imposed under straight and level flight conditions in calm air. The operator of an airplane must make sure that an airplane is not flown at speeds or under conditions which may apply loads exceeding the safe load factor for the airplane. If, during flight, severe turbulence or any other condition causes excessive loads to be imposed on the airplane, a very thorough inspection must be given all critical structural parts before the airplane is flown again. Damage to the structure is often recognized by bulges or bends in the skin, "popped" rivets, or deformed structural members. When these are found, the airplane must be "grounded" until adequate repairs are accomplished.

EFFECTS OF ATMOSPHERIC CONDITIONS

Air temperature

Air temperature is one of the very important factors affecting the flight of an airplane. It has a pronounced effect on the flight of all aircraft, but the pilot of a particular airplane should make sure that he knows how temperature affects the performance of his craft. One of the operations most critically affected by temperature is the takeoff. If an airplane will take off in 500 ft at sea level with standard temperature, it will require about 700 ft to take off when the temperature is at 110°F. If the airplane is operating from a very short field, this much difference in takeoff distance may be quite important.

Air temperature is also a factor in determining true airspeed. As temperature rises, the indication on the airspeed indicator decreases. For this reason, if it is necessary to determine exact airspeed, a temperature correction must be applied. This correction can be obtained from a chart, or if a flight computer is used, the temperature correction is provided by the computer.

Another effect of air temperature is noted in the power output of the engine. Here again, an increase in temperature causes a decrease in engine power. This is because the air is less dense and a smaller charge is taken into the engine during each intake stroke of a piston.

Air pressure

Atmospheric pressure has an effect upon the flight of an aircraft even more pronounced than air temperature. This pressure varies somewhat owing to weather conditions, so it is necessary to obtain a correct barometric pressure reading when one wishes to compute the effect accurately. Standard atmospheric pressure at sea level is 14.7 psi, 29.92 in. Hg, or 1,013.2 millibars. These are all the same pressure but are given in different units.

Atmospheric pressure varies with altitude because of the weight of the air above the ground. As altitude above the earth increases, the air pressure decreases rapidly, and at 18,000 ft the air pressure is about half the sea-level air pressure. At 50,000-ft altitude the air pressure is just a little more than one-tenth sea-level air pressure. Because of these changing pressures a pilot landing or taking off in an airplane at high altitudes must make sure that he has correctly estimated or computed his takeoff distance. As an example of the effect that air pressure has upon takeoff distance, we can compare the distance required for the takeoff of an airplane at 10,000-ft altitude with the takeoff distance required at sea level. A typical airplane which takes off in a distance of 500 ft at sea level under standard conditions requires about 1,500 ft at 10,000-ft altitude.

It is also important to note that air pressure affects the power of an engine. A normally aspirated (nonsupercharged) engine will take in only one-half the air per stroke of a piston at 18,000-ft altitude that it will at sea level; hence the power developed will be one-half of that produced at sea level at the same rpm.

The pressure and temperature of air together determine density. As air density increases, lift increases and engine power increases. Therefore all power and performance charts use air density as a principal factor for computation.

TAKEOFF AND LANDING PROBLEMS

Effects of wind on takeoff

In general, a takeoff should be made into the wind. This is not always possible because a runway may not be exactly in line with the wind; however, it is the practice to use a runway which is most nearly aligned with the wind. The reason for taking off into the wind is that a head wind reduces the amount of runway necessary for takeoff. This can be demonstrated by the following example:

A runway is 2,100 ft in length, and 100 ft from the end of the runway are power lines 50 ft above the ground. An airplane of a certain type, fully loaded, requires 100 ft to take off in calm air conditions. After takeoff the airplane gains altitude at the rate of 400 ft per min or 6.6 ft per sec while climbing 80 mph and has 1,200 ft to travel before it reaches the power lines. At 80 mph the airplane is traveling about 117 ft per sec, so it requires 1,200/117 or 10.3 sec to reach the power lines. Since it is gaining altitude at the rate of 6.6 ft per sec for 10.3 sec, the airplane is at approximately 68-ft altitude when it crosses the power lines. This provides about 18-ft clearance over the 50-ft obstruction. If this same airplane took off with a 10-mph tail wind, we find that it would be in trouble. With a 10-mph tail wind the airplane would take about 1,241 ft of runway before takeoff. This would leave 959 ft to go before the obstruction is reached. Also, with the tail wind the airplane would be traveling at a ground speed (speed of aircraft relative to the ground) of 90 mph or 132 ft per sec during the climb. It would therefore take it 959/132 or 7.2 sec to reach the obstruction. Climbing at the rate of 6.6 ft per sec for 7.2 sec, the airplane would reach an altitude of only 47.5 ft. This, of course, would not clear the obstruction and the airplane would crash into the power lines.

If the airplane in the foregoing example takes off into a 10-mph head wind, it requires only about 748 ft of runway before takeoff. This leaves 1,452 ft to travel before the obstruction is reached. The airplane is now traveling at only 70 mph ground speed, so it takes about 14.2 sec to reach the obstruction. At this speed it reaches an altitude of about 94 ft, so it clears the obstruction with a wide margin of safety.

The effect of wind on ground speed can easily be determined by means of a vector diagram. If we draw one vector representing the airplane heading and true airspeed (TAS) and another vector representing the direction from which the wind blows and the speed of the wind, we can form a triangle from which the actual direction and ground speed of the airplane can be determined. In the diagram of Fig. 4·13 we have drawn the vector **AB** for the airplane true heading and TAS and a vector **BC** for the wind direction and speed (30 mph from 50°). We then draw **AC,** which represents the actual track and ground speed of the airplane. By measuring, we find that the track of the airplane is approximately 105° and the ground speed is about 61 mph.

A **crosswind** at the time of takeoff may cause considerable trouble unless the pilot understands its effect and makes proper allowances for it. The effect of a crosswind is to make the airplane tend to move sideways at the same time that it is traveling down the runway. The wind also has a weather-vane effect which causes the airplane to try to turn toward the wind. The first correction a pilot must make in taking off with a crosswind is to apply rudder and aileron in a direction which will counteract the weather-vane effect of the wind. If the crosswind is from the left, the pilot

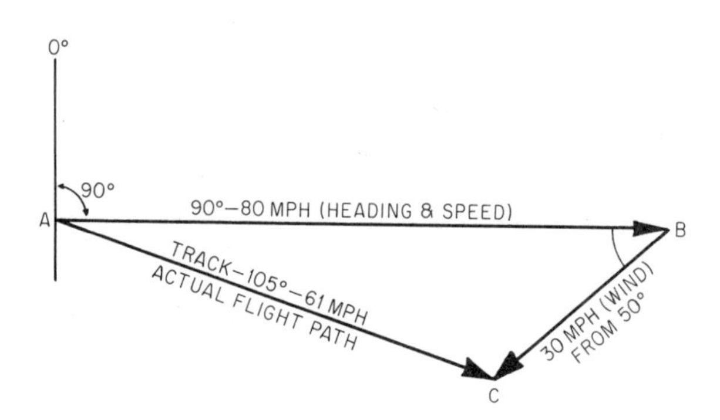

Figure 4·13 Diagram to determine the effects of the wind on flight path.

must apply more right rudder and left aileron than he would for a normal takeoff.

The foregoing examples and discussions are given to emphasize the need for extreme care in the operation of an airplane. Since the airplane "rides on the air," the condition of the air is of prime importance and the pilot must give careful attention to wind and weather if he hopes to fly safely.

Effects of wind on landing

Landing an airplane safely is somewhat more difficult than taking off for most pilots; hence conditions on landing are of more concern to the pilot than at any other time during a flight. Before making an approach for a landing, the pilot must determine wind direction and speed so he can use a runway which is most nearly into the wind. On a tower-controlled airport the tower operator will radio instructions for landing and will also give wind direction and speed. This prepares the pilot to make any corrections necessary for crosswind.

In a landing on any field the effect of wind is important, but on short fields or runways it may be critical. A good head wind, directly down the runway toward the landing aircraft, has the effect of lengthening the runway. That is, the airplane will require less runway for landing than it otherwise would because the ground speed is reduced by an amount equal to the speed of the head wind. If an airplane normally lands at 50 mph TAS in calm air, it will land at only 35 mph ground speed when landing into a 15-mph head wind. The wind not only decreases the landing speed but also shortens the landing roll.

If it is necessary to make a downwind landing, the pilot must use extreme care because the ground speed will be increased and the landing roll will be extended in accordance with the speed of the wind.

Crosswind landings are somewhat hazardous, depending upon the direction and speed of the crosswind. There are two general methods for making a crosswind landing. The pilot may choose to use either one or a combination of both methods. As the airplane approaches the runway where a crosswind exists, the pilot will immediately notice that his airplane is drifting with respect to the runway. He can then choose to "crab" the airplane, that is, fly it on a heading which will cause it to move straight down the runway but not aligned with the runway, or he can put the airplane into a side slip by applying aileron into the wind and rudder to hold the aircraft aligned with the runway. In this way he can keep the airplane flying down the runway with one wing low. In either method, immediately before the airplane wheels touch down, the pilot will usually align the airplane with the runway and level the wings. Some pilots let the airplane touch down with one wing low and hold this attitude until the crosswind effect is no longer felt. Upon landing, the pilot continues to apply aileron and rudder against the effects of the crosswind.

THE HELICOPTER

One of the most versatile and useful aircraft for a wide variety of applications is the helicopter. The word **helicopter** is derived from two Greek words: *helix* meaning spiral and *pteros* meaning wing. Hence, we may say that a helicopter has a spirallike or rotating wing.

The great usefulness of the helicopter is due to its ability to fly straight up, sideways, forward, or backward or remain still in a hovering position. Because of its ability to land in almost any small clear area, the helicopter is used for air taxi service, police work, intercity mail and passenger service, power-line patrolling, fire fighting, agricultural work, air-sea rescue, and a variety of other services.

Helicopter flight

The helicopter flies in accordance with the same laws of aerodynamics which govern the flight of a conventional airplane. In the helicopter, however, these laws are applied differently.

The principle of lift in a helicopter can be easily demonstrated with a small propeller rotated by means of a spool, with two holding pins, mounted on a handle as shown in Fig. 4·14. A string wound around the spool serves to rotate the spool and spin the propeller. As the propeller generates lift, it rises from the holding pins and flies into the air.

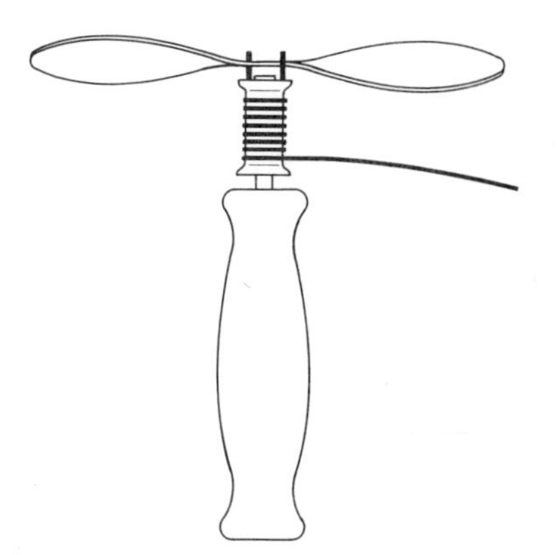

Figure 4·14 Demonstrating the principle of lift in a helicopter.

The blades of the helicopter rotor are airfoils with a very high aspect ratio (length to chord). The rotation of the blades causes air to flow over them and produce lift. The angle of incidence is adjusted by means of the controls in the control cabin, and the velocity of the blades is governed by engine power. Essentially, the rotor is at constant speed because the blade pitch is increased as engine power is applied to produce lift. As the blade pitch increases, more power is required to maintain rotor speed and this power is converted to lift.

The main rotor of the helicopter may have two, three, four, or five blades, depending upon the design. The rotor is driven by means of a conventional aircraft engine, a gas turbine, or small jets mounted on the ends of the rotor blades. When the rotor is driven by a conventional engine, it is connected to the engine by means of a **power train.** The power train usually consists of a clutch, a free-wheeling mechanism, reduction gears, and a drive shaft with necessary couplings and bearings.

The main rotor blades are hinged to the rotor head in such a manner that they have limited movement up and down and also so they can be rotated axially to change the pitch (angle of incidence). The controls for the main rotor are called **collective pitch** and **cyclic pitch.**

Collective pitch

The collective-pitch control increases or decreases the pitch of all the rotor blades simultaneously. Hence, when it is desired to cause the helicopter to rise from the ground, collective pitch is increased while engine power is increased. The collective-pitch control is usually a lever mounted beside the seat in the control cabin. The engine throttle control is a motorcycle-type grip mounted on the end of the collective-pitch lever to provide for minor adjustments to engine power in accordance with lift requirements. When it is desired to increase the altitude, the collective-pitch control is pulled up. To reduce altitude the collective-pitch control is moved down.

Cyclic pitch

The **cyclic-pitch** control causes a variation in the pitch of the rotor blades as they rotate about the circle. The purpose of this pitch change is to cause the rotor disk to tilt in the direction in which it is desired to move. When we consider only the aerodynamic effects of the blades, it would seem that, when the pitch of a rotor blade is high, the lift would be high and the blade would rise. Thus, if the blades had high pitch as they passed through one side of the disk and low pitch as they passed through the other side of the disk, the side of the disk having the high pitch should rise and the side having the lower pitch should fall. This would be true except for another dynamic force called **gyroscopic precession.**

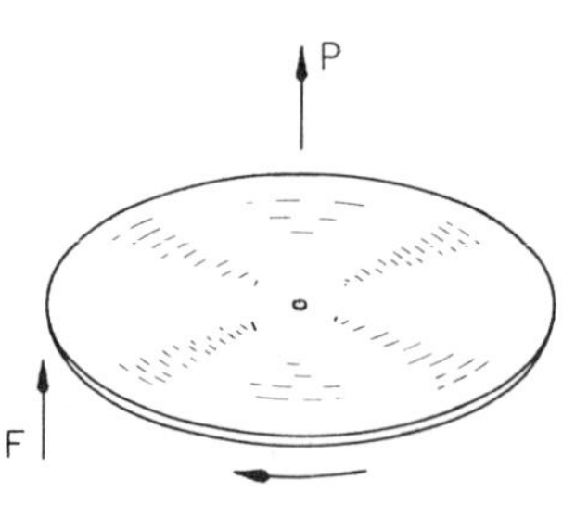

Figure 4·15 Disk representing the rotor of a helicopter.

In Chap. 14 the nature of gyro precession is explained. However, we must describe the effect here so the forces involved in cyclic pitch control are made clear. In Fig. 4·15 is a drawing of a spinning disk which represents the main rotor of a helicopter. If the disk is spinning in the direction indicated by the arrow and a force is applied upward at *F*, the disk will precess in the direction shown at *P*. Thus, if the force is applied upward at one point, the gyroscopic precession will cause an upward force 90° from the applied force in the direction of rotation.

As a result of the foregoing principle, if it is desired to cause the main rotor of a helicopter to tilt in a particular direction, the applied force

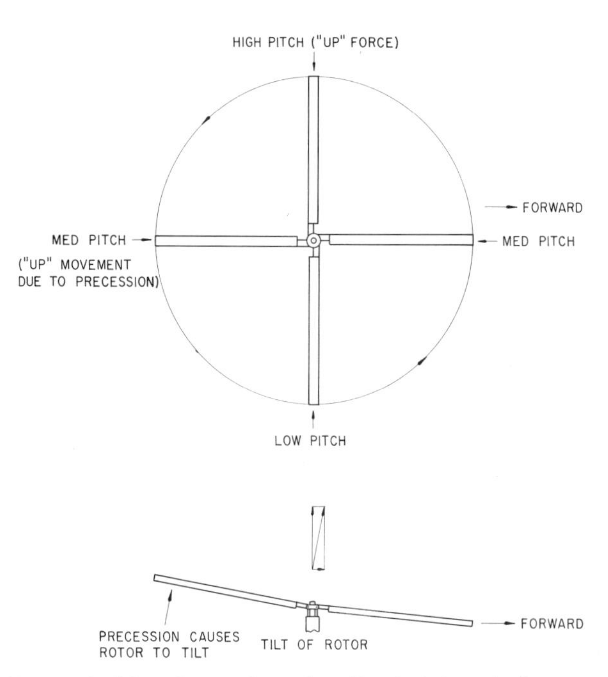

Figure 4·16 Operation of cyclic pitch in a helicopter rotor.

must be at an angular displacement 90° ahead of the desired direction of tilt. The required force is applied aerodynamically in changing the pitch of the blades by adjusting the angle of the **swashplate** with the cyclic control. This action is illustrated in Fig. 4·16. Observe that, as the blades rotate, the blade is at high pitch 90° ahead of the point where the actual "up" movement is desired. With the rotor tilted as shown, a forward lift component is developed which causes the helicopter to move forward with a resultant loss of vertical lift.

The helicopter can be caused to move in any direction desired merely by moving the cyclic-pitch control in that direction. The main rotor tilts in the direction called for by the control, and the helicopter moves in that direction. If the control is in neutral, the helicopter will **hover,** that is, remain still in the air. In a wind the helicopter will drift in the direction in which the wind is blowing.

Main rotor control

The control of collective pitch and cyclic pitch for a helicopter rotor requires a rather complex system of levers, bearings, and linkages. These controls vary with different makes and models; however, they usually have similarities in methods for obtaining similar results.

Figure 4·17 is an example of the drive and control mechanism for the main rotor of a helicopter manufactured by the Bell Corporation. The collective pitch is controlled through the large ring bearing at the lower part of the mast. The inner part of this ring is linked to the pitch-control mechanism and rotates with the main rotor blades. When the ring is moved up and down by means of the collective-pitch lever, the pitch of the blades is changed simultaneously to increase or decrease lift.

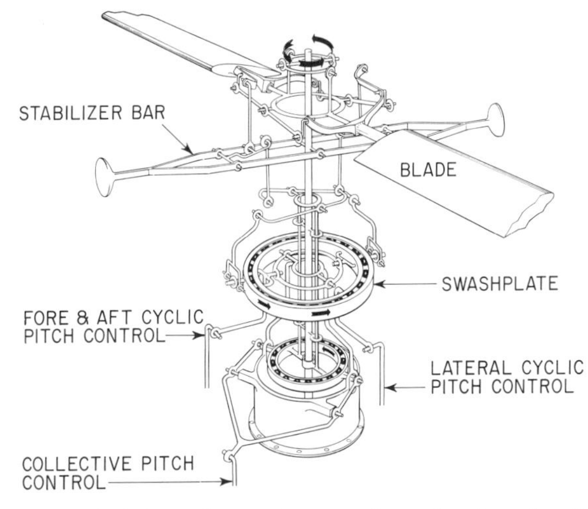

Figure **4·17** *Drive and control mechanism for the main rotor of a helicopter. (Bell Corporation, Texas Division.)*

The cyclic pitch is controlled through the swashplate, which can be tilted as desired by means of the cyclic-pitch control. The inner ring of the swashplate is linked to the levers of the control. Through this linkage the swashplate is tilted for fore-and-aft control or lateral control. The outer ring of the swashplate turns with the main rotor and is linked through a stabilizer bar to the pitch-changing mechanism. When the swashplate is parallel with the plane of rotation, the pitch of the rotor blades is equal and uniform throughout the complete cycle. When the swashplate is tilted, the pitch of the blades changes throughout the circle of rotation. On one side of the rotor disk the pitch will be decreasing and on the other side the pitch will be increasing, thus causing the rotor disk to tilt.

Directional control

Direction (heading) of the helicopter is controlled by the **tail rotor,** which, in turn, is controlled by the rudder pedals. The tail rotor is mounted on the tail of the helicopter, so that it rotates in a vertical plane. Its pitch can be changed as required to turn the helicopter in the direction desired. A rudder will not stabilize and control the direction of the helicopter because there is not sufficient slipstream to develop directional control and because of main rotor torque. The torque necessary to drive the main rotor creates an equal and opposite torque in the fuselage, so the fuselage tends to turn in a direction opposite to the rotation of the main rotor. For this reason the tail rotor pitch must be adjusted by means of the rudder pedal to compensate for the changing torque forces of the main rotor. The tail rotor usually rotates at a speed of about one-half engine speed and is driven by means of a shaft extending from the engine. The pitch of the tail rotor is controlled by means of cables and linkages from the rudder pedals in the cockpit. Pressing the right pedal reduces the tail rotor pitch and allows the main rotor torque to turn the helicopter to the right, and pressing the left pedal increases the tail rotor pitch and causes the helicopter to turn to the left. This is assuming that the main rotor is turning clockwise as viewed from underneath.

Autorotation

The helicopter must incorporate a safety feature to provide for the condition which exists in the event of power failure. This is called **autorotation.** If a power failure occurs, the pilot moves the collective-pitch control down to reduce the main rotor pitch. He also moves the cyclic-pitch control forward to control the forward flight speed and establish the proper forward speed for autorotation. Under these conditions the main rotor will maintain its speed of rotation and provide normal lift. In effect, then, the helicopter glides and remains under good control. While descending, the pilot selects a clear spot in which to land, and just before landing, he pulls back on the cyclic-pitch control to reduce forward speed and increases collective pitch to increase lift. This, of course, slows the rate of descent, and the helicopter lands without difficulty. The rate of rotation developed by the main rotor during descent provides the inertial forces necessary to sustain the rotation of the main rotor long enough to provide a normal zero-rate-of-descent landing.

REVIEW QUESTIONS

1. Why is it important for the maintenance technician to understand the stresses which may be imposed on an aircraft in flight?
2. What is the difference between *structural* members and *nonstructural* members in an airplane?
3. What are the three principal airfoils used for the control of an airplane in flight?
4. Explain how each of the control surfaces is operated from the cockpit.
5. Name the three axes of an airplane and give the direction of each.
6. What is meant by a *coordinated* turn in an airplane?
7. Explain the operation of the *ruddervator.*
8. What is the function of the *elevon?*
9. Explain the purpose of the *trim tabs.*
10. What is the difference between a *balancing tab* and a *servo tab?*
11. Under what conditions are flaps useful in the flight of an airplane?
12. Why is it necessary to consider the effects of air impact forces in the design of an airplane?
13. What loads are imposed upon a wing during the course of a flight?
14. What loads are carried by the flying wires and landing wires on a biplane?
15. What effect does a turn have on the loading of an airplane structure in flight?
16. What is the load factor in a 60° turn?
17. What flight conditions may lead to a stall?
18. What events are taking place when an airplane spins?
19. What effect does the use of flaps have on the stalling speed of an airplane?
20. How does air temperature affect the takeoff speed of an airplane?
21. If the destination of an airplane is due north 200 miles, the airplane flies at 120 mph, and there is a crosswind of 20 mph from due west, what heading should the airplane take and how long will it fly in order to reach its destination?
22. Explain two methods for making a crosswind landing.
23. In the operations of a helicopter, what is meant by *collective* pitch and *cyclic* pitch?
24. How is directional control provided in a helicopter?

CHAPTER 5

Blueprint Reading

Blueprints are drawings which describe objects by means of lines and symbols. Through a blueprint, an engineer can convey to those who build, inspect, operate, and maintain airplanes and spacecraft his instructions for ordering the materials, making the parts, assembling the units, and finishing the surfaces. Blueprints constitute the abbreviated written language of the aerospace industry, a shorthand method for presenting information which it would take many pages of manuscript to transmit.

Blueprints are not always blue. They may be blue and white, black and white, brown and white, or some other combination of colors, depending upon the method of reproduction. Since they are not always blue and they are usually printed copies of drawings, the words **blueprint, drawing,** and **print** are commonly used to mean the same thing, and they are thus used in this text.

Blueprint reading is the interpretation of the abbreviations, lines, symbols, measurements, notes, and other information on a blueprint for the purpose of fabricating, assembling, installing, inspecting, and repairing parts, units, and assemblies. Blueprint reading is not a job in itself; it is merely one of the several skills required of any technical employee of the aerospace industry.

DUPLICATION PROCESSES

The word blueprint comes from the method of reproducing mechanical drawings which has been in common use in all industries for many years. A draftsman usually makes a pencil drawing because in methods used today it is seldom necessary to ink the drawing. The drawing is placed over a chemically treated white paper, called blueprint paper. The drawing and the blueprint paper are held together as they are passed through the blueprint machine by means of rollers. While moving through the machine they are exposed to a strong light which passes through the drawing paper (usually called **vellum**) and activates the sensitized surface of the blueprint paper. The lines of the drawing hold back the light and do not permit activation of the chemically treated paper where the lines cast a shadow. During the exposure to the light the chemical turns gray. When the blueprint paper is rinsed in water, wherever the paper was protected from the light by the lines of the drawing, a white surface is left. The remainder of the blueprint paper, corresponding to the areas where the untouched areas of the drawing paper let the light come through, turns blue. The result is a blueprint, with the mechanical drawing shown in white on a blue background.

Other methods of reproducing mechanical drawings are similar in principle, the difference depending upon the developing processes and the types of paper used. For example, ammonia prints may be black, brown, maroon, purple, or blue against a white background. Ammonia prints are widely used today in the aerospace industry. "Vandykes," sometimes called "brownies," are brown and white and are used as "originals" from which to make other prints. The "brownline" prints are made on a highly translucent paper so light can penetrate easily.

Negative photostats have white lines against a dark gray or black background. There are also black-and-white prints which have black lines on a white background. Thus, the word **blueprint** has been given a wide meaning. In the loose sense of the term, it refers to any reproduction of a mechanical drawing, regardless of whether the color blue is present or not.

CARE AND USE OF BLUEPRINTS

Blueprints are valuable, permanent records which can be used repeatedly if they are handled carefully. There are a few simple rules which always apply wherever blueprints are used. The observation of these rules tends to establish a worker's reputation as a competent employee.

Blueprints are usually kept in a room referred

to as "blueprint files." It may be a darkroom, somewhat similar to a photographer's darkroom, because exposure to strong light for a long time causes blueprints to fade. A master copy of each print is filed for use if all other copies are destroyed or lost. The original drawing is carefully preserved in the engineering department where it was made.

When a blueprint is received from the files, it is usually folded to a size convenient for filing. If the drawing has been folded properly, the number is visible on the outside. If the drawing number is not readily visible, the print should be unfolded when it is received to make certain that it is the one requested.

In use, the blueprint should not be bent back on the folds or folded in any other manner than the way it was when delivered. Blueprint paper is somewhat brittle because of the exposure to strong light during its reproduction, and it will crack easily if it is folded incorrectly or too often. The ammonia-process papers are not so brittle as the blueprint paper, but this does not mean that they may be handled carelessly.

The person receiving or using a blueprint should have clean hands regardless of the nature of his work. The print is taken to the job, spread out on a large, flat, clean surface, and kept free from dirt, grease, perspiration, hydraulic fluid, or any other destructive materials or substances. An airplane wing is sometimes a convenient place to spread out the print, or there may be a clean work stand or bench for this purpose. If an airplane wing is used, care must be taken that it does not have oil or other substances on it. Tools must not be placed on the print. If it must be anchored in place, some clean, heavy, smooth object should be used to avoid tearing or soiling the print.

Any person using a print may find an error on it. If an error is found, it should be brought to the attention of the engineering department. In most factories only the engineering department can correct a drawing, and then not by marking the print. Instead, a new drawing is prepared, or the old one is corrected, and new blueprints are issued.

Pencil, ink, or crayon marks must never be put on a print because they cause wear to the print and confuse others who may later refer to the same print. In exceptional cases, where permission is granted by competent authority, prints may be marked with a special pencil, but an ordinary lead pencil is never used because lead pencil marks are difficult to see.

When the worker is through with a print, he should refold it **along the original fold lines** and either place it in a nearby safe place, such as the drawer of a workbench, if it is to be used again soon or return it to the blueprint files.

VIEWS AND PROJECTIONS

The perspective drawing

Figure 5·1 is a photograph of an airplane. Compare this with the perspective drawing in Fig. 5·2. There is not any difference in the shape or arrangement of parts, but there is a difference in shading. Both illustrations show the airplane as it would look to the eye, but they do not present the information needed by the maintenance technician. The left wing of the airplane seems longer than the right wing because it is closer to the observer than the right wing, although both wings obviously must be of the same length. This is called **foreshortening.**

The tip of the right wing appears to be narrower than the tip of the left wing. Even if the leading edge of the wing were parallel with the trailing

Figure **5·1** *Photograph of an airplane.*

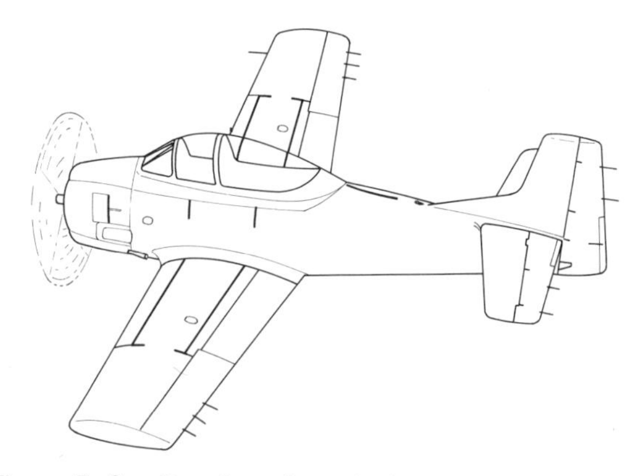

Figure **5·2** *Drawing of an airplane.*

edge, the parallel lines would converge for the same reason that the rails of a railroad seem to meet in the distance.

The oblique view—isometric projection

Figure 5 • 3 shows two views of the same object, one in **perspective** and the other an **oblique view.** The oblique view is somewhat similar to the perspective, but the line representing the edge farthest from the observer is drawn the same length as the line nearest the observer. The lines are parallel and of the same length, yet the farthest one from the observer seems to be longer because of an optical illusion.

An **isometric projection** is an oblique drawing without the optical illusion of perspective. In this type of drawing, the object appears distorted, but it shows equal distances on the subject as equal distances on the drawing, thus enabling the draftsman to make the dimensions clear to the reader.

Figure 5 • 4 is an **isometric drawing.** All vertical lines are drawn as verticals, and all horizontal lines are drawn at an angle of 30°. It shows that certain lines are parallel to each other and at right angles to other lines. There is no foreshortening, and there is no convergence of lines as in the true perspective drawing. The isometric drawing provides a bird's-eye view, it gives proportions, and it is often very useful in explaining the design and construction of complicated assemblies. Its faults are that the shape of the object is distorted and the angles do not appear in their true size.

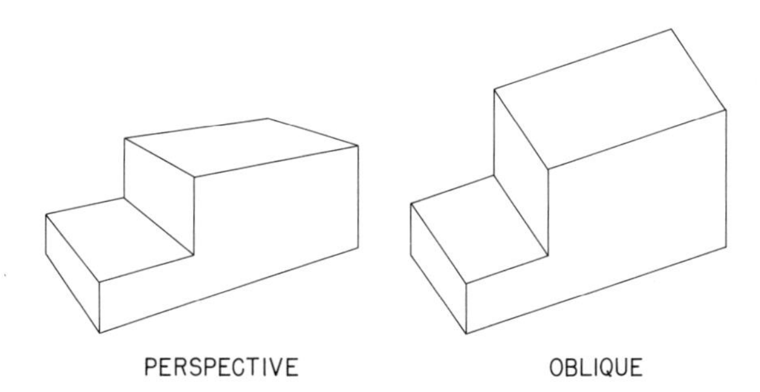

Figure **5 • 3** *Perspective and oblique views of the same object.*

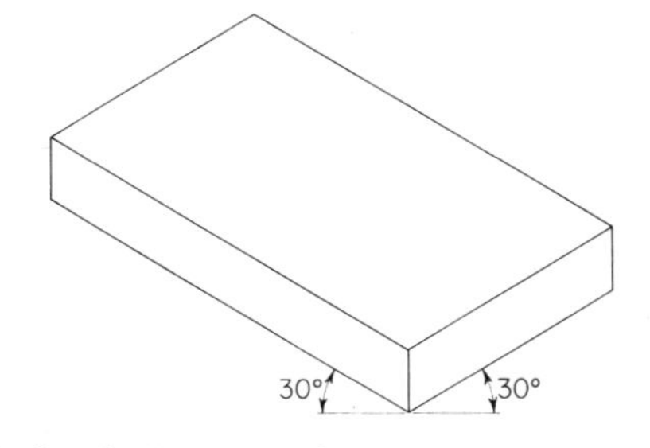

Figure **5 • 4** *An isometric drawing.*

The term isometric is derived from two Greek words *isos* and *metron,* meaning **equal** and **measure.** Thus we see that isometric means **of equal measure.**

Orthographic projections

The three types of drawings we have already discussed (perspective, oblique, and isometric) give a bird's-eye view of an object, but the man who reads a blueprint must have more than one view, especially if the object shown is three-dimensional, and he must have each view presented without distortion in most cases.

Figure 5 • 5 is an **orthographic projection** of a bracket. There is a **front view,** a **top view,** and a **right-side view.** The **front view** is what you would see if you were directly in front of the bracket. It would be impossible to see any of the top, the bottom, or the sides. The **top view** is what you would see if you were looking directly down on the bracket. You would not see the front, the bottom, or any of the other surfaces. The **right-side view** is what you would see if you looked directly at that side. You would not see the top, the bottom, or any other surface except the right side.

The purpose of this portion of the text is to prepare the student to read shop drawings, so a detailed explanation of how orthographic projections are drawn will not be given here but will be presented in the chapter on "Fundamentals of Drafting."

THE MEANING OF LINES

Lines

Standards for lines used in drafting are set forth in MIL-STD-1A, General Drawing Stand-

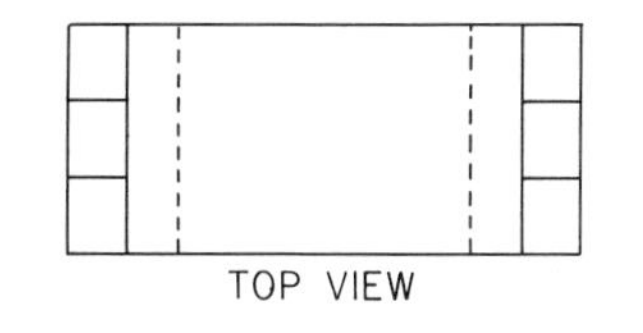

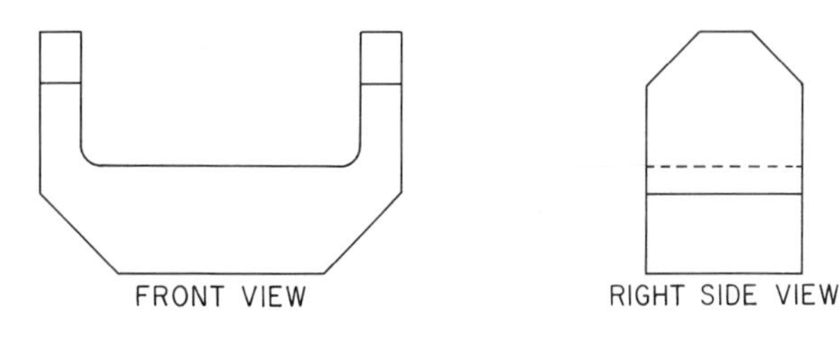

Figure **5 • 5** *Orthographic projection of a bracket.*

ards. Figure 5·6 shows the types and forms of lines used in preparing the drawings from which blueprints are made. These are numbered, named, and described in the illustration. Copy these lines on a piece of paper, and see if you can name them without looking at the book. Next, write the names of the lines on another sheet of paper and then try to draw the lines from memory. The few minutes required for this exercise will help fix this important topic in your memory.

Most drawings use three widths or intensities of lines: **wide, medium,** and **narrow.** These lines may vary somewhat on different drawings, but on any one drawing there is a noticeable contrast between a wide line and a narrow line and the medium line is somewhere between.

The **visible outline** (object line) is a medium to wide line which should be the outstanding feature of the drawing. The thickness may vary to suit the drawing, but it should be at least 0.015 in. in width. This line represents edges and surfaces that can be seen when the object is viewed directly.

The **invisible outline,** more correctly called a **hidden line,** is a medium-width line made up of short dashes and is sometimes called a **dotted** or **broken line.** It represents edges and surfaces behind the surface being viewed and therefore not visible to the observer.

The **center line** is drawn narrow or thin and consists of alternate long and short dashes. It shows the location of the center of a hole, rod, symmetrical part, or symmetrical section of a part. Center lines are the first lines drawn, and they provide the basic reference for the rest of the drawing.

Phantom lines are not used by all draftsmen; however, they serve a good purpose and should be understood. The phantom line is a medium-width line and is made up of a series of long dashes with two short dashes between the long dashes. The purpose of the line is to indicate the position of an adjacent part for local reference.

The **dimension line** is a narrow line and is unbroken except where a dimension is written in. Having determined the general shape of an object, the man reading the blueprint wants to know the

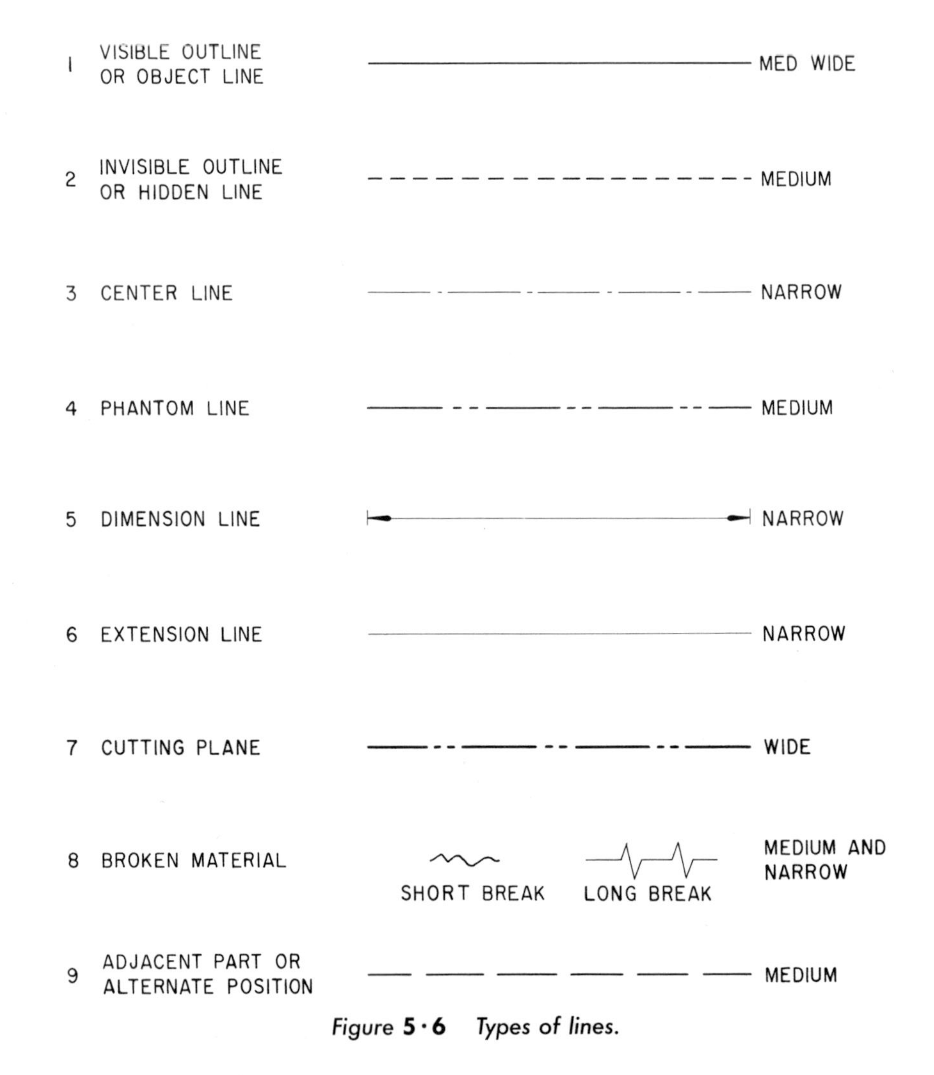

Figure 5·6 Types of lines.

size. The length, width, or height of a dimensioned part is customarily shown by a fraction or a number placed in a break in the line.

An **extension line,** or **witness line,** is used to extend the line indicating an edge of the object for the purpose of dimensioning. The extension line is drawn very narrow or thin.

The **cutting-plane** line is a heavy, wide, broken line made up of one long and two short dashes, alternately spaced. It is used where the draftsman wants to refer the reader to another view and direct his attention to a section, or "slice," which reveals the interior.

The **broken material line,** often simply called a **break** line, can be used where the draftsman is cramped for space on his drawing. If he drew all of an object, the drawing would run off the paper; hence he uses a medium line of the form illustrated to show that he has reduced the drawing, although the length of the actual object is not reduced. The narrow ruled line with zigzags is for long breaks. The wider freehand wavy line is used for short breaks, and it is especially useful where the draftsman has removed an outer surface to reveal an interior part of the object.

The break line is also used simply to avoid the necessity of repeating the second half of a symmetrical part. This saves drafting time and has been done in the case of the pulley in Fig. 5·7, section *A-A*. There is obviously enough room to

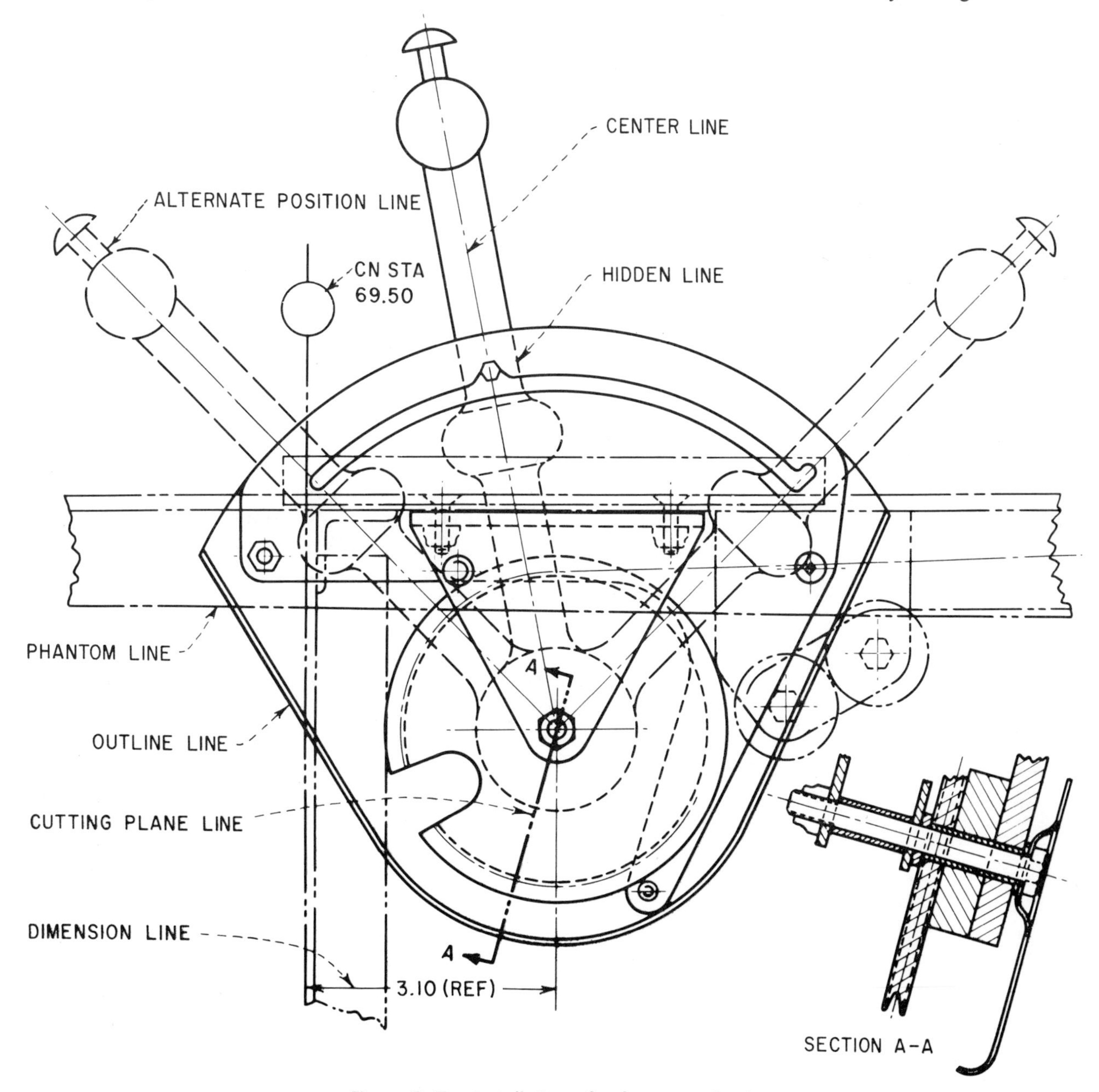

Figure 5·7 Installation of a flap-control unit.

complete the drawing, but it is quicker and simpler to do it as shown.

The **adjacent part,** or **alternate-position,** line is a medium, broken line made up of long dashes. It can be used to show the relationship between a part and an assembly or to show the alternate positions of a moving part.

Figure 5·7, Installation of a flap-control unit, illustrates the use of many of the lines described in the foregoing. Notice the visible outline line, the invisible outline line labeled **hidden line,** the center line, the dimension line, the phantom line, the alternate-position line, and the cutting-plane line. In this particular drawing, three alternate positions are shown for the lever, since it is a moving part. The break lines are not labeled, but they are easily found.

When a surface has been cut away to reveal a hidden, inner feature of an object, **section lines** are used. These are narrow, solid lines, spaced evenly to present a shaded effect. Notice that the large letter *A* appears twice in Fig. 5·7, connected by a cutting-plane line. This shows where a section was taken. In the lower right-hand corner of the drawing, the **section** itself is shown. It must be pointed out here that the shading or line pattern used to indicate a cutaway section usually varies according to the material from which the object is constructed. Some of the patterns used for various materials are shown later in this chapter.

Visible and hidden lines

Figure 5·8 shows that all edges or sharp corners are projected into other views as outlines or visible edges. Figure 5·9 shows that any line or

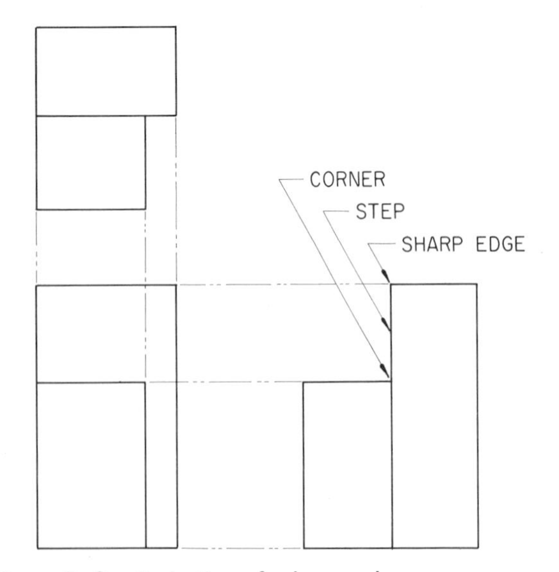

Figure **5·8** *Projection of edges and corners.*

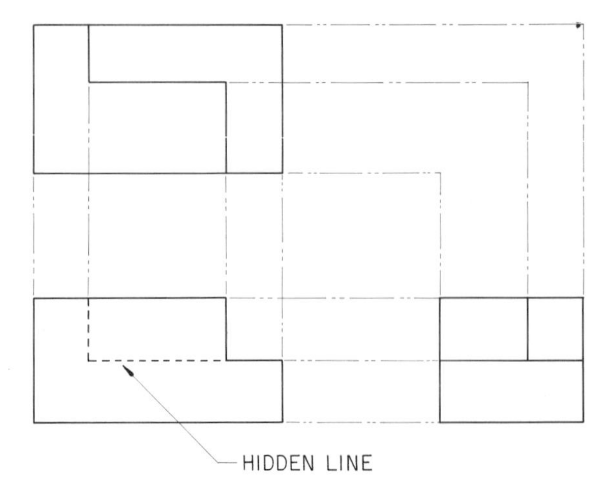

Figure **5·9** *Use of hidden lines.*

edge that cannot be seen from one particular view must be shown as a **hidden line** (invisible edge) in that view by means of the appropriate line symbol. Hidden lines are often omitted for clarity, especially on drawings of very complex parts, if the drawing is clear without them.

Conventional breaks

A pipe, tube, or a long bar having a uniform cross section is not always drawn for its entire length. When one or more pieces of the object are broken out and the ends moved together, a larger and more legible scale can be used. The true length will not be shown, but that does not matter because the dimensions give the measurements to be taken on the work.

Different types of breaks are used for different shapes and materials. Figure 5·10 shows the conventional breaks used in drawing a round, solid object; a round, hollow object; a metal object; and a wood object.

Curved surfaces

Figure 5·11 illustrates the general rule that a curved surface or a circle appears in one view only in that form. In other views, the curve or the circle is shown as a straight line or by a pair of straight lines, according to circumstances. For example, there is a hole through the object in

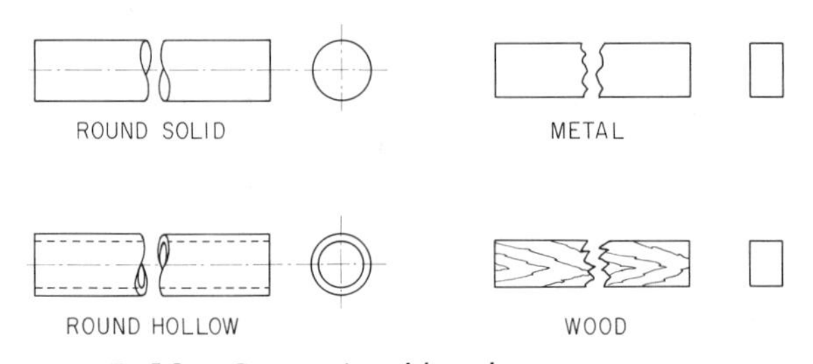

Figure **5·10** *Conventional breaks.*

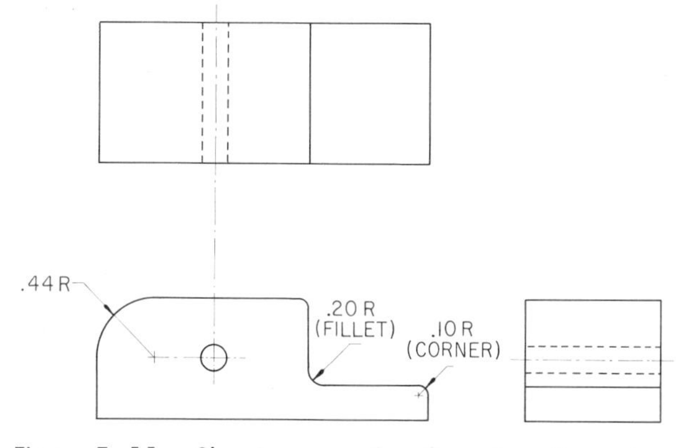

Figure 5 • 11 Showing curved surfaces in a three-view drawing.

Fig. 5 • 11 which appears as a circle in the front view, as two parallel lines in the top view, and as two parallel lines in the right-side view. In the top view and in the right-side view, the lines representing the hole are dashed lines because the hole cannot be seen from the top or the side of the object.

The fillet in Fig. 5 • 11 is shown as a curved line in the front view and as a straight line in each of the other views. Since it is visible, it is represented by a solid, straight line in the top view and right-side view and by a solid curved line in the front view.

Two-view drawings

It is a general practice to present three views of an object, but it is also a common practice to illustrate such simple parts as bolts, collars, studs, and simple castings by means of only two views.

Figure 5 • 12 includes drawings of two entirely different objects, with two views of each object. The one at the top is a simple casting, illustrated by what we may call a front view and a top view, although the naming of the views in a case like this may vary according to the whims of the draftsman. The second drawing shows a tubular object such as a bushing. In both drawings, a circle is shown in only one view as a circle, in accordance with the general rule previously explained.

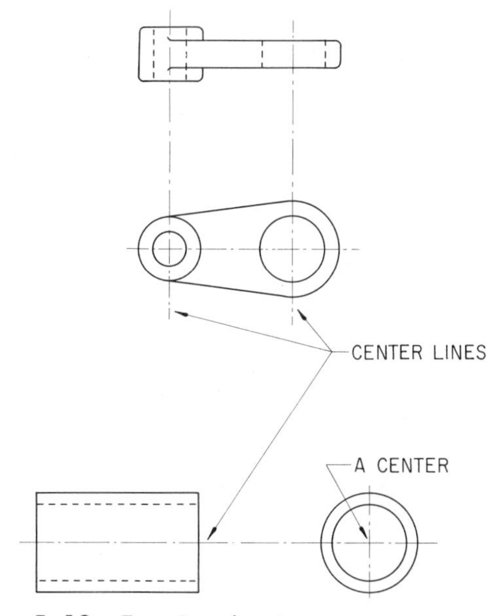

Figure 5 • 12 Two-view drawings.

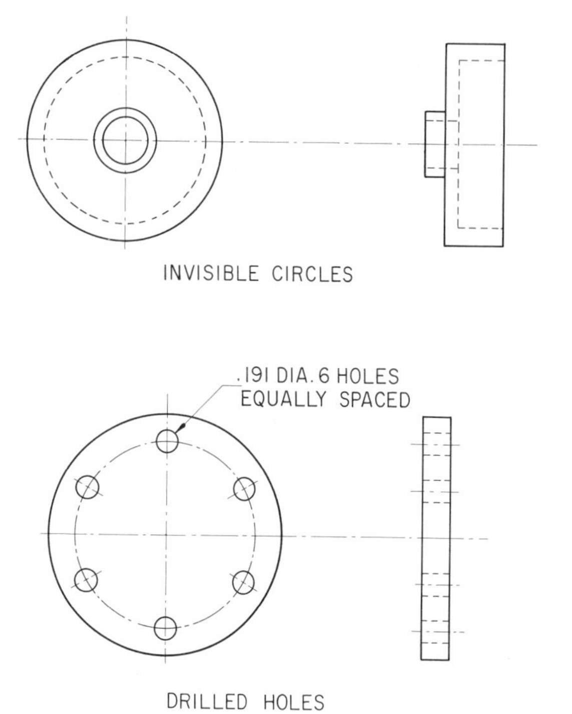

Figure 5 • 13 Two-view drawings showing drilled holes.

Figure 5 • 13 includes drawings of two different objects. The object at the top has invisible circles. It is customary to use two-view drawings such as these to illustrate objects having either drilled holes or invisible circles. The object at the bottom shows the drilled holes as small circles in the front view and as dotted lines in the side view.

Single-view drawings

There are some objects which are so simple that their shape can be shown by only one view. Figure 5 • 14 shows two views of this type. The object at the top of the drawing is a cylindrical part with a groove which must be made according to the directions shown near the root of the arrow. The letter *D* indicates that the long cylindrical section has a uniform diameter throughout its length. The object at the bottom of the illustration is a piece of sheet metal of regular shape; hence only one view is needed. Since the kind of material to be used and its thickness are impor-

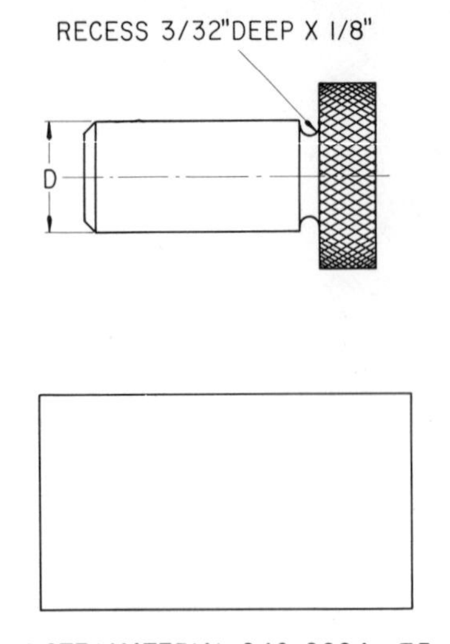

Figure **5 · 14** *Single-view drawings.*

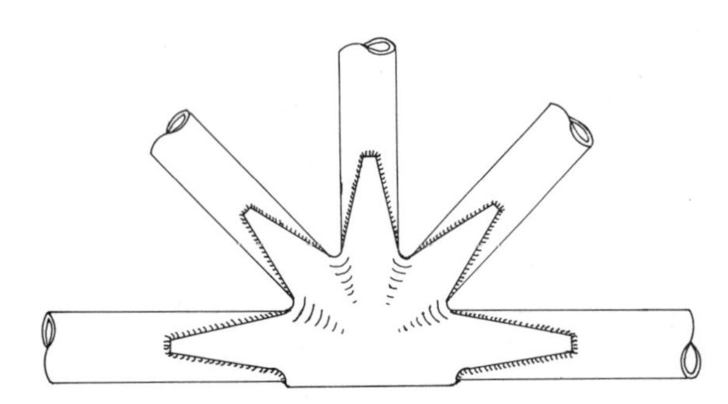

Figure **5 · 15** *Single-view drawing of a welded patch.*

tant, these are given in coded language in a note at the bottom of the picture.

Figure 5 · 15 is an illustration from Civil Aeronautics Manual 18 showing a patch formed and welded to tubes. This is another good example of a single-view drawing.

DIMENSIONS

The approved method for the dimensioning of drawings has been standardized in accordance with Military Standard (MIL-STD)-8A which also gives the specifications for tolerancing. This standard is issued by the Office of Standardization of the United States Defense Department.

Types of dimensions

Figure 5 · 16 shows several types of dimension lines. These are the **continuous,** or **consecutive, dimension;** the **simplified base-line dimension;** the **double base-line dimension;** the **center-line dimension;** and the **progressive base-line dimension.**

Even though there is a wide variety of types of dimension lines, they can be broken down into two principal classes according to their purpose. When a mechanic locates holes for drilling or

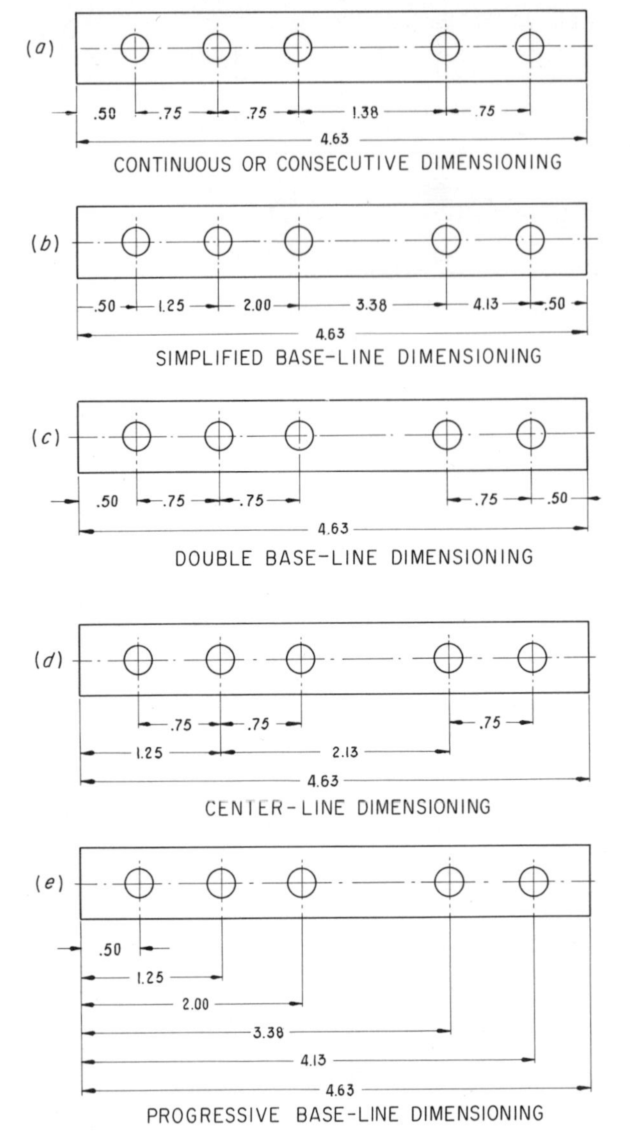

Figure **5 · 16** *Dimension lines.*

positions for slots, he uses **location dimensions.** When he cuts a piece of stock to the size and shape for a part, he uses **size dimensions.**

Continuous or consecutive dimensioning

Continuous or consecutive dimensioning can be used for small parts that have few location dimensions. Referring to Fig. 5 · 16*a*, if a plus error of 1/32 in. is made in laying out each hole, there may be a total error of 5/32 in. for the five holes because each dimension is made dependent upon the previous one in a series of consecutive measurements. In order to avoid such errors, it is obvious that each measurement should be made from the same reference point.

Simplified base-line dimensioning

In the simplified base-line dimension, all measurements are taken from some reference line, such as the left edge of the part. The dimension quantities are additive from the point of reference as shown in *b* of Fig. 5·16. Note that each dimension figure is the sum of the separate dimensions from the reference point. Notice also that the arrowheads are on one end only of each dimension line.

Double base-line dimensioning

In double base-line dimensioning, *c* of Fig. 5·16, measurements are taken from two base lines or reference points, such as the right and left edges of the part. This will cause any errors to fall in the center area of the part rather than at one end as in other methods of dimensioning. Double base-line dimensioning is somewhat less subject to error than consecutive dimensioning.

Center-line dimensioning

When a pattern of holes is located around a center line on an object, it shows that something must be fastened to that object; hence the holes must be accurately located. Referring to *d* in Fig. 5·16, there are three holes at the left in the illustration of this type of dimension. The distance from the left edge to the center line of the middle hole of the three holes on the left is 1.25 in. The holes on each side are located by measuring 0.75 in. from the center line of the middle hole, and a distance of 2.13 in. is measured to the right to locate the center line of the left of the two holes at the right end. Then 0.75 in. is measured from the center line of this hole to locate the hole on the right. In this way all holes are more accurately placed from the key point than might otherwise be the case.

Progressive base-line dimensioning

The progressive base-line dimension is measured from some reference line, such as the left edge, but the dimension lines are drawn parallel to each other, one under the other, as shown in *e* of Fig. 5·16. In principle this is the same as the simplified base-line dimension, but it requires too much space to be practical.

Location of dimensions

The illustration of Fig. 5·17 shows how dimensions are located for a simple drawing. A **dimension line** has an arrowhead at each end. The arrowhead shows where the dimension ends. The **dimension** is the distance shown by the fraction or number at the break in the dimension line. The short lines at right angles to the arrowheads are **extension lines** made by the draftsman before drawing the dimension lines. Dimensions common to two views are usually placed **between** the views.

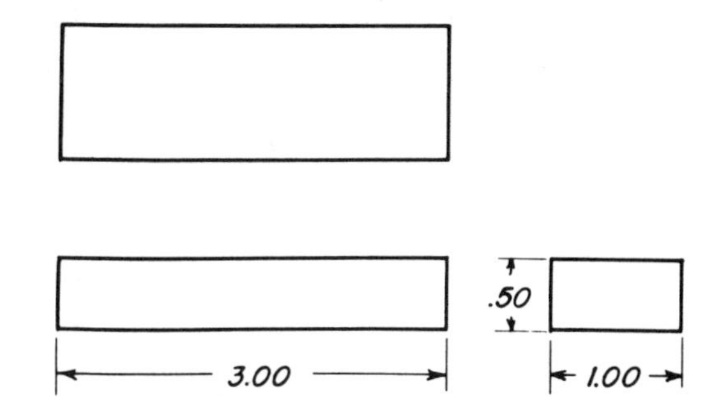

Figure 5·17 Dimension lines for a simple object.

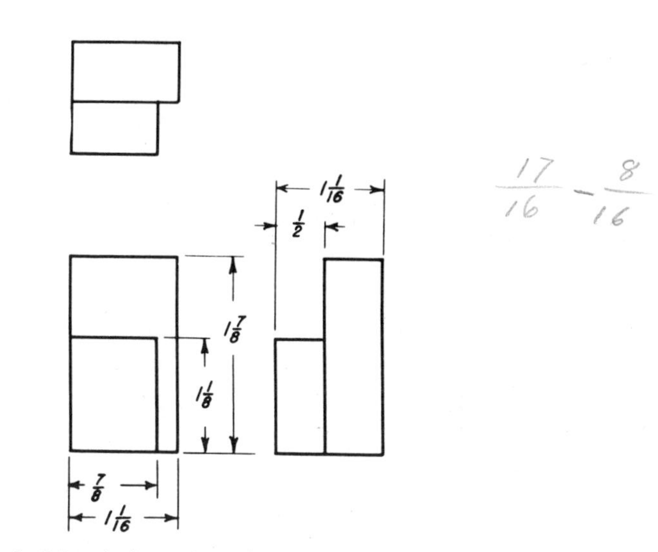

Figure 5·18 A three-view drawing with dimensions.

On drawings of simple parts, the length is given under the front view while the width and thickness are given in the right-side view.

The illustration of Fig. 5·18 shows three views of an object which is solid but can be regarded for purposes of discussion as two blocks joined together. The front view shows the length of the small block as ⅞ in. and the length of the large block as 1$\frac{1}{16}$ in. The front view also shows the height of the small block as 1⅛ in. and the height of the large block as 1⅞ in. The right-side view gives the width of the small block as ½ in. and the width of the whole object as 1$\frac{1}{16}$ in.

A slightly more complex object is shown in Fig. 5·19. The general rule that dimensions are given to visible and not to hidden lines is also illustrated in the drawing. The three views show that there is a cutaway section and a hole in the object. The hole is dimensioned in the top view, where it is indicated that the hole is ⅜ in. from the right side. The right-side view shows that the top of the hole is 1 in. below the upper surface of the object.

In the upper right-hand corner of Fig. 5·19 are shown several approved methods for dimensioning parts or holes where the space on the drawing

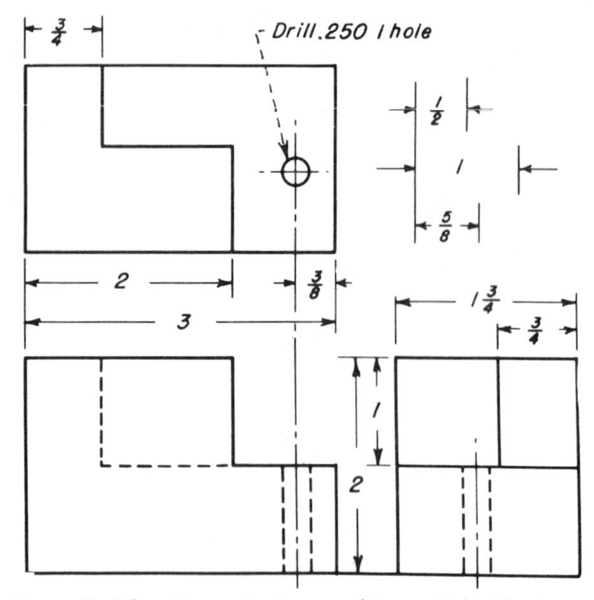

Figure 5·19 Dimensioning an object with hidden lines.

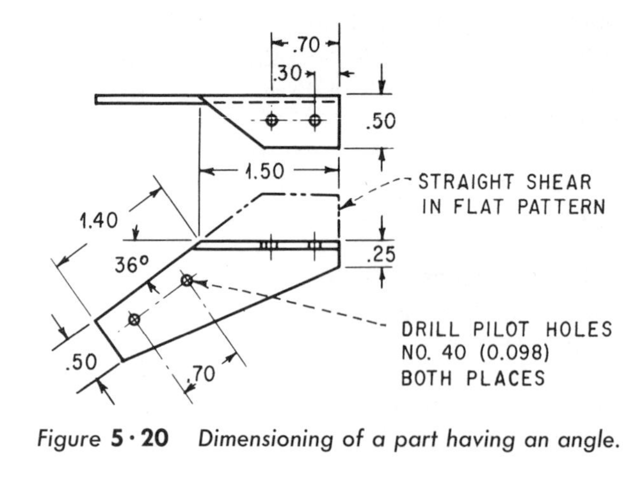

Figure 5·20 Dimensioning of a part having an angle.

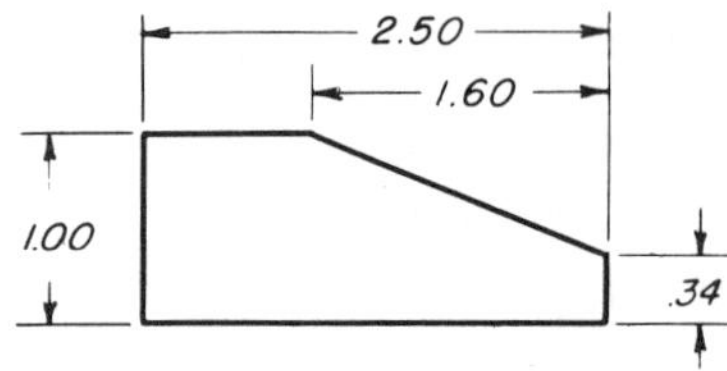

Figure 5·21 Dimensioning a tapered object to establish the angle of taper.

is limited. The one at the top is the method used for locating the center of the hole in the top view of the main drawing. The lower of the three methods shown is followed for giving the other dimensions on the drawing.

Dimensions are always given in inches unless some other unit is indicated, but the symbol ″ is omitted from aircraft and missile drawings to save space and time. When dimension lines and extension lines cross each other, they are often broken at the intersection.

Measuring Angles

An **angle** is formed by the intersection of two straight lines. The amount of opening between the lines determines the size of the angle. If two straight lines intersect so that they form four equal angles, each angle is a right angle. It will be remembered that two right angles form a straight angle (180°) and four right angles together produce the full circle of 360°.

As explained previously, angles are measured in degrees, minutes, and seconds. When a circle is divided into 360 equal divisions, each division is one degree. A **minute,** represented by the symbol ′, is one-sixtieth of a degree. A **second,** represented by the symbol ″, is one-sixtieth of a minute.

Since there are 360° in a circle, a right angle, which is one-fourth of a circle, is 90°. A protractor, which is a graduated circle or part of a circle, is used to measure or lay out angles.

When any angle on a drawing **looks** like a right angle and is not dimensioned to show that it is not a right angle, it is to be considered 90°. All angles other than right angles must be dimensioned on the drawing.

In Fig. 5·20, which is a drawing of a sheet-metal clip, there is a 36° angle in the front view. An arrow points to an area bounded in part by alternate position lines to show the shape and position of the flange before it is bent at a 90° angle to take the form shown in the top view.

In Fig. 5·21 another method is used to dimension an angle. The dimensions of the large and small ends of the object are given, the distance from where the taper begins to the small end, and the total length.

Taper

The word taper is used to describe a shape which is changed in size uniformly along its length. For example, tapered pins and bolts, which are widely used in aircraft and spacecraft work, usually have a uniform change of size along their lengths. Taper can be expressed in various ways, but the preferred method is to give it in inches per foot. Thus, a part with a taper of ⅛ in. per ft can be described as taper ⅛ per ft.

Limits, tolerance, and allowance

The dimensions on a blueprint which represent the perfect size are sometimes called the **basic dimensions.** For example, the basic dimension for the length of an object might be 4 in. All basic dimensions have **limits.** From these limits, the person reading the blueprint can tell the extreme permissible dimensions which he can safely allow. For example, the limits for the 4-in. dimension already might be 4.005 and 3.995 in. The part could be made 0.005 in. longer or 0.005 in. shorter than the basic dimension and still pass inspection. In other words, the **limits** are the extremes of size allowable. The limits are usually written with one over the other. For example, a drawing may read DRILL $\frac{0.293''}{0.290}$.

The **tolerance** is the difference between the extreme permissible dimensions. It is the range of error between the limits that will be accepted or tolerated. For example, if the limits are ± 0.005, then the plus limit is the dimension plus 0.005, the minus limit is the dimension minus 0.005, and the tolerance is 0.010.

Allowance is generally defined as the difference between the nominal dimensions and the upper or lower limit. It represents the condition of the tightest permissible fit for the correct construction and operation of the mating parts. For example, when a permanent assembly is being put together, it may be desirable to have a driving or heavy force fit which can be described as a tight fit. On the other hand, if clearance is required between moving parts, a loose fit is desired.

The American Standards Association has established eight classes of fits, ranging from the large allowance or loose fit to the considerable negative allowance or heavy force and shrink fit. These classes of fits are used by the engineers to determine the limits or tolerances to be used, but a class is not ordinarily used as a designation on a drawing. Actual sizes will usually be "called out." The term "called out" means **indicated** on the drawing.

Basic hole system

The American Standards Association has developed a **basic hole system** which is a method of determining the size of the hole in which a shaft is to be fitted. The basic diameter is the minimum diameter of the hole. The hole may be made larger than the basic diameter, but it must not be made smaller. Hence the limits are plus limits, and since there are no minus limits, the plus limits constitute the tolerance. For this reason, the tolerance in this system is described as a "plus tolerance."

Scale

The word **scale** has many meanings. One of them is the proportion in dimensions between a drawing, map, or plan and the object that is represented on paper. For example, a map may be drawn on a scale of 1 in. to 1 mile, which means that 1 in. on the map represents 1 mile on the earth. In a like manner, a drawing from which a blueprint is to be made may be prepared to any desired scale, and this scale is shown in the title block on the drawing. Most aerospace drawings are made "full scale," "½ size," "¼ size," or "1⁄10 size." Occasionally other scales may be used.

TITLE BLOCKS AND NUMBERING SYSTEMS

Title blocks

The **title block** is the index to the drawing. It provides all necessary information that is not shown in or near the actual drawing. It is usually located in the lower right-hand corner of the drawing, although it may occupy the whole bottom portion of a drawing made on a small sheet of paper.

Figure 5·22 illustrates a typical title block used in the aerospace industry. It is exceptionally complete and yet is flexible enough in its design to cover many unforeseen details. Since the one title block can be used on many different blueprints, it is standardized and printed on the drawing paper with the spaces left blank. When the draftsman executes a drawing, he fills in the required information as far as he can, and then additional blanks are filled in by various members of the engineering department as the drawing is submitted through channels to the higher authorities for approval.

Figure 5·23 is a small drawing prepared by the engineering department of an aerospace company. The title block is somewhat similar to the one shown in Fig. 5·22, but there are some variations. All companies do not prepare their drawings exactly alike, and even within the same organization it is impossible and often undesirable to standardize completely the manner of preparing drawings. In order to explain the component parts of the title block, each feature will be discussed separately.

Drawing or blueprint number

The **drawing number** is customarily printed in large numerals in the lower right-hand corner of the title block and repeated elsewhere on the same drawing so that it can be read when the drawing is folded and to provide for the possibility of one of the numbers being torn off or otherwise obliterated. In some companies, the drawing number is repeated in the upper left-hand corner or in some other location where it will not interfere with other information.

The **universal number system** has been used for many years by some manufacturers and is still

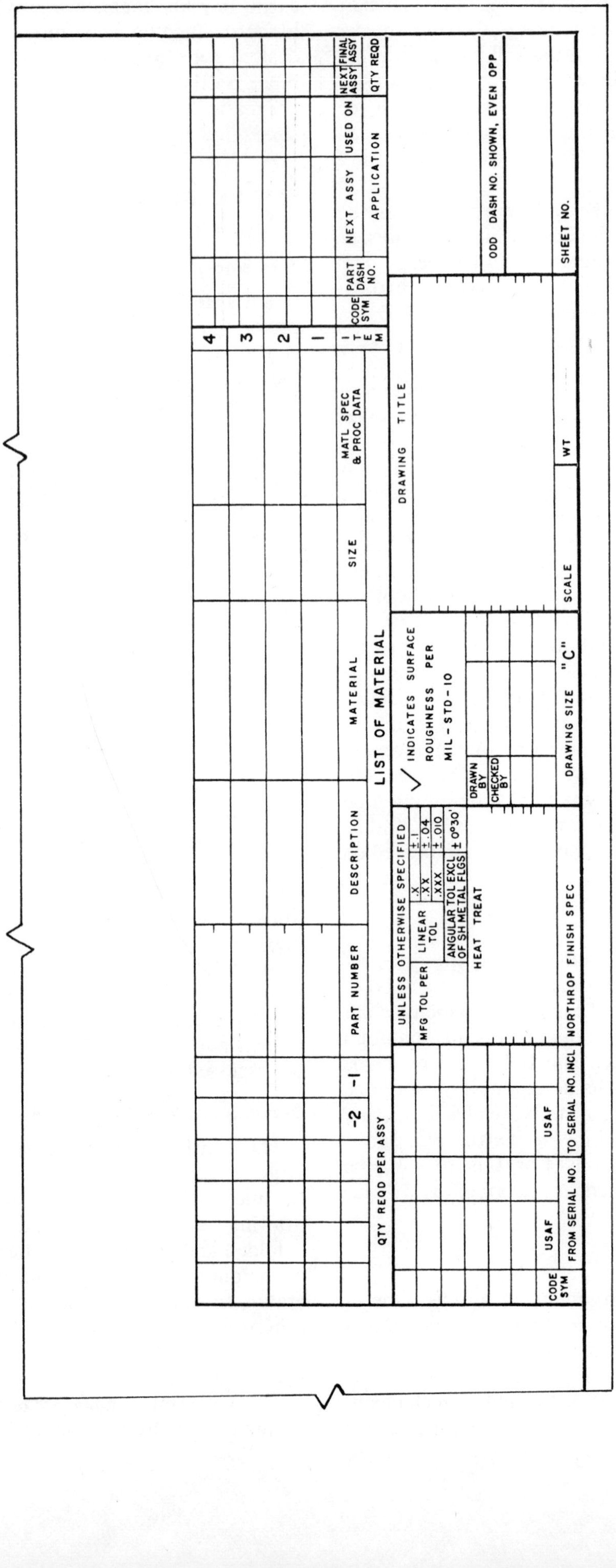
QTY REQD PER ASSY
-2
-1
PART NUMBER
DESCRIPTION
MATERIAL
SIZE
MATL SPEC & PROC DATA
ITEM
4
3
2
1
CODE SYM
PART DASH NO.
NEXT ASSY
USED ON
NEXT ASSY
FINAL ASSY
APPLICATION
QTY REQD
LIST OF MATERIAL
CODE SYM
USAF
USAF
FROM SERIAL NO.
TO SERIAL NO. INCL
UNLESS OTHERWISE SPECIFIED
MFG TOL PER
LINEAR TOL
.X ±.1
.XX ±.04
.XXX ±.010
ANGULAR TOL EXCL OF SH METAL FLGS ± 0°30'
HEAT TREAT
NORTHROP FINISH SPEC
INDICATES SURFACE ROUGHNESS PER MIL-STD-10
DRAWN BY
CHECKED BY
DRAWING SIZE "C"
SCALE
WT
DRAWING TITLE
ODD DASH NO. SHOWN, EVEN OPP
SHEET NO.

Figure **5·22** *A title block.*

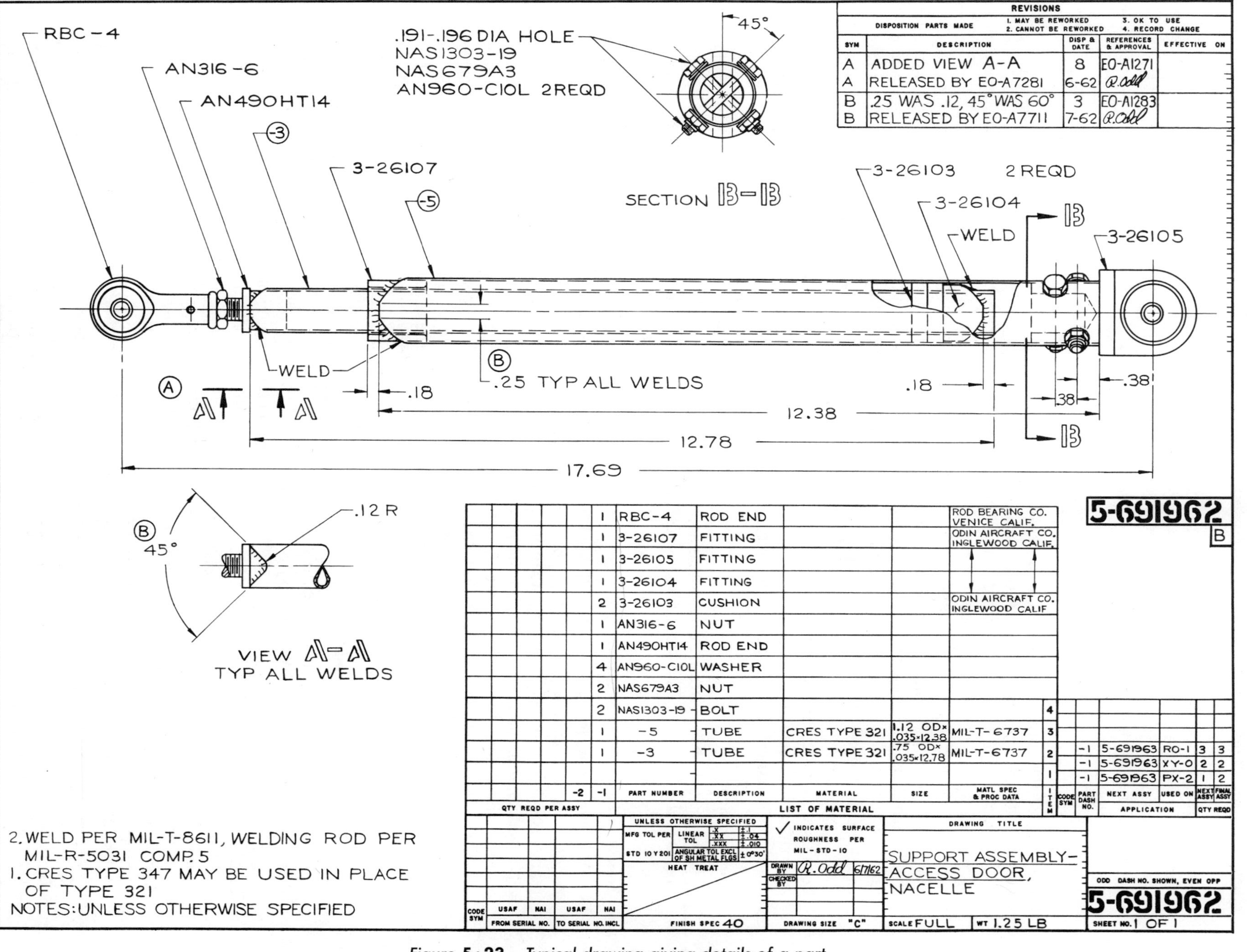

Figure 5·23 Typical drawing giving details of a part.

used by a few. This system is so named to distinguish it from other systems and to signify that it is applicable to all classes of drawings. In the universal system each drawing number consists of six or seven digits, for example, 110798 or 2005226. The first indicates the size of the drawing as follows: No. 1 is for the *A* size (8½ by 11 in.), No. 2 is for the *B* size (11 by 17 in.), No. 4 is for the *C* size (17 by 22 in.), and No. 5 is for the roll size. The other digits in the number form the serial number as assigned in consecutive order but are never used without the first digit, and for all purposes of filing and reference, the first digit can be considered a part of the number.

When a drawing consists of more than one sheet, each sheet is identified by the basic drawing number and the sheet number. The sheet number is entered in the number block.

In recent years a variety of number systems has been used by different companies. To understand any particular system, it is necessary to consult the **drafting-room manual** of the company concerned.

Drawing sizes

In general, drawing sizes are established according to MIL-STD-2A. The designated sizes are given in Table 5 · 1.

Zone number

Roll-size drawings are usually divided into zones to make it easy to find what the blueprint reader is looking for. The zoning is identified by alphabetical and numerical entries in the margin and by subdivision of the margin. The size of the zone spacings is designed to suit the type and scope of the drawing. Zoning can also be employed on flat sheet drawings if necessary to clarify locations. Zone numbers are illustrated in Fig. 5 · 24.

Name of part, unit, or assembly

The name of the part, unit, or assembly is given first followed by descriptive terms, just as the family name is given in a telephone directory followed by the given or Christian name, such as **Jones, John J.** In like manner, in the aerospace industry, the name of a carburetor air intake flange would read: **Flange, Carburetor Air Intake.** Likewise, the assembly shown in Fig. 5 · 23 is **Support Assembly, Access Door, Nacelle.** In other words, the noun is given first and this is followed by the descriptive terms.

The location may be a part of the name, such as **Elevator and Tab Assembly–Left,** showing that it belongs on the left side of the airplane. Another example is **Installation–C.N. sta. 77 flap control cable pul. brkt. assemb.** When analyzed, it is apparent that this is an installation, it is located at crew nacelle station 77, and it is the flap-control pulley bracket assembly.

Table 5 · 1

Flat sizes			Roll sizes		
Size	Width, in.	Length, in.	Size	Width, in.	Length (min), in.
A	8½	11	T	11	34
B	11	17	G	11	42
C	17	22	H	28	50
D	22	34	J	34	50
E	34	44	K	40	50
F	28	40			

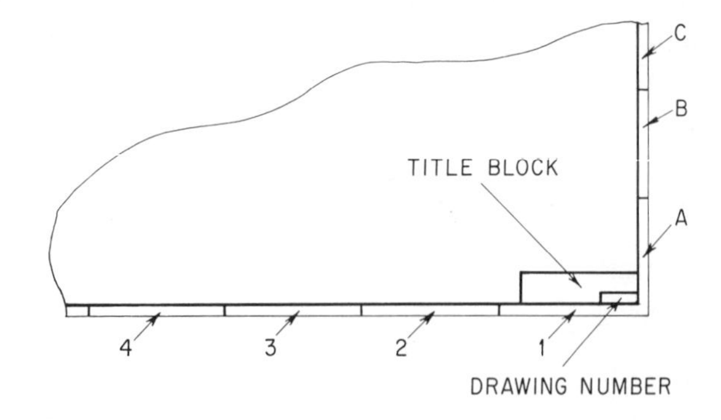

Figure **5 · 24** *Zone numbers.*

Revisions

On the drawing of Fig. 5 · 23 there is a space in the upper right-hand corner labeled **Revisions,** and it will be noted here whether any revisions have been made in the drawing, the disposition and date of the revision, the name or initial of the person making it, an indication of approval, and the serial number on which it is to be effective. The disposition of previously made parts may also be indicated.

Dimensions and limits

On the drawing of Fig. 5 · 23 there are spaces for the dimension of the standard stock from which the part is made. In this case the standard stock is tubing, MIL-T-6737. Limits and tolerances are shown in a supplementary block adjacent to the basic title block.

Right-hand and left-hand parts

A profile or silhouette drawing of a person's right shoe is the same as the outline of his left shoe viewed from the side, even though the shoes have different shapes as viewed from the top. In like manner, many parts of large assemblies are right-hand and left-hand mirror images of each other and not two identical parts.

The usual practice in drawing a part for one side only is to show the left-hand part and left-hand part number, and also to give the right-hand part number, which is the same as the basic number with -2 added. For example, the title block might read "135795-1, LH shown; 135795-2, RH opposite." Both parts have the same basic number, but the right-hand part has the -2 added.

This is not a universal practice. Some companies use odd numbers for left-hand parts and even numbers for right-hand parts, while others do the opposite. Still others assign numbers with no regard to whether they are odd or even. There is no fixed rule. The man reading the blueprint must learn the practice of the manufacturer of the device on which he is working and follow that.

Dash numbers

The dash number system, in general, is used when detailed parts of an assembly are dimensioned on their assembly drawing. At least one manufacturer places each of the dash numbers in a circle having a diameter not less than 0.38 in. or more than 0.40 in., close to the part it identifies, followed by the name (noun only), with an arrow running from the circle to the border of the part. An encircled dash number will not appear in more than one place on a drawing. On roll-size drawings, dash numbers can be found by zone numbers in the material block.

The -1 number is usually the left-hand part, and -2 is used only to indicate the right-hand part of the basic number, as previously explained.

Part number

Each part of an aerospace vehicle always has a number of its own. On a blueprint, the part number and the blueprint number may be the same, but if they are not, then the part number is a dash number shown in the title block.

Station numbers

A station numbering system can be used to help the blueprint reader find such things as fuselage frames, wing frames, stabilizer frames, etc. For example, the nose of an airplane or some other point that can be easily identified is designated as the zero station, and other stations are located at measured distances in inches behind the zero station. Thus, when a blueprint reads: "Fuselage Frame-Sta. 182," that means that the frame is 182 in. back of station zero. In a similar manner, the fore-and-aft center line of an airplane may be a zero station for objects on its right and left. Thus, the wing and stabilizer frames can be located as being a certain number of inches to the right or left of the airplane center line. On some drawings the firewall is a zero station, and on other drawings the leading edge of the wing can be used as a zero station for certain purposes. Always locate the zero station before looking for other stations.

Model and next assembly information

When an object shown on a blueprint is to be a part of an assembly, then the next assembly number is given in the title block to indicate the drawing number of another blueprint which gives the necessary information for completing the assembly. The number of parts required, such as 1 for the right hand and 1 for the left hand, is also given. In the vicinity of these facts is found the model designation. A letter X precedes the designation while it is in the experimental stage. Thereafter, any modifications are shown by a dash and the number of the modification or by a letter and a dash followed by a number, such as J79-23.

Material

Every blueprint carries information regarding the material, and the specifications are also given. For example, a blueprint may have "C.M. Sh't" in the material space, that is, chromemolybdenum steel sheet. The specification space may show that this is SAE4130 or some other particular type of chrome-molybdenum steel sheet. In a similar manner, a blueprint may show that 0.040 sheet aluminum (0.040 in. thick) is required and then specify that it must be 2024-T3, which is a grade of heat-treated structural aluminum alloy.

The material specification is coded when it is for the Army, Navy, or Air Force. For example, it might read "ANQQ - - -," or it might have some other combination of letters and numerals which have a definite meaning to those handling military contracts.

The finish, or protective coating, may be indicated in clear language, or it may be coded, especially for a military contract.

Heat treatment

When heat treatment is required, it should be specified in the title block, although it is sometimes placed on the drawing itself. The word "normalize" may appear on a drawing. **Normalizing** is similar to annealing, but the steel is allowed to cool in still air. It softens the metal less than annealing, increases the strength of the steel above that of annealed material, and relieves internal strains. Normalizing is merely one of the many kinds of heat treatment which may be specified on a blueprint.

Weight

In a space of the title block for a drawing, the weight of the object shown in the blueprint is given. This quantity may be the calculated weight, the actual weight, or both weights. This information is particularly useful for the weight and balance engineers and others who are concerned with the balance of the device involved.

Notes

Information which cannot be given completely and yet briefly in the title block is placed on the drawing in the form of notes, but such information does not duplicate information given elsewhere in the same drawing. Notes may be used to tell the size of a hole, number of drill to be used in making the hole, the number of holes required, and similar information but only when it cannot be conveyed in the conventional manner without notes or when it is desirable to avoid crowding the drawing. If the notes apply to specific places on the part, they are placed on the face of the drawing. If they apply to the part in general, they go in the "General Notes" at the bottom and to the left of the title block.

SYMBOLS AND ABBREVIATIONS

Purpose

A symbol is a visible sign used instead of a word or words to represent ideas, operations, quantities, qualities, relations, or positions. It may be an emblem, such as a picture of a lion to represent courage or an owl to represent wisdom. Likewise the cross represents Christianity, the Star of David represents Judaism, and the crescent stands for Islam. It may be an abbreviation, a single letter, or a character. In other words, symbols constitute picture writing.

Symbols and abbreviations are used extensively in place of long explanatory notes on drawings and blueprints. A few of these symbols and abbreviations are common to every trade, whereas special trades have special symbols and abbreviations of their own.

Material symbols

The American Standards Association has standardized certain symbols used to represent materials in section views. The military services have adopted some of these symbols and added others of their own, and these are all included in the design handbooks used by aerospace manufacturers. Figure 5·25 shows an important group of such symbols.

It must be clearly understood that, when used, these symbols are intended only for general information and not to indicate specific types of materials. For example, in the upper right-hand corner of Fig. 5·25, there is a symbol for iron, including cast iron and malleable iron, but it does not tell the specific type of iron to be used. Such information appears elsewhere on each blueprint.

To simplify drawing-room changes, the symbol for cast iron and malleable iron is often used by many companies to refer to all metals. The blueprint reader must make sure that he knows what metal is intended in each case.

These material symbols are not generally used on section views unless it is desired to call special attention to section parts; hence their appearance is an invitation to observe the drawing closely.

Color is used more and more in modern illustrations in manuals and other textbooks or reference material, especially to show the flow of fluids or the movement of parts. For example, in a hydraulic system, the direction of the flow of the hydraulic fluid may be shown in red where it is under pressure, yellow for supply lines, and green for return lines. A legend explaining the meaning of the different colors is then provided on the drawing. However, the blueprinting process does not permit the use of color on ordinary shop drawings.

Finish and surface-roughness symbols

The surface of a metal part is "finished" by performing a machining, coating, or hand-finishing operation on that surface. Scraping, file-fitting, reaming, lathe turning, shaping, and grinding are a few of the finishing operations.

On many existing blueprints the symbol for a finished surface is a letter V with its point touching the surface to be finished, drawn with an angle of 60° between the sides of the V.

Numbers may be placed within the angle formed by the sides of the V to represent the type of finish to be applied to that particular surface. When a part is to be finished on all surfaces the abbreviation F.A.O. is sometimes used to represent "finish all over."

Some factories use symbols on shop orders, but not necessarily on drawings, according to what they call a "finish code." Examples taken at random are: 1, zinc chromate primer; 2, darkened primer; 3, aluminized primer; 9, dope; 10, shellac; etc. However, it is a more common practice to write a finish specification to show how each

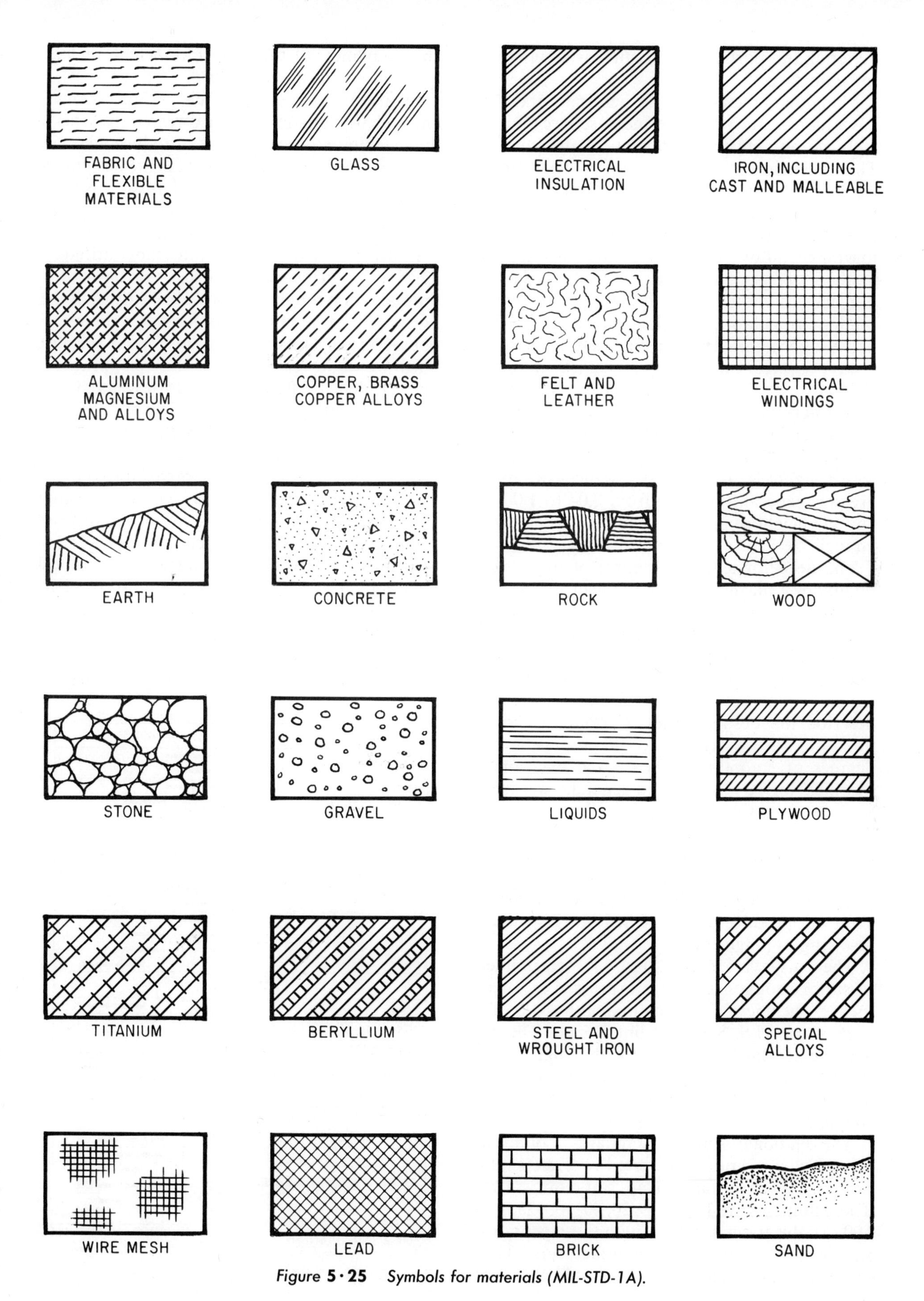

Figure **5·25** *Symbols for materials (MIL-STD-1A).*

material and portion of a particular assembly is to be finished.

Many manufacturers in the aerospace industry have adopted the rms (root-mean-square) microinch system of surface-roughness designation. This system has been standardized by the National Aircraft Standards Committee in Specification NAS30 and is also set forth in MIL-STD-10A. All new drawings of machined castings, machined forgings, and other machined parts will use this method of specifying surface finishes. **Surface roughness** is a term used to designate recurrent or random irregularities which may be considered as being superimposed upon a plane surface or upon a wavy surface. On "smooth machined" surfaces, these irregularities generally have a maximum crest-to-crest distance of not greater than 0.010 in. and a height which may vary from 0.000001 to 0.00005 in. "Waviness" should not be confused with roughness, as the crest distances are much greater, generally running from 0.04 to 1.00 in., and the height as much as several thousandths of an inch.

The need for a simple control of the surface quality of a machined part, by means of production drawings, has long been apparent. Dimension tolerances as well as process notes such as "rough machine," "smooth machine finish," "grind," "polish," etc., limit the surface characteristics in a general way but are not sufficiently specific to describe the desired result. Certain machining processes, such as grinding, could produce several degrees of smoothness; hence the decision as to which degree was intended generally was made in the past by the shop or the vendor.

By means of the rms system of surface-roughness designation, it becomes possible for the engineering department of any company to specify precisely the degree of finish required and for the shop to produce the specified finish without resorting to judgment.

The rms average is a unit of measurement of surface roughness and is expressed in microinches. The microinch is one-millionth (0.000001) part of the U.S. Standard linear inch. The rms average is chiefly affected by the highest and lowest deviations from a mean surface and is a mathematical indication of average surface roughness.

The National Aircraft Standards Committee has selected a series of preferred roughness numbers that cover the range of aircraft requirements. These numbers are 1, 2, 5, 10, 20, 40, 100, 250, and 500. All the above numbers, with the exception of number 1, are used by manufacturers. These numbers indicate maximum allowable or acceptable roughness of the surface on which they are specified in rms microinches.

Engineers have a fairly clear conception of finish characteristics when expressed in terms of the machining process used to produce a surface finish. It is therefore necessary for the designer to designate this surface condition as an rms finish number. Figure 5·26 is a table of roughness numbers for surface-finish designation.

In order to allow the machine shop latitude in developing the specified finish, drawings specify the maximum roughness allowable. Any smoother finish will be acceptable as long as economy is not sacrificed. The shop may develop the specified finish by whatever method is the most practical. Surface defects, flaws, irregularities, and waves which generally occur in only a few places will be handled by the inspection department.

The shop and engineering departments must use the standard reference samples for comparison with machined parts. By visual inspection and by feel, they can check the completed surfaces. In borderline cases the surface can be checked by instruments called the profilometer and the Bush analyzer. These are tracer-point instruments which measure the surface roughness when drawn along the surface to be measured.

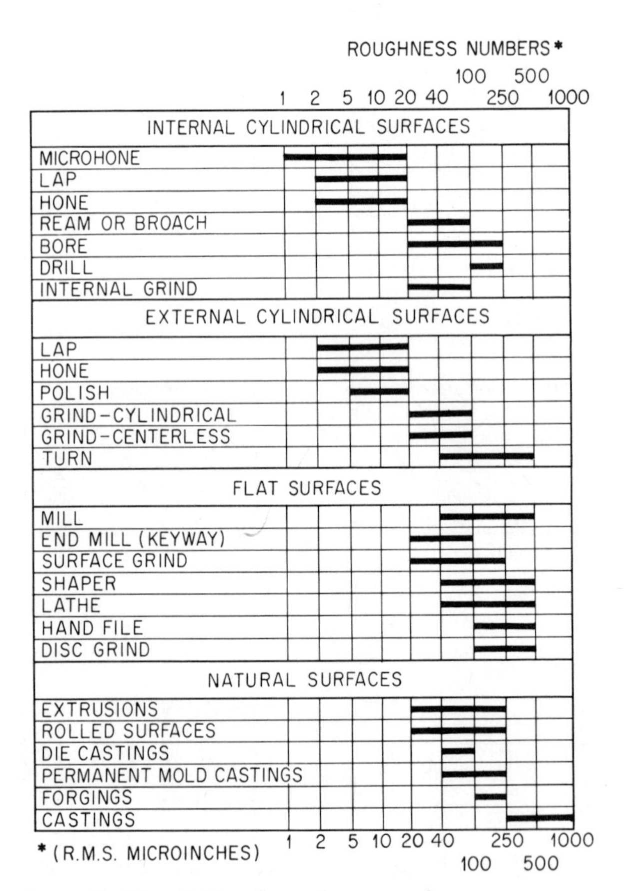

Figure **5·26** *Table of roughness numbers.*

The rms numbers on drawings always are called out by the use of the standard symbol illustrated in *a* of Fig. 5·27. The roughness number must always be on the left side of the long leg close to the horizontal bar as indicated by *xx* in the illustration.

The roughness of natural surfaces is not specified unless such surfaces are critical because of functional or manufacturing requirements.

The finish of such items as drilled holes, reamed holes, and spot faces is not usually specified if the maximum roughness to be produced will be acceptable. The roughness of fillets and chamfers conforms to the rougher of the two connected or adjacent surfaces, unless otherwise indicated.

Unless otherwise specified, a symbol used on a plated or coated surface always signifies that a control applies to the parent-metal surface before plating or coating.

"Lay" may be defined, for the purpose of this discussion, as the direction of tool marks or the grain of the surface roughness. Waviness and tool lay designations also covered in the National Aircraft Standards Committee Specification NAS30 are not yet adopted by all manufacturers.

The symbol at *b* in Fig. 5·27 indicates rms 500. This is a very rough, low-grade machine surface resulting from heavy cuts and coarse feeds in milling, turning, shaping, and boring, as well as from rough filing and rough disk grinding. This is also the natural finish of some forgings and sand castings. It is not used for aluminum alloys or other soft metals, for surfaces in tension, or where notch sensitivity is a factor. It may be used on secondary items but is generally not called out as a finish for aircraft or missile parts.

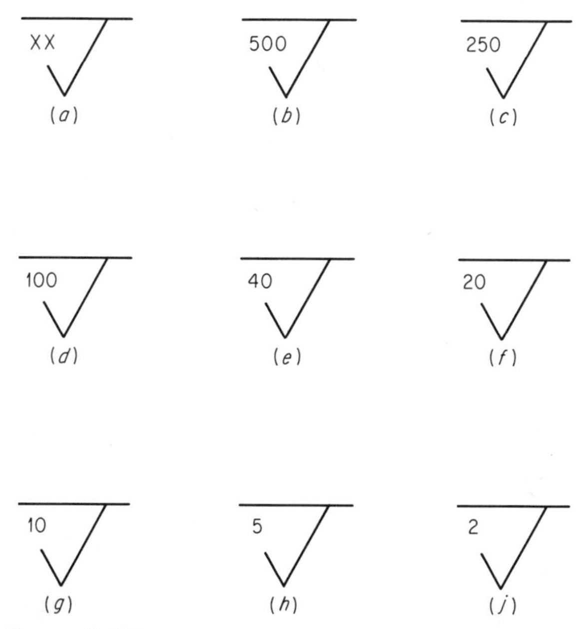

Figure **5·27** *Root-mean-square finish symbols and numbers.*

In Fig. 5·27, *c* is the symbol for rms 250. This is a medium machine finish and is fairly inexpensive to produce.

Figure 5·27*d* is the symbol for rms 100. This finish is generally known as smooth machine finish and is the product of high-grade machine work in which relatively high speed and fine feeds are used in taking light cuts with well-sharpened cutters.

Figure 5·27*e* is the symbol for rms 40. This is a fine machine finish produced by a carbide or diamond bore, a medium surface or cylindrical grind, a rough emery buff, ream, burnish, and similar operations.

Root-mean-square 20, a very fine finish, is indicated by the symbol of Fig. 5·27*f*. This finish is produced by fine cylindrical or surface grind, very smooth ream, smooth emery buff, and coarse to medium lap or hone.

The extremely smooth finishes are indicated by *g*, *h*, and *j* in Fig. 5·27. These finishes are produced by honing, lapping, microhone, polishing, or buffing.

Root-mean-square 10 and the finer finishes may have either a dull or bright appearance, depending upon the method used to produce them. The surface appearance must not be considered in judging quality, but the degree of smoothness must be determined by "feel" or roughness-measuring instruments.

Process code

Many manufacturers in the aerospace industry use symbols in what they call their "process code." Examples are: A, anodize; B, chromodize; C, cadmium plate; D, dichromate (Dow No. 7); H, degrease in vapor degreaser; and S, sand blast. These code letters simplify the instructions required on drawings and consume much less space than would otherwise be required.

Abbreviations

The use of abbreviations is not encouraged in the aerospace industry except where a saving of space is necessary. Most companies prefer the use of capital letters on drawings and generally restrict the use of small (lower-case) letters to reports, manuals, and other technical publications, where they are used along with capital letters.

The period (.) is used after an abbreviation only when the abbreviation spells an English word. For example, ADD. for additional, and AIL. for aileron are used with periods because the words **add** and **ail** are common English words. In any case of doubt about the use of an abbreviation, the word or words should be given in full. Each company standardizes its abbreviations in accordance with MIL-STD-12, a military specification for government drawings.

REVIEW QUESTIONS

1. What is meant by the term *blueprint?*
2. Describe a method for reproducing a drawing.
3. What precautions must be taken in handling a blueprint?
4. What should be done if an error is found in a blueprint?
5. Describe a *perspective* drawing.
6. What is an *isometric* drawing?
7. What is meant by an *orthographic* projection?
8. Draw lines representing the following: visible outline, hidden line, center line, dimension line, extension line.
9. What kind of a line is used to indicate broken material?
10. What is the purpose of a *conventional break?*
11. Compare *location* dimensions and *size* dimensions.
12. What is meant by continuous dimensioning?
13. Where is a dimension placed when it is common to two views?
14. What unit of measurement is generally used for dimensions?
15. What is a dimension *limit?*
16. Explain *tolerance.*
17. With respect to a drawing, what is meant by *scale?*
18. List the information which may be contained in the title block.
19. Describe the universal number system.
20. Give the standard drawing sizes.
21. What is the purpose of notes on a drawing?
22. How is surface roughness indicated on a drawing?

CHAPTER 6

Fundamentals of Drafting

As pointed out in the preceding chapter, blueprints are an essential means of communication between the engineer and the technician or craftsman. In order to produce drawings which can be correctly interpreted, the draftsman must learn the language of drafting and how to use this language in the preparation of engineering drawings.

Great care must be used in drafting to produce drawings from which good reproductions can be made. This means, particularly, that drawing lines be clean, sharp, and dense and that the drawing paper (vellum) be kept clean and free of extraneous marks, smudges, or other defacing conditions.

It is also most essential that symbols, letters, figures, and notes be accurately placed on drawings. A drawing released with inaccurate information can be very costly when it reaches the tooling or production department. Many hours of work may go into producing a part, but if the part is incorrectly made because of a poor drawing, all the time and money spent in producing the part are lost.

It is the purpose of this chapter to describe standard practices for the preparation of engineering drawings and to explain the proper techniques for drafting.

DRAFTING EQUIPMENT

Drawing boards

A standard drawing board is illustrated in Fig. 6·1. This board is 18 by 24 in. in dimensions and is made of wood laminations with a birch surface on each face. The board can be used on a drafting table or any solid surface which is free from movement. The edges of the board are very straight and smooth and make accurate 90° angles at the corners. It is common practice to cover the surface of the drawing board by cementing on a layer of linoleum or other suitable material to provide a hard, smooth surface. If this is not done, the wood surface can become grooved and marred, especially when very hard drawing pencils are used.

A drawing board made in the form of a table is shown in Fig. 6·2. Boards of this type are often used in engineering departments where large drawings must be produced. Figure 6·3 shows an engineer at work on a similar board.

Figure 6·1 *Drawing board.*

Figure 6·2 *Drawing table.*

Figure 6·3 Engineer at a drawing table.

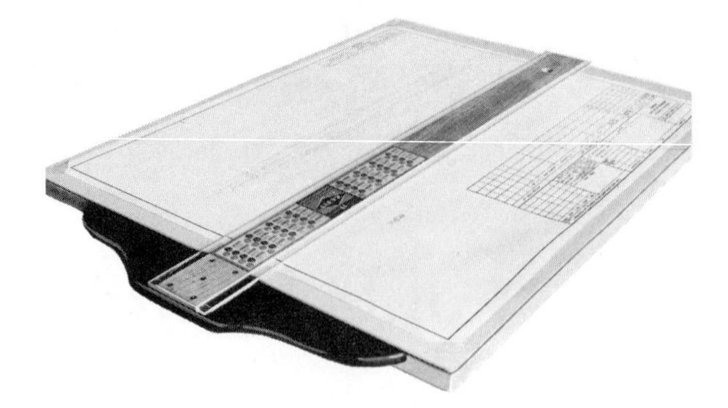

Figure 6·5 Using a T square with a drawing board.

It was once the practice to fasten the drawing paper or vellum to the drawing board by means of thumbtacks. This practice has long been in discard, and the universal method today is to use masking tape or drafting tape at the corners of the paper to secure it to the board. The paper should be aligned with the edge of the board so the drawing will bc squarc on the paper.

The T square

The T square, shown in Fig. 6·4, is designed to make possible the rapid and accurate alignment of drawing lines. The head of the square is perpendicular to the blade, and it is arranged so it will extend over the edge of the board while the blade lies flat on the surface. When the T square is placed properly on the board as shown in Fig. 6·5, the blade will be parallel to two edges of the board and perpendicular to the other two edges. The head of the square can be quickly and smoothly moved along the edge of the board so that parallel lines can be drawn at any location on the paper without the necessity of measuring the alignment each time.

A properly constructed T square is made of hardwood with the blade rigidly secured to the head. The edges of the blade are made of a clear plastic to provide a hard, smooth edge and visibility through the blade. The visibility feature aids considerably in the accurate placing of lines. If the T square gets dirty, it will smudge the drawing. It can be cleaned with a cloth dampened with a petroleum solvent or similar fluid or **slightly** moistened with water. It should never be held under a faucet or washed with a **wet** rag, since water will warp it and destroy its accuracy.

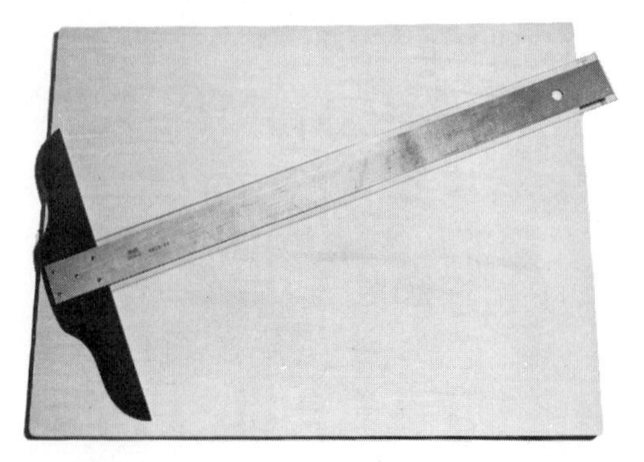

Figure 6·4 A T square.

Scales

A wide variety of scales can be obtained for use in drafting, but the most commonly used types are the engineer's scale and the architect's scale. For use in the aerospace industry the engineer's scale, shown in Fig. 6·6, is the most popular. The triangular engineer's scale has six faces calibrated in tenths, twentieths, thirtieths, fortieths, fiftieths, and sixtieths of an inch. Other divisions of the inch are also used on some scales. The draftsman uses the scale division which is most convenient for his particular drawing.

Scales are principally used for measuring distances accurately; however, they can also be used as straightedges for drawing lines. It is essential that the scales be properly cared for because the sharp, smooth edges can be easily damaged, and when this occurs, the edge can no longer be used for straight lines.

Drafting machines

A drafting machine is a mechanical device which can be used to perform the functions of a number of other items of drafting equipment including the straightedge, T square, protractor, triangle, and scale. As shown in Fig. 6·7, the drafting machine is designed to mount on the edge of the drafting table. The machine is constructed with bands or rods which hold the scales at any desired angle when they are locked

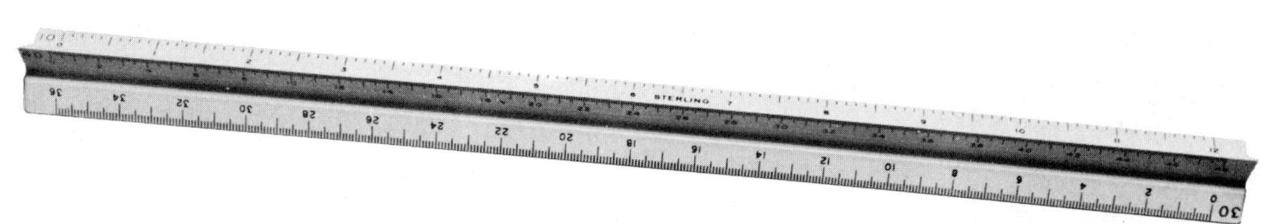

Figure 6·6 Engineer's scale.

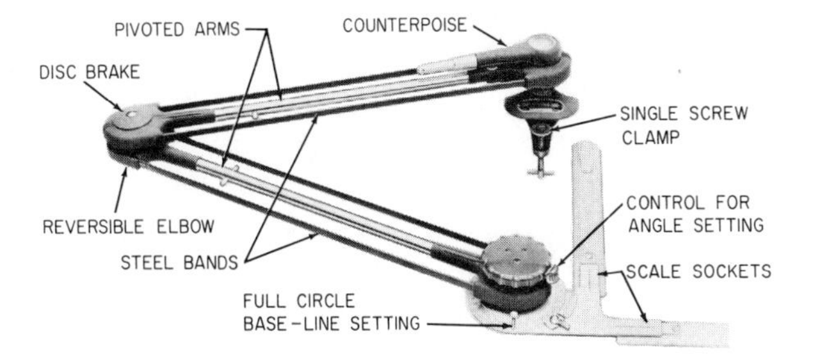

Figure 6·7 Drafting machine.

in place, regardless of the movement of the machine on the board.

The scales are mounted on the machine at an angle of 90° to each other, but they can be rotated together through any angle when the lock is released. A protractor scale makes it possible to select a desired angle accurately; thus it is possible to draw a line at any angle required.

Triangles

An adequate set of drafting equipment includes two right-angle triangles, one having 45° acute angles and the other having acute angles of 30 and 60°. These triangles are shown in Fig. 6·8. The triangles are made of clear plastic to provide good visibility. Sizes may be from 6 to 24 in. in the maximum dimension of one leg of the right angle.

Through the use of the 45° and 30/60° triangles together with a T square, any angle which is a multiple of 15° can be produced without the use of a protractor. As explained in a previous chapter, a protractor is a curved scale for measuring angles.

French curve

The French or irregular curve, shown in Fig. 6·9, is a curved ruler with a wide range of curvatures designed to make possible the production of smoothly curved lines. Any curved line which is a portion of a circle can be drawn with a compass. However, there are many curves which are portions of parabolas, hyperbolas, or ellipses, and these cannot be drawn with a compass. The French curve is made of a plastic material similar to that used for the triangles.

Templates

Templates are special patterns made of plastic or a similar material. These patterns are designed to speed the work of the draftsman by providing him with ready-made designs for letters, circles, ellipses, and symbols. In order to produce a certain figure or symbol, the draftsman places the desired pattern in the correct position on the drawing paper and then follows the outline of the pattern with his drawing pencil. Typical drafting templates are shown in Fig. 6·10.

Drawing instruments

A standard set of drawing instruments is shown in Fig. 6·11. This set includes some items which may not be used often; however, there are occasions when each item becomes useful. Probably the most widely used instrument in the set is the large **compass.** The compass is used for drawing all curves which are portions of circles, and it is

Figure 6·8 Triangles.

Figure 6·9 French curves.

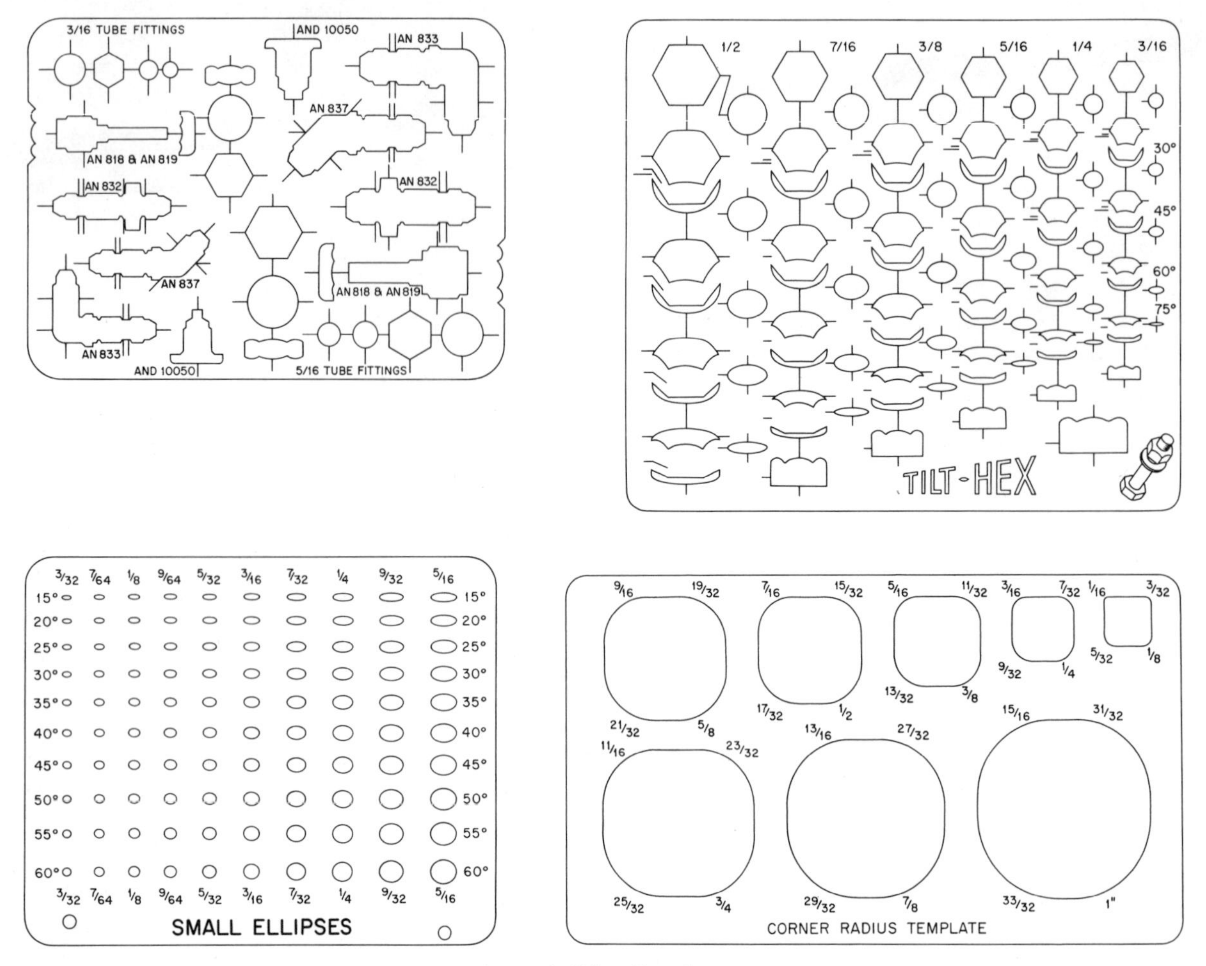

Figure **6·10** *Templates.*

also very useful for layout and drawing construction work.

The small compass, called a **bow compass,** is used for curves with small radii (1 in. or less). This provides for more accuracy because the longer compass may spring slightly when drawing very small circles. The bow compass is shown in Fig. 6·12.

The **divider,** which is very much like the compass, consists of two legs joined together at the top with a friction joint. The friction is sufficient to hold the adjustment under normal use, but it permits easy change of adjustment with one hand. The tips of the legs are equipped with steel needle points as shown in Fig. 6·13.

Accessories for the compasses include an extension and a pen attachment. The extension makes it possible to draw larger circles than would otherwise be possible. The pen attachment is used when it is necessary to draw ink curves and circles.

The **ruling pen,** shown in Fig. 6·14, is used to draw straight lines on ink drawings. For the majority of drawings, inking is not required. However,

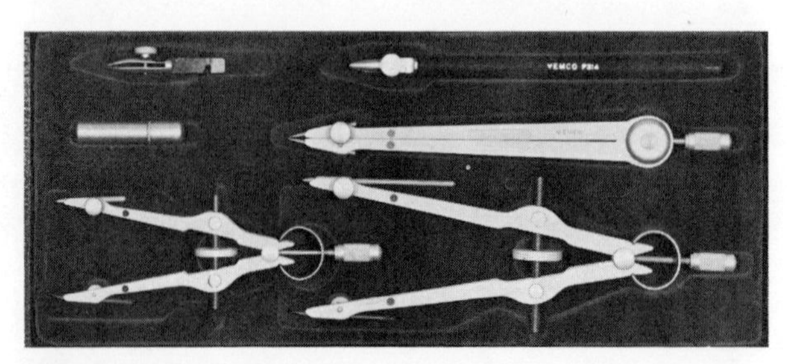

Figure **6·11** *A set of drawing instruments.*

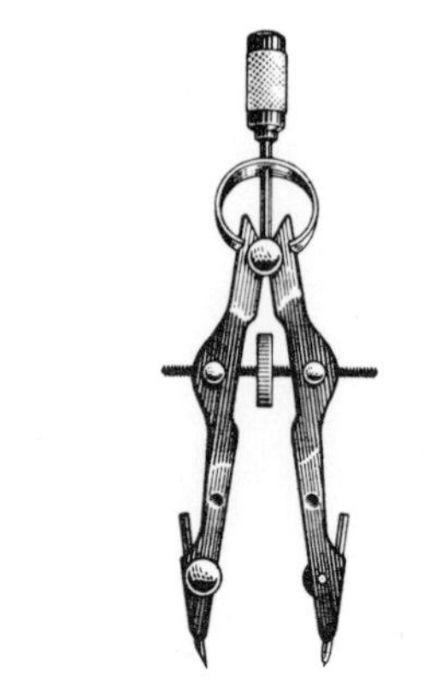

Figure **6·12** *A bow compass.*

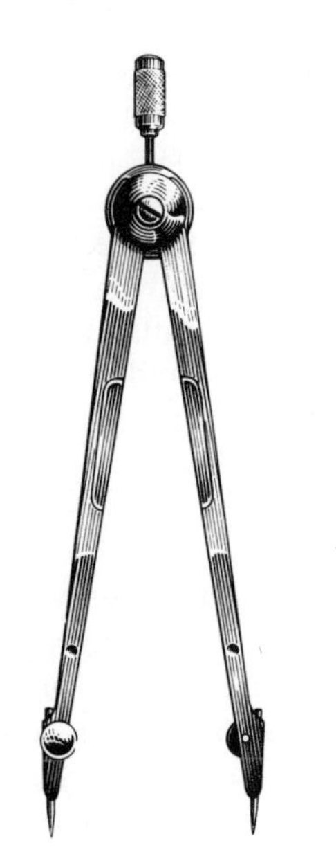

Figure **6 · 13** *A divider.*

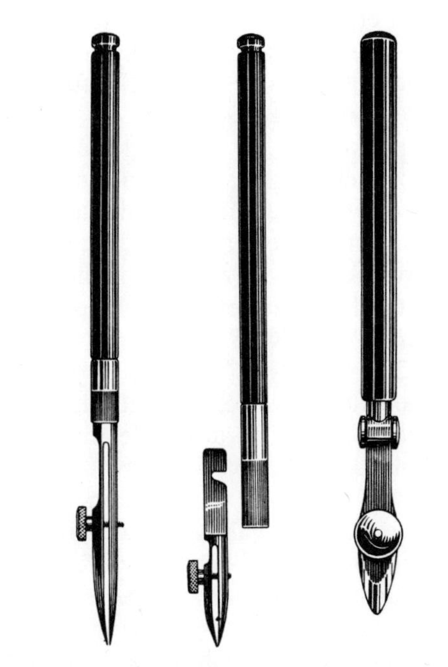

Figure **6 · 14** *Ruling pens.*

if a drawing is made for publication, a much higher quality reproduction can be obtained from an ink drawing. For this reason, the ruling pen is considered an essential instrument for the draftsman.

Drafting materials

The materials used for drafting, other than the instruments and equipment previously described, are drawing paper (vellum), drawing pencils, erasers, pencil sharpeners or pointers, and a dusting brush.

The drawing paper used for the preparation of drawings for reproduction is 100 per cent rag content and treated to make it translucent. The translucence is required so the light of the printing machine can shine through it and cast shadows of the drawing lines on the sensitized printing paper.

In addition to various papers used for drawing, a specially prepared cloth is sometimes used, particularly for ink drawings. The cloth may be made of finely woven linen or cotton, heavily sized to provide a good surface for drawing. Another material used for ink drawings is a heavy plastic film, frosted on one side. This material has the appearance of a good-quality vellum.

Drawing pencils are made with very fine grain lead which must be uniform in quality and hardness. These pencils are made in 18 degrees of hardness from 7B (very soft) to 9H (very hard). For typical drawings the medium range, H to 2H, is commonly used for lines.

Mechanical refill pencils are preferred by most draftsmen. The leads for these pencils can be procured in the hardness desired so they can be changed or adjusted as necessary for the work being performed. To change or adjust a lead it is merely necessary to turn the cap of the pencil to the left and then move the lead to the position desired. Rotating the cap to the right will then grip the lead and hold it in place.

Pencil sharpeners used for wood drawing pencils are specially designed so they will cut only the wood from the pencil and leave the full diameter of the lead extending for about ⅜ in. The point is then prepared with a pencil pointer such as that shown in Fig. 6 · 15. The pencil pointer consists of a wooden paddle with layers of sandpaper attached to the surface. The pencil lead is shaped by rubbing it and rotating it on the sandpaper. When the top layer of sandpaper becomes filled with lead particles, it is removed to expose a clean layer.

A mechanical pointer is a useful tool. To point the lead the pencil is inserted in the hole at the

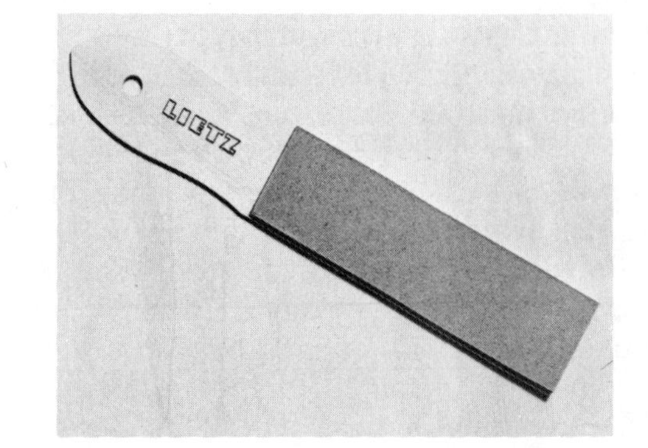

Figure **6 · 15** *Pencil pointer.*

Figure **6·16** *Erasers.*

top and then the top is turned with a "cranking" motion of the pencil. This will produce a fine point on the lead, and with practice the draftsman can adjust the fineness of the point to his desire by proper manipulation of the pointer.

A variety of erasers is used for drafting work. Drafting erasers are made of a rubber material which wears away and carries the pencil line with it. The best eraser, of course, is one which will remove the line without damage to the paper or tracing cloth. White rubber or gum erasers usually leave a clean surface and no stain or marking on the paper. It is best to try several different drawing erasers for a particular pencil and paper combination and then use the one which serves the purpose best. Typical erasers are shown in Fig. 6·16.

Ink erasers are made of a firmer rubber than those designed for pencil work, and they also contain a fine abrasive. Care must be used with such an eraser to avoid damaging the paper or tracing cloth.

DRAWING TECHNIQUES

Although this text is primarily written for the technician whose need for a knowledge of drafting techniques may not be extensive, it is deemed useful for such a person to know the basic techniques employed by draftsmen because of the necessity for preparing shop sketches, diagrams, and drawings as required for reports on work projects. When certain repairs are made on certificated aircraft, it is required that drawings of such repairs be prepared for submission to the Federal Aviation Agency (FAA) on the repair and alteration form. The technician who knows how to make good drawings will be able to prepare reports which are well illustrated and easy to understand. Technicians may also be required to make drawings of alterations or modifications to be submitted to the engineering department of an organization for study and approval. If prepared in a manner familiar to the engineers, the drawings will be easily understood and much time will be saved in trying to determine exactly what the drawings mean.

Necessary equipment

Although the technician may have all the items mentioned in the foregoing section, good drawings or shop sketches can be prepared with only a few of the items. All that is actually needed to make a suitable diagram or sketch is a smooth table or board on which to place the drawing paper, some masking or drafting tape to hold the paper, a good scale, a compass, some drawing pencils, and erasers. To increase the speed with which the drawing can be made, a T square, drawing board, triangles, French curves, and drawing templates are desirable.

For shop sketches, a good grade of white, smooth (not slick) high-rag-content paper should be used. If drawing vellum is available, it can be used, but it is not essential unless the drawing is to be reproduced by Ozalid or other contact methods. Standard sizes of paper for engineering drawings are 8½ by 11 (1 size), 11 by 17 (2 size), and 17 by 22 (4 size).

To prepare for drawing, the technician should see that all necessary or desirable items are on hand and placed within easy reach. It is best that the position of each item be maintained until the job is completed so it will be unnecessary to look for something which has been misplaced.

The proper size and quality of paper should be selected and attached to the drawing board with a small strip of tape at each corner. The bottom edge of the paper should be at least 3 in. in from the bottom edge of the board. This makes it possible to use the T square to the bottom edge of the paper.

Drawing pencil lines

Before starting to draw pencil lines the draftsman should make sure that he has a pencil with the proper hardness of lead for the results which he wishes to obtain. This will depend upon the type of paper upon which he is drawing and the type of line which he wishes to produce. For sharp, fine lines the pencil should be reasonably hard, 2H to 4H. Heavy, dark lines can be made more satisfactorily with a softer lead such as H or

Figure 6·17 Drawing horizontal lines.

F. The pencil should be pointed properly by using a pointer such as that shown in Fig. 6·15.

When drawing horizontal lines, the draftsman should use the method similar to that illustrated in Fig. 6·17. The pencil point should be held snugly against the edge of the T square or rule, and the top of the pencil should be slanted a few degrees away from the rule. This is to make sure that the point remains against the rule so it will produce a perfect straight line. The pencil

Figure 6·18 Drawing vertical lines.

Figure 6·19 Drawing vertical lines using a triangle.

should be held at a slant of about 60° in the direction of movement. A right-handed draftsman will draw the pencil from left to right as shown in the illustration. The pencil should be continuously rotated while it is being drawn across the paper in order to keep the point sharp and to produce a line of uniform width.

Vertical lines are drawn by changing the position of the T square so the rule points in a vertical position as shown in Fig. 6·18 or by placing a triangle on the horizontal rule as shown in Fig. 6·19. The pencil line is started at the required point near the draftsman, and the pencil is moved toward the upper edge of the drawing board. The pencil is rotated as explained before, and the angle of slant is about 60° away from the draftsman.

Angle lines can be drawn with the triangles provided the angles are in increments of 15°. Otherwise, a protractor must be used to establish the correct angle. In drawing any angle line, the right-handed draftsman will generally use a direction such that the pencil moves to the right.

Using the compass

For drawing circles and arcs of circles, the compass is used. As explained previously, the large compass is used for drawing arcs with radii of more than 1 in. and the small bow compass is used for arcs or circles with radii of less than 1 in. The pencil end of the compass is pointed with the pencil pointer to produce the weight of line required. The needle in the other leg of the

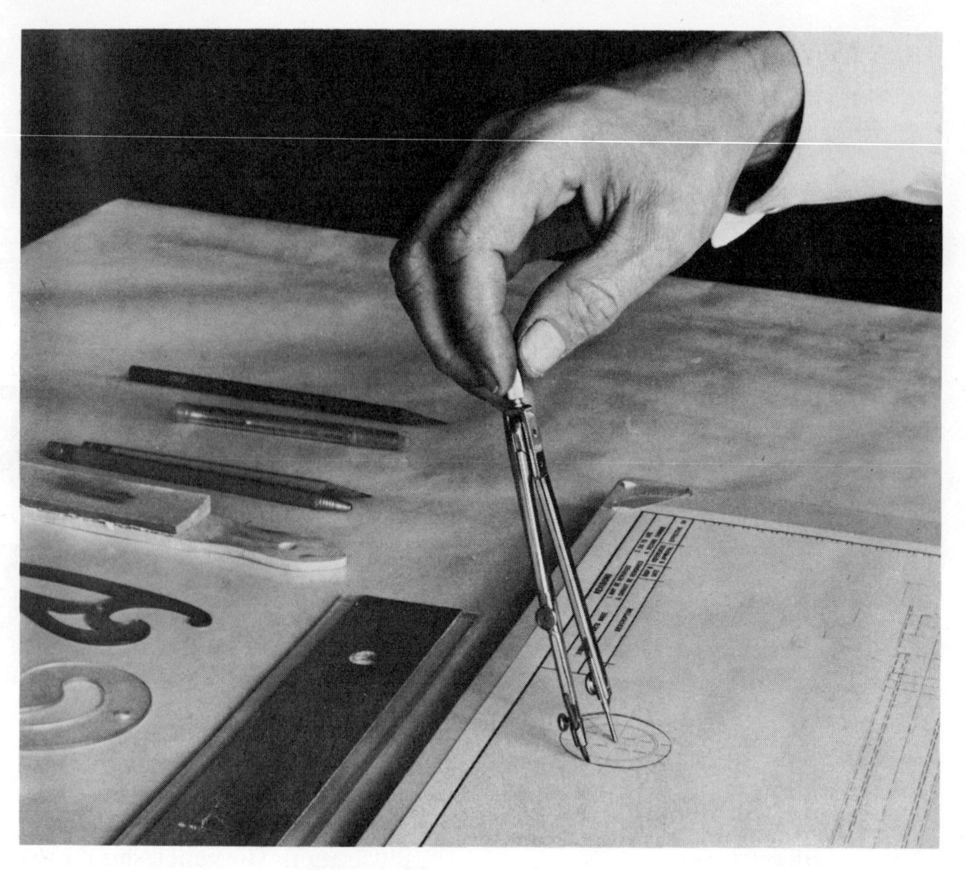

Figure 6 • 20 Using the compass.

compass should have a shoulder to prevent excessive penetration into the drawing paper.

To use the compass, it should be held as shown in Fig. 6 • 20. It is slanted a small amount in the direction of rotation so it will move smoothly without a tendency to catch on the paper. Constant pressure must be maintained on both legs of the compass, first to hold the center leg in place and second to keep the pencil lead on the paper so a solid line will be drawn. The lead should be pointed to produce the desired line.

A standard compass usually can be fitted with a ruling-pen attachment for ink drawing. When ink drawings are to be made with a compass, the ruling pen must be properly adjusted so both sides of the pen will touch the paper. Before the pen attachment is used, the legs of the compass with their attachments should be adjusted so the pen is even with the needle point as shown in Fig. 6 • 21. The width of the point is set correctly, and ink is placed in the pen with the dropper from the ink bottle. It is important that only good-quality drawing ink be used.

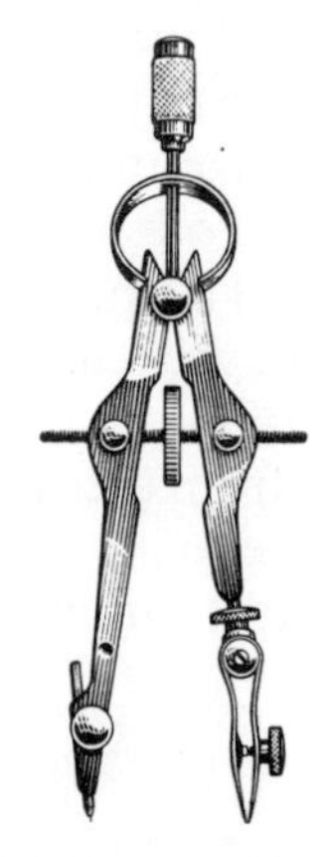

Figure 6 • 21 Compass with a pen point.

The ruling pen

The point of a typical ruling pen is shown in Fig. 6 • 22. The pen consists of two flattened points mounted together with an adjusting screw

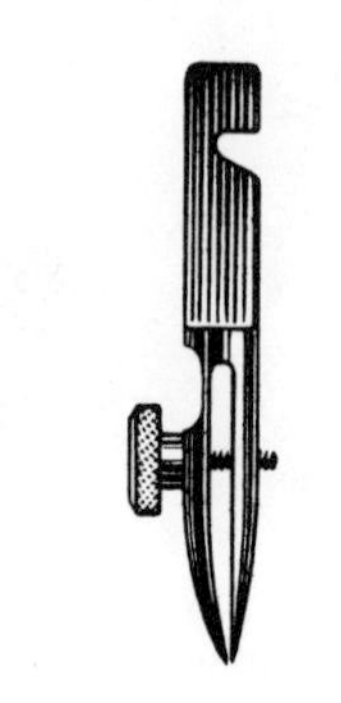

Figure 6 • 22 The point of a ruling pen.

Figure 6·23 Using a ruling pen.

to establish the width of the line to be drawn. The points are sharp and smooth, but they are not sharpened to the extent that they will cut the drawing paper when used with the proper drawing pressure. If they become worn, they should be sharpened with a fine honing stone and rounded slightly chordwise.

The ruling pen should be used as shown in Fig. 6·23. The point of the pen should not be allowed to touch the junction of the rule and the paper because this will allow the ink to flow under the rule and ruin the drawing.

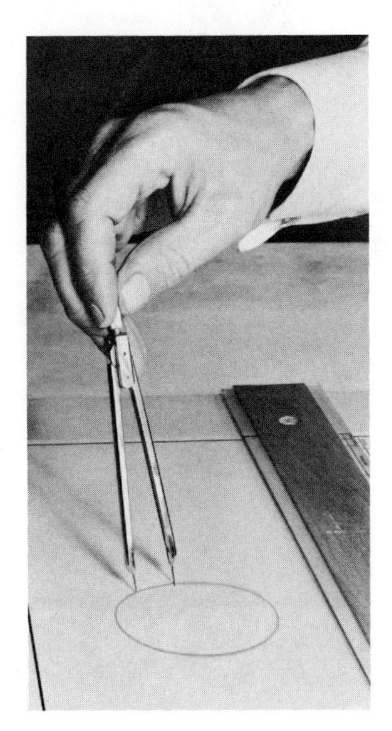

Figure 6·24 Use of a divider.

Dividers

Dividers are used to divide lines, transfer measurements, and, in combination with a scale, determine dimensions. The use of dividers is illustrated in Fig. 6·24. The dividers are held as shown so they can be adjusted with one hand while taking a measurement.

The points of the dividers are sharp steel needles. A very light pressure will cause the needles to penetrate paper or wood sufficiently to keep the points from slipping. When it is desired to lay off equal segments of a line, the divider can be "walked" along the line by fixing one leg with the needle point and swinging the other leg around it. The second line is then fixed, and the first leg is swung around it.

The irregular (French) curve

The irregular curve is used to draw curved lines which cannot be drawn with a compass. As mentioned previously such curves may be portions of parabolas, hyperbolas, or ellipses. Several points are first established along the line to be drawn. These points are then connected by a light curved line drawn freehand. The irregular curve is then matched to as much of the line as it will conveniently fit, and a solid line is drawn using the irregular curve as a guide. It may be necessary to use several portions of the irregular curve to produce the desired line because of changes in curvature. It is important that each section of the curved line drawn be a continuation of the section previously drawn so the finished curve will be free from bumps or other irregularities. A typical line drawn with an irregular curve is shown in Fig. 6·25.

Pencil lines

As explained in the previous chapter, pencil lines are usually drawn light, heavy, or medium. The light lines are usually 0.003 to 0.008 in. in width, the medium lines are 0.012 to 0.017 in., and the heavy lines are 0.015 to 0.020 in. These measurements may vary somewhat from the foregoing dimensions, but the widths given provide a good guide.

The draftsman should make sure that his lines

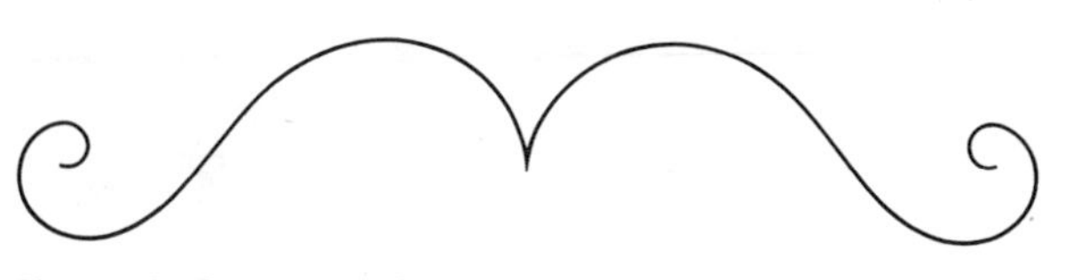

Figure 6·25 Line drawn with an irregular curve.

are clean, solid, and black. This requires the proper choice of lead and the right pressure when drawing. A line which is not solid and black will make a poor reproduction.

Lettering

The application of good lettering to a drawing is essential if the drawing is to convey the necessary information to the technician or engineer. The ability to produce good lettering is easily developed with practice and the use of proper techniques.

The letters on a drawing should normally be about ⅛ in. in height and may be drawn vertically or on a slant. Slanted letters make an angle of about 68° from the horizontal. Figure 6·26 shows standard lettering and the direction for making each stroke. Straight portions of letters are drawn with one stroke from top to bottom or from left to right. Curved portions may be made with a clockwise or counterclockwise stroke, depending upon which direction will produce the best results.

In order to make words in straight lines, the draftsman should draw very light guide lines for the top and bottom of the letters. This will aid in keeping the letters of uniform height and will make the line of words straight. The draftsman may also use a set of guide lines which have been drawn in ink or printed on a sheet of paper. This guide is placed under the vellum, and the lines show through.

Since all notes, dimensions, material specifications, etc., are read from the bottom of a drawing, all lettering and numbering should be made in horizontal lines with the letters and figures upright as viewed from the bottom of the drawing. This makes it unnecessary for the person using the drawing to turn it at an angle or sideways in order to read it easily.

The lettering pencil should be of a hardness which will make a solid, black line on the drawing paper but should not be so soft that it smears easily. An H pencil will usually serve the purpose well. The point of the pencil should be reasonably sharp but should have a slightly rounded point. This is necessary so the pencil will not cut through the paper and so the line will be of the proper width. From time to time, as the lettering is being done, the pencil should be turned so the point will not become flattened on one side.

The spacing of letters and words is important so that each word and figure will be clear and

Figure 6·26 Standard lettering style.

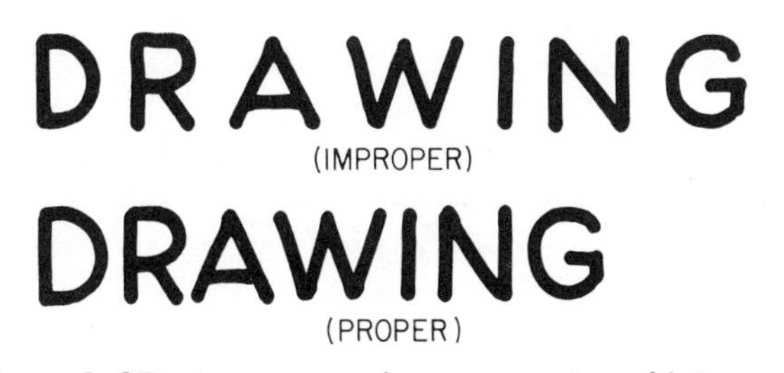

Figure **6·27** *Improper and proper spacing of letters.*

distinct from the others. The letters in each word should be close together with a uniform amount of white paper between each letter. Because of the different shapes of various letters it is somewhat difficult to produce an appearance of uniform spacing, but practice will aid in accomplishing this. Letters should not be spaced with equal distances between the ending of one letter and the beginning of the next because this will produce an appearance of very irregular spacing. This is illustrated in Fig. 6·27. Observe that there is more white space between some letters than between others because of the shape of the letters.

DRAWING VIEWS

The orthographic projection

The orthographic projection was described briefly in the previous chapter; however, the method for drawing such a projection was not described. An orthographic projection is defined as a projection in which the projecting lines are perpendicular to the plane of projection. We enclose an object in a rectangular glass box, as shown in Fig. 6·28, and we can see several views of the object by observing it on lines of sight perpendicular to the glass surfaces. The views we see are projected to view 1, front; view 2, side; and view 3, top. When we study all three views, knowing that they are different views of the object, we can determine the actual configuration of the object drawn.

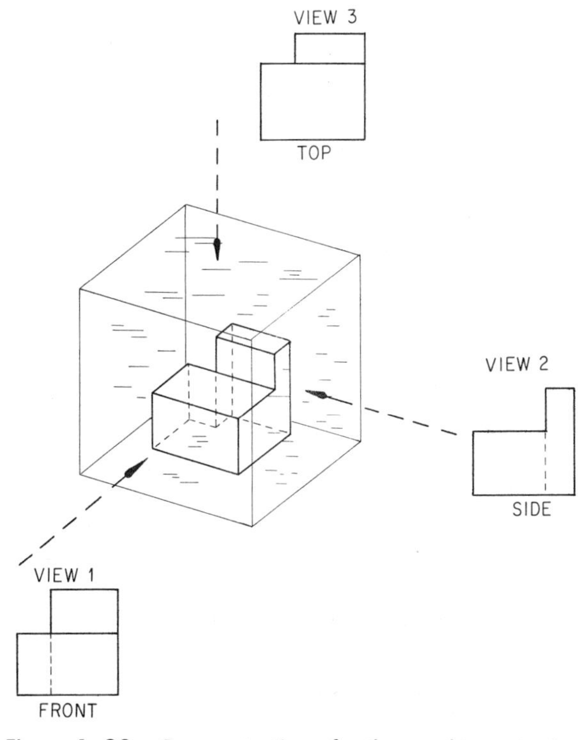

Figure **6·28** *Demonstration of orthographic projection.*

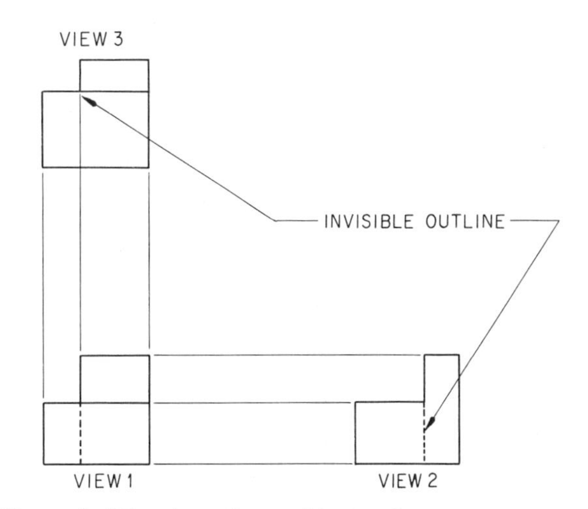

Figure **6·29** *An orthographic drawing.*

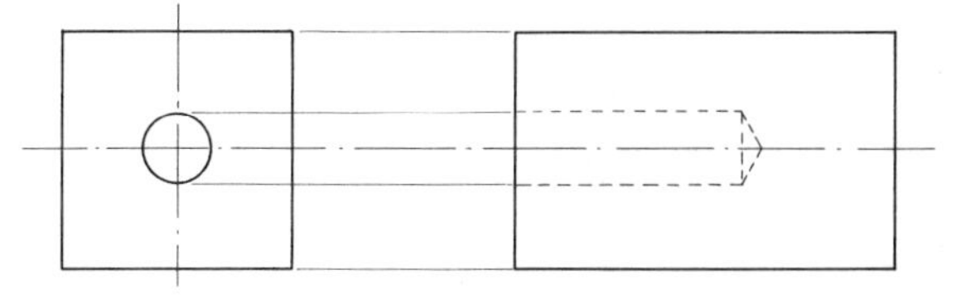

Figure **6·30** *Invisible outlines to show a hole in material.*

The three-view orthographic drawing of the object described in Fig. 6·28 is accomplished as shown in Fig. 6·29. Observe that projection lines from view 1 establish the positions of views 2 and 3. Observe that invisible outlines of a view are shown in the drawing by the dashed line established for this purpose. The note "invisible outline" shown in Fig. 6·29 is not included in standard drawings. Invisible outlines are also used to show a hole inside an object. This is illustrated in Fig. 6·30.

Oblique views

The oblique views such as **perspective** and **isometric** are not usually shown on engineering drawings. They are useful for the purposes of illustration to show three-dimensional configurations. A discussion of such views was given in the previous chapter.

DRAWING INFORMATION

On every engineering drawing, every shop sketch, and any drawing which is intended to convey information, the proper type of information must be supplied. This is accomplished by means of the title block, supplementary blocks, notes, dimensions, etc. The information supplied should be arranged in a standardized manner so it is readable and understandable by anyone using the drawing.

The title block

The **title block** was described and explained in the previous chapter, but it is well to consider important aspects of this device again. Title blocks for production drawings prepared for government contract items are described in MIL-STD-3A. This standard also describes other aspects of the drawing format. A typical title block for a drawing is shown in Fig. 6·31. This basic block is divided into subblocks marked *A*, *B*, *C*, *D*, and *E*.

The *A* section is the space provided for the name and address of the preparing agency. When a drawing is prepared by a contractor for issue as a government agency drawing, this space shows the name and address of only the cognizant government agency. When the government agency accepts a manufacturer's drawing, the manufacturer's name and address only appear in this block.

The portion of the block shown as *B* is the space provided for the title of the drawing. The *C* area is provided for the signatures necessary to record the preparation, checking, approval, and date of the drawing. Block *D* shows the area provided for the information on the scale of the drawing (dimensional scale), and block *E* can be used for weight information or for reference to a specification or other pertinent data.

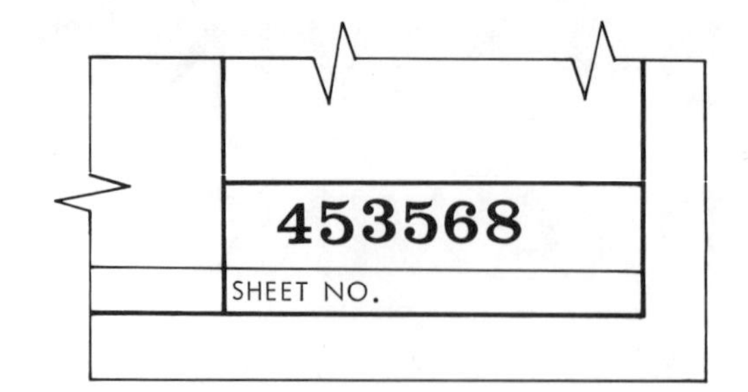

Figure **6·32** *Identification number.*

The lower right-hand section of the title-block area is used for the drawing number. Usually the first digit of the drawing number indicates the size of the paper used, that is, 1, 2, 4, etc. The digits following the first digit provide identification for the drawing and the part or parts shown on the drawing. The number is printed in large, bold letters as shown in Fig. 6·32.

Supplementary blocks

Supplementary blocks are used for dimensional notes, material, treatment, or finish. These blocks are located adjacent to the basic title block as shown in Fig. 6·33. The block marked *F* gives dimensional information, and the block *G* is used for a description of the material, reference to a specification, heat treatment, finish, etc.

List of materials

When it is desired to show a complete material record on a drawing by listing all the parts forming the assembly, a supplementary block can be located on the right-hand side of the drawing above the basic title block. This arrangement is shown in Fig. 6·34. The information shown in the illustration presents the minimum requirements necessary for the preparation of a complete ma-

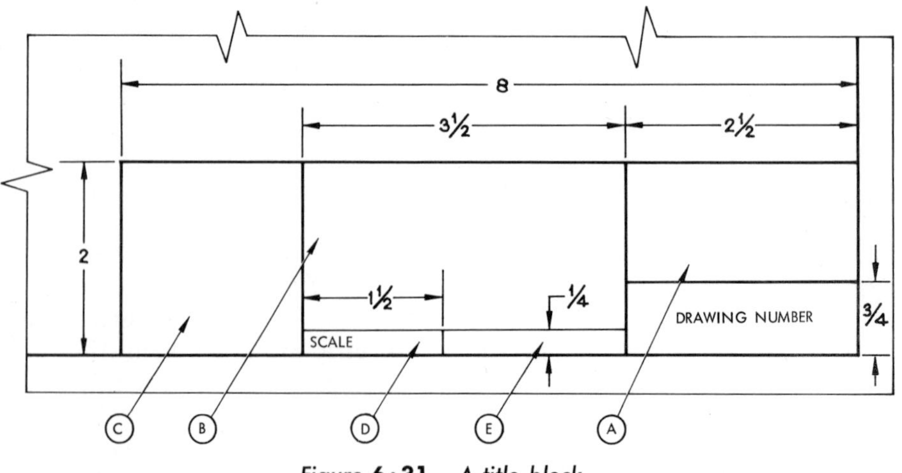

Figure **6·31** *A title block.*

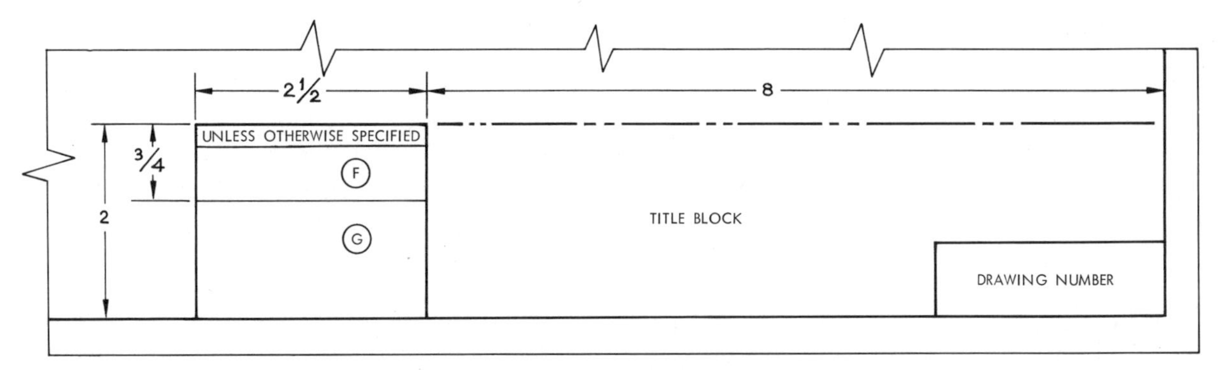

Figure 6·33 Supplementary blocks.

terial record. Additional columns can be included if required.

Parts included in the list of material which are detailed on other drawings need show only the quantity required, part number, description, and weight.

The REQD column shows the number of parts required to make one assembly such as that to which the list pertains. The PART NO. column shows the part number or applicable dash number of each part detailed on the drawing. Parts detailed on other drawings are listed by giving the drawing number and applicable dash number.

The DESCRIPTION column shows the name which clearly classifies the part. The MATL column shows the name or description of the material from which the part is to be made and may include the stock size. The MATL SPEC column identifies the applicable specification of the material from which the part is to be made.

The UNIT WT column, when required, shows the actual unit weight of the finished part. Where the actual weight is not available, the calculated weight can be entered, preceded by the abbreviation CALC.

On those drawings where it is desired to include information concerning the physical properties of the material, this information can be shown in another supplementary block such as that illustrated in Fig. 6·35.

When stock numbers for catalog identification of an item are required to be shown on a drawing, one such number can be included with the title of the drawing, or if there is more than one number, they can be placed in a tabular form within a supplementary block adjacent to the title block. Where a list of material is shown on the drawing, a column can be added to include the stock numbers or they can be indicated adjacent to an assembly view.

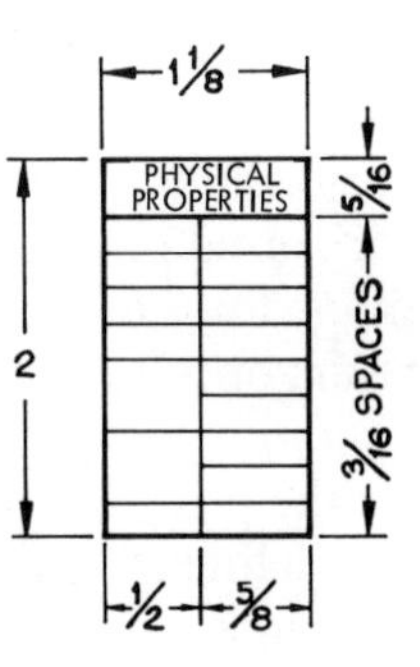

Figure 6·35 Supplementary block to show physical properties of materials.

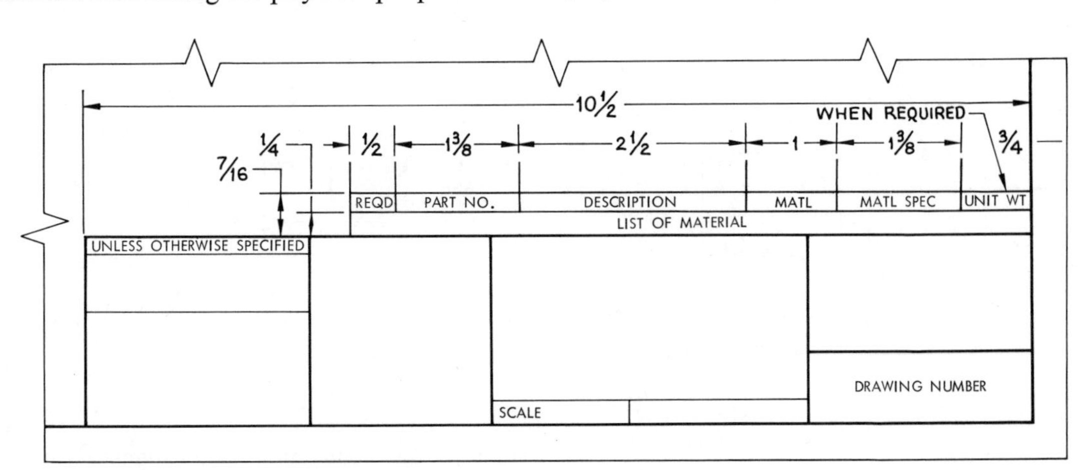

Figure 6·34 List of material.

Dimensioning

Methods of dimensioning and tolerancing are given in MIL-STD-8A. Dimensions are indicated by the use of lines, symbols, numerals, and notes on drawings to define geometric characteristics such as lengths, locations, diameters, and angles. It is important that the statement of a dimension be clear and permit only one interpretation. It is permissible to deviate from the ordinary rules of dimensioning in unusual instances only if clarity can be improved by so doing.

All dimensions should be complete without repetition. That is, each surface, line, or point is located by one, and only one, set of dimensions which is not repeated in other views.

Size, form, and location can be specified by means of two fundamental dimensional systems, rectangular dimensioning, and angular dimensioning. Both of these systems can be used on one drawing. However, any given surface or any given angle must be located only by the rectangular system or only by the angular system except where points of tangency are determined by radii.

In cases where no tolerance is shown, it is assumed that permissible variations in the dimensions are covered by a general tolerance note in a supplementary block.

Figure 6 • 36 illustrates the rectangular dimensioning system. In this system the extension lines for horizontal dimensions are placed in a vertical position and extension lines for vertical dimensions are placed in a horizontal position. All dimension numbers are arranged in horizontal lines so they can be read from the bottom of the drawing.

Angular dimensioning is shown in Fig. 6 • 37. It is used to indicate the position of a point, line, or surface by means of a linear dimension and angle, other than the 90° angle implied by the horizontal and vertical center lines. The advantage of angular dimensioning for certain drawings is shown in Fig. 6 • 38. It will be observed that the angular system is more suitable for this type of drawing. The rectangular method generally is preferred, especially when tolerances are close. However, where the angular system provides a better indication, it should be used. This is particularly true when specifying the location of several holes on a common arc or dimensioning graduations on a circular scale.

The dimensioning of curved surfaces is shown in Fig. 6 • 39. When it is desired to give the dimensions for the spacing of holes and other features

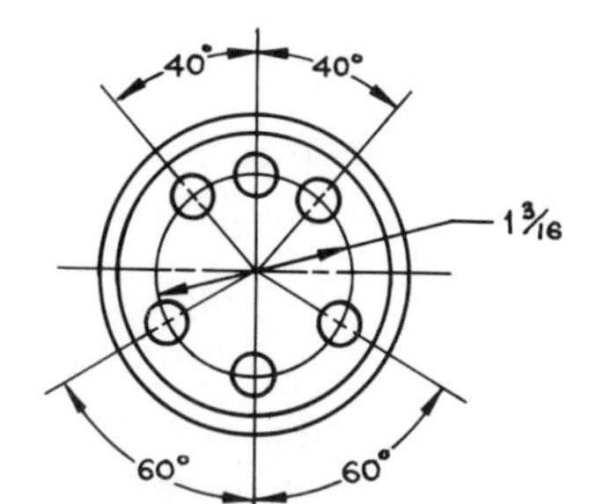

Figure **6 • 37** *Angular dimensioning.*

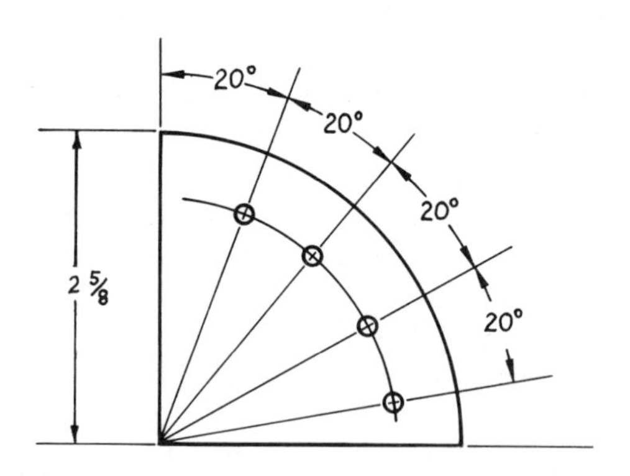

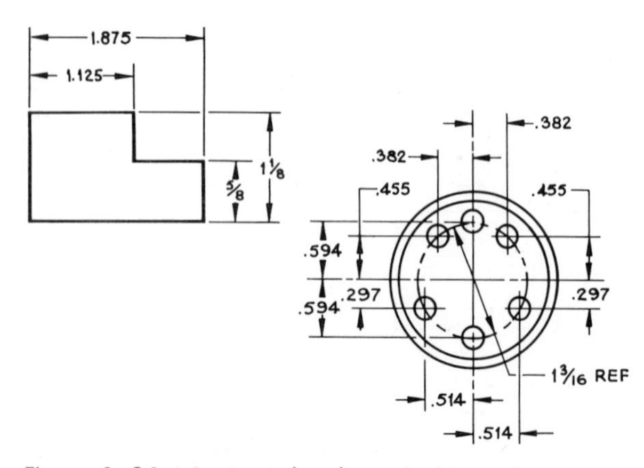

Figure **6 • 36** *Rectangular dimensioning system.*

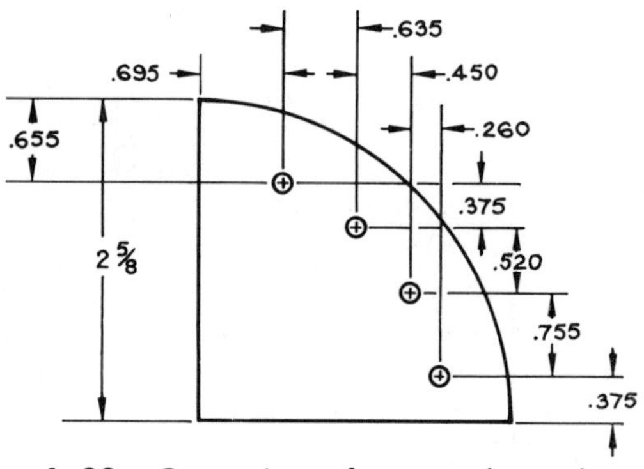

Figure **6 • 38** *Comparison of rectangular and angular systems.*

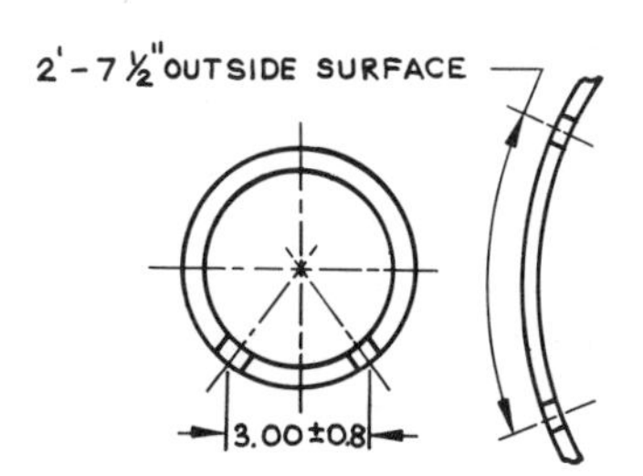

Figure **6·39** *Dimensioning curved surfaces.*

on such a surface, care should be taken to indicate clearly the surface on which the dimensioned points are to be measured and whether the dimensions are chordal or circumferential. A **chordal** dimension is a straight-line measurement between two points on a circle.

Application of dimensions and tolerances

The rules and practices established by MIL-STD-8A for the application of dimensions and tolerances to drawings provide an excellent guide for the draftsman or anyone preparing shop sketches, detail drawings, etc. The following rules generally agree with those established by the foregoing standard:

1. The thickness and composition of dimension, extension, center, and other lines are specified in MIL-STD-1A.
2. Dimension lines are used to show the extent of lengths, breadths, thicknesses, etc., to which the dimensions apply.
3. The spacing suitable for most drawings is about 3/8 in. between parallel dimension lines or between a dimension line and the outline of the object.
4. Extension lines are used to denote locations such as points or surfaces between which the dimension applies. They are drawn perpendicular to the dimension lines. However, when required, they may be drawn at an angle provided their starting point is not questionable. They must start generally about 1/16 in. from the outline of the part and extend about 1/8 in. beyond the outermost dimension line.
5. All numerals used for dimensioning and all lettering used for dimensional notes must conform to MIL-STD-1A, General Drawing Practice.
6. It is important to provide ample spacing between letters or numerals in order to prevent their becoming blurred when reproduced on a reduced scale. For the same reason decimal points should be slightly heavier than the lettering lines and must be properly spaced.
7. All dimensional notes should be placed on the drawing in accordance with MIL-STD-1A.
8. It is preferred that the tolerance be placed just to the right of the dimension and at the same level, but it is permissible to place the tolerance directly beneath the dimension. The numerals should be placed in a break of the dimension line, or when the numerals are parallel to the dimension line and written one above the other, the line may pass between them (see Fig. 6·40).
9. When limited space requires dimensions to be placed outside the extension lines, the dimensions and tolerances may be placed either in line with the dimension line or above and below its level, and in such case the dimension line should be extended to the dimension.
10. Center lines are used to indicate points and axes of symmetry. They may be extended to show relationships between symmetrical features and also to serve as extension lines for dimensional purposes.
11. Two center lines are drawn at right angles to each other in views showing the contour of a symmetrical feature in order to indicate the center of a circle. The lines have an actual intersection at the center.
12. A center line shall be dimensioned when it is used as a reference in locating related holes or features.
13. Leaders composed of straight ruled lines are used to indicate exactly where dimensions and dimensional or explanatory notes are to be applied. The note end of the leader is always run either to the beginning or to the end of the note or dimension, never to the middle.
14. Drawings will present a better appearance if all adjacent leaders are drawn parallel. However, leaders should not be parallel to adjacent dimension or extension lines.
15. Leaders drawn to symmetrical features should be in line with the center of the feature, and the arrowhead of the leader should terminate exactly on the line which represents the profile of the feature.
16. The unit of measurement on drawings is the inch unless other units are specifically indicated. Where there is a combination of units of measurements, the units must be expressed accord-

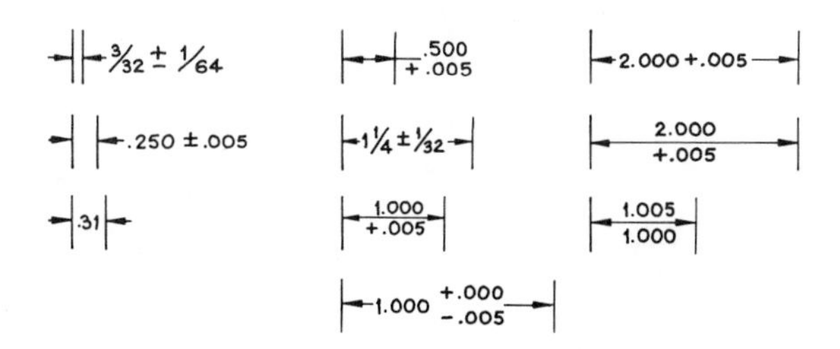

Figure **6·40** *Dimension lines and tolerances.*

ingly, but where the dimension is in units of inches only, the inch marks may be omitted.

17. Divisions of the inch may be expressed in terms of decimals or common fractions. Where it is desired to convert from fractions to decimals, a standard conversion table may be used.
18. The tolerances on decimal dimensions are expressed in decimals, and the tolerances on fractional dimensions are expressed in fractions.
19. The smallest fractional division used in dimensions is 1/64 and the smallest tolerance specified by a fraction is 1/64. Decimals are used when finer divisions must be made.
20. All dimensions expressed in terms of decimals are carried to the same number of places as the required tolerance. For example, use .050 −.005; do not use .05 −.005. The cipher is omitted before decimal points.
21. Angles are expressed in units of degrees, with divisions of minutes and seconds, or may be expressed as degrees, minutes, and decimals thereof.
22. Angular dimensions and their tolerances should contain the same unit of measurement. For example, use 10°30′0″ ± 0°0′30″ or 10°30.0′±0° .5′; do not use 10°30′±30″. It will be noted that this method follows that established for decimal dimensions as previously explained.
23. Indicate as many dimensions as practicable, without crowding, in the principal view. The principal view is the one which most completely shows the characteristic contour of the object. In general, all dimensions for surfaces which show in profile in this view should be given in this view. Dimensions are usually given in the auxiliary views only for those lines or surfaces which are not shown in their true shape in the principal view.
24. In general, crossing of lines used in dimensioning a drawing should be avoided wherever practicable.
25. To avoid crossing, the dimension line for the shortest length is placed nearest the outline of the object and adjacent parallel dimension lines are added in the order of their size, with the longest dimension line the outermost. This is illustrated in Fig. 6·41.
26. When crossing dimension lines with extension or leader lines is unavoidable, a break may be made in the extension or leader line at the point of crossing.
27. When it is necessary to cross an extension line, it is permissible to break the extension line to improve clarity.
28. Care should be taken to avoid crossing leaders, but where crossing is absolutely necessary, a break should be made in one of the leaders at the point of crossing.

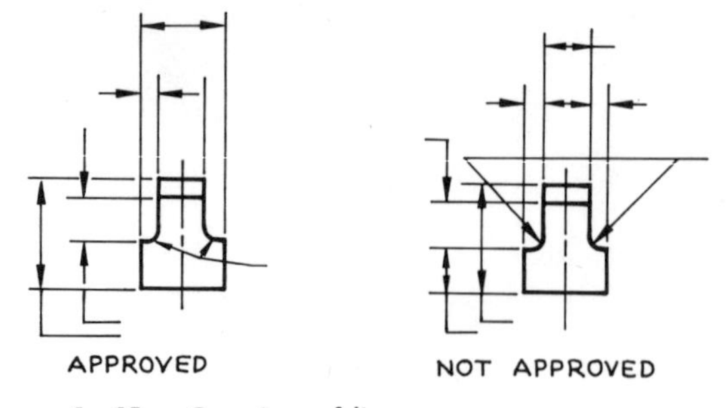

Figure **6·41** *Crossing of lines.*

29. When dimensions are grouped as shown in Fig. 6·42, clarity is improved by placing dimension lines and numerals in line where space permits.
30. When space is restricted, it is desirable to stagger columns of dimensions in two or more rows.
31. Wherever practicable, dimensions should be placed outside the view being dimensioned. In general, it will be found preferable to place overall dimensions above and to the right of the principal view. Overall dimensions of surfaces which show in profile in two views are preferably placed between these views.
32. The abbreviation DIA may be written after diametral dimensions in order to avoid showing an end view of a cylindrical object (see Fig. 6·43). However, the end view must be drawn if the cylindrical surface includes any special features such as keyways, flats, etc.
33. The size and location of holes and curved surfaces should be shown in view where they appear as circles or curves unless the abbreviation DIA is being used as mentioned before. An exception to this rule occurs where a sectional or side view is taken along the axis of two or more concentric cylindrical surfaces, in which case it usually

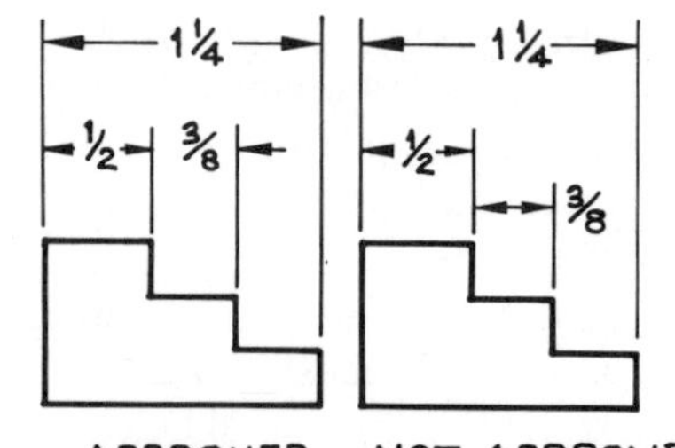

Figure **6·42** *Grouping of dimension lines.*

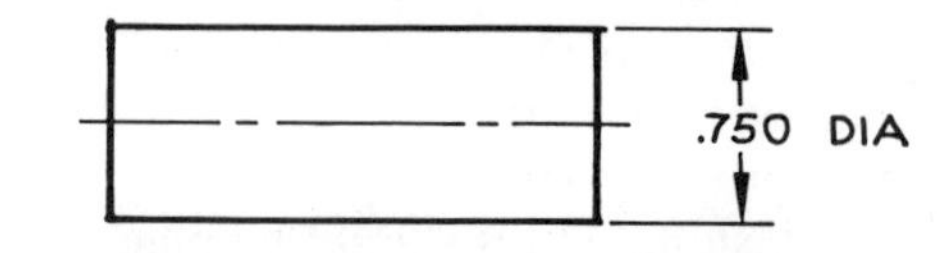

Figure **6·43** *Use of the abbreviation DIA.*

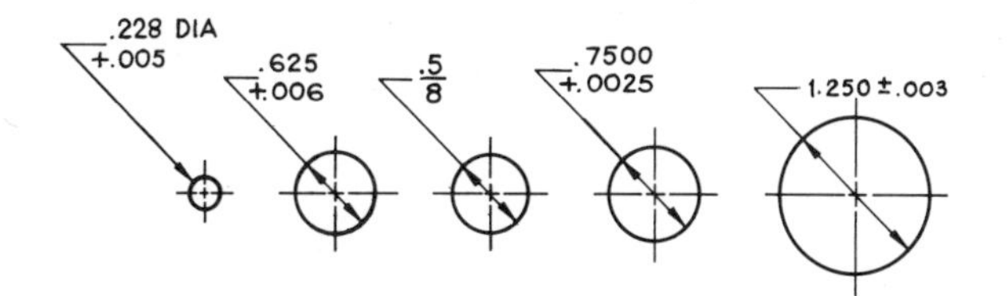

Figure 6·44 Dimensioning of holes.

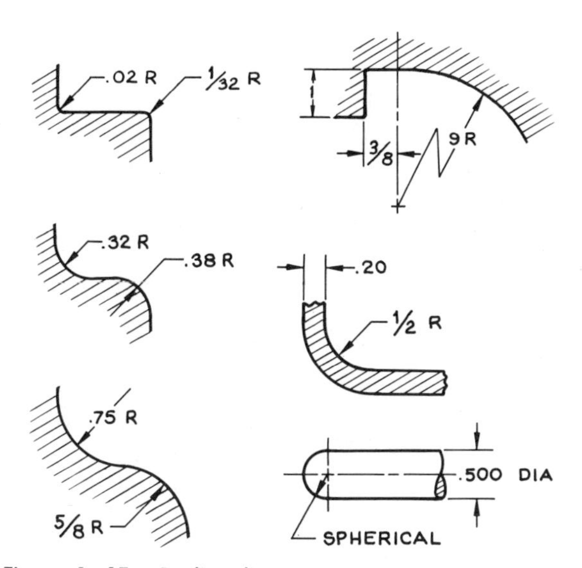

Figure 6·45 Radius dimensioning.

is clearer and more convenient to show the magnitude of the diameters in the sectional views.

34. Do not dimension to lines representing hidden surfaces or draw dimension lines directly to the outline of the object. Place dimensions between extension lines wherever practicable.
35. Specific information pertaining to holes is given by means of a leader drawn in the view where the hole appears as a circle. This is illustrated in Fig. 6·44.
36. Curved surfaces shown on arcs of circles are dimensioned by drawing a radial dimension line through the origin of the radius to the surface in question. On small radii, the radial dimension line may be drawn on the side opposite the center instead of through it. The letter *R* always follows the dimension of the radius. The preferred placement of the dimensions for various sizes and types of radii is shown in Fig. 6·45.
37. In specifying the dimensions of a large number of fillets and rounded edges of the same size, it is acceptable to specify them in the form of a note instead of dimensioning each individual radius.

There are many other rules and practices for the details of complex drawings; however, it is believed that the foregoing list will give the student a good understanding of dimensioning practices.

Tolerances

Tolerances have been explained to some extent in the chapter on "Blueprint Reading." However, additional information will be given here, including some of the general rules established by MIL-STD-8A.

To determine suitable tolerances, it is necessary first to establish the requirements to be imposed on the part involved, the tolerance which can be obtained under normal manufacturing processes, and the maximum tolerance which can be allowed without impairing the function of the product.

Tolerances should be assigned which are a reasonable compromise between those most desirable for functioning characteristics on the one hand and machining processes on the other. When tolerances are assigned to commercially available stock such as drill rod, plate, bars, etc., consideration should be given to the commercial tolerances available, and if requirements permit, the specific tolerances should not be closer than those commercially available.

There are three methods by which the maximum and minimum values of a dimension may be indicated on a drawing. They are classified as the **unilateral tolerance, bilateral tolerance,** and **limit dimensioning** methods. In the unilateral method the tolerance is taken all plus or all minus from an explicitly stated dimension. The dimension represents the size or location which is nearest the critical condition (maximum material condition), and the tolerance is applied in either a plus or minus direction, but not in both directions, in such a way that the permissible variation in size or location will be away from the critical condition. This method is illustrated in Fig. 6·46.

In the bilateral method the dimension indicates the preferred or desired size or location and the tolerance indicates the permissible variations therefrom. These variations are not necessarily required to be equal in both directions. This method is illustrated in Fig. 6·47. If variations in size or position are not more critical in one direction than the other, the mean position or size

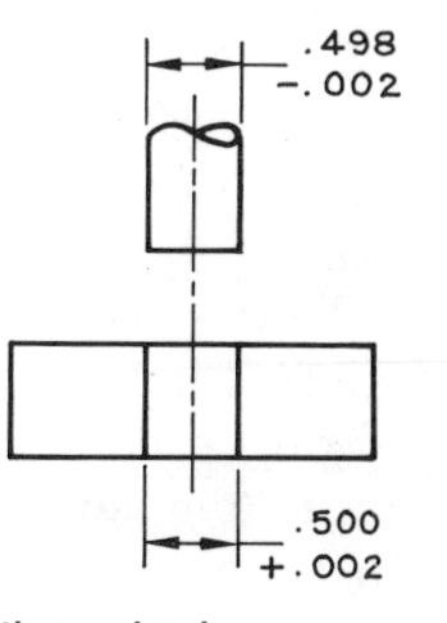

Figure 6·46 Unilateral tolerances.

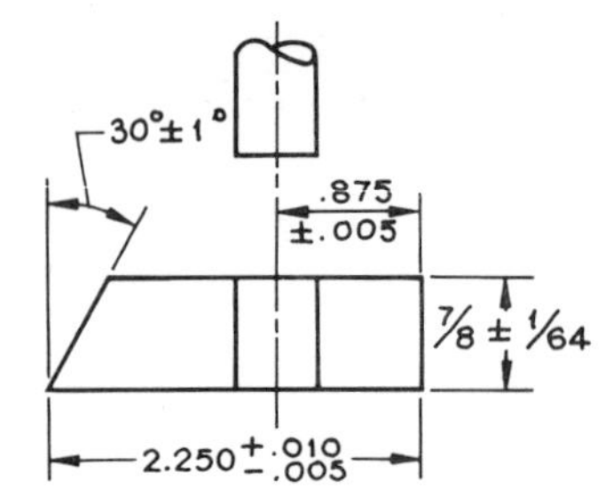

Figure **6·47** *Bilateral tolerances.*

should be taken for the stated dimension and equal tolerances assigned for each direction.

In the limit dimensioning method the maximum and minimum permissible values for a dimension are stated specifically to indicate the size or location of the element in question. In the case of location dimensions the high limit (maximum dimension) is placed above the dimension line and the low limit (minimum dimension) is placed below the line. In the case of size dimensions, the limit representing the maximum material condition is placed above the dimension line and the limit representing the minimum material condition is placed below the line. When the limits are specified in the form of a note, the dimension which otherwise would appear above the line precedes the other.

The direction in which tolerances are to be taken is indicated by placing at the left of the tolerance one of the symbols +, −, or ±. Tolerances, like dimensions, are applied in such a way as to provide all essential information without duplication. All dimensions applied to the drawing, except dimensions labeled **basic, datum, reference, maximum,** or **minimum,** must have an exact tolerance, either applied directly to the dimension or indicated by means of a general tolerance note, other notes, or referenced associated documents. It is advisable to specify in the general tolerance note the tolerances which are most generally applicable.

TYPES OF DRAWINGS

Detail drawings

A **detail drawing** is a drawing of a small part of a larger assembly. For example, a bulkhead in a missile may consist of flat sheet parts, angular brackets, angle stiffeners, and various other components. The detail drawing will give all the information required for the production of each of the parts. This will include material, all dimensions, heat treatment (if required), identification numbers, related drawing numbers, and any other information needed.

Assembly drawings

Assembly drawings are made up from the information contained in detail drawings. The purpose of an assembly drawing is to show how the detail parts are to be put together. The assembly drawing does not show the dimensions of the detail parts except as necessary for location purposes. Assembly drawings are often drawn to reduced scale because of the size of the assemblies. An assembly which is 6 ft wide may be drawn to one-fourth scale and would measure 18 in. on the drawing.

Production drawings

Any detail or assembly drawing used for the production of parts or assemblies may be classified as a **production drawing.** A production drawing must have been checked and approved for release to the production department before it can be used for production, and it must be up to date on revisions and changes.

Shop sketches

A shop sketch may be anything from a simple line drawing such as that shown in Fig. 6·48 to a rather complex and detailed drawing something like a standard engineering drawing. The purpose of a shop sketch is to convey information concerning the repair of a part or structure, to illustrate a proposed modification, to provide information for engineering draftsmen from which they can make standard engineering drawings, and for various other uses where an illustration is necessary to convey technical information. Due care should be exercised in the preparation of a shop sketch so it will present a good appearance, the information it contains is complete and accurate, and it conveys the information which it is intended to convey. The principles of drafting described in this chapter can be used to good advantage in the preparation of shop sketches.

REVIEW QUESTIONS

1. How is drawing paper usually fastened to a drawing board?
2. What precaution is taken to assure that the drawing is square on the paper?
3. Describe the use of a T square.
4. What is the purpose of the engineer's scale (rule)?
5. Describe a drafting machine.

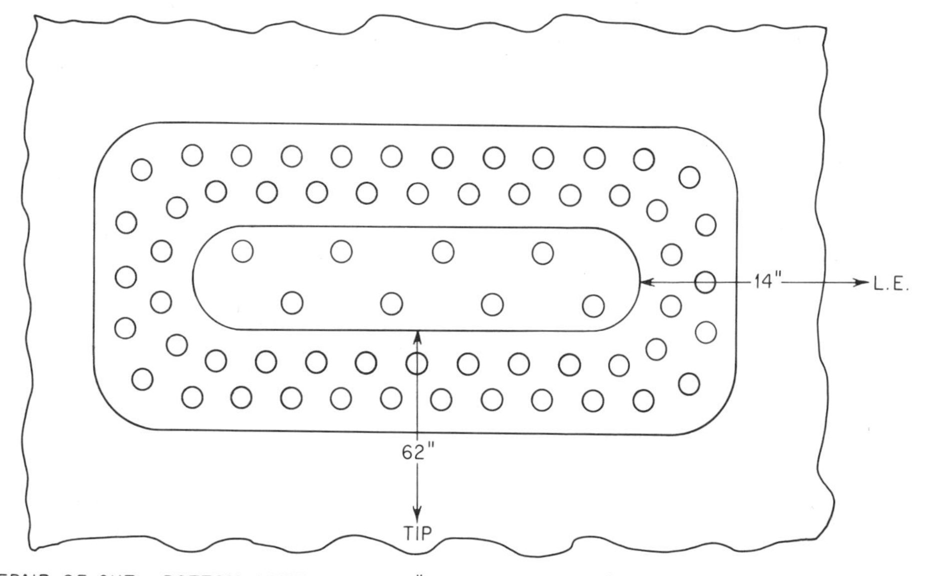

REPAIR OF CUT — BOTTOM, LEFT WING — 14" REAR OF L.E.—62" INBOARD OF WING TIP — CUT 3 7/8" — DAMAGED MATERIAL CUT OUT-SKIN MATERIAL — 2024-T3 —0.032" ALCLAD — PATCH SAME MATERIAL—RIVETS-AN 426-AD-4-3 —PATTERN EXCEEDS ORIGINAL IN STRENGTH PATCH INSIDE WING—SKIN MADE FLUSH WITH PLUG

Figure **6·48** *A shop sketch.*

6. How are drawing triangles used in mechanical drawing?
7. What is the purpose of a French curve?
8. What is the advantage of using a template in drawing?
9. What are the principal units in a drawing instrument set?
10. Give another name for the paper used in engineering drawings.
11. What pencil hardness is most commonly used for lines?
12. Explain the importance of proper pencil pointing (point sharpening).
13. Under what conditions does the maintenance technician find a knowledge of drawing practices useful?
14. What is the essential equipment for making an acceptable drawing?
15. Why is a drawing pencil rotated while drawing a line?
16. Explain the use of a compass.
17. What is the purpose of a ruling pen?
18. What precautions must be taken in the use of a ruling pen?
19. Why is it important that the lines in a pencil drawing be solid and black?
20. What does the draftsman do to assure that lines of lettering are straight and that the letters are of uniform size?
21. How does the draftsman vary the width of lines?
22. What document provides the standards for dimensioning?
23. What is meant by a *rectangular* dimensioning system?
24. Compare *detail* drawings and *assembly* drawings.
25. What is the value of a shop sketch?

CHAPTER 7

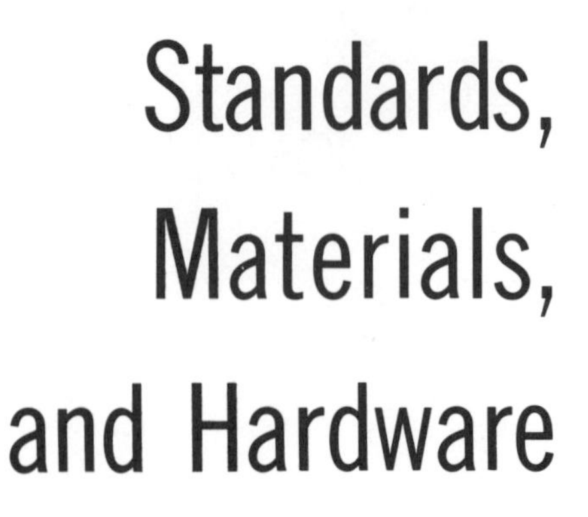

Standards, Materials, and Hardware

STANDARDS AND SPECIFICATIONS

In the production of aircraft, missiles, space vehicles, or any other device for which specific performance and quality requirements are established, it is necessary that standards and specifications be followed. Generally speaking, standards and specifications establish quality, size, shape, performance, strength, finish, materials used, and numerous other conditions for the manufacture and design of aerospace vehicles and their components. Because of the almost infinite number of sizes, shapes, materials, etc., involved in mechanical devices, a wide variety of standards and specifications have been developed covering hardware, metals, plastics, coatings, nonmetallics, and manufactured components.

In order to provide measures of uniformity, the military services, technical societies, manufacturers, and other agencies have attempted to establish uniform standards which would be universally acceptable for particular materials, products, dimensions, etc.

A **standard** is variously defined as (1) **something established for use as a rule or basis of comparison in measuring or judging capacity, quantity, content, extent, value, quality, etc.**; (2) **a level or grade of excellence;** (3) **any measure of extent, quality, or value established by law or by general usage or consent.**

A **specification** may be defined as **a particular and detailed account or description of a thing; specifically, a statement of particulars, describing the dimensions, details, or peculiarities of any work about to be undertaken, as in architecture, building, engineering, or manufacturing.**

For government procurement purposes a specification is a purchase document that contains (1) a clear, accurate description of the technical requirements for a product, material, or service; (2) the procedure used to determine that the requirements have been met; and (3) the packaging requirements.

Standards

In the normal performance of his duties a technician will encounter an extensive array of standards establishing the characteristics of the materials and components which he may use from day to day in repair and maintenance work. Among these standards are AC (Air Corps), AF (Air Force), AN (Army and Navy or Air Force and Navy), AND (Air Force–Navy Aeronautical Design), MS (Military Standard), NAS (National Aircraft Standard), NAF (Naval Aircraft Factory), and AS (Aeronautical Standard).

AC standards are not generally used at present because they have been replaced by standards which are more applicable to modern items. Hydraulic fittings were manufactured before World War II according to AC standards, and some of these are still to be found, especially on older airplanes. Such fittings are now found to be covered by AN and MS standards. For example, an elbow fitting having a pipe thread on one end and a flared tube thread on the other end is designated by AN822. The size of the fitting is indicated by dash numbers following the design number.

AF standards have been used for parts limited to Air Force use. These are not often found among modern materials because almost all items are now covered by more popular standards.

The most widely used standards for aircraft and missile hardware are the AN and MS standards. As pointed out above, these standards have been established as approved by the Air Force and the Navy Bureau of Aeronautics. Items manufactured according to these are not limited to use by the Air Force and Navy but are found in all classifications of aircraft including those certificated by the FAA. Typical AN parts are bolts, nuts, washers, screws, rivets, cable fittings, etc. The following is a list of a few typical AN standard items which should be familiar to all technicians working on aircraft and missiles:

AN3 through AN20	Bolt, machine, aircraft
AN21 through AN36	Bolt, clevis
AN42 through AN49	Bolt, eye
AN60	Bolt, hexagon head, fine thread
AN65	Bolt, hexagon head, coarse thread
AN70	Bolt, carriage
AN73 through AN81	Bolt, aircraft, drilled head
AN100	Thimble, wire cable
AN111	Bushing, cable
AN115	Shackle, cable
AN130 through AN170	Turnbuckles and parts
AN173 through AN186	Bolts, aircraft, close tolerance
AN200 through AN213	Bearings, ball
AN214	Pulley, control, plain bearing
AN219 through AN221	Pulleys, control, aircraft
AN226 through AN229	Fasteners
AN230	Grommet, metallic
AN231	Grommet, drainage, plastic
AN250 through AN253	Hinges
AN280	Key, Woodruff
AN286 and AN287	Fitting, lubricator, pressure-grip
AN290	Cup, oil
AN301	Nail, flathead
AN310	Nut, castellated, airframe
AN315	Nut, plain, airframe
AN325	Nut, plain hex, fine thread
AN335	Nut, plain hex, coarse thread
AN350	Nut, wing
AN355	Nut, engine, slotted
AN363	Nut, self-locking, 550°F
AN365	Nut, self-locking (elastic stop nut)
AN366	Nut, plate, noncountersunk, 250°F
AN380	Cotter pin, steel
AN385	Cotter pin, stainless steel
AN386	Pin, tapered, threaded
AN392 through AN406	Pin, flathead
AN420	Rivet, countersunk head
AN426	Rivet, countersunk head, 100°
AN430	Rivet, roundhead
AN442	Rivet, flathead
AN455	Rivet, brazier head
AN456	Rivet, modified brazier head
AN458	Rivet, blind, countersunk head
AN470	Rivet, universal head
AN500	Screw, machine, fillister head, coarse
AN501	Screw, machine, fillister head, fine
AN509	Screw, machine, flathead, 100°
AN520	Screw, machine, roundhead, fine thread
AN545	Screw, wood, roundhead
AN658 through AN669	Terminal, cable, for swaging
AN671 through AN708	Tie rods
AN737	Clamp, hose
AN757 through AN849	Fittings, hose and tube
AN935	Washer, lock, spring
AN960	Washer, flat
AN970	Washer, flat, large area

Some of the above listed items are illustrated in Fig. 7·1. It must be understood that there are hundreds of additional items under AN standards.

Some of the common items covered by MS standards are listed below, and a few are illustrated in Fig. 7·2. Technicians should be generally familiar with MS standards and should know where to obtain MS standard parts.

MS9013	Ring, retaining, external, steel
MS13928	Expander, piston ring, oil
MS13953	Piston, aluminum, 4 by 4¾ in.
MS13963	Bushing, piston pin
MS13964	Bearing, main, flanged, 2⅞ by 3¼ in.
MS13996	Pin, piston
MS15002	Fitting, lubrication
MS15249	Fuse, cartridge, ferrule contact
MS16251	Attachment, crowfoot wrench
MS20000	Turnbuckle assembly, pin eye
MS20602	Rivet, blind, explosive, brazier head
MS21905	Fitting, tee, flareless tube
MS24585	Spring, compression, helical
MS28775	Packing, O ring, hydraulic
MS35489	Grommet, rubber, hot-oil resistant

The NAF standards are those which were developed and approved for use by the Naval Aircraft Factory. Items or parts manufactured under these standards are almost all covered by AN or MS standards at the present time. If an NAF number is called out for a particular part in an older airplane, it is likely that a comparable part can be found under an AN or MS standard;

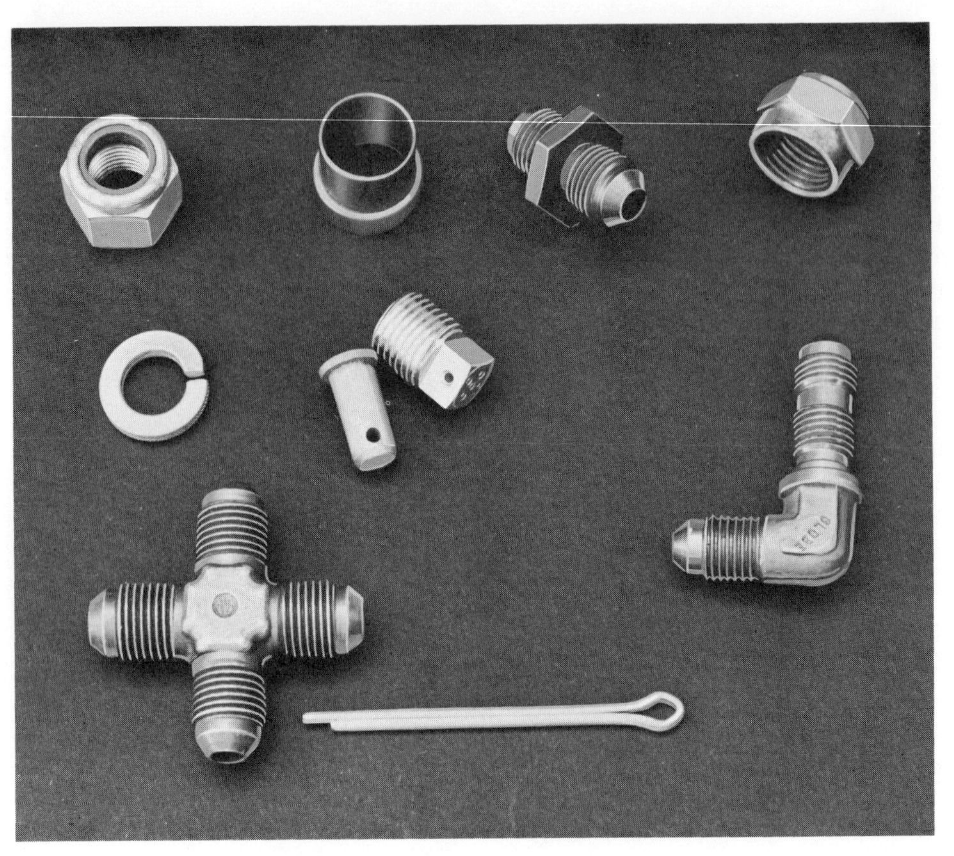

Figure 7 · 1 A few AN standard parts.

hence there should be no difficulty in obtaining a replacement.

AND standards are generally of more interest to the engineer than the technician because they are concerned principally with design. It is well, however, that the technician know the meaning and purpose of AND standards.

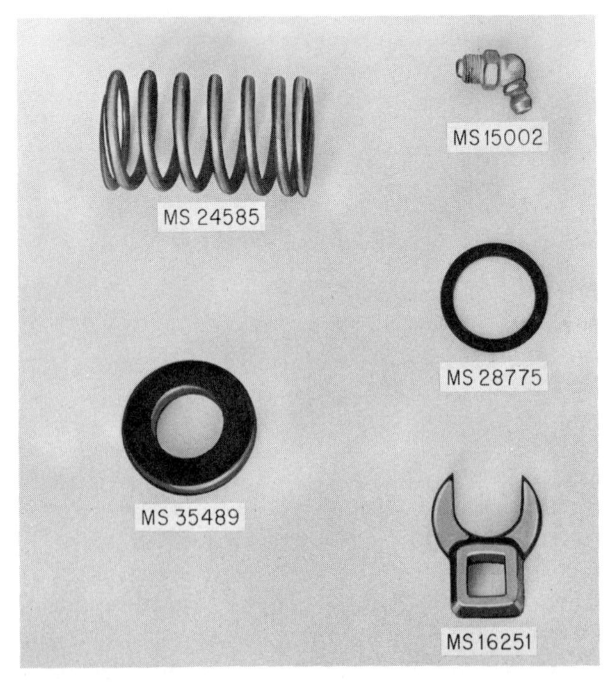

Figure 7 · 2 MS standard parts.

When manufactured items have not yet been covered by other standards, it is common practice for the manufacturers to assign NAS (National Aircraft Standard) numbers to them. If the item later comes into general use, it will probably be placed under an AN or MS standard.

AS (Aeronautical Standards) have been established by the Society of Automotive Engineers (SAE). They include design standards, parts standards, and specifications which have not already been assigned AMS (Aeronautical Materials Specifications) numbers. Materials manufactured under AMS specifications are often required for use on civil aircraft by the FAA; for example, grade A fabric used for covering aircraft is designated AMS3806.

Industry standards

In addition to the standards previously described, industry organizations have also developed standards and specifications which are not necessarily covered by other standards. The American Society for Testing and Materials (ASTM) is one of the most active organizations in the establishment of material standards.

The American Standards Association (ASA)

is a federation of other organizations. Its function is to serve as a clearinghouse for standards. When a standard is established by the ASA, the item standardized is generally accepted by all groups concerned with the particular item.

One of the leading organizations concerned with standards for iron and steel products is the American Iron and Steel Institute (AISI). Standards established for iron and steel products are therefore designated by AISI numbers. Many iron and steel products are also covered by standards issued from the SAE, ASA, and ASTM. Special types of products are also standardized by the Alloy Casting Institute (ACI), the Investment Casting Institute (ICI), the Gray Iron Founders' Society (GIFS), the Steel Founders' Society of America (SFSA), and the Metal Powder Association.

The SAE, ASA, and ASTM are concerned with almost all types of materials used in the aircraft and missile field. Other organizations concern themselves with limited fields such as iron and steel, nonferrous metals, plastics and rubber, nonmetallics, and finishes and coatings.

Military specifications

Of greatest concern to persons working in the aircraft and missile field are the military specifications for materials and products. Such specifications are designated MIL followed by a letter and a number. For example, the specification for standard aircraft cable, 7 by 19, carbon steel, is MIL-C-5424. MIL is the abbreviation for military, C is the first letter of the first word in the title of the specification (cable), and 5424 is the basic serial number. The number could be followed by a letter, which would indicate a revision in the basic specification.

MATERIALS

Ferrous metals

Ferrous metals are those whose principal content is iron (Latin, *ferrum*), such as cast iron, steels, and similar products. Because of the vast number of different steels and steel alloys, we shall not attempt to describe more than a few of the more commonly used types.

A large percentage of the steels used for general aircraft work are of the wrought type and are designated as shown in Table 7·1.

Table 7·1 SAE Identification for Wrought Steels

Carbon Steels	
10xx	Nonsulfurized carbon steel (plain carbon)
11xx	Resulfurized carbon steel (free machining)
12xx	Resulfurized and rephosphorized carbon steel
Alloy Steels	
13xx	Manganese 1.75% (1.60–1.90%)
23xx	Nickel 3.50%
25xx	Nickel 5.00%
31xx	Nickel-chromium (Ni 1.25%, Cr 0.65%)
32xx	Nickel-chromium (Ni 1.75%, Cr 1.00%)
33xx	Nickel-chromium (Ni 3.50%, Cr 1.50%)
40xx	Molybdenum 0.25%
41xx	Chromium-molybdenum (Cr 0.50 or 0.95%, Mo 0.12 or 0.20%)
43xx	Nickel-chromium-molybdenum (Ni 1.80%, Cr 0.50 or 0.80%, Mo 0.25%)
46xx	Nickel-molybdenum (Ni 1.75%, Mo 0.25%)
47xx	Nickel-chromium-molybdenum (Ni 1.05%, Cr 0.45%, Mo 0.20%)
48xx	Nickel-molybdenum (Ni 3.50%, Mo 0.25%)
50xx	Chromium 0.28 or 0.40%
51xx	Chromium 0.80, 0.90, 0.95, 1.00, or 1.05%
5xxxx	Chromium 0.50, 1.00, or 1.45%, Carbon 1.00%
61xx	Chromium-vanadium (Cr 0.80 or 0.95%, V 0.10 or 0.15%)
86xx	Nickel-chromium-molybdenum (Ni 0.55 or 0.05 or 0.65%, Mo 0.20%)
87xx	Nickel-chromium-molybdenum (Ni 0.55%, Cr 0.50%, Mo 0.25%)
92xx	Manganese-silicon (Mn 0.85%, Si 2.00%)
93xx	Nickel-chromium-molybdenum (Ni 3.25%, Cr 1.20%, Mo 0.12%)
98xx	Nickel-chromium-molybdenum (Ni 1.00%, Cr 0.80%, Mo 0.25%)

In addition to the standard group of wrought-carbon and alloy steels, a substantial number of heat- and corrosion-resistant steels are used in aircraft and missiles. The principal designations for these steels are given in Table 7·2.

Table 7·2 AISI Identification for Heat- and Corrosion-resistant Steels

2xx	Chromium-nickel-manganese (nonhardenable, austenitic, nonmagnetic)
3xx	Chromium-nickel (nonhardenable, austenitic, nonmagnetic)
4xx	Chromium (hardenable, martensitic, magnetic)
4xx	Chromium (hardenable, ferritic, magnetic)
5xx	Chromium (low chromium, heat-resisting)

In Table 7·1, the first digit of each number indicates the general classification of the steel, that is, carbon, nickel, etc. The number 1 indicates a carbon steel. The second digit of the number indicates the approximate percentage of the principal alloying element; for example, a 2330 steel contains more than 3 per cent nickel. The last two digits of the number indicate the approximate amount of carbon in hundredths of 1 per cent.

One of the most important considerations for ordinary carbon steel is the quantity of carbon it contains. A low-carbon steel contains 0.10 to 0.15 per cent carbon. Medium-carbon steels contain 0.20 to 0.30 per cent carbon. The higher the carbon content of steel, the greater are its hardness and also its brittleness. High-carbon steels are used for cutting tools, springs, etc. For general purposes, low or medium steels are best because they are more easily worked, they are tougher, and they have a much greater impact resistance. Such steels were used for many years in the manufacture of aircraft structures and fittings.

Probably the most commonly used steel for general aircraft structural purposes today is **SAE 4130 chromium-molybdenum (chrome-moly) steel.** When properly heat-treated, it is approximately four times as strong as 1025 mild-carbon steel. SAE 4130 chrome-molybdenum steel is easily worked, readily weldable by any method, hardenable, heat-treatable, easily machined, and well adapted to high-temperature conditions of service. The technician should remember the name and number of this steel because he is likely to use it often in the repair of aircraft.

Nickel steels, SAE 23xx and 25xx, contain from 3.5 to 5 per cent nickel and a small percentage of carbon. The nickel increases the strength, hardness, and elasticity of the steel without appreciably affecting the ductility. Nickel steel is used for making various aircraft hardware including nuts, bolts, clevis pins, and screws.

Nickel-chromium and chromium-vanadium steels are used where still greater strength, hardness, and toughness are required. Such steels are often found in highly stressed machine parts such as gears, shafts, springs, bearings, etc.

It is not essential that the technician know the type of steel used in a particular factory-made part. However, if he needs to fabricate a steel part which is no longer available, he must make sure that it is made from a material as good or better than the original and that it is properly stress-relieved and heat-treated if such treatment is necessary to provide the correct degree of hardness and strength. The nature and temper of the original part can often be determined by means of a Rockwell or Brinnell hardness tester.

Corrosion-resistant (stainless) steels

During the past two decades the term "stainless steel" has become a household word because of its many applications in consumer items as well as in aircraft and missiles. The development of stainless steel has made possible many of the outstanding advances in aircraft, jet engines, rockets, and missiles. The most important characteristics of stainless steels are corrosion resistance, strength, toughness, and resistance to high temperatures.

Stainless steels can be divided into three general groups based on their structures: (1) **austenitic,** (2) **ferritic,** and (3) **martensitic.**

The austenitic steels are chromium (Cr)-nickel (Ni) and chromium-nickel-manganese alloys. They can be hardened only by cold-working, and heat treatment serves only to anneal them. They are nonmagnetic in the annealed condition, although some may be slightly magnetic after cold-working.

Austenitic steels are formed by heating the steel mixture above the critical range and holding to form a structure called **austenite.** A controlled period of partial cooling is allowed followed by a rapid quench just above the critical range.

Ferritic steels contain no carbon; hence they do not respond to heat treatment. They contain a substantial amount of chromium and may have a small amount of aluminum. They are always magnetic.

Martensitic steels are straight chromium alloys which harden intensely if they are allowed to cool rapidly from high temperatures. They differ from the two preceding groups because they can be hardened by heat treatment.

The most widely used stainless steels for general use are those in the 300 series, called 18-8 because they contain approximately 18 per cent chromium and 8 per cent nickel. Typical of these types are 301, 302, 321, and 347.

Although stainless steels have many advantages, there are certain disadvantages which must be faced by the fabricator and designer. (1) Stainless steels are more difficult to cut and form than many materials. (2) Stainless steels have a much greater expansion coefficient than other steels, and they conduct heat at a lower rate. This makes welding more difficult. (3) Many of the stainless steels lose their corrosion resistance under high temperatures.

Aluminum and its alloys

Since the days of the "stick and wire" airplanes, aluminum has been the principal structural metal for aircraft. Pure aluminum was much too soft for structural use, so alloys were developed to provide for the strength and stiffness required. The most widely used alloy was originally designated 24ST and is now 2024-T3 and 2024-T4. The T3 and T4 are temper designations which will be more fully explained later. When structural aluminum alloys first came into use, they were called "duraluminum" or "dural." These were bare alloys and were subject to considerable corrosion unless specially treated. Eventually the corrosion problem was largely solved by the process of "cladding." This consisted of rolling a thin layer of pure aluminum on the outer surface of both sides of the alloy sheet. Since pure aluminum is highly resistant to corrosion because of a very thin layer of oxide which forms on the surface immediately upon exposure to the air, the surface of the clad material is effectively protected. The trade name for aluminum alloy sheet prepared in this manner by the Aluminum Company of America is Alclad.

Aluminum and aluminum alloys are designated by a four-digit system with the first digit of the number indicating the principal alloying element. Standard aluminum alloys are given in Table 7·3.

Table 7·3

Number	*Alloy Type*
1100	Pure aluminum
2014	Copper, silicon, manganese, magnesium
2017	Copper
2020	Copper and lithium
2024	Copper plus manganese and magnesium
2117	Copper (modified)
2219	Copper plus manganese, vanadium, and zirconium
2618	Copper, iron, magnesium, nickel, titanium
3003	Manganese
4043	Silicon
5052	Magnesium
6061	Magnesium and silicon
7075	Zinc, magnesium, copper, chromium
7079	Zinc, magnesium, copper, iron, silicon

The foregoing list does not include all the aluminum alloys, but those most commonly used are listed. The alloys shown have a wide variety of characteristics; hence each one has particular applications.

Another factor important for aluminum alloys is the temper or hardness value. Heat-treatable alloys are followed by the letter T and a number to indicate the type and degree of heat treatment. Non-heat-treatable alloys are followed by the letter O to indicate soft or annealed condition or H and a number to indicate the degree of work-hardening. For example, 1100-H12 indicates one-fourth hardened while 1100-H18 indicates that the aluminum is fully hardened. With the 5052 alloy, H38 is the fully hardened condition.

The most commonly used aluminum alloys for aircraft and missile structures are 2024-T3 and -T4 and 7075-T6. Where elevated temperatures are encountered, other aluminum alloys or other types of metal may be used.

Pure aluminum (1100) and the softer alloys (3003 and 5052) are generally used for tubing, junction boxes, nonstressed panels, deep-drawn parts, or other parts which require considerable forming but are not subjected to high loads. These materials are easily worked and readily weldable.

The alloy 2014 is particularly well adapted to the manufacture of forged parts requiring high strength.

The alloys 2117, 2024, and 7075 are all used for structural rivets. The 2024 and 7075 rivets require heat treatment before driving.

Aluminum alloy sheet as it comes from the manufacturer is usually marked with letters and numbers in rows about 5 in. apart. These identification symbols may include a Federal specification number, the alloy number with temper designation, and the thickness of the material in thousandths of an inch.

Magnesium

Magnesium alloys are used frequently in aircraft and missile structures in cast, forged, and sheet form. The greatest advantage of magnesium is that it is one of the lightest metals for its strength.

The disadvantages in the use of magnesium sheet are that it is more subject to corrosion than many metals, it is not easily worked at room temperatures, and if it becomes ignited, it is extremely difficult to extinguish.

When magnesium is used in an airplane structure, it can often be recognized by the fact that it has a yellowish surface due to the chromate treatment used to prevent corrosion and furnish a suitable paint base. When the technician encounters magnesium in an aircraft, he must know that it cannot be cut easily but is likely to tear, it cannot be bent or otherwise worked under normal temperatures, it is subject to corrosion and therefore should be treated with the proper coating, and it presents a certain degree of fire hazard.

When standard parts are made of magnesium, this fact will usually be stated in the manufacturer's overhaul and service manuals. Also in the manuals will be the directions for the proper treatment of such parts.

Titanium

Since the isolation of titanium in pure form in 1945, its use has increased tremendously, especially in aircraft and missiles where high temperatures are encountered and light weight is required.

Titanium is light, strong, and ductile. In density it falls between aluminum and steel, being 56 per cent of the weight of steel while aluminum is 35 per cent of the weight of steel. It is twice as strong as the better aluminum alloys and is superior or comparable to all but the highest strength steels. In relation to its density, its strength is unsurpassed among structural metals. Not only is titanium strong, but it retains its useful strength and favorable strength/weight ratio at temperatures up to 800°F. This is far above the service temperature range for aluminum alloys.

One of the most outstanding properties of titanium is its resistance to corrosive substances, including some of the most troublesome industrial chemicals. It is uniquely resistant to inorganic chloride solutions, chlorinated organic compounds, chlorine solutions, and moist chlorine gas. It also has excellent resistance to oxidizing acids such as nitric or chromic acids. Strong reducing acids, however, will attack titanium. The resistance of titanium to corrosion by natural environmental substances is unequaled by other structural metals. It is completely inert when exposed to stagnant water, urban atmosphere, marine atmosphere, salt-water spray, and sea water.

Titanium has a very low thermal coefficient of expansion, being much lower than other structural metals such as monel metal or stainless steel. The thermal conductivity is approximately the same as that of stainless steel. The low thermal-expansion coefficient simplifies the design of complex structures made with titanium because it is unnecessary to make such large allowances for expansion as those required for the metals with high expansion coefficients. Table 7·4 gives some characteristics of titanium alloys.

Titanium is used extensively in both military and commercial aircraft and in missiles because of its high strength/weight ratio, freedom from stress corrosion and cracking, its ability to withstand high operating stress, and its high temperature resistance. It is used for major aircraft structures, engines, and numerous small parts and components.

An example of the use of titanium in missiles is the Project Mercury space capsule manufactured by the McDonnell Aircraft Company. Selected for the internal skin of the capsule was commercially pure titanium with usable strengths up to 900°F. Hat section stringers are fabricated from titanium alloy Ti-5A1-2.5Sn, a medium-strength alloy providing excellent weldability, resistance to oxidation up to 1200°F, and a fatigue endurance limit of approximately 60 per cent of its ultimate strength of 125,000 psi.

Illustrating the adaptability of titanium to pre-

Table 7·4 Titanium Alloy Properties

Specification No.		Producers						1,000 psi		
AMS	Military	Crucible	M-STC	Republic	TMCA	Composition, % max. (Bal. Ti)	Forms*	Y.S.	T.S.	% E. in 2 in.
4900A	...	A55	MST-55	RS-55	T00025	Unalloyed	S, B, E, W	55	65	18
4901B	(MIL-T-7993-CL1)	A70	MST-70	RS-70	T00035	Unalloyed	S, B, E, W	70	80	15
4902	...	A40	MST-40	RS-40	T00020	Unalloyed	S, B, E, W, T	40	50	20
4908A	(MIL-T-9046-CL1)	C110M	MST-8Mn	RS-110A	...	8Mn	S	110	120	10
4911	(MIL-T-009046-CL2)	C120AV	MST-6Al-4V	RS-120A	T34615	6Al-4V	S, B, E, W	120	130	10
4921A	(MIL-T-9047-CL1)	A70	MST-70	RS-70	T00035	Unalloyed	B, F	70	80	15
4923	(MIL-T-9047-CL4)	...	...	...	T96035	2Fe-2Cr-2Mo	S, B, E, W, F	120	130	15
4925A	(MIL-T-9047-CL6)	C130AM	MST-4Al-4Mn	RS-130	...	4Al-4Mn	B, W, F	130	140	10
4926	...	A110AT	MST-5Al-2.5Sn	RS-110C	T00820	5Al-2.5Sn	S, B, W	110	115	10
4927	(MIL-T-9047-CL3)	...	MST-3Al-5Cr	...	...	3Al-5Cr	B, F	135	145	10
4928	(MIL-T-9047-CL5)	C120AV	MST-6Al-4V	RS-120A	T34620	6Al-4V	B, F	120	130	10
4929	...	...	...	...	T94520	5Al-1.5Fe-1.5Cr-1.2Mo	B, F	135	145	10
4941	...	A40	...	...	T00020	Unalloyed	T (welded)	40	50	20
4951	...	A40	MST-40	RS-40	T00020	Unalloyed	W	...	50	
4953	...	A110AT	...	RS-110C	T00820	5Al-2.5Sn	W	...	115	
...	...	...	...	RS-140	...	5Al-2.75Cr-1.25Fe	B	140	150	10
...	...	...	...	RS-110	...	3Mn-1.5Al	S, B, W	100	110	12
...	...	...	...	RS-110B	...	3.25Mn-2.25Al	S, B, W	110	120	10
...	...	C105A	MST-2.5Al-16V	...	...	2.5Al-16V	S, B, W	55	90	12
...	...	C115A	...	...	Ti-4Al-3Mo-1V	4Al-3Mo-1V	S	90	125	16
...	...	...	...	...	Ti-6.5Al-3Mo-1V	6.5Al-3Mo-1V	B	150	155	17
...	...	C130AMO		...	...	6.5Al-3.75Mo	B	152	162	
...	...	...	MST-821	...	...	8Al-2Cb-1Ta	S, B	120	127	16
...	...	...	...	...	Ti-8Al-1Mo-1V	8Al-1Mo-1V	B	132	137	18
...	...	C120VCA	...	...	Ti-13V-11Cr-3Al	13V-11Cr-3Al	S, B, W	120	125	10
...	...	...	MST-881	...	...	8Al-8Zr-1(Cb + Ta)	S, B, F	125	135	16
...	...	...	...	...	...	7Al-4Mo	B, F	130	140	10

* S, rolled flat products—sheet, strip, plate E, extrusions T, tube B, bar and billet W, wire F, forgings

cision operating equipment is the use of Ti-6Al-4V alloy for turbine wheels in the 155-lb Sidewinder missile. This application calls for a high-strength, heat-resistant material with low inertia forces because the wheel must attain a speed of 60,000 rpm in a fraction of a second.

The working of titanium can be accomplished in much the same manner as that employed for sheet or stainless steel. It can be sheared, sawed, stretched, punched, and formed into a variety of shapes. It is not what would be called "easy" to work, but with care and proper tools and techniques it can be handled satisfactorily. Since molten titanium absorbs gases rapidly, it cannot be welded by oxyacetylene or simple arc welding. Inert-gas welding, on the other hand, is quite satisfactory because in this case the titanium is protected from the air.

If a technician should find that he must do a substantial amount of work with titanium, he should make sure that he understands the peculiarities of the metal and governs his operations accordingly.

High-temperature and super alloys

Because of recent advances in aircraft and missile design which involve elevated temperatures, it has become necessary for the industry to develop metals which can withstand very high temperatures and still retain their strength. Some of these alloys are described briefly below:

Types 321 and 347 stainless steel: Stabilized 18 per cent chromium (Cr) and 8 per cent nickel (Ni). Basic nonhardenable stainless steel with excellent fabrication characteristics, weldable, and fully corrosion-resistant. Used in elevated-temperature applications to 1500°F where medium strength and corrosion resistance are required.

Type 310 stainless steel: 25 per cent chromium, 20 per cent nickel, with excellent scaling resistance up to 2000° and over. Used where high-temperature strength to 2200° is needed.

Inconel X: An 80 per cent nickel-chromium-iron alloy containing titanium and aluminum for age hardening. Excellent strength up to 1600°F.

Hastelloy C: A Haynes stellite which is a nickel-base alloy containing substantial amounts of molybdenum (Mo) and chromium for increased scale resistance. Used for high-strength applications up to 1800°F.

S-816: A cobalt-base alloy containing 20 per cent nickel and 20 per cent chromium with substantial amounts of molybdenum (Mo), tungsten (W), and columbium (Cb) [also called niobium (Nb)]. Used for forged turbine blades.

L-605: A cobalt-base alloy that is one of the strongest of the high-temperature materials above 1600°. Widely used in the 1700 to 2200° range.

Udimet 700: A nickel-base alloy with large amounts of cobalt and chromium together with aluminum, titanium, and molybdenum. Has outstanding tensile and stress-rupture strength.

Astroloy: A vacuum-melted nickel-base alloy similar in composition to Udimet 700. Designed to operate in the 1800 to 2000° range in an oxidizing environment while under load for considerable periods.

The foregoing alloys are only a few of the special alloys designed for use under high-temperature conditions in aircraft, jet engines, and missiles. However, their descriptions give an indication of the extensive developments which have been made by manufacturers to meet the requirements of the space age. Figure 7·3 gives the heat-resistant properties of some high-temperature alloys.

PLASTICS

In the manufacture and repair of aircraft, many plastic materials are used because they can be manufactured to provide strength, light weight, freedom from corrosion, good insulating proper-

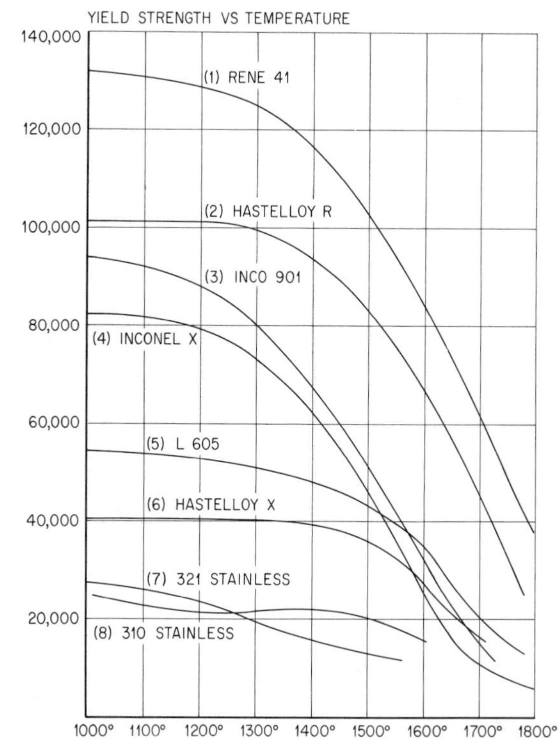

Figure 7·3 Heat-resisting properties of high-temperature alloys.

ties, and other desirable features. Furthermore, the manufacture of plastic parts is often less expensive than the manufacture of parts with other materials.

Types of plastics

Plastic materials may be classified in a number of ways; however, there are two general types, based on their reaction to heat. These are **thermoplastic** plastics and **thermosetting** plastics. The thermoplastic material becomes softened by the application of heat, and the thermosetting material is hardened by heat. This means, of course, that a thermosetting material cannot be reshaped after it has been formed and set by heat. Thermoplastic materials can be heated and reshaped a number of times.

Plastics are also classified according to the material from which they are made. For transparent sheet to be used in aircraft windshields and windows, **acrylic** and **cellulose acetate** plastics are used. For the manufacture of parts, the synthetic resins **polyester, epoxy, and phenolic** are most often used. The resins are usually reinforced with various fabrics or glass fiber to provide a maximum of durability and strength.

Windshields and windows

The most suitable clear plastic material for windows and windshields is acrylic sheet. One of the best known brand names for this material is Plexiglas manufactured by the Rohm and Haas Company. This material is manufactured in almost any size and thickness desired and can be used for many purposes other than windows and windshields.

Great care should be exercised in the handling and storing of acrylic sheet. The surface can be easily scratched if it is allowed to rub against any kind of a rough surface. In handling the material it is best that soft gloves be worn and that the sheets be stored on edge in a specially prepared rack. The new sheet is often protected with a paper mask which is held to the surface by an adhesive. This masking paper can be easily peeled off when the material is installed. Acrylic sheet can be stored horizontally with the sheets stacked together provided that the supporting surface is perfectly flat and smooth and that no particles of metal, wood chips, sand, or other foreign material are on the surface. If the sheet is masked, there will not be so much danger of damage as otherwise. When the material is stacked horizontally, large sheets should be placed at the bottom of the stack and then smaller sheets can be stacked in order of their size. This is to assure that all sheets have full support so they will not sag and become deformed.

In the replacement of windows and windshields in aircraft it is essential to make sure that the type of material to be installed is of the same quality as that being replaced. There are many types of transparent plastics, and their properties vary greatly, particularly with respect to expansion characteristics, brittleness under low temperatures, strength, etc. It may be noted here that acrylic plastics are stronger and more durable than the cellulose acetate types. Furthermore, the acrylics have a lower expansion coefficient.

When an acrylic plastic panel is installed, it should never be forced into place to make it fit. If the fit is poor, the panel should be trimmed or a new one should be obtained. When an acrylic plastic sheet is clamped or bolted in place, care must be taken that the material is not placed under excessive stress. If it is held in place by a nut and bolt or machine screw, the nut must not be turned up tight. The correct method is to tighten the nut to a firm fit and then back it off one turn. The purpose of this procedure is to allow for expansion and contraction of the material and to avoid crushing the point of attachment. In many cases where bolts are used to hold plastic sheet in place, the bolts are used with spacers or stops which prevent overtightening. In the replacement of panels, the spacers, washers, and other parts should be installed as in the original configuration.

The edges of plastic sheet should be mounted between rubber, cork, or other protective material to reduce the effects of vibration and to distribute compressive stresses on the material.

Acrylic plastics expand and contract about three times as much as the metal channels in which they are installed. It is therefore necessary that adequate provision be made to allow for this expansion and contraction. Clearances of ⅛ in. minimum should be allowed around the edges of small panels, and larger clearances around the edges of large panels. Where holes are drilled in the plastic material for bolts or screws, the holes should be oversize by ⅛ in. diameter and centered so there will be no binding or cracking at the edges of the holes. Slotted holes are also recommended.

Panels of plastic must be mounted in the channels to a sufficient depth to prevent the panels from coming out when they shrink as the result of cold temperatures.

Cellulose acetate panels are mounted in the same manner as acrylics; however, allowance must be made for greater expansion and contraction.

Plastic panels may be repaired when cracked or damaged, but when the damage is extensive, it is best to replace the panel with a new one. Small cracks can be stopped with ⅛-in. holes drilled at the end of the crack.

Cracks and holes may be patched in accordance with directions given by the manufacturer of the plastic or according to directions provided by the FAA in the Civil Aeronautics Manual 18.

Clear plastic panels should be cleaned by washing with soap and water. Solvents and chemical cleaners should not be used because there is danger that the cleaner will attack or soften the surface of the plastic. If, after dirt and grease are removed, no great amount of scratching is visible, the plastic should be finished with a good grade of commercial wax. The wax should be applied in a thin, even coat and brought to a high polish by rubbing lightly with a soft cloth.

If the surface of a plastic panel has small scratches, it can be polished with a fine grade of polish and a soft cloth or buffing wheel. Care must be taken that the surface is not heated appreciably because this will cause the material to soften and damage may result.

Glass fiber plastics

As mentioned previously, certain parts for aircraft are made of synthetic resin plastic reinforced with glass fiber or other reinforcing agents. Methods for applying synthetic resins to glass fiber are usually furnished by the manufacturer of the material used, and the directions given should be carefully followed.

If it is desired to make a particular item, the first step is to make a wooden or plaster form or die in the shape of the item desired. This form is coated with a type of varnish which will prevent the plastic material from sticking.

The resin is usually a clear, siruplike liquid which will become hard after the addition of a suitable catalyst. The catalyst can be obtained from the same source as the resin. The type and amount of catalyst will usually determine how soon the resin will "set up." In any case, the manufacturer's directions must be followed closely to obtain the desired result.

When the form has been made and the proper finish applied, the actual construction of the part may begin. The first step is to coat the form or die with a thick layer of the resin to which the proper type and amount of catalyst have been added. Strips of glass cloth are then carefully applied to the surface, completely covering the form over the area delineating the part to be made. After the layer of glass cloth is firmly in place, another coating of the resin is applied by brushing or spraying. A second layer of glass cloth is then applied and pressed firmly into place. This is followed by a coating of the resin. The number of layers of glass cloth and resin is determined by the thickness required.

If it is desired to have a perfectly smooth finish inside and outside the part, it is necessary that male and female dies be provided. The glass cloth and resin are laid up on one die, and then the other die is mated to it and the two sections are firmly pressed together. They are kept in this position until the resin has set.

After removal from the form or die it is usually necessary to trim the part and smooth the rough spots. The trimming can be done with several types of cutting tools such as shears, a saw, or a knife. Smoothing can be accomplished with sandpaper, a sanding machine, or other means.

AIRCRAFT WOODS

Even though we are accustomed to metal aircraft as the most modern type, many aircraft are still in operation which are largely of wood construction. For this reason the aircraft repair technician must be familiar with the approved types of wood used for aircraft structures.

The standard wood for aircraft structures has for many years been aircraft-grade spruce. Aircraft spruce is a uniform, straight-grain wood classified as a soft wood (coniferous woods are generally classed as soft woods).

Among woods which can be substituted for spruce are Douglas fir, Noble fir, western hemlock, northern white pine, white cedar, and yellow poplar.

Douglas fir can be used in the same sizes as spruce or in slightly reduced sizes if the reduction can be substantiated. It is more difficult to work with hand tools than spruce and has some tendency to split and splinter during fabrication.

Noble fir has satisfactory characteristics with respect to workability, warping, and splitting. It is slightly lower in shear strength; however, it can be used in the same sizes as spruce if shear is not a critical factor.

Western hemlock is less uniform in texture than spruce but can be used as a direct substitute. It must, of course, meet all requirements for quality.

Northern white pine is excellent in working qualities and uniform in properties, but it is somewhat low in hardness and shock resistance. It cannot be used as a substitute for spruce unless the size is increased to compensate for lower strength.

Port Orford white cedar can be used as a substitute for spruce in the same sizes or slightly reduced sizes provided that reductions can be substantiated. It is more difficult to glue, but satisfactory joints can be obtained with suitable precautions.

Yellow poplar can be used in place of spruce if sizes are increased sufficiently to make up for slightly lower strength.

Defects in woods

Woods used for aircraft may have certain slight defects provided that these defects do not appreciably affect the strength of the wood. Normally a straight grain is preferred, but if cross grain or spiral grain does not exceed a slope of 1:15, the wood can be used. The wood should be inspected on all four faces to be sure that the grain deviation is not excessive. Wavy, curly, or interlocked grain that does not exceed the 1:15 limitation is acceptable.

Sound, hard **knots** of not more than ⅜ in. in diameter are acceptable provided that they are not in the projecting portions of I beams, along the edges of rectangular or beveled, unrouted beams, or along the edges of flanges of box beams. They must not cause grain divergence at the edges or in the flanges of beams. They must be in the center third of the beam and not closer than 20 in. to another similar defect. It is preferable, however, to use material without knots. Small pin-knot clusters are acceptable if they do not cause an appreciable grain deviation.

Pitch pockets are acceptable if they are in the center portion of a beam, are at least 14 in. apart when they lie in the same growth ring, and do not exceed 1½ in. in length by ⅛ in. in width and ⅛ in. in depth. They must not be in the projecting portions of I beams, along the edges of rectangular beams, or along the edges of the flanges of box beams. Here again, it is preferable to avoid using lumber with pitch pockets.

Mineral stains or streaks are not cause for rejection if they are checked to make sure that there is no decay in the area.

Spike knots are not acceptable. These knots are those which cut across the growth rings (see Fig. 7·4).

Checks in wood are longitudinal cracks extending across the growth rings. These are illustrated in Fig. 7·5. **Shakes** are longitudinal cracks between the annual rings. These are also illustrated in Fig. 7·5. **Splits** are longitudal cracks caused by artificial stress. Wood containing checks, shakes, or splits must be rejected.

Compression wood is not acceptable. It is difficult to recognize. However, it has the appearance of an excessive growth of summer wood and it is higher in specific gravity than the normal wood. If compression wood is suspected, it should be subjected to a toughness machine test to establish its quality. Any piece of wood containing compression wood should be rejected.

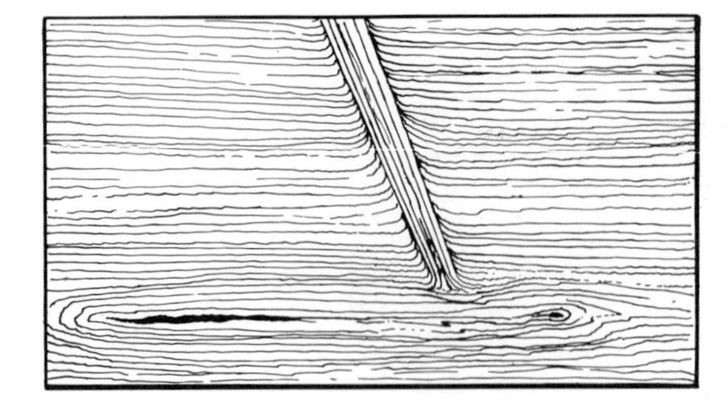

Figure 7·4 A spike knot in wood.

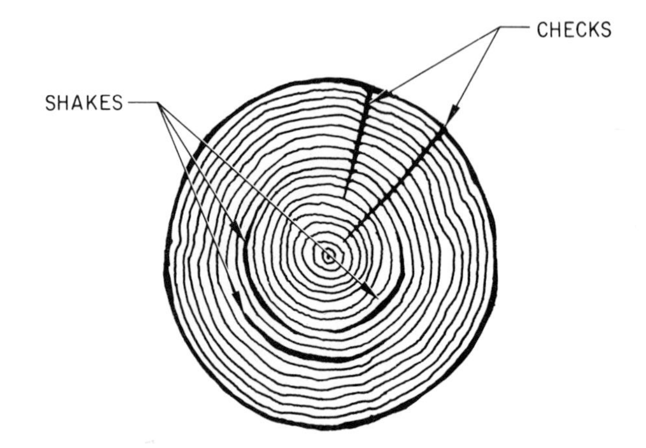

Figure 7·5 Defects in wood.

Compression failure is caused from the wood being overstressed in compression owing to natural forces during the growth of the tree, felling trees on rough or irregular ground, or rough handling of logs or lumber. Compression failures are characterized by a buckling of the fibers that appear as streaks on the surface of the piece substantially at right angles to the grain. They vary from pronounced failures to very fine hairlines that require close inspection to detect. Wood containing such failures should be rejected.

All stains and discolorations should be inspected carefully to see that no decay is present. Any wood containing detectable decay must be rejected.

Joining aircraft wood parts

Wood parts for aircraft are usually joined by means of approved-type glues. Glues for aircraft woodwork are of two general types. These are casein glues and resin glues. In the early days of wood aircraft structures, casein glues were used almost exclusively, and these glues in an improved form are still suitable. Casein glues for use in aircraft should contain suitable preservatives, such as the chlorinated phenols and their sodium salts, to increase their resistance to organic deterioration under high-humidity exposures. Most casein glues are sold in powder form ready to be mixed with water at ordinary room temperatures.

Synthetic-resin glues for wood are outstanding in that they retain their strength and durability under moist conditions and even after exposure to water. The best known and most commonly used synthetic-resin glues are the phenol-formaldehyde, resorcinol-formaldehyde, and urea-formaldehyde types.

Liquid resin glues may come ready for use or in a form which requires only the addition of a catalyst to cause them to set up. In all cases the mixing, glue consistency, assembly time, etc., should comply with the glue manufacturers' recommendations and instructions. Cold-setting synthetic-resin glues, when prepared for use, are usually sharply limited in working life, and care must be taken to discard the glue and clean the equipment before the end of the working-life period.

When wood structures are assembled, glue should be spread on both surfaces to be joined. **Open assembly,** where the glued surfaces are left open for a time, is preferred by many technicians to speed the setting of the glue. In **closed assembly** the surfaces are joined immediately after the glue is spread, and it takes much longer for the glue to set. In general, it is recommended that glue joints be kept under pressure of clamps or other devices for at least 7 hr unless the manufacturer specifies a different time. When a joint is made using the open-assembly method, the joint should not be left open for more than 20 min.

Complete information concerning woods for aircraft and the construction of aircraft wood structures is given in the government publications ANC18 and ANC19.

AIRCRAFT FABRICS

Because many aircraft still employ fabric and dope for covering, it is essential that the technician be familiar with the fabrics used. For aircraft with wing loadings of more than 9 psf and a placarded never-exceed speed of more than 160 mph, grade A aircraft mercerized cotton fabric or an equivalent is required. Fabric conforming to AMS3806 or MIL-C-5646 meets the requirements. This fabric when new has a tensile strength of 80 lb per in. or more in either warp or fill. This means that a 1-in. strip of the fabric will lift a weight of 80 lb without breaking. Technical Standard Order TSO-C15 sets forth the FAA requirements for aircraft fabric.

Predoped fabrics must conform to MIL-C-5643 for nitrate dope and MIL-C-5642 for acetate butyrate dope.

An intermediate-grade fabric for airplanes with a wing loading of less than 9 psf and a never-exceed speed of less than 160 mph must conform to AMS3804 and is described in TSO-C14. This fabric has a minimum tensile strength of 65 lb per in. of width.

Fabric for gliders with wing loading of 8 psf or less and a placard never-exceed speed of 135 mph or less must meet the requirements of AMS3802A or AAF16128.

Aircraft linen cloth is also used by many owners for covering their airplanes. Linen cloth meeting the British Specification DTD540 meets the requirements of TSO-C15.

Since the discovery of synthetic fabrics, a number of new materials have been approved for aircraft use. Satisfactory methods have been developed using nylon, Dacron, and Fiberglas as well as other materials for covering aircraft and control surfaces. Some of these materials have a much longer life than grade A cotton fabric. All such coverings must be approved by the FAA before they are used on aircraft certificated for the standard categories.

In addition to the fabric, various other materials must be used for the application of aircraft covering. These are hand-sewing thread, rib-stitching cord, reinforcing tape, and finishing tape. All these materials should meet the requirements established for aircraft use. Aircraft fabric should be applied according to the methods described in Civil Aeronautics Manual 18 or the directions of the material manufacturer.

AIRCRAFT HARDWARE

General-purpose hex-head bolts for aircraft are manufactured in accordance with AN specifications. The basic specification numbers for aircraft bolts are AN3 through AN20. AN3 bolts are 3/16 in. in diameter, AN4 bolts are 1/4 (4/16) in. in diameter, AN5 bolts are 5/16 in. in diameter, etc. It is seen that the first number indicates the diameter of the bolt in sixteenths of an inch. The dash number or the number following a descriptive letter indicates the length of the bolt. The lengths of AN bolts increase by 1/8-in. increments.

AN bolts may be made of cadmium-plated alloy steel, corrosion-resistant steel, or aluminum

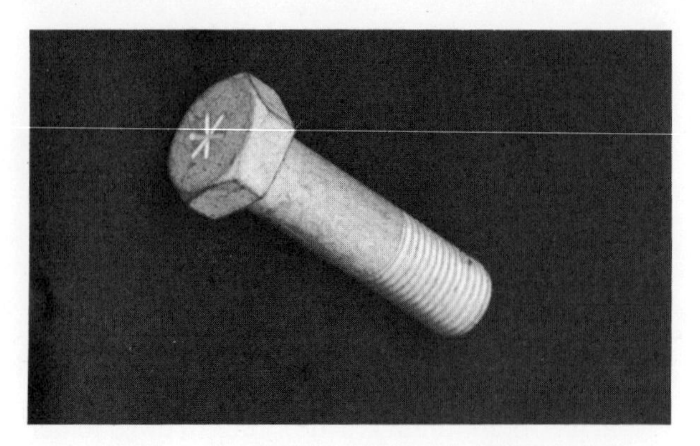

Figure 7·6 An AN general-purpose aircraft bolt.

alloy. Markings on the head of the bolt indicate the type of material used. Figure 7·6 is a photograph of an AN general-purpose aircraft bolt.

NAS internal wrenching bolts are designated under the numbers NAS144 through NAS158 and NAS495. These are extra-strength bolts for use in applications where high tension and shear loads are developed. An internal wrenching bolt of more recent design and even greater strength than the NAS bolt is the MS20004 through MS20024. The MS-series bolt is of very high strength and requires special washers and nuts for proper installation. An internal wrenching bolt is shown in Fig. 7·7.

A clevis bolt is shown in Fig. 7·8. The AN specifications for these bolts are AN21 through AN36. These bolts are made from cadmium-plated alloy steel. The first number indicates the diameter of the bolt, and the second number indicates the length. Clevis bolts are generally used for applications where shear is the principal stress.

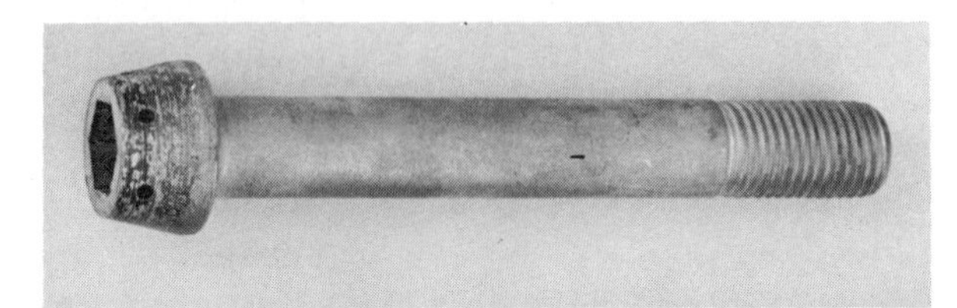

Figure 7·7 An internal wrenching bolt (NAS).

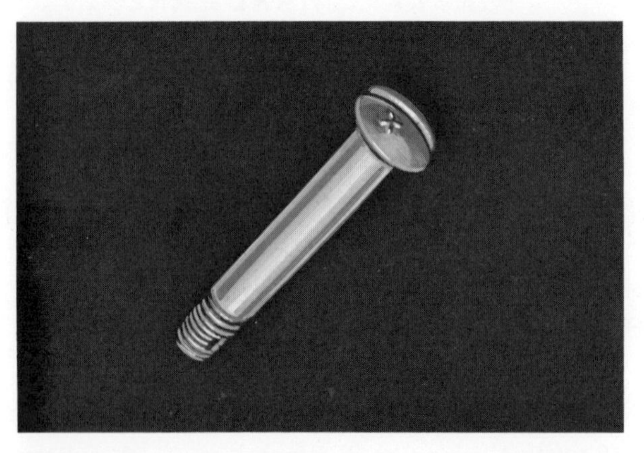

Figure 7·8 A clevis bolt.

Nuts

Typical AN nuts for aircraft bolts are shown in Fig. 7·9. The AN315 is a plain nut, AN310 is a plain castle nut, and AN365 is a standard self-locking nut. Castle (castellated) nuts are secured with cotter pins or safety wire, plain nuts are locked with lock washers or lock nuts, and self-locking nuts do not require safetying devices. Self-locking nuts should not be used in applications where there is rotation between the bolt and the member through which it is placed.

Machine screws

Several standard AN machine screws are shown in Fig. 7·10. Machine screws differ from wood screws and some other screws in that the machine screw has a constant thread diameter. Screws are usually made of a carbon steel rather than the alloy steel used for AN bolts. Certain high-strength screws, however, require the use of alloy steel.

The basic AN number of a machine screw indicates the type of screw, the dash numbers indicate the diameter and length, and the letters

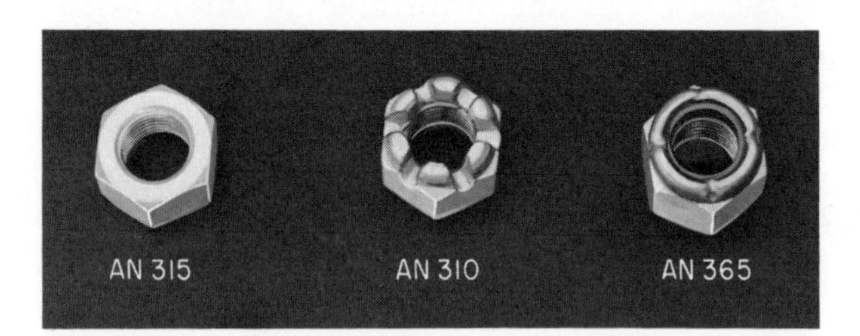

Figure 7·9 Typical AN nuts.

Figure 7·10 AN machine screws.

indicate the type of material and other features such as a drilled head.

Thread types for machine screws are included in the basic AN number. For example, the AN500 fillister head screw has a coarse thread and the AN501 fillister head screw has a fine thread. A No. 10 screw with a coarse thread has 24 threads per inch, and the same screw with a fine thread has 32 threads per inch. Most of the standard machine screws are covered by AN specifications 500 through 526.

Machine screw sizes under ¼ in. in diameter are designated by numbers ranging from 2 to 10. The diameters for numbered screws are as follows:

No. 2	0.086 in.
No. 4	0.112 in.
No. 6	0.138 in.
No. 8	0.164 in.
No. 10	0.189 in. (approx. 3/16 in.)

Washers

Plain washers for use under nuts and for spacing are covered by AN specifications 960 and 970. The AN960 flat washer is a general-purpose washer and is used for all normal installations requiring washers. Standard washers with an inside diameter for Nos. 2 through 8 screws are made 0.032 in. thick, sizes 10 through ⅝ in. are made 0.63 in. thick, and sizes for a ¾-in. bolt and larger are made 0.090 in. thick. AN960 washers are also made in a light (thin) series. Washers of this type are indicated by an L after the dash number.

The AN970 washer has a large outside diameter and is designed for use with wood or other soft materials. Figure 7·11 shows an AN960 washer compared with an AN970 washer.

Lock washers are designed to prevent the turning of nuts and may be used for limited applications in aircraft. Lock washers of the AN935 and the AN936 types may be used with machine screws or bolts whenever the self-locking or castellated type of nut is not applicable. They should not be used as fastenings to primary or secondary structures or where they are subject to frequent removal or corrosive conditions. AN935 and AN-936 shakeproof washers are shown in Fig. 7·12.

Figure 7·12 Shakeproof washers.

Special washers are necessary for particular applications where plain flat washers will not suffice. Ball-seat and socket washers, AN950 and AN955, are used in special applications where the bolt is installed at an angle to the surface or where perfect alignment with the surface is required at all times. These washers are used together to provide the required angle between the surface and the nut.

Special washers for use with NAS internal wrenching bolts are the NAS143 and the MS-20002 washers. The type C washer is countersunk to seat the bolt-head shank radius, and a plain-type washer is used under the nut. Both of these washers are heat-treated to a tensile strength of 125,000 to 145,000 psi.

Self-tapping screws

Self-tapping screws are often used to join nonstructural parts and for temporarily joining parts prior to riveting. The AN504 and AN506 screws are used for attaching minor removable parts. AN530 and AN531 screws are used for temporary blind applications and for the permanent assembly of nonstructural parts. One of the commonly used self-tapping screws is the Parker-Kalon screw, commonly called a "PK." Typical PK screws are illustrated in Fig. 7·13. The pointed screws are type A, and the blunt or square-

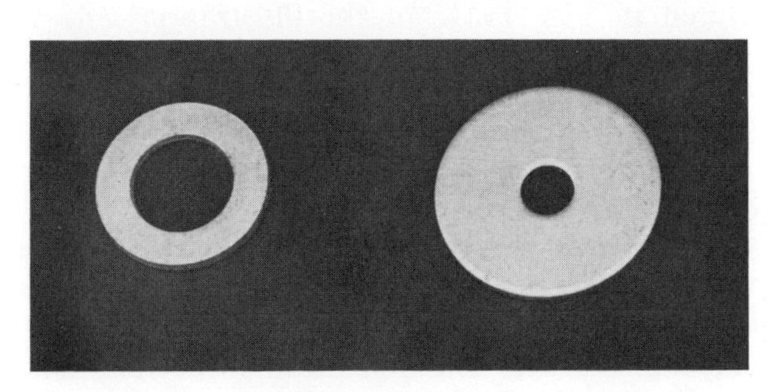

Figure 7·11 Standard and large-area washers.

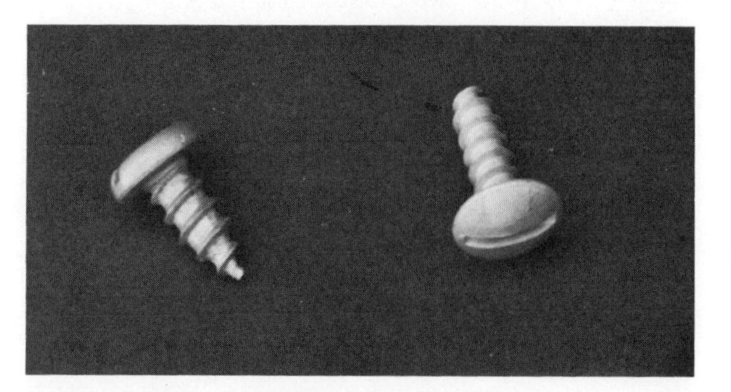

Figure 7·13 PK self-tapping screws.

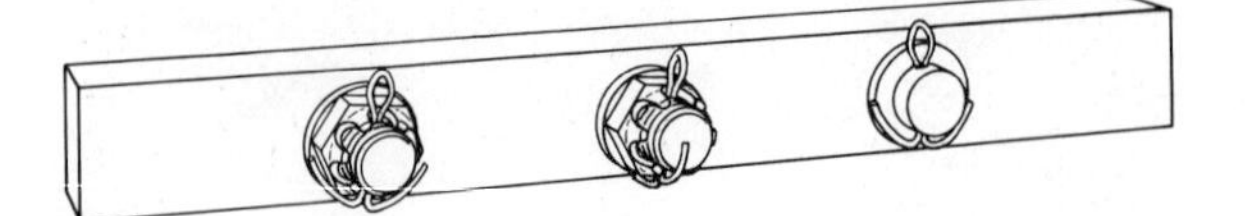

Figure 7·14 Applications of cotter pins.

ended screws are type Z. The type U, AN535 screw is a self-tapping screw designed to be driven into a hole. It is therefore called a drive screw.

Cotter pins

There are two principal types of cotter pins with which the technician should be familiar. These are the AN380 and AN381. The AN380 is a cadmium-plated, low-carbon-steel cotter pin used for safetying bolts, screws, nuts, and other pins and in various other applications where safetying is necessary. The AN381 cotter pin is made of corrosion-resistant, nonmagnetic steel and is used in safetying applications where these features are desired. The applications of cotter pins are shown in Fig. 7·14.

Pal-nuts

A common safetying device for plain nuts is the Pal-nut illustrated in Fig. 7·15. This is a formed-sheet-steel lock nut which is applied to the extending portion of a bolt after the plain nut has been properly torqued. The Pal-nut must not be overtorqued or its effectiveness will be destroyed.

Rivets

Standard aircraft rivets are designated by AN numbers as follows:

AN420	90° countersunk head
AN425	78° countersunk head
AN426	100° countersunk head
AN430	Roundhead rivet
AN435	Roundhead rivet
AN441	Flathead
AN442	Flathead
AN455	Brazier-head
AN456	Modified brazier-head
AN470	Universal-head

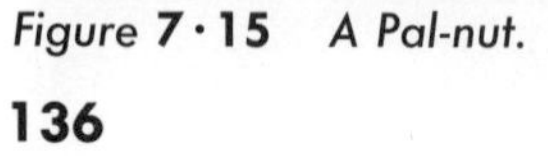

Figure 7·15 A Pal-nut.

Rivet sizes and materials are indicated by the numbers and letters following the basic AN number. For example, AN470-AD-3-4 indicates a universal-head rivet made of 2117 aluminum alloy (AD), $\frac{3}{32}$ in. in diameter and $\frac{4}{16}$ in. in length. The first dash number indicates the diameter in thirty-seconds of an inch, and the second dash number indicates the length of the rivet in sixteenths of an inch.

The letters indicate the type of material from which the rivet is made. A, B, D, AD, and DD indicate different types of aluminum alloys; C indicates copper; F indicates stainless steel; and M indicates monel metal. The materials are also indicated by markings on the heads of the rivets.

Tube fittings

Tube fittings are required for joining the many sections of tubing and the various operating devices in the systems of aircraft, including hydraulic systems, fuel systems, oxygen systems, and others. Some hydraulic systems and oxygen systems are subjected to pressures up to 5,000 psi; hence it is of extreme importance that the fittings be of a quality suitable for the application.

Tube fittings are covered by a number of specifications, but the most widely used fittings are designated by AN numbers from the late 700s to the 900s. The specifications MS21900 to MS21918 also give the requirements for special tubing fittings.

Tube fittings are discussed in more detail in the chapter covering plumbing.

Turnbuckles

Turnbuckles are commonly used for adjusting the tension of control cables. A standard turnbuckle consists of a **barrel** and two steel ends, one end having a right-hand thread and the other having a left-hand thread. Thus, when the barrel is rotated, the ends are caused to move together or away from each other. A typical turnbuckle is illustrated in Fig. 7·16.

Turnbuckles may be supplied with several different types of ends. Some of these are illustrated in Fig. 7·17. In the illustration *a* is a **cable eye** for use with a cable thimble, *b* is a **fork** by which the turnbuckle can be attached to a flat fitting, *c* is a **pin eye** to be inserted into a forked or double-sided fitting, and *d* is a swage fitting by which the cable can be attached to the turnbuckle after having been swaged into a sleeve.

The barrel of the turnbuckle is made of brass and is grooved around one end to indicate the left-hand thread. The hole through the center of the turnbuckle is used for the purpose of turning the barrel.

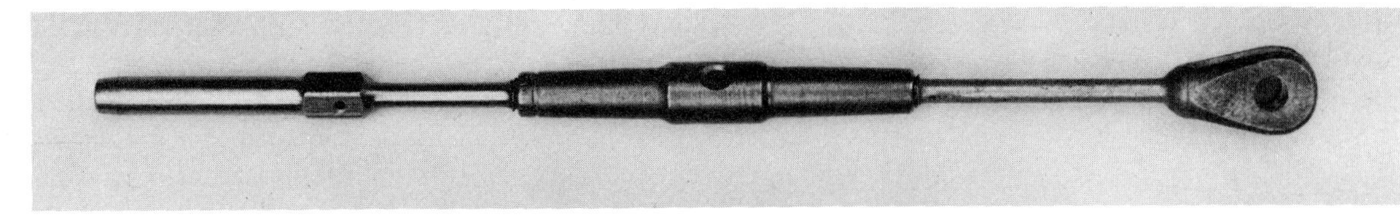

Figure 7·16 A turnbuckle.

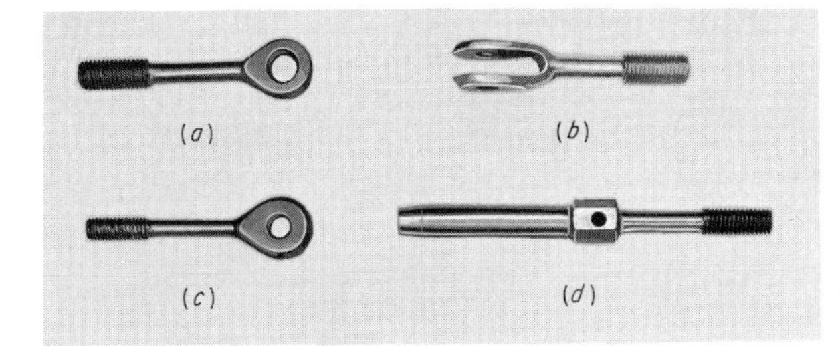

Figure 7·17 Ends for turnbuckle. (a) Cable eye; (b) fork; (c) pin eye; (d) swage fitting.

Two principal factors must be considered in the installation and adjustment of turnbuckles. (1) When the turnbuckle is tightened, not more than three threads must show outside the barrel at each end. (2) The turnbuckle must be properly safetied. The proper methods for safetying turnbuckles are shown in Fig. 8·59 in the next chapter.

Some turnbuckle parts are designated by AN numbers as follows:

AN155	Standard barrel
AN161	Fork
AN170	Cable eye
AN165	Pin eye
AN669	Swaging terminal

Cable fittings

Cable fittings are required to connect a cable to control arms, to other fittings, to turnbuckles, and to other sections of cable. When it is necessary to attach a cable to a turnbuckle or other device and swageable fittings are not available, the AN100 cable thimble is used. This thimble is illustrated in Fig. 7·18 and is attached by means of the five-tuck splice.

Figure 7·18 A cable thimble.

When swaging equipment is available, it is desirable to use swaged fittings because these fittings develop the full cable strength when properly installed. The AN664 ball end and the AN666 stud end, the AN667 fork end, and the AN668 eye end are shown in Fig. 7·19.

To install a swaged fitting, the cable is inserted to the full depth of the barrel in the fitting and is held firmly in this position while the swaging operation is completed. The swaging can be done either with a hand machine or with a power swaging machine. The machine presses the metal of the fitting barrel into the cable to the extent that there is no visible division between the fitting and the cable when a cross-sectional cut is made through the swaged portion. After the swaging operation is completed, the swaged barrel should be checked with a "go no-go" gage to make sure that the proper degree of swaging has been accomplished. It is also advisable to mark the cable with adhesive tape when it is inserted into the barrel of the fitting to make sure that it does not slip during the swaging operation. It is good practice to paint the junction of the terminal or fitting and the cable with red paint to provide a means of detection for slipped cable at later inspections.

A method for splicing cable around a thimble or bushing, which may be used in place of the five-tuck splice, is the **Nicopress** swaged-sleeve method. The Nicopress sleeve and a spliced cable fitting are shown in Fig. 7·20. The Nicopress sleeve is composed of copper and is pressed (swaged)

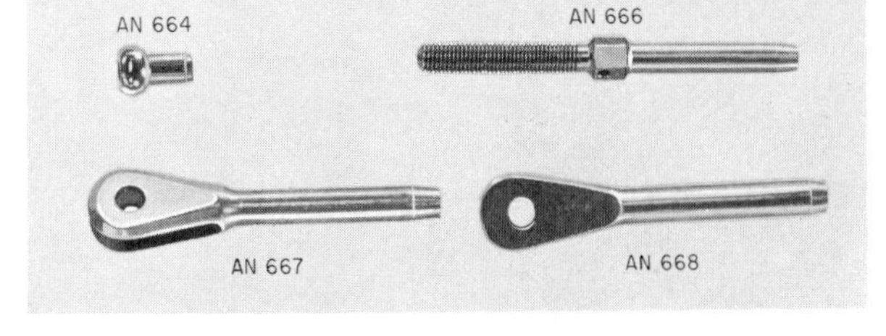

Figure 7·19 Swaged fittings.

Figure 7·20 A Nicopress cable splice.

on the cable by means of a special tool. The specifications for a properly installed sleeve are established by the manufacturer.

It must be emphasized that new standards are constantly being issued and that older standards become obsolete. Nevertheless, many of the older standards are still effective, and it is up to the maintenance technician to see that he is using approved parts and materials. It is always safe to select materials and parts which are specified in the manufacturer's overhaul or maintenance manual for a particular airplane, powerplant, or accessory.

REVIEW QUESTIONS

1. Define a *standard.*
2. Define a *specification.*
3. List the meanings of the following standard designations: AC, AF, AN, MS, NAS, NAF, AS.
4. What type of hardware is covered by AN5, AN365, AN470, AN500?
5. What is the meaning of MIL-C-5424?
6. What are ferrous metals?
7. What can you determine by the following SAE steel designations: 1020, 2340, 4130, 6130?
8. What do you know concerning a type-302 stainless steel?
9. What types of aluminum alloys are generally used for aircraft structures? (Give numbers.)
10. What common elements are used as alloying materials for aluminum alloys?
11. What are some of the advantages and disadvantages of magnesium?
12. Describe some of the properties of titanium which make it useful for aerospace structures.
13. Name some of the metal alloys which are particularly useful for high-temperature applications.
14. Compare *thermosetting* and *thermoplastic* plastics.
15. What types of plastics are generally used for aircraft windows and windshields?
16. Name three types of synthetic resins.
17. Describe some of the precautions required in handling plastic materials for windows and windshields.
18. Why is it necessary to leave mounting bolts for plastic sheet slightly loose?
19. Discuss the size of bolt holes which should be drilled in plastic sheet for mounting purposes.
20. What precautions should be taken in cleaning plastic windows and windshields?
21. Describe the general procedure for making a glass fiber part.
22. Name some of the woods which may be used for aircraft structural parts.
23. Name five defects in wood which will make it unsuitable for aircraft use.
24. How are woods usually joined in a wooden aircraft assembly?
25. What is meant by *open assembly* and *closed assembly?*
26. What types of glues are suitable for aircraft wood assembly?
27. What is the minimum drying time usually required before removing pressure from a glue joint?
28. What is the maximum time a glue joint may be left open after applying glue?
29. Where would you obtain instructions for the use of a particular type of glue?
30. Give the general requirements for grade A cotton fabric which may be used for covering aircraft.
31. What TSO gives the specifications for aircraft fabric?
32. What should you know about nuts, bolts, and other hardware items before you use them for aircraft structural assembly?
33. What is the meaning of the number AN470-AD-4-4?
34. What is a *swaged* cable fitting?

CHAPTER 8

Structures for Aerospace Vehicles

The purpose of this chapter is to familiarize mechanics, technicians, and pilots with the fundamentals of the design and construction of the principal structural units of airplanes, missiles, and spacecraft. Emphasis is placed upon fuselages, wings, and control surfaces, and considerable attention is given cockpits, cabins, compartments, canopies, windshields, windows, landing gear, and powerplant structural parts. It is not intended to describe the details of all aircraft or all the details of any particular aircraft because to do so would require far more space than is available. We shall, however, describe and explain aircraft structures in general and shall use specific examples of particular airplanes and missiles to illustrate certain devices and different types of construction.

NOMENCLATURE

Although we have discussed and described certain parts of airplanes in previous chapters of this text, we shall in this section give a more comprehensive listing of the parts and related nomenclature for aircraft together with definitions of the parts, measurements, conditions, and actions.

Figure 8 · 1 is a drawing of a light airplane with many parts labeled. In the following, the definitions of these parts will be given together with numerous other definitions.

aileron: One of a pair of movable control surfaces attached to the trailing edge of each wing tip, the purpose of which is to control the airplane in roll by creating unequal or opposing lifting forces on the opposite sides of the airplane.

angle of attack: The angle at which an airfoil or a system of airfoils, such as a helicopter rotor, meets the airflow. It may also be described as the angle between the chord line of a wing and the relative wind.

angle of incidence: The acute angle between the chord of an airfoil and the horizontal axis of an airplane.

angle of landing: The acute angle between the wing chord and the horizontal when the airplane is on the ground.

angle of stabilizer setting: The same as the angle of incidence as applied to a vertical or horizontal stabilizer.

angle of sweep: The acute angle between a reference line in a swept or tapered airfoil and some other chosen reference line. For fixed airfoils, the angle is measured from a plane perpendicular to the longitudinal axis of the aircraft to the reference line of the airfoil, frequently the mean chord line.

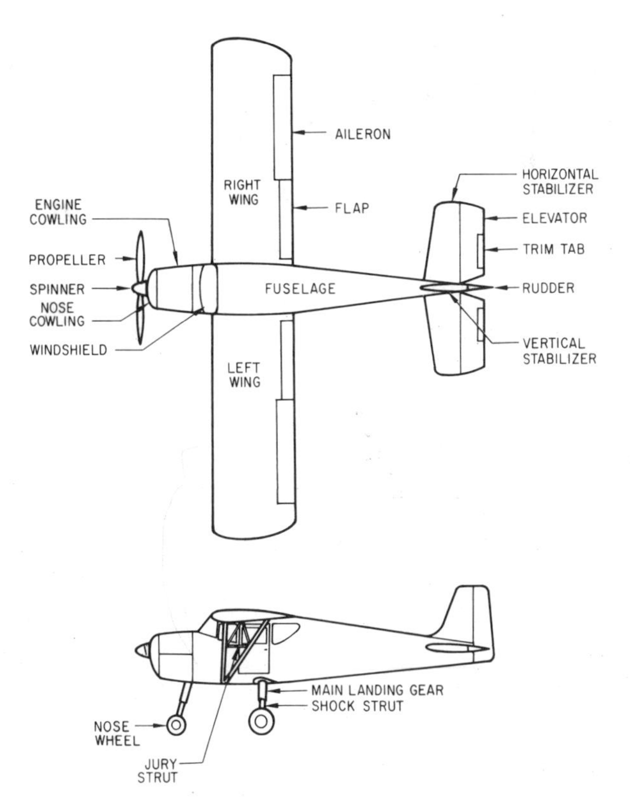

Figure 8 · 1 Light airplane with nomenclature.

angle of wing setting: The same as the angle of incidence.

antidrag wire: A wire in certain kinds of wing structures, running from an inboard point near the trailing edge to an outboard point near the leading edge, designed to resist forces acting on the wing in the direction of flight.

antilift wire: Same as landing wire.

balanced control surface: A control surface that is in a desired condition of equilibrium about its hinge axis. Such a surface can be balanced for either static or aerodynamic conditions.

balancing tab: A tab so linked that, when the control surface to which it is attached is deflected, the tab is deflected in an opposite direction, creating a force which aids in moving the larger surface.

cabane: An arrangement of struts used to support a wing above the fuselage of an airplane.

camber: The curvature of the mean line of an airfoil or airfoil section from leading edge to trailing edge.

canard: An aircraft or aircraft configuration having its horizontal stabilizing and control surfaces in front of the wing or wings.

cantilever: A beam or member supported at or near one end only, without external bracing.

center of thrust: A line coincident with the center line of the propeller shaft, about which the thrust forces are balanced.

center section: The middle or central section of an airplane wing to which the outer wing panels are attached.

chord of a wing: A straight line joining the ends of the mean line of a wing profile.

cockpit: An open space in the top of an airplane for the accommodation of a pilot or passenger. On cabin airplanes, if the pilot's compartment is separated from the rest of the cabin, it is often called the cockpit.

cockpit canopy: A transparent cover for the cockpit.

control cables: Cables connecting the control levers with the control surfaces.

control stick: A vertical lever by means of which the pilot operates the longitudinal and lateral control surfaces of the airplane. The elevator is operated by a fore-and-aft movement of the stick, and the ailerons are moved by a sideways movement of the stick.

control surface: A movable airfoil or surface, such as an aileron, elevator, ruddervator, flap, trim tab, or rudder, used to control the attitude or motion of an aircraft or missile and to guide it through the air.

control wheel: A wheel or semiwheel used in connection with the control column in an airplane. Rotation of the wheel operates the ailerons for control about the roll axis.

cowling: A removable cover or housing placed over or around an aircraft component or section, especially an engine.

decalage: The difference between the angles of incidence for two airfoils on the same airplane. It generally refers to the two wings of a biplane.

dihedral angle: The acute angle between a line perpendicular to the plane of symmetry and the projection of the wing axis of the airplane. If the tip of the wing is higher than the root section, the dihedral angle is positive.

drag strut: Any strut used to resist drag or antidrag forces. In a wing it is a fore-and-aft compression member. In landing gear it is a strut which runs diagonally up into the airplane to resist drag forces.

drag wire: A wire in certain kinds of wing structures, running from a forward inboard point to an aft outboard point to resist drag forces.

elevator: A movable auxiliary airfoil or control surface designed to impress a pitching moment on the airplane, that is, to cause rotation about the lateral axis.

fairing: A piece, part, or structure, having a smooth streamlined contour, used to cover a nonstreamlined object or to smooth a junction.

fin: The vertical stabilizer.

firewall: A fireproof or fire-resistant wall or bulkhead separating an engine from the rest of the aircraft structure to prevent the spreading of a fire from the engine compartment.

flap: A hinged, pivoted, or sliding airfoil or plate, normally located at the trailing edge of a wing, extended or deflected to increase the lift and/or drag, generally used at takeoff or landing.

fuselage: The main or central structure of a heavier-than-air aircraft, typically elongated and approximately streamlined, which carries the crew and passengers and to which the wings are attached.

gap: The distance between the chords of two superimposed airfoils.

horizontal stabilizer: A stabilizer mounted horizontally on an airplane affording horizontal stability and to which elevators are attached.

horn: A short lever fastened to a control surface to which an operating cable or rod is attached.

inspection door: A small door used especially for inspection of the interior of an airplane.

interplane strut: A strut between two wings or other surfaces.

jury strut: An auxiliary strut that braces a main strut or struts.

landing gear: The understructure which supports the weight of the airplane, also called alighting gear.

landing wires: Wires or cables which brace the wings against the forces which are opposite to the normal direction of lift. These wires attach to the upper wing above the fuselage and to the lower wing near the outboard end.

leading edge: The foremost or front edge of an airfoil or a propeller blade. The rearmost edge is called the trailing edge.

lift wires: Wires or cables which brace the wings against the forces of lift. They are also called flying wires.

longeron: A principal longitudinal (fore-and-aft) member of the framing of an airplane fuselage, usually continuous across a number of points of support.

propeller blade: That portion of a propeller which cuts the air.

propeller boss: The thick central portion of a propeller.

propeller hub: The part of the propeller which comes into contact with the shaft.

propeller root: The part of the propeller blade near the hub.

propeller tipping: The protective covering placed on the blade of a wooden or plastic propeller at or near the tip.

rudder: A hinged or movable auxiliary airfoil used to impress a yawing moment on the aircraft.

rudder pedal: Either one of a pair of cockpit pedals for operating a rudder or other directional-control device.

ruddervator: A control surface, set at a pronounced dihedral (forming a wide V), that serves as both a rudder and elevator.

shock absorber: A device built into the landing gear to reduce the shock during landing or taking off.

span: The maximum distance, measured parallel to the lateral axis, from tip to tip of any airfoil.

spar: A principal spanwise structural member of a wing or other airfoil.

spinner: A fairing of approximately conic or paraboloidal shape, fitted coaxially with the propeller hub and spinning with the propeller.

stabilizer: A fixed or adjustable airfoil or vane that provides stability for an aircraft.

stagger: With two or more superposed objects or objects fixed in a row, the advance or the amount of advance of one object ahead of another. The amount of advance of one wing of a biplane ahead of the other, of a compressor blade ahead of another, or of one rotor of a tandem-rotor helicopter ahead of the other.

stagger wire: On a biplane, a diagonal wire, usually one of a pair forming an X, running fore and aft between the two wings and helping to maintain a constant stagger.

struts: A supporting brace which bears compression loads, tension loads, or both, as in a fuselage between the longerons, in a landing gear to transmit the airplane loads, etc.

sweepback: The backward slant from root to tip of an airfoil.

tail skid: On certain older airplanes, a skid attached to the rear part of the airplane on the underside and supporting the tail.

tail wheel: A wheel at the tail of certain airplanes used to support the tail section on the ground. A tail wheel may be steerable, retractable, fixed, castering, etc.

trim tab: A tab attached to the trailing edge of an airfoil.

wing rib: A chordwise member used to give the wing its shape and to transmit the load from the fabric or other covering to the spars.

wing spar: A principal spanwise member in the structure of a wing.

wing tip: The outermost extremity of a wing.

STRUCTURAL SHAPES

It is well at this time to describe briefly some of the common structural members used in the construction of sheet-metal assemblies. Figure 8·2 shows three formed sections and seven extruded

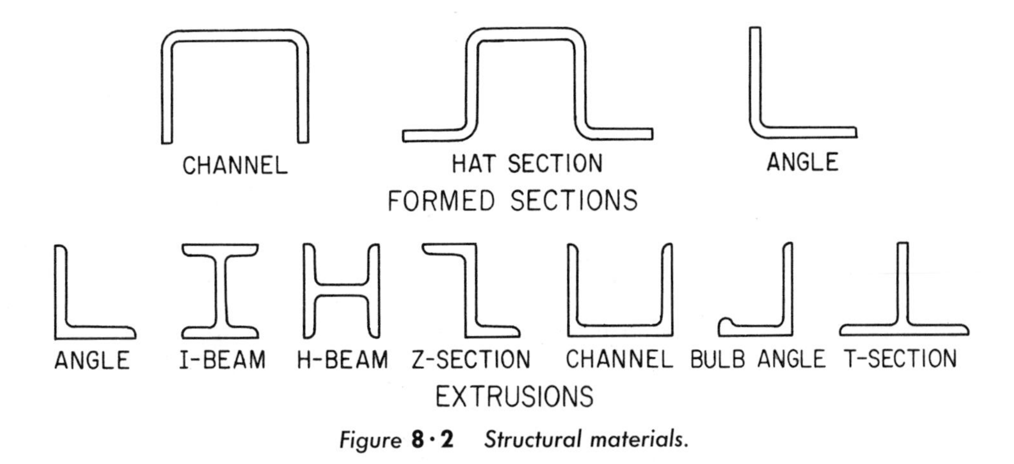

Figure **8·2** *Structural materials.*

sections commonly used for stiffeners, stringers, spars, and longerons.

As indicated, the formed sections are made from sheet stock of the proper thickness and material for the purpose desired. Any one of the shapes illustrated may be used to provide a framework for a sheet-metal assembly. Channels are sometimes formed into rings to provide formers, rings, or bulkheads for fuselages. Channels may be riveted together back to back to provide built-up I beams where it is desired to increase the strength. Hat sections are often used as stringers in wings and to strengthen sections of flooring. They may also be used as fuselage stringers where extra strength is required. Formed angle sections are often used as stiffeners to prevent buckling or **oil canning** of large sheet areas.

The expression "oil canning" refers to a metal skin which has upward bulges between rows of rivets. When the finger is pressed on one of these bulges and released, the bulge behaves like the bottom of an oil can; that is, it is first depressed and then it bounces back. The cause of oil canning is improper riveting and fitting, which forces metal out of line.

Extrusions are made by squeezing (extruding) soft aluminum alloy through a steel die having the shape of the desired section. A preheated billet of the proper alloy is placed in a giant press which applies hundreds of tons of force to squeeze the metal through a die, even as a person squeezes toothpaste from a tube. As the extruded shape comes from the die, it is passed through straightening rollers which eliminate any irregularities of alignment. There is practically no limit to the variety of shapes which can be produced by extrusion; hence, those illustrated in Fig. 8·2 are only a few of the standard shapes commonly used for aircraft structures. After extrusion the metal regains a substantial degree of hardness; however, the strength can be improved by heat treating.

The dimensions shown for the extruded sections vary over a wide range, and such parts must be ordered according to required sizes and thicknesses. Flange sizes and overall depth and thickness of material must all be given.

Any one of the extruded sections shown may be used for a stringer or stiffener; however, certain shapes serve specific purposes better than others, depending upon the design strength required and the problems in fabrication. Where the sections must be bent, it is desirable to use angles, because these are the easiest shapes to form. With the proper type of a roller equipped with suitable dies, it is possible to bend any of the shapes within certain limits; however, the more complex shapes are more expensive to form.

As a typical example of the use of extruded sections, the stringers for the wing of the Boeing 720 jet airliner are principally cut from extruded Z-section material. Z sections are also often used for fuselage stringers.

FUSELAGES

The **fuselage** is the body to which the wings and the tail unit of an airplane are attached and which provides space for the crew, passengers, cargo, controls, and other items, depending upon the size and design of the airplane. It should have the smallest streamline form consistent with desired capacity and aerodynamic qualities of the airplane. If the airplane is of the single-engine type, the engine is usually mounted in the nose of the fuselage and the engine nacelle must be of such a construction that the engine accessories such as the carburetor, magnetos, ignition leads, strainers, fuel lines, and other parts are easily accessible for service and inspection.

The main structure of a spacecraft or missile may be called a fuselage but is more commonly called the body or tank. In a typical rocket or guided missile, the greater part of the body consists of a tank to hold the large quantities of fuel and oxidizer required for the operation of the rocket engine.

The fuselage must have points of attachment for the wing or wings, tail surfaces, and landing gear, so arranged and installed that they can be inspected, removed, repaired, and replaced easily. The fuselage must be strong enough at the points of attachment to withstand flying and landing loads. Finally it should be shaped to offer low resistance to the air and provide good vision for the pilot.

The structure of the fuselage should be strong enough to protect the passengers and crew in the event of a complete turnover. Emergency exits must be provided, the number of which is determined by the capacity of the cabin.

Types of fuselages

In general, we can say that fuselages are classified in three principal types, depending upon the method by which stresses are transmitted to the structure. The three types according to this classification are (1) **truss,** (2) **semimonocoque,** and (3) **monocoque.**

A **truss** is an assemblage of members forming a rigid framework which may consist of bars, beams, rods, tubes, wires, etc. The truss-type fuselage may be subclassified as the **Pratt truss** and the **Warren truss.** The primary strength members of both Pratt and Warren trusses are

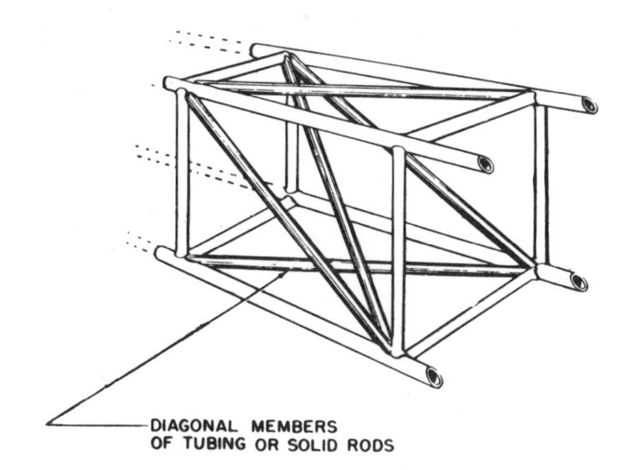

Figure **8·3** *A Pratt truss.*

the four longerons. As defined previously, the longeron is a principal longitudinal member of the airplane fuselage. In the truss-type fuselage, lateral bracing is placed at intervals. The lateral structures may be classed as bulkheads, although this is not strictly true from the technical standpoint, and the spaces between the bulkheads are called **bays.**

A Pratt truss similar to the type used in present aircraft with tubular fuselage members is shown in Fig. 8·3. In the original Pratt truss the longerons were connected with rigid vertical and lateral members called struts, but the diagonal members were made of strong steel wire and were designed to carry tension only. In the Pratt truss shown in Fig. 8·3, the diagonal members are rigid and can carry either tension or compression.

A Warren truss is illustrated in Fig. 8·4. In this construction, the longerons are connected with only diagonal members. Normally, all members in the truss are capable of carrying both tension and compression. When the load is acting in one direction, compression loads are carried by every other member while the alternate members

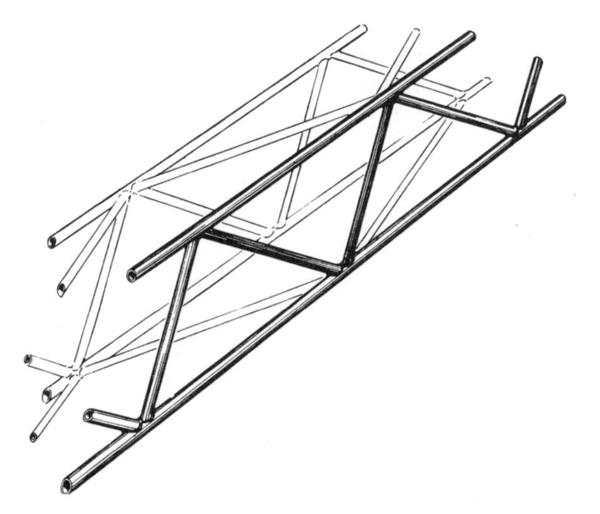

Figure **8·4** *A Warren truss.*

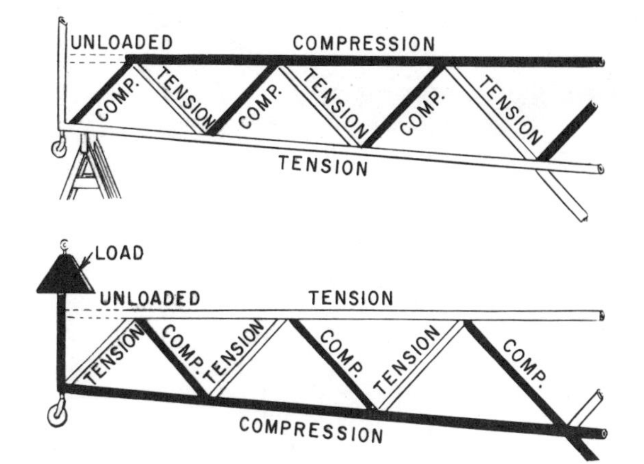

Figure **8·5** *Reversal of loading.*

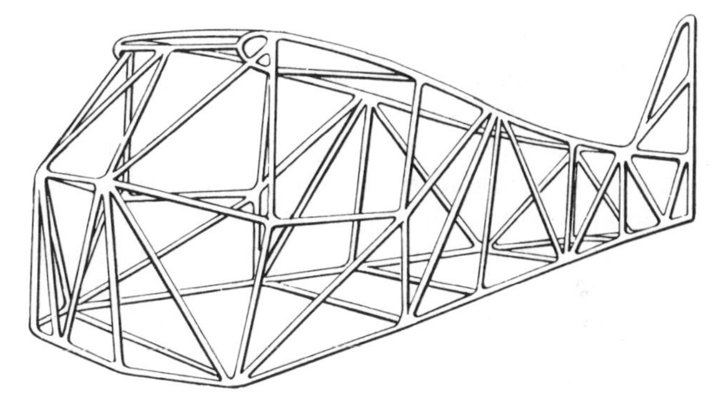

Figure **8·6** *Welded-steel fuselage.*

carry the tension loads. When the load is reversed, the members which were carrying tension previously now carry compression and those which were carrying compression now carry tension. This reversal of loading is shown in Fig. 8·5.

The welded-steel fuselage shown in Fig. 8·6 is

Figure **8·7** *All-metal semimonocoque fuselage.*

Figure 8 • 8 Semimonocoque construction.

essentially a Warren truss, even though it does have some nondiagonal members in vertical and lateral position. The members of this fuselage are made of steel tubing and are welded in place. Such a fuselage could also be made of aluminum-alloy structural members riveted together.

A **semimonocoque** fuselage consists of a framework of vertical and longitudinal members covered with a structural skin which carries a large percentage of the stresses imposed upon the fuselage. Figure 8 • 7 illustrates the construction of an all-metal semimonocoque fuselage. The vertical members of the fuselage frame are called **frames** or **bulkheads.** Between the principal vertical members are lighter **formers** or **rings** to maintain the uniform shape of the structure. The longitudinal members are called **stringers,** and they serve to stiffen the metal skin and prevent it from bulging or buckling under severe stress. The semimonocoque construction is also illustrated in Fig. 8 • 8.

The construction of a semimonocoque wood fuselage is illustrated in Fig. 8 • 9. Although there are not many airplanes constructed in this manner, it is still important that the maintenance technician be aware of this type of construction and be prepared to make repairs if necessary.

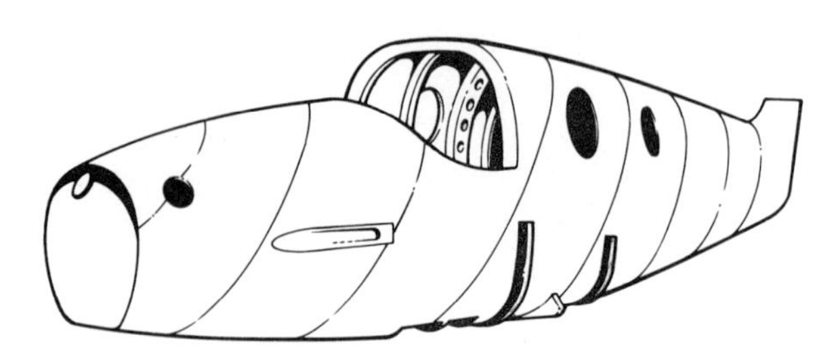

Figure 8 • 9 Semimonocoque wood construction.

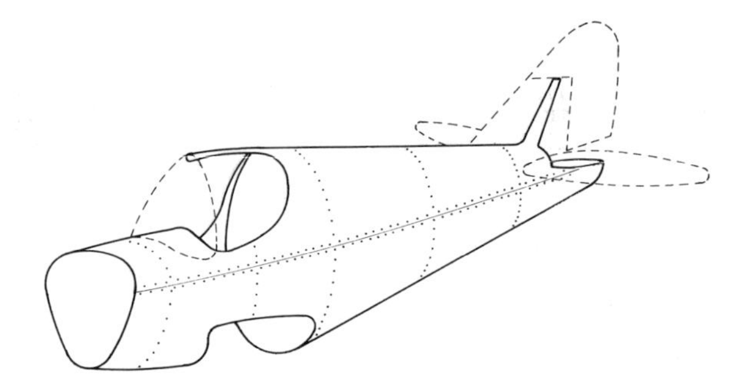

Figure 8 • 10 Full monocoque metal fuselage.

The bulkheads of the wooden semimonocoque fuselage are made of aircraft-quality plywood and are cut to a shape to fit the configuration of the fuselage. Between the bulkheads are longitudinal wooden stringers attached to the bulkheads by means of an approved glue. Small wooden corner blocks are often glued into the corners to provide reinforcement. Over the inner framework a strong skin of aircraft plywood is glued. A variety of manufacturing and repair techniques have been developed to hold the skin firmly in place while the glue sets (hardens). After such a fuselage is constructed, it is essential that the inside be thoroughly coated with spar varnish or some other waterproof protective material. One of the principal problems in the maintenance of wooden aircraft structures is the slow deterioration resulting from the penetration of moisture through the protective coatings.

A full monocoque fuselage is shown in Fig. 8 • 10. This construction merely involves the construction of a metal tube or cone without internal structural members. In some cases it is necessary to have former rings to maintain the shape, but these do not carry the principal stresses imposed upon the structure. Very often this type of fuselage will be constructed by riveting two preformed halves together. Many of the missile bodies constructed today are merely metal tubes and do not have internal structural members. Some use pressurized tanks for structural support. This method will be discussed in more detail later.

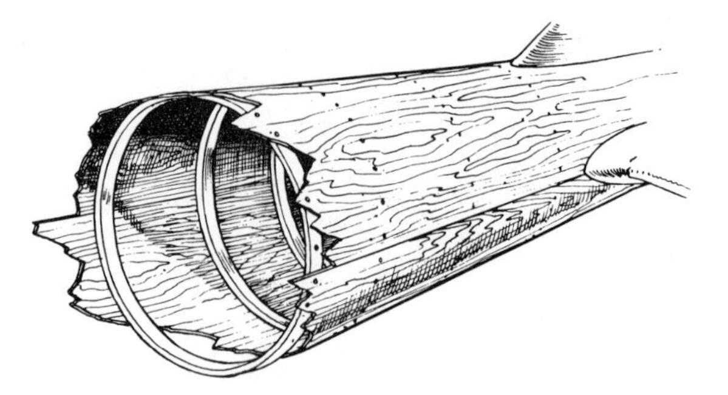

Figure 8 • 11 A wooden monocoque fuselage.

A wooden monocoque structure is illustrated in Fig. 8 • 11. It can be seen that this is merely a plywood shell with formers to hold the proper cylindrical or conical shape.

Jet airliner fuselages

To provide a good example of the construction of a fuselage for a modern jet airliner, some construction features of the Douglas DC-8 fuselage will be discussed. Figure 8 • 12 is a picture of the DC-8 in flight.

The fuselage of the DC-8 may be classed as a semimonocoque structure incorporating a number of fail-safe features. This means that, if there is failure in any part, the surrounding parts will take the additional load without failing. The fail-safe feature is developed through the use of titanium rip-stop doublers which reinforce the skin at strategic frames and surround every door and window. In addition, beaded doublers are used in the window belt area forward of the front spar. These can be seen in Fig. 8 • 13, which is a photograph of fuselage panels in various stages of construction.

The riveting of a fuselage section assembly is shown in Fig. 8 • 14. The large machine in the

Figure 8 • 12 A Douglas DC-8 jet airliner in flight.

Figure 8 • 13 DC-8 fuselage panels under construction.

Figure 8 • 14 Riveting of a fuselage section.

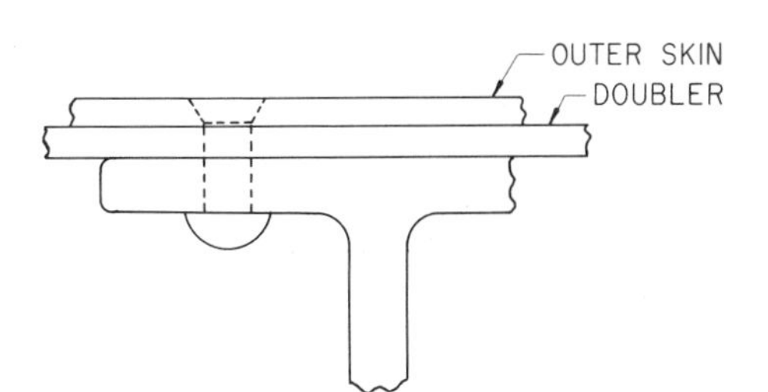

Figure 8 • 15 NASA rivet installation.

drawing is a Manco-Crispin semiautomatic riveting machine by which NASA-type riveting is accomplished. By means of these machines, a uniform fastening is made while a clamping action holds the members together under a pressure of 1,720 psi. On the external surface of the skin, the rivets are upset into countersunk cavities and then they are shaved smooth. This results in a very smooth, low-drag surface on the outside of the fuselage and is illustrated in Fig. 8 • 15. Sealing qualities and fatigue life are greatly improved by this method of riveting.

The rear portion of the DC-8 fuselage is lined with extra-thickness plating and closely spaced longitudinal stiffeners of a flattened hat section. This construction is shown in the photograph of Fig. 8 • 16. The aft section is covered with 7075-T aluminum-alloy skin, and the forward area, which is supported by conventionally spaced stiffeners, is covered with 2014-T6 skin. The stress level in the aft section is only about one-half that of the forward area. Skin gages in the forward portion are typically 0.060 in., and those in the aft section are typically 0.080 in. A minimum skin thickness of 0.050 is used in the pressure cabin section.

The lower fuselage, which is built in two sections, contains 16 panels. These sections are constructed in an upside-down position and secured in turning rings to place them physically in their proper positions. Next they are trans-

Figure **8 · 16** *Rear section of the DC-8.*

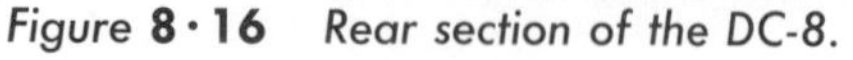

ferred to dollies before movement to the fuselage joining line.

Special fixtures are attached to the lower sections during assembly. These fixtures are used subsequently through the lower-half pickup, turnover position, fuselage joining line, fuselage installation line, and ultimately the wing-to-fuselage joining position. Once attached to the lower sections, the fixtures need not be removed and are used to index, carry, handle, and support the structures through all the fuselage major positions plus the critical wing and fuselage joining position.

The upper fuselage, containing 18 panels, has stretch-formed, rolled, or extruded Z transverse frames which are flush-riveted to the skins. After completion of the upper fuselage as a continuous section, it is hoisted into position directly above the two lower sections in the mating jig and the fuselage is riveted together. This operation is shown in Fig. 8 · 17.

The **nose section** of the fuselage is manufactured in three major sections called the **lower nose, upper nose,** and **cockpit enclosure.** The material is 0.060-in. 2014-T6 aluminum alloy,

Figure **8 · 17** *Joining fuselage sections.*

Figure **8 · 18** *Joining nose section and fuselage.*

Figure **8 · 19** *Tail assembly of the DC-8.*

with the exception of a 0.100-in. panel above the cockpit. When the fuselage line movement reaches the nose subassembly area, the nose and fuselage are joined together as shown in Fig. 8 · 18.

The tail assembly of the DC-8 is shown in Fig. 8 · 19. Observe that the construction is semimonocoque with transverse former rings and longitudinal stringers. It will also be noted from the photograph that large diagonal members extend from the inside of the tail section into the fin (vertical stabilizer) to transmit stresses from the fin to the fuselage.

WINGS

The purpose of this section is to explain the basic principles of wing design and construction which can be applied to any conventional airplane and in most respects to modern transport

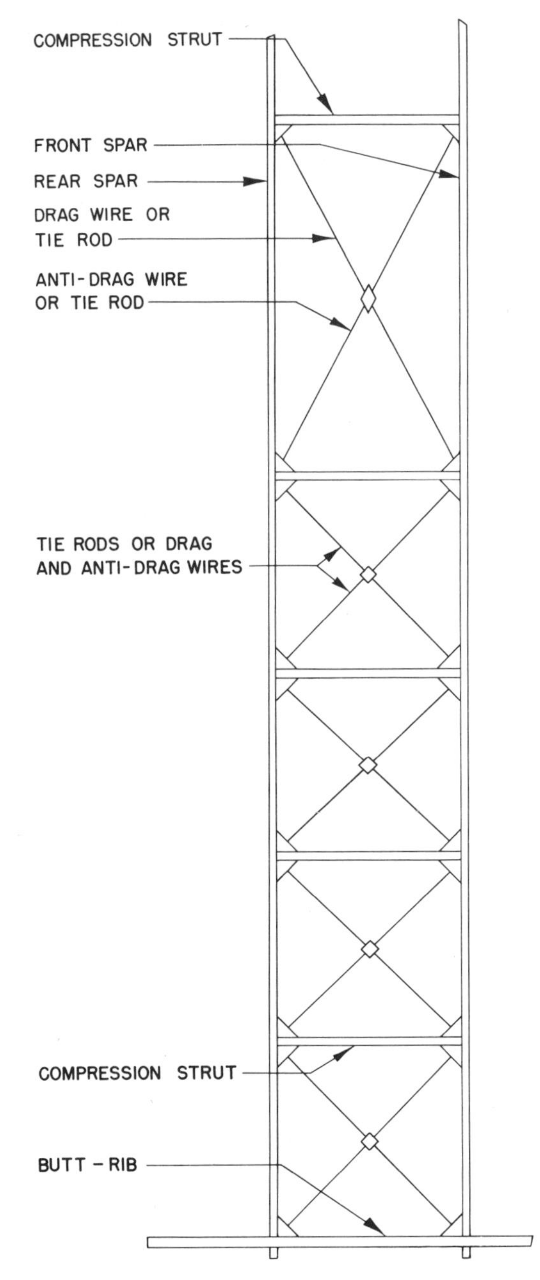

Figure **8 · 20** *Basic structure of a light-airplane wing.*

aircraft. It will be noted that any wing requires longitudinal (lengthwise with the wing) members of great strength to withstand the bending stresses, which are greatest during flight and upon landing. This is particularly true of the cantilever wings, which are normally employed for high-performance aircraft. Light aircraft often have external struts for wing bracing, and these do not require the type of internal structure needed for the cantilever wings.

Basic features of wing construction

Conventional wings are of three general types: **monospar, two-spar,** and **multispar.** True stressed-skin wings may have shear webs but no true "spars." The monospar wing has only one spar, the two-spar wing has two spars as the name indicates, and the multispar wing has more than two spars. A **wing spar,** sometimes called a **wing beam,** is a principal spanwise member of the wing structure. The spars in the basic structure for a light-plane wing are shown in Fig. 8 · 20. The structure shown in the illustration can be used in either a metal wing or a wood wing. In the metal wing all principal parts are made of aluminum alloy and the tie rods or brace wires are made of steel. In the wood wing, the spars may be the only members made of wood or both the spars and the compression struts (ribs) may be made of wood. Observe the two names for the tie rods or brace

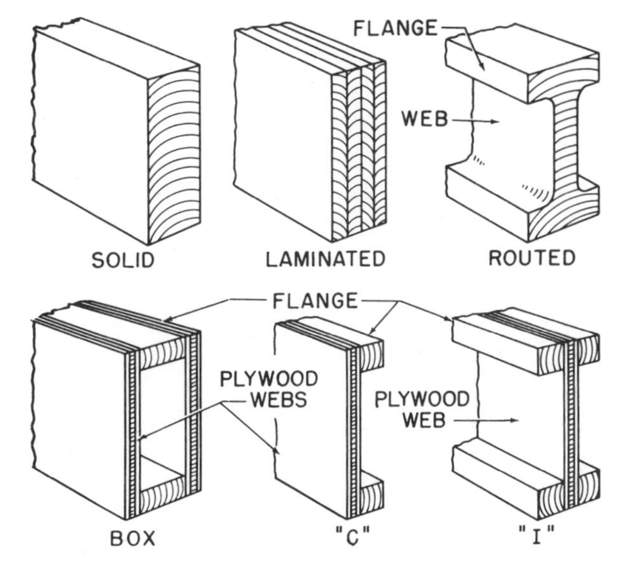

Figure **8 · 21** *Wood spar sections.*

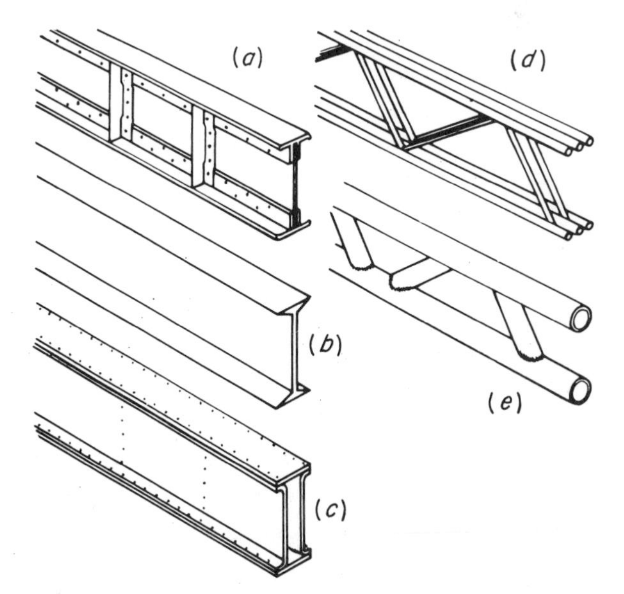

Figure **8 · 22** *Metal spar construction. (a) Built-up I beam; (b) extruded I beam; (c) built-up double-web spar; (d) welded-steel small-tubing structure; (e) welded-steel large-tubing structure.*

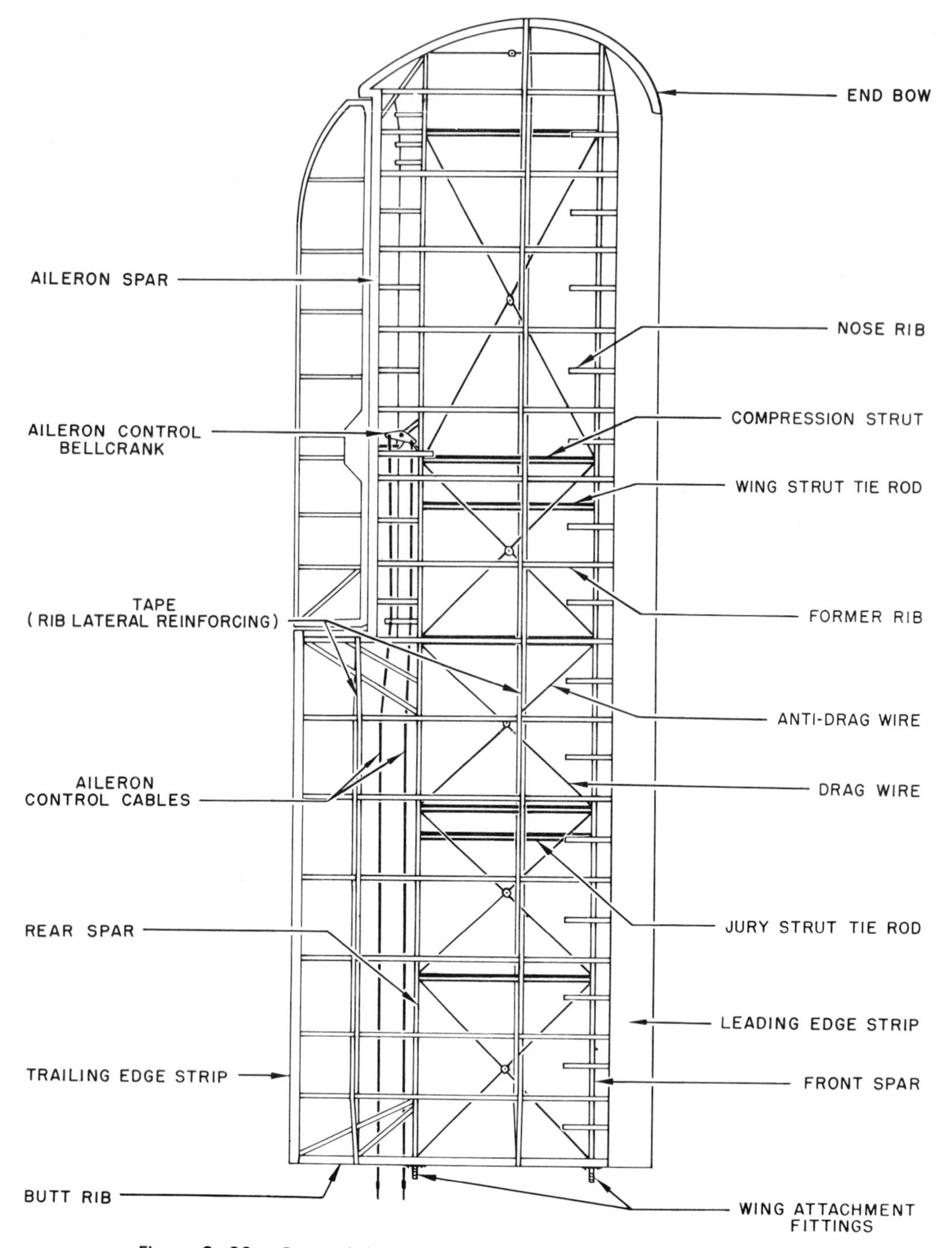

Figure **8·23** *General design of a light-plane wing with nomenclature.*

wires. The wires carrying drag loads are called **drag wires,** and those carrying the loads opposite drag are called **antidrag wires.**

The wing spars for a wood wing must be made of aircraft-quality spruce meeting the requirements set forth in Civil Aeronautics Manual 18 or some other type of wood meeting the same requirements. Wood spars may be solid or may be built up as shown in Fig. 8·21 and must be constructed of aircraft-grade woods.

Metal spars may be made in a variety of designs, such as those in Fig. 8·22. *a* is a built-up I beam, *b* is an extruded I beam, *c* is a built-up spar with a double web, *d* is a welded-steel tubing structure using small tubing, and *e* is a welded-steel structure using large tubing.

Figure 8·23 shows a general design for a light-aircraft wing to be covered with fabric. This type of structure may be made of wood or metal; however, the drawing indicates steel compression members.

A **wing rib,** sometimes called a **plain rib,** is

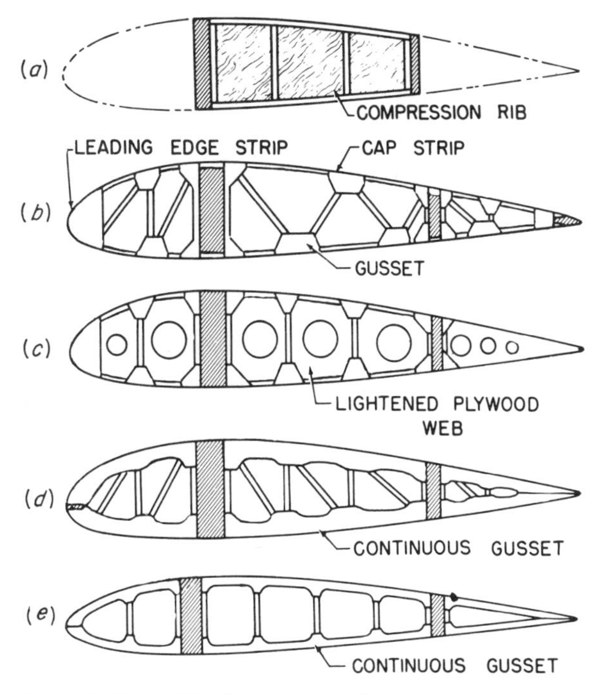

Figure 8·24 Ribs for wooden wings.

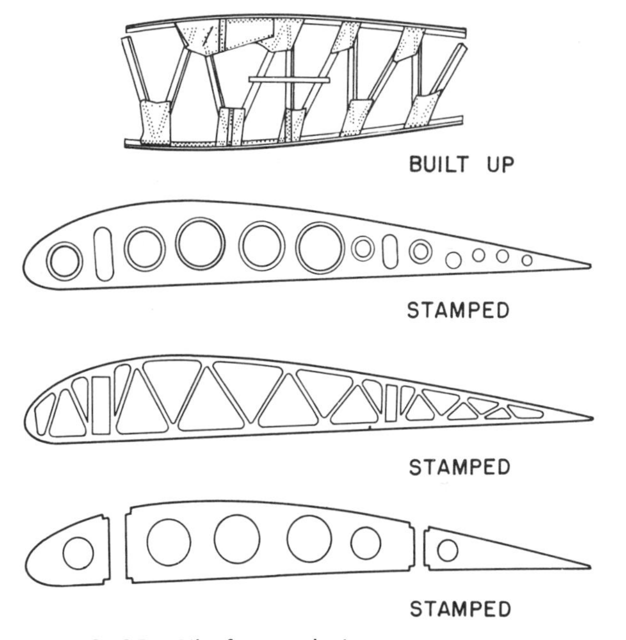

Figure 8·25 Ribs for metal wings.

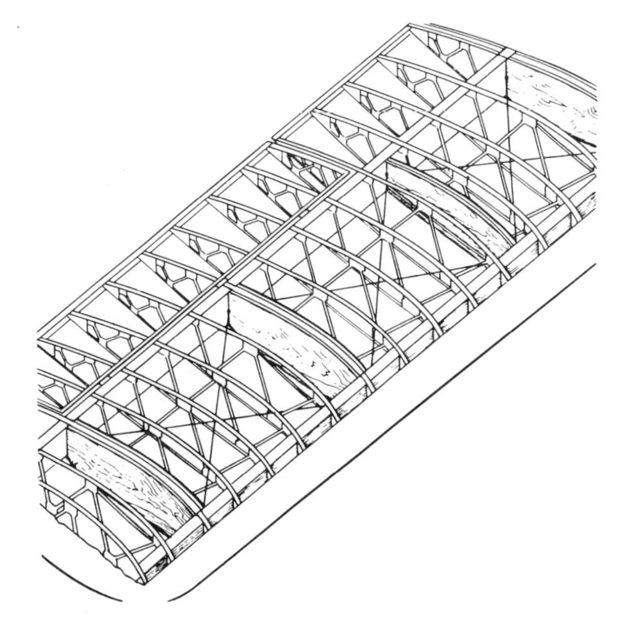

Figure 8·26 Wood wing construction.

a chordwise member of the wing structure used to give the wing section its shape and also to transmit the air loads from the covering to the spars. The rib may extend from the leading edge of the wing to the trailing edge or it may extend only to the rear spar, depending upon the type of construction. Ribs for wood wings are shown in Fig. 8·24. The rib shown in drawing *a* illustrates the use of compression ribs with heavy cap strips and solid plywood webs. The rib in drawing *b* is a typical built-up rib with cross bracing secured to the cap strips with plywood gussets. Ribs of this type are glued or glued and nailed. If nails are used, they must be of an approved type and coated with a rust-inhibiting cement. The cap strips are usually made of aircraft-grade spruce, first cut in straight strips and then bent to fit the rib configuration.

Drawing *c* shows a built-up rib with a plywood web which has been lightened by cutting large holes in the portions having the least stress. The ribs shown in drawings *d* and *e* have continuous gussets which eliminate the need for leading-edge strips. The only important difference between *d* and *e* is the method of bracing.

Typical metal ribs are shown in Fig. 8·25. Starting at the top of the illustration, the built-up rib is used in conjunction with metal spars and is riveted to them. The stamped rib with lightening holes and the stamped rib with a truss-type cross section are used with either metal or wood spars. The rib at the bottom of the picture is stamped in three sections and is usually riveted to metal spars.

An assembled wood wing is shown in Fig. 8·26. Either a fabric or a plywood covering can be applied to this type of wing structure. Notice that wood compression ribs are used instead of the tubular members used in the illustration of Fig. 8·23. When plywood or fabric is used for the covering, some of the stress is carried by the covering.

Typical stressed-skin metal construction is shown in Fig. 8·27. The skin of the wing is 2024-T4 aluminum alloy riveted to the ribs and

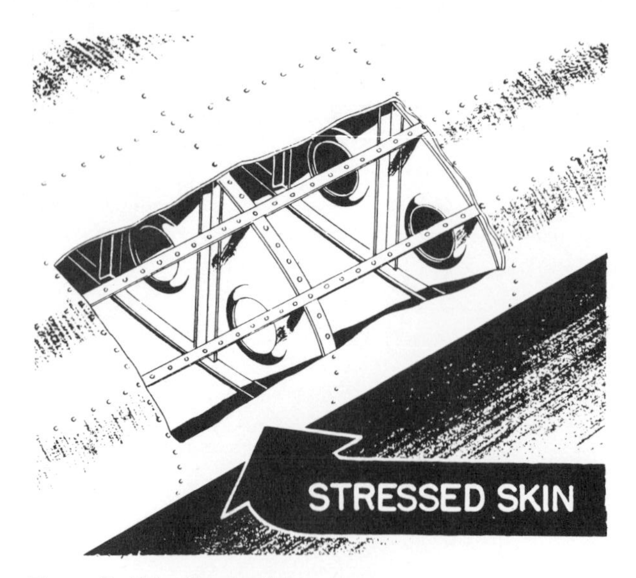

Figure **8 · 27** *Stressed-skin wing construction.*

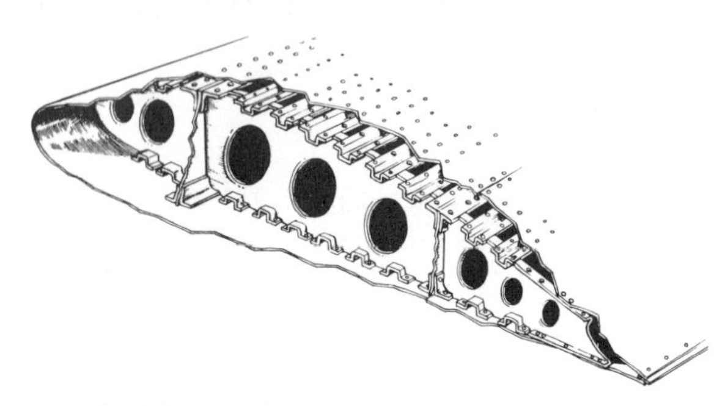

Figure **8 · 28** *Reinforced stressed-skin wing construction.*

stringers. It serves not only as a covering but also as a part of the basic structure of the wing.

The construction of another stressed-skin wing is shown in Fig. 8 · 28. In this design, the skin is reinforced with hat-section stringers used as stiffeners. The stringers are riveted to the ribs and to the skin.

Wing for a jet airliner

The construction of the wing for a modern jet airliner such as the Douglas DC-8 provides an understanding of how the great strength required for such a wing is attained. When we consider the weight of the wing itself plus the two jet engines hung under the wing on each side of the airplane plus the weight of the fuel carried in the wing, it seems almost impossible that the wing could be made strong enough to carry the weight alone, much less the additional loads imposed upon it in flight and upon landing.

The basic structure of the wing consists of three spars with conventional sheet-aluminum alloy webs and vertical stiffeners. Between the spars are ribs and bulkheads to provide additional strength and to form separations between the

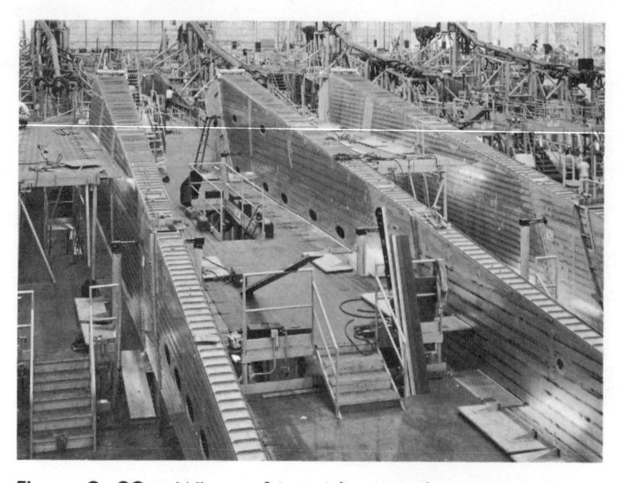

Figure **8 · 29** *Wings of jet airliner under construction.*

tank sections. Main-wing sections are shown on edge, rear spar down, in Fig. 8 · 29. Here the wing sections are in the assembly jigs during construction.

The inboard wing skins are stretch-formed across the sweepback and dihedral break. Prior to forming on a four-way stretch press, the skins are stored at a temperature of −30°F to prevent age hardening. The inboard skins are 10 by 50 ft in dimension and are taper-rolled to provide a maximum thickness in areas of heavy loading and a minimum thickness in the areas of reduced load. The skin is the thickest at the root and across the fuselage, where there are high bending and torsional loads.

When a skin is ready for forming, a lifting device with suction cups moves it into position on the press. The complex contour of the airfoil surface is shaped on the dies of the giant stretch press mentioned previously. On the press, the sheet is gripped by four jaws while hydraulically powered hold-down clamps fix the skin against spanwise movement. Each jaw pulls with a force of 300 tons to stretch the airfoil contour in the area of the dihedral break. The stretch-press operation is shown in Fig. 8 · 30.

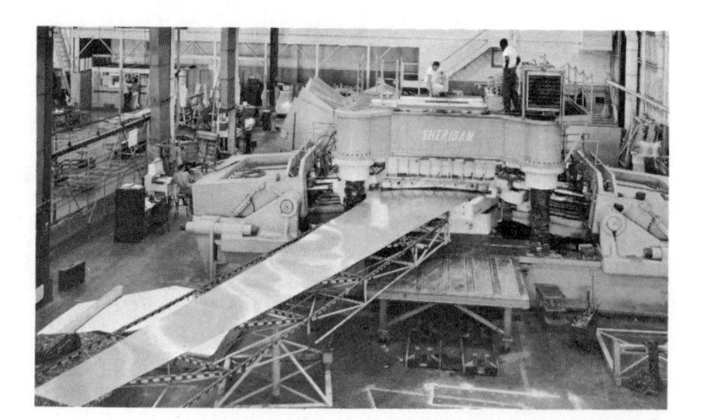

Figure **8 · 30** *Forming of wing skins on the stretch press.*

Figure 8·31 Sealing of wing for fuel tank.

The wing is fabricated entirely of 7075 aluminum-alloy sheet clad with pure aluminum on each side. Wing ribs are of formed 7075 sheet with tab segments along their periphery. These tabs are tied into the skins by clips milled from 7075 forgings. Each wing box beam is divided into four individual tanks separated by solid bulkheads. When the two wing sections are joined with top and bottom splices, a ninth tank is created by the wing junction. The wing halves thereby form a complete integral wing with a minimum of joints and splices. This design results in considerable weight saving over previous configurations.

During wing tank assembly operations, specified areas are hand-filleted with PR1422 Thiokol sealing compound. This is a brown paste which cures in about 4 hr at room temperature. The sealing compound is easily seen in the illustration of Fig. 8·31, which also shows some of the construction features of the wing.

After the wing halves are assembled, they are moved into a horizontal position for the joining of the right and left halves at the center line of the airplane. During the mating of the wing halves, final tank sealing and testing are accomplished. At this time the wing weighs about 28,000 lb. From one closing bulkhead to the other, the length is 136 ft without the wing tips. The chord range is from 340 to 74 in. The mated wing halves are shown in Fig. 8·32.

After the wings are assembled as shown in the illustration, they are coated inside by a fill and drain method. The entire wing is installed on a tilted platform, and the tanks are filled. The platforms are then tilted by means of hydraulic cylinders to ensure complete coating of the interior surfaces. After the mixture of synthetic-rubber compound and solvent is pumped out of the wing, hot air is circulated through the interior to cure the coating.

Of somewhat different construction from that described for the DC-8 airplane is the wing for the Boeing 720 jet airliner. The complete main structure of the wing consists of five sections: one center section, a right and left inboard wing, and a right and left outboard wing.

The wing primary structure is a box beam consisting of two spars, closely spaced inspar ribs, and longitudinally stiffened skins. In the wing center section the ribs are replaced by full-depth spanwise beams. The rear spar carries heavier loads than the front spar because of the swept-wing configuration and is therefore heavier. It is straight to a point just outboard of the outboard nacelle, where it increases its angle of sweep slightly. This point of change is the production break at which the outboard wing assembly can be removed when necessary.

Figure 8·32 Mated wing halves.

Details of wing design and construction

Wing structures carry some of the heaviest loads found in the aircraft structure; hence there are a number of details which must be understood, not only by the designer but also by the technician who performs the inspection, maintenance, overhaul, and repair of aircraft.

Fittings and joints in wings must be carefully proportioned so they can pick up loads in a gradual and progressive manner and redistribute these loads to other portions of the structure in a similar manner. Special attention must be paid to minimizing stress concentrations by avoiding too rapid changes in cross sections and to providing ample material to handle stress concentrations and shock loadings which are unavoidable.

The principles mentioned above are of special importance in considering the wing carry-through structures which carry landing loads to the fuselage. Allowance must be made for the fact that landing loads are of the impact type. This makes it necessary to provide adequate bearing areas for all attachments which carry such loads into the basic structure.

In addition to introducing these loads locally into the structure in a proper manner, they must be properly distributed throughout the structure. Bulkheads designed and built for this purpose in stressed-skin wings must have ample rigidity, and allowance must be made for the fact that considerable distance is required before these loads are completely distributed into the structure.

The principles already mentioned apply with full force when a landing gear is attached directly to a wooden spar, and in some instances they are even more important, because wood is more susceptible to stress-concentration effects than the average person realizes. For example, allowance must be made for stress concentration caused by holes through the spar.

A **filler block** is a wooden block sometimes placed in the routed-out portion of a spar between the flanges. When holes through a spar pierce both the spar cap strip and a filler block (if one is used), the filler block should extend a sufficient distance away from this part so that it can distribute the loads. In addition, filler blocks should be liberally tapered in order to avoid rapid changes in the effective cross section of the spar.

It is generally considered a sound practice to distribute the landing loads into wooden spars by means of several small bolts rather than by means of a few large bolts. Bolts alone may not provide an adequate attachment of the landing gear to the spar, especially when the bolt area required would cut out too much of the spar. In such a case, it is recommended that a hardwood block be incorporated under the spar to assist in distributing the landing-gear load.

Details of wing design and construction given below are mandatory FAA rules in the United States and sound practices in other countries. They must be understood not only by designers but also by technicians engaged in the inspection, maintenance, overhaul, and repair of aircraft.

When monoplanes are externally braced by wires only, the right and left sides of the bracing must be independent of each other so that an unsymmetrical load from one side will not be carried through the opposite wires before being counteracted unless the design complies with the following conditions: (1) the minimum true angle between any external brace wire and spar is 14°, (2) the landing wires are designed to remain in tension at least up to the **limit load,** and (3) the landing and flying wires are double. A limit load is a load or load factor or force which must be demonstrated to be safely experienced without damage or permanent set to the structure.

Multiple-strand cable must not be used in lift trusses. It must not be used in drag trusses unless such use is substantiated to the satisfaction of governmental authority.

When clamps are used for the attachment of jury struts to lift struts, the design must be such as to prevent misalignment or local crushing of the lift strut.

Wing beams must be reinforced against torsional failure, especially at the point of attachment of lift struts, brace wires, and aileron hinge brackets. Wing beam joints in metal beams (except pinned joints) and joints in mid-bays of wood beams must maintain 100 per cent efficiency of the beam with respect to bending, shear, and torsion.

Fabric-covered wing structures having a cantilever length of overhang such that the ratio of span of overhang to chord at the root of the overhang is greater than 1.75 must have a double system of internal-drag trussing spaced as far apart as possible or other means of providing equivalent torsional stiffness. When the double system of internal-drag trussing with wide spacing is used, counter wires must be of the same size as the drag wires. Whenever double-drag trussing is employed, all drag wires must incorporate a multiplying factor of safety varying linearly from 3.0 when the ratio of overhang to root chord of overhang is 2.0 or greater to 1.20 when such ratio is 1.0 or less, assuming an equal division of drag load between the two systems. This paragraph is primarily of interest to design engineers and need not be studied carefully by technicians, although a technician working on biplanes should understand that there are definite rules for drag trussing which must be observed.

Aileron and flap attachment ribs or brackets must be rigidly constructed and firmly attached to the main wing structure in order to reduce wing-flutter tendencies.

Fabric covering material and processes must comply with the requirements of the FAA as set forth in Civil Aeronautics Manual 18. Such covering must be attached in a manner which will develop the necessary strength, with due consideration for slip-stream effects.

Internally braced biplanes must be provided with N or I struts to equalize deflections, and the effect of such struts must be considered by the engineers conducting the stress analysis of the airplane.

When streamline wires are used for external lift bracing, they must be double unless the design complies with the "lift-wire-cut condition" which is an engineering problem beyond the usual duties of a technician.

Metal-covered wings must be designed to incorporate provisions to prevent the buckling or wrinkling of the metal covering. The covering must be sufficiently strong and adequately supported to withstand critical air loads and handling without injury or undesirable deformations. Deflections or deformation at low load factors which may result in fatigue failures should be avoided. In general, skin which shows deformations commonly known as **oil canning** is considered unsatisfactory.

EMPENNAGE AND CONTROL SURFACES

The stabilizers and the control surfaces of an airplane are constructed in a manner similar to the wings but on a much smaller scale. They usually include one or more main longitudinal members (spars) and ribs attached to the spars. The vertical stabilizer (fin) may be constructed as a part of the fuselage or may be a separate member which is both adjustable and removable.

The horizontal stabilizers often appear as the forward part of a wing, with the elevator serving as the rear part. Usually the airfoil section is symmetrical; that is, it has the same degree of camber for both top and bottom.

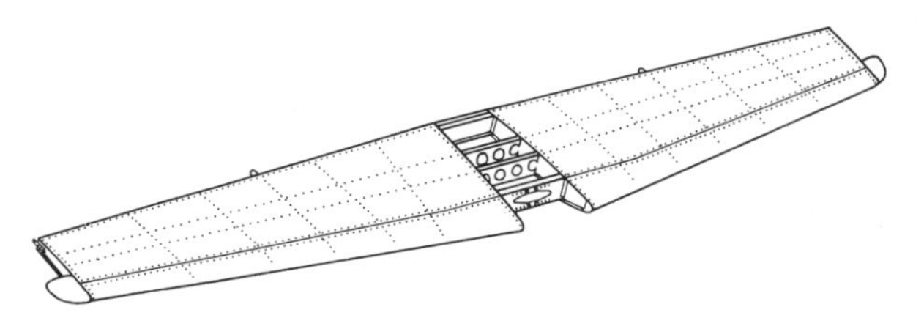

Figure **8·33** *Horizontal stabilizer for a light twin-engine airplane.*

Horizontal stabilizer

The appearance of the horizontal stabilizer for a Cessna 310 airplane is shown in Fig. 8·33. The internal structure consists of two main spars which extend the full length of the span. Across the spars are ribs, as indicated by the rows of rivets in the drawing. At the rear is an auxiliary spar to which four hinges are riveted to provide for installation of the elevators.

The construction of a horizontal stabilizer for a large jet airplane is illustrated in Fig. 8·34. This drawing shows the left-hand horizontal stabilizer for the Boeing 720 airliner. As indicated in the drawing, the principal structural members of the unit are the front and rear spars and the ribs. The outside of the unit is covered with sheet-aluminum alloy, which adds considerably to the strength. Attachments are provided at the inboard end to secure the unit to the center section, which is within the fuselage.

Vertical stabilizer

The vertical stabilizer for an airplane is the airfoil section forward of the rudder. This unit is commonly called the fin. The construction of the vertical stabilizer is very much like that of the horizontal stabilizer, and as mentioned previously, it may be constructed as an integral part of the fuselage. The rear structural member of the fin is provided with hinges for the support of the rudder.

Control surfaces

The control surfaces of an airplane include the ailerons, rudder, and elevator. The functions of these units have been described previously. The construction of the control surfaces is similar to that of the stabilizers; however, the movable surfaces usually are somewhat lighter in construction. They often have a spar at the forward edge to provide rigidity, and to this spar are attached the ribs and the covering. Hinges for attachment are also secured to the spar. Where it is necessary to attach trim tabs to the trailing edges of control surfaces, additional structure is added to provide for transmission of the tab

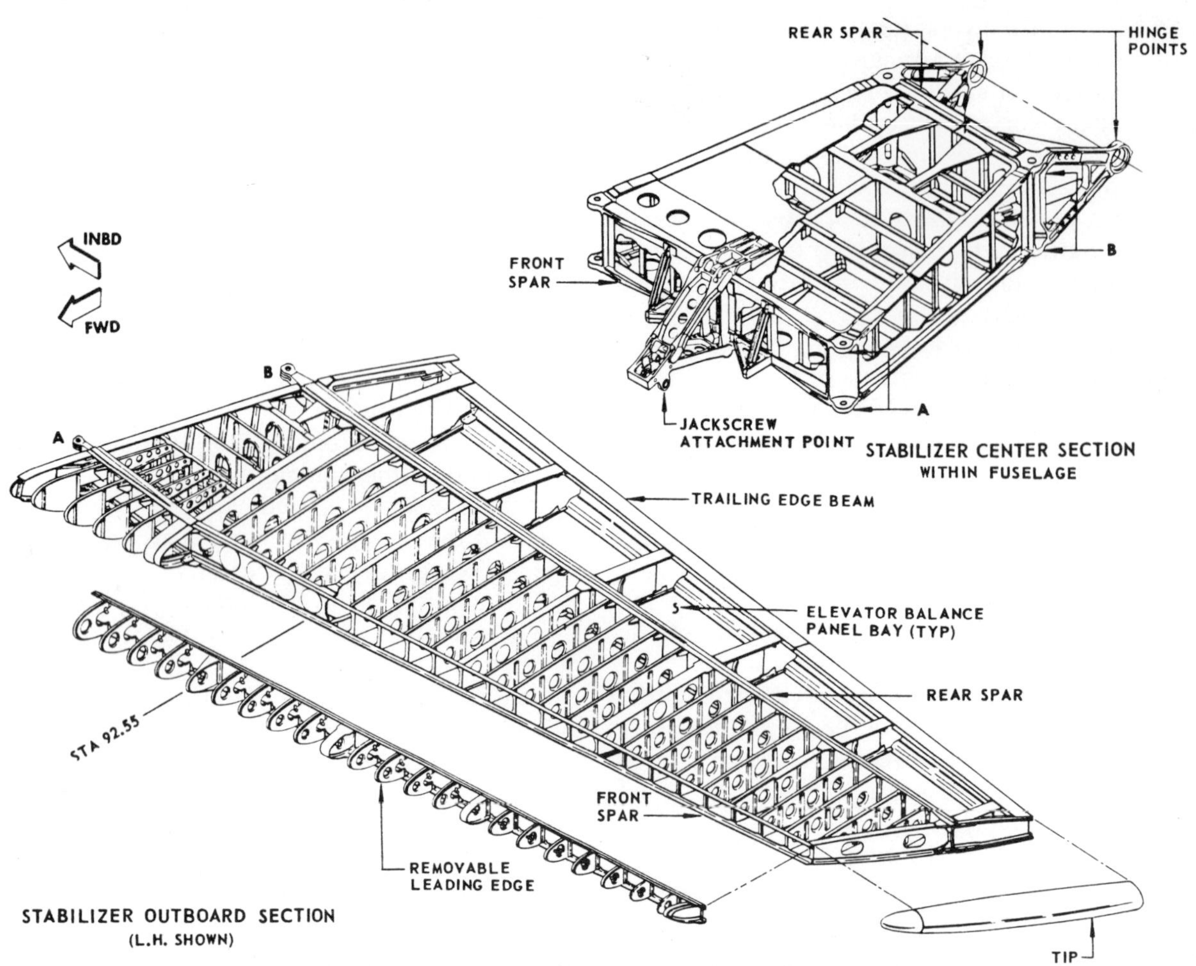

Figure **8·34** *Construction of horizontal stabilizer for jet airplane.*

loads to the surface. Typical of such an arrangement is the aileron assembly shown in Fig. 8·35.

Detail design of tail and control surfaces

The FAA sets forth certain requirements for the design and construction of the tail and control surfaces for an airplane, and because the technician must perform repair and maintenance in conformance with such requirements, they are listed here.

Movable tail surfaces shall be so installed that there is no interference between the surfaces or their bracing when any one is held in its extreme position and any other is operated through its full angular movement.

When an adjustable stabilizer is used, stops must be provided at the stabilizer to limit its movement, in the event of failure of the adjusting mechanism, to a range equal to the maximum required to balance the airplane.

Elevator trailing-edge tab systems must be equipped with stops which limit the tab travel to values not in excess of those provided for in the structural report. This range of tab movement must be sufficient to balance the airplane under all speeds of normal flight except those specified by Civil Air Regulations which are in excess of cruising speed or near stalling speed.

Hinges of the strap type bearing directly on torque tubes are permissible only in the case of steel torque tubes which have a multiplying factor of safety of 1.5 for ultimate strength. In other cases sleeves of suitable material must be provided for bearing surfaces.

Clevis pins may be used as hinge pins provided that they are made of a material conforming

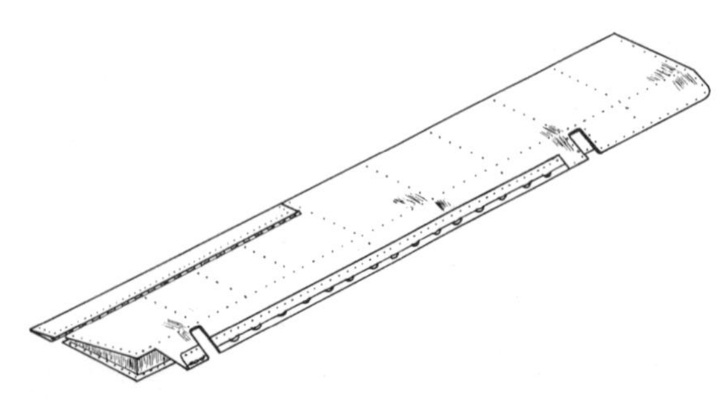

Figure **8·35** *Aileron with trim tab.*

with or equivalent to SAE specification 2330 (nickel-steel alloy).

When separate elevators are used, they must be rigidly interconnected so they cannot operate independently of each other.

All control surfaces must be dynamically and statically balanced to the degree necessary to prevent flutter at all speeds up to 1.2 times the design diving speed.

Flaps must be installed in such a manner that they will not induce flutter or appreciable buffeting.

The installation of trim and balancing tabs must be such as to prevent any free movement of the tab. When trailing-edge tabs are used to assist in moving the main surface (balancing tabs), the areas and relative movements must be so proportioned that the main surface is not overbalanced at any time.

COCKPITS, CABINS, AND COMPARTMENTS

Cockpit or pilot's compartment

The **cockpit** is that portion of the airplane occupied by the pilot (or the pilot and copilot). From this cockpit radiate all controls used in flying and landing the airplane. The word **controls** is a general term applied to the means provided to enable the pilot to control the speed, direction of flight, attitude, power, and altitude of an aircraft.

In designing an airplane, the engineers allow sufficient headroom, visibility, clearance for controls, and space for the movement of the hands and feet, keeping in mind the fact (for certain aircraft) that parachutes may be worn. These provisions are especially important in the case of airplanes designed for acrobatic use, and they are equally desirable when an airplane is to be used for a demonstration of flying ability during a pilot's flight tests or for other special purposes.

The fuselage and cabins must be designed to protect the passengers and crew in the event of a complete turnover, and adequate provision must be made to permit egress of passengers and crew in such an event. The requirements may be modified when the possibility of a complete turnover in landing is remote.

When the space occupied by the pilot (or the pilot and copilot) is completely enclosed, it may be referred to as a **cabin.** The word **compartment** is loosely used to mean any space occupied by personnel or cargo. For example, on a large airplane, it is possible to speak of the pilot's compartment, the navigator's compartment, the flight engineer's compartment, and the passenger's compartment or compartments.

The arrangement of the cockpit or pilot compartment and its appurtenances must provide safety and assurance that the flight crew will be able to perform all their duties and operate the controls in the correct manner without unreasonable concentration and fatigue.

A door equipped with a lock must be provided between the pilot compartment and the passenger compartment. The lock is provided to prevent passengers from entering the cockpit without the pilot's permission.

On a propeller-driven airplane the seats for the pilot and copilot and the primary control units for the airplane, excluding cables and control rods, must be so located with respect to the propellers that no portion of the pilots or controls lies in the region between the plane of rotation of any propeller and the surface generated by a line passing through the center of the propeller hub and making an angle of 5° forward or aft of the plane of rotation of the propeller. This requirement is necessary to protect the pilot and the airplane in case a propeller blade should be thrown from the engine shaft and should pass through the fuselage.

The pilot compartment in airplanes certificated for air-transportation service must be so constructed as to prevent any leakage into it when the airplane is flying in rain or snow. Leakage is prevented by the proper application of seals and sealing compound around the windshield, windows, and doors.

Vibration and noise characteristics of cockpit appurtenances must be such that they will not interfere with the safe operation of the airplane. The installation of insulating material and soundproofing and vibration-damping materials usually lowers the noise level and vibration characteristics to a point where a long flight can be made with little or no discomfort.

Single-place airplanes have one cockpit and provide accommodations for only the pilot. Two-place airplanes may have either one or two cockpits with the seats in tandem or side by side. Except for some agricultural aircraft and certain older types, there are few open-cockpit airplanes still in operation.

In any airplane there must be sufficient room for the installation of the required instruments, furnishings, and equipment in accessible positions. In two-place airplanes with dual controls, certain instruments, controls, and equipment are either duplicated or placed in positions where they are accessible to either pilot.

When a second pilot is required, two seats must be installed side by side in the pilot compartment of airplanes certificated for air-transportation service from either of which the airplane must be fully and readily controllable. If any difference exists as to convenience of the instruments and controls necessary for safe flight, such difference should favor the left-hand seat. The left-hand seat is known as the first pilot's seat and the right-hand seat is known as the second pilot's seat.

The arrangement of the cockpit, or pilot's compartment, for a modern light airplane is shown in Fig. 8·36. It can be seen from the illustration that the cockpit is attractively and functionally designed to provide for safe and comfortable flight.

The pilot's compartment of a modern jet airliner is shown in Fig. 8·37. Emphasized in this photograph are the many instruments and controls needed for the operation of the complex systems of a great airplane which flies through the air at more than 800 ft per sec.

The pilot compartment must be so constructed that it affords adequate ventilation and vision to the pilot under normal flying conditions. In cabin aircraft the windows must be so arranged that they can be readily cleaned or easily opened in flight to provide forward vision for the pilot. Of course, they cannot be opened when the cabin is pressurized [see Civil Aeronautics Manual 4a.505(b) and 4b.351(b)(2)].

The portion of the windshield that can be opened in flight is for the purpose of giving the pilot vision in case the windshield wiper and/or windshield heating system becomes inoperable during stormy conditions. The storm window must be so arranged that the airstream and the snow or rain are deflected across the opening.

Figure **8·36** *Cockpit for a light airplane.*

The windows and windshield sections for the pilot's compartment must be installed in such a manner that there will be no glare or reflections which will interfere with the vision of the pilot, particularly while flying at night.

The windshield panes which the pilots will be directly behind in the normal conduct of their duties and the supporting structures for such panes must have sufficient strength to withstand without penetration the impact of a 4-lb bird when the velocity of the airplane relative to the bird along the flight path of the airplane is equal to cruising speed Vc at sea level.

Some typical methods for installing transparent plastic sheet for windows and windshields are shown in Fig. 8·38. In *a* the opening for the window is reinforced with a flanged doubler riveted all around the opening. Retaining strips are placed on both the inside and the outside of the opening to form a channel into which the edge of the plastic sheet is placed. The inside retaining strip is joggled to accommodate the thickness of the plastic sheet. The edges of the sheet are protected with a waterproof adhesive tape or thin rubber channel.

The installation for the window in a door is shown in Fig. 8·38*b*. The outside retainer is a flat strip of metal, and the inside retainer is flanged and joggled for stiffness and to accommodate the thickness of the window. As before, the edge of the plastic sheet is protected by means of waterproof tape.

A method for retaining the lower edge of a windshield on a light plane is shown in Fig. 8·38*c*. An extruded channel section with a flange is formed to fit the contour of the airplane. The lower edge of the windshield is protected with a rubber channel section and then fitted into the metal channel as shown.

An understanding of the installation of cabin windows for pressurized airliners can be obtained from a study of Fig. 8·39. This illustration shows the details for the installation of a window in the Boeing 720 airliner. One passenger window consists of outer, center, and inner panes. The inner pane is nonstructural and is mounted in the cabin sidewall lining. It is not shown in Fig. 8·39. The outer and center panes are each capable of taking the full cabin pressurization load. Fail-safe structure is ensured by the center pane, which can take shock loadings subsequent to outer pane failure. All three panes are of acrylic plastic with the structural panes being stretched and formed

1. Autopilot disengage
2. Navigation marker lights
3. Airspeed indicator
4. Pilot directional indicator
5. Gyro horizon
6. Compass card
7. Altimeter
8. Clock
9. Rate of climb
10. Emergency pneumatic brake
11. Autopilot axis indicator
12. Altimeter
13. Ice-detector lights
14. Engine pressure ratio
15. Low spool engine rpm
16. Thrust reverser operating light
17. Tail pipe temperature
18. High spool engine rpm
19. Master warning light
20. Flap position indicators
21. Gear down, locked lights
22. Fuel flow
23. Landing-gear control handle
24. Static air temperature
25. Machmeter
26. Navigation radio selection
27. Glide slope light
28. Autopilot disengage light
29. Oil-pressure warning lights
30. Radio and radar controls
31. Air brake handle
32. Weather radar scope
33. Thrust levers
34. Parking brake latch
35. Engine start levers
36. Turn-and-bank indicator
37. Hydraulic system pressure
38. Brake system pressure
39. Flap control handle
40. Stabilizer trim wheel
41. Autopilot controls
42. Rudder trim

Figure **8 · 37** *Pilot's compartment for a jet airliner.*

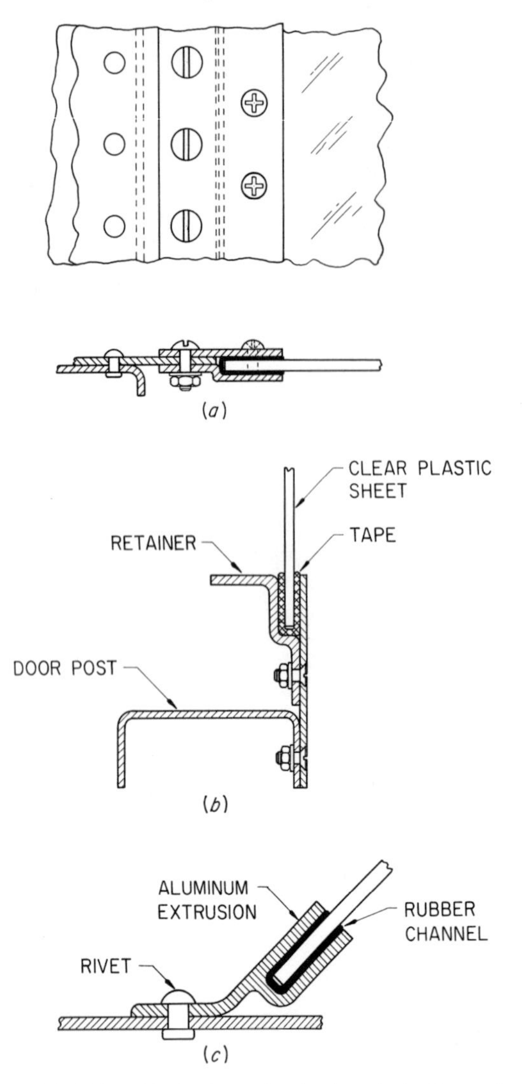

Figure **8·38** *Typical methods for installing plastic sheet.*

to improve resistance to crazing and to increase the strength.

The outer pane, which is rectangular with rounded corners, is curved to suit the fuselage contour and has a peripheral seal of sponge rubber. A steel spring assembly holds the outer pane against the window-frame forging. Spring retainers, which slip over special shouldered screws mounted on the window-frame forging, hold the spring assembly and outer pane in position. The center pane seats in a plastic reveal which is pressure sealed, and both pane and reveal are held in position on the window-frame forging by retaining brackets.

Passenger compartments

Passenger compartments must be designed and equipped to provide a maximum of comfort and safety for the passengers. This is particularly true for those aircraft certificated as air carriers for passenger service.

Passenger compartments must be adequately ventilated by means of a system which precludes the presence of fuel fumes and dangerous traces of carbon monoxide. The ventilation system is usually integrated with the heating system, and if the airplane needs to be pressurized, the pressurization system is also included in the design.

The passenger compartment of a jet airliner is illustrated in Fig. 8·40. This photograph shows the three-seat arrangement for coach configurations, the "tracks" in the floor to which the seats are anchored, and the overhead compartments in which the emergency oxygen-dispensing equipment is stored. Some details of the seat construction and finish are visible. The compartment shown illustrates one arrangement of the Boeing 720 airliner. The Douglas DC-8 cabin is shown in Fig. 8·41.

The seats in the passenger compartment must be securely fastened to the aircraft structure in all types of aircraft, regardless of whether or not the safety-belt load is transmitted through the seat. Each seat must be equipped with a safety belt which has been approved by the FAA.

Cargo compartments

Baggage and cargo compartments must be designed in such a manner that they will carry their approved capacity under all normal conditions of flight and landing without failure of any structural part. Each compartment must bear a placard stating the maximum allowable weight of contents as determined by the structural strength of the compartment and the flight tests conducted for certification of the airplane. Suitable means must be provided to prevent the contents of baggage and cargo compartments from shifting.

Doors

The doors for aircraft are usually constructed of the same materials used for the other major components. Typically, the main framework of a door consists of a formed sheet-metal structure to provide rigidity and strength, and to this framework is riveted the sheet-metal outer skin. The metal used is aluminum alloy such as 2024-T4. The door frame is formed on a hydropress, stamp press, or drop hammer.

If the door is used for entrance to an upholstered cabin, the inside of the door will be covered with a matching upholstered panel. Inside the door structure will be located the door latching and locking mechanisms. The upper portion of the door will often contain a window made of a clear plastic similar to that used for the other cabin windows. The edge of the plastic sheet used

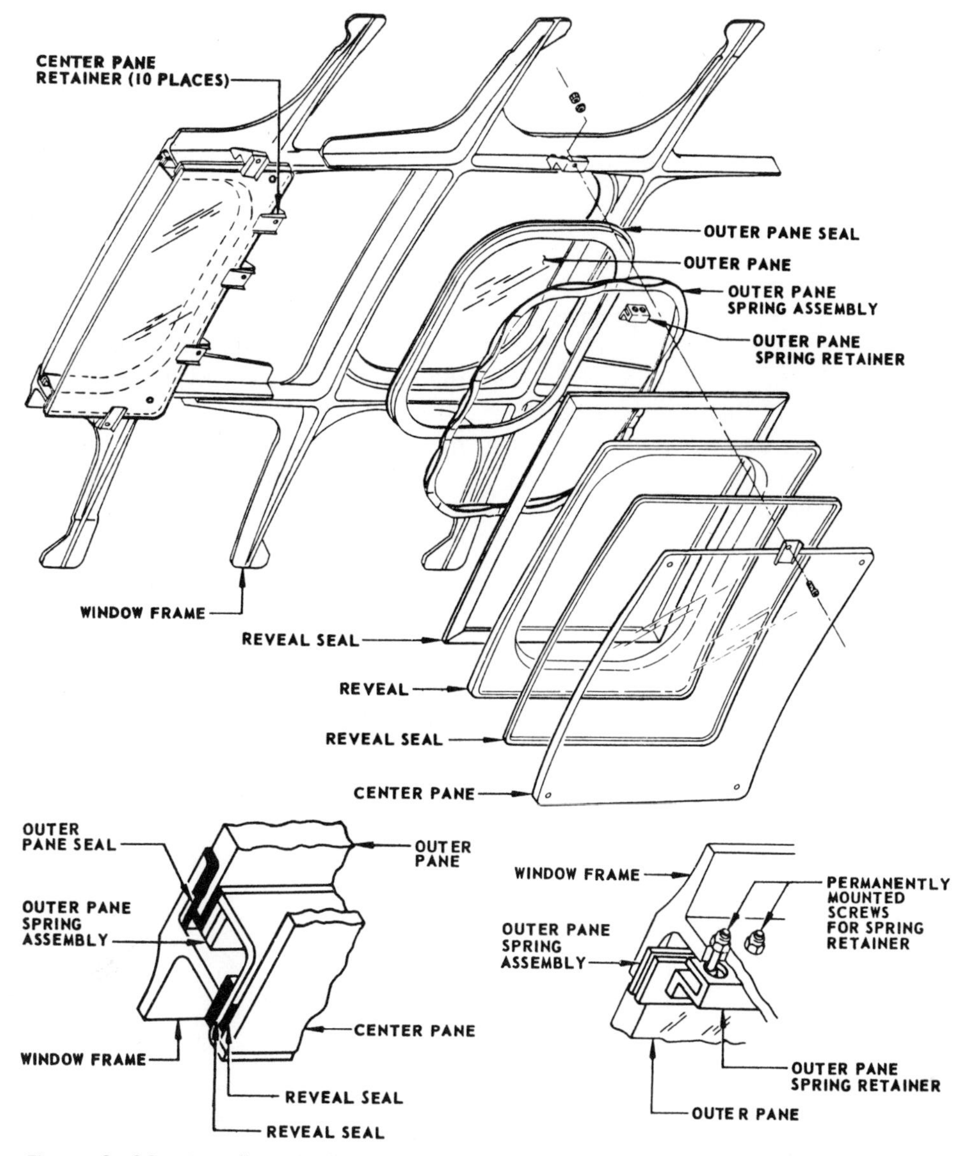

Figure **8·39** *Installation of a window for a pressurized jet airplane (Boeing Airplane Co.).*

Figure **8·40** *Passenger compartment of jet airliner (Boeing Airplane Co.).*

Figure **8·41** *Passenger compartment of the DC-8 (Douglas Aircraft Co.).*

for the window is protected with waterproof tape and is held in the frame by means of one or more retainers designed to form a channel. The retainers are secured by means of screws.

The doors for a pressurized airliner must be much stronger and much more complex than the door for a light airplane. Typical of a door for the main cabin of a jet airliner is that shown in Fig. 8·42. This illustration is a drawing of the forward entry door for the Boeing 720 airliner. As shown in the drawing, the door consists of a strong framework of aluminum alloy to which is riveted a heavy outer skin formed to the contour of the fuselage. At the top and the bottom edges of the door are hinged gates which make it possible, in effect, to decrease the height of the door so it can be swung outward through the door opening.

The hinging and controlling mechanism of the door is rather complex in order to provide for the necessary maneuvering to move the door outside the airplane when loading and unloading passengers. For safety in a pressurized airplane, the door is designed to act as a plug for the door opening, and the pressure in the cabin seats the door firmly in place. To accomplish this, the door must be larger than its opening and must be inside the airplane with pressure pushing outward. This prevents the rapid decompression of the cabin which could occur if the door should be closed from the outside and the securing mechanism should become unlatched.

The operation of the door is shown in Fig. 8·43. The door is opened from the airplane interior by rotating the **inside handle** counterclockwise as shown in steps 1 and 2. Initial rotation of the

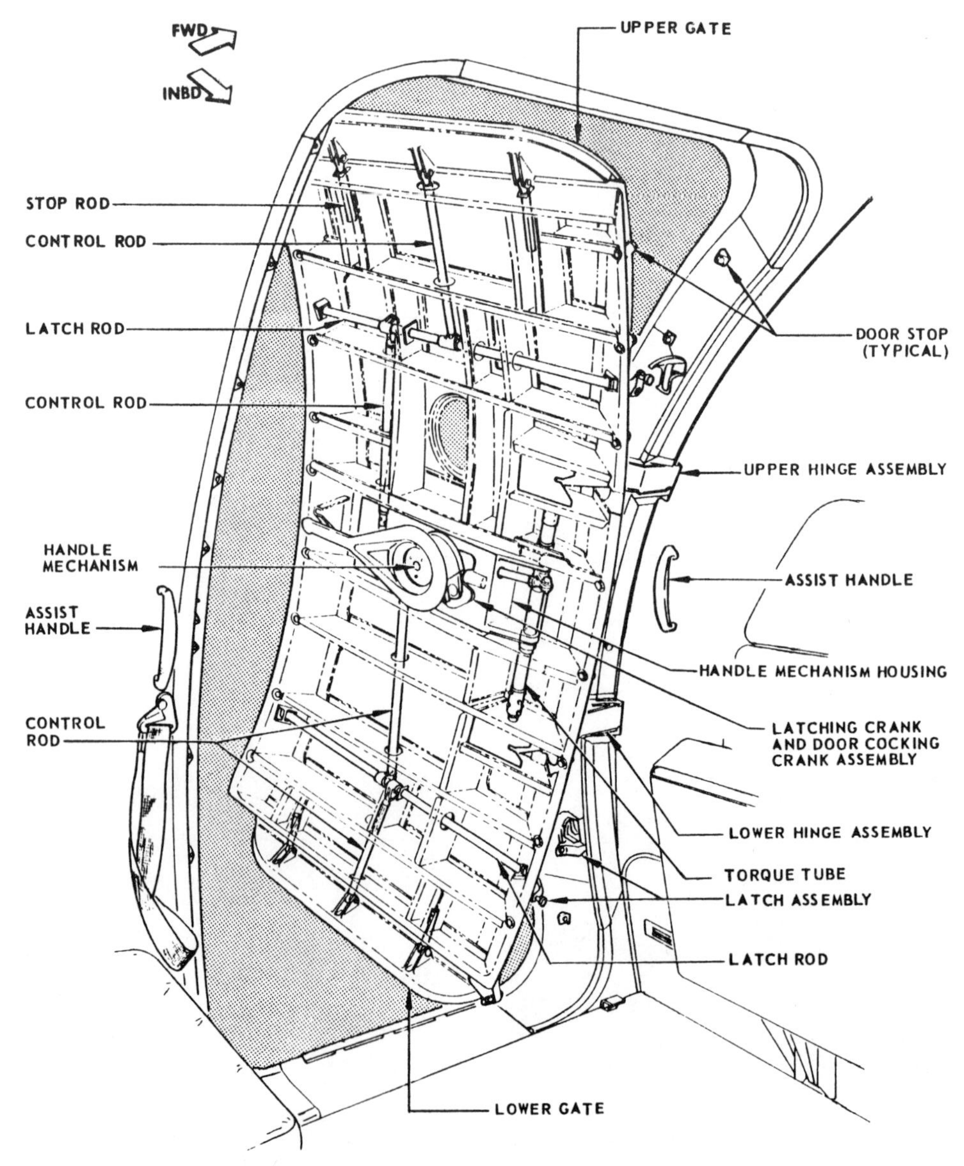

Figure **8·42** *Main cabin door for a jet airliner.*

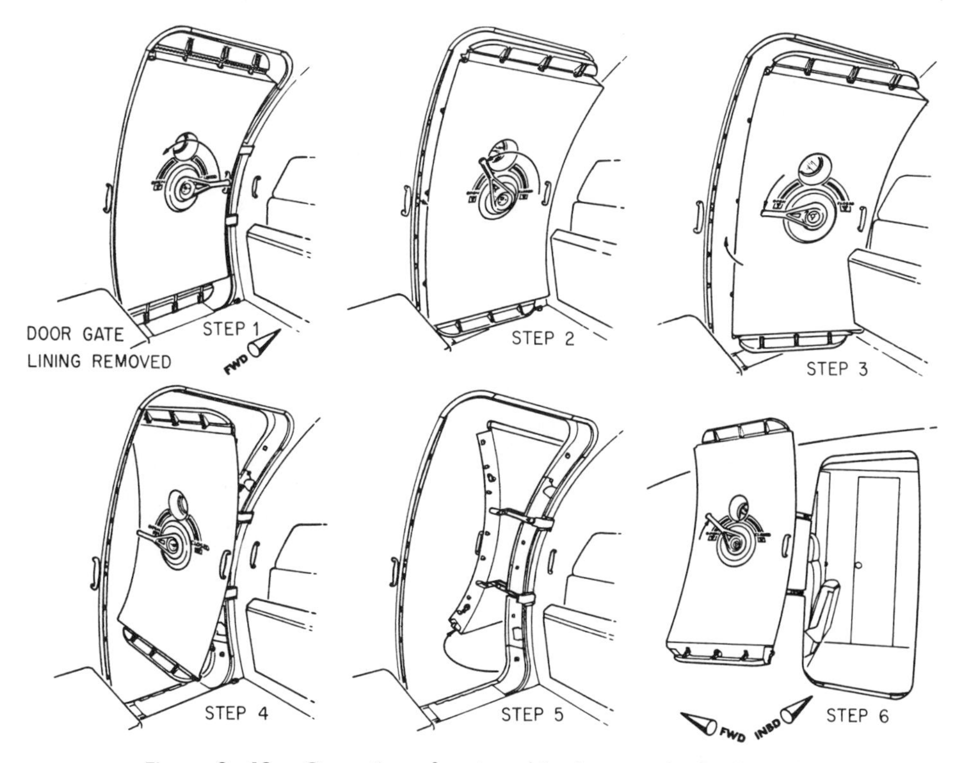

Figure **8·43** *Operation of main cabin door on the Boeing 720.*

cam plate transmits angular movement to the **latching-crank assembly.** The control rods at each end of the **latching crank** turn the **latch rods** and withdraw the latch rollers from the latches, thus allowing the door to move inward (step 3). The **latch rods** also operate the **control rods** attached to the **upper** and **lower gates,** causing them to fold inward and push the **stop rods** away from their **stops.** Further rotation of the handle to its full travel of 180° allows the cam plate to transmit angular movement to the **cocking-crank assembly** (see Fig. 8·42). The **cocking crank** operates the push rod connected to the **torque-tube crank.** Movement of the push rod is resisted by the torque tube, causing the door to rotate on the hinge arms and pivot about the torque-tube axis. This motion is due to the change in relative positions of the hinge arm and guide arm at the upper hinge and the hinge arm and snubber at the lower hinge. Tracking of the door is controlled by the guide-arm roller in the roller-guide plates. As the door rotates to the cocked position (step 3, Fig. 8·43), the guide arm and snubber deflect the upper and lower hinge flaps inward on their hinges. The door is swung through the opening by means of an **assist handle** (step 4). The outward lateral travel of the hinge arm transmits motion through the radius link to the guide arm, which in turn causes the door to rotate in an outward direction about the pivot axis of the torque tube. The inside handle on the door automatically rotates approximately 45° clockwise during the final movement of the door to the latched position (steps 5 and 6). This is due to the change in relative position of the hinge arms, guide arm, and snubber, passing beyond 180° from the door cocked position and causing the door to counterrotate and operate the **cocking crank** and cam plate in reverse. When the door is approximately parallel with the airplane exterior, the stop pin contacts the stop plate and prevents further movement of the door. The door is latched in the open position by the **latch pin** engaging the **latch-pin hole.**

The door is closed by depressing the **door-open stowing latch lever** which releases the latch pin. The remainder of the closing is essentially the reverse of the opening process. The door can also be opened and closed from outside the airplane by means of a recessed handle on the outside of the door.

It must be noted that the foregoing description represents only one of several door designs for pressurized aircraft. It does, however, emphasize the complexity of such doors necessary as a result of cabin pressurization, which imposes loads of several tons on each door.

Requirements for doors and exits

The doors and special exits for passenger-carrying aircraft must conform to certain regulations designed to provide for the safety and well-being of passengers. These regulations are established by the FAA, and they must be followed in the design and manufacture of all certificated aircraft for passengers.

Closed cabins on all aircraft carrying passengers must be provided with at least one adequate and easily accessible external door.

No passenger door may be located in the plane of rotation of an inboard propeller or within 5° thereof as measured from the propeller hub.

The external doors on transport aircraft must be equipped with devices for locking the doors and for safeguarding against opening in flight either inadvertently by persons or as a result of mechanical failure. It must be possible to open external doors from either the inside or the outside even though persons may be crowding against the door from the inside. The use of inward-opening doors is not prohibited if sufficient measures are provided to prevent occupants from crowding against the door to an extent which would interfere with the opening of the door. The means of opening must be simple and obvious and must be so arranged and marked internally and externally that it can be readily located and operated even in darkness.

Reasonable provisions must be made to prevent the jamming of any external door as a result of fuselage deformation in a minor crash.

External doors for a transport airplane must be so located that persons using them will not be endangered by the propellers of a propeller-operated airplane when appropriate operating procedures are employed.

Means must be provided for a direct inspection of the door-locking mechanism by crew members to ascertain whether all external doors for which the initial opening movement is outward, including passenger, crew, service, and cargo doors, are fully locked. In addition, visual means must be provided to signal to appropriate crew members that all normally used external doors are closed and in the fully locked position. This requirement is often met by placing indicator lights in the cockpit. These lights are operated by switches incorporated in the door-locking mechanisms.

Closed cabins on aircraft carrying more than five persons must be provided with **emergency exits,** in addition to the one external door mentioned previously. The exits consist of movable windows or panels or of additional external doors which provide a clear and unobstructed opening, the dimensions of which are such that a 19- by 26-in. ellipse may be inscribed therein. The location and the method of operation must be approved by governmental authority. If the pilot is in a compartment separate from the cabin, passage through such compartment must not be considered as an emergency exit for the passengers.

Aircraft with a total seating capacity of more than 5 persons, but not in excess of 15 persons, must be provided with at least one emergency exit or one suitable door in addition to the main door. This emergency exit or additional door must be on the opposite side of the cabin from the main door. If desired, an additional emergency exit may be provided in the top of the cabin, but such an installation will not eliminate the necessity for an exit on each side of the aircraft.

Aircraft with a seating capacity of more than 15 persons must be provided with an additional emergency exit or door in either the top or side of the cabin for every additional 7 persons or fraction of 7 above 15, except that not more than four exits, including doors, will be required if the arrangement and dimensions are suitable for the purpose intended.

Passenger-carrying transport aircraft such as those used by the schedule airlines must be equipped with sufficient emergency exits to permit rapid egress in the event of crash landings, whether with the landing gear retracted or extended, taking into account the possibility of the airplane being on fire. If the airplane is divided into separate compartments arranged so that the minimum unobstructed passageway (20 in.) between such compartments is not available, the emergency-exit requirements must be applied to each compartment independently. Passenger and crew entrances and service doors shall be considered as emergency exits if they meet the applicable requirements stated above.

Flight-crew emergency exits must be located in the flight-crew area, one on each side of the airplane, or alternatively, a top hatch must be provided. Such exits must be of sufficient size and must be so located as to permit rapid evacuation by the crew. Such exits are not required in airplanes having a passenger capacity of 20 or less if the proximity of passenger emergency exits to the flight-crew area offers a convenient and readily accessible means of evacuation for the flight crew.

The passenger emergency exits are classified according to size and arrangement. There are four types of exits classified as follows:

Type I: A rectangular opening not less than 24 in. wide by 48 in. high, with corner radii not greater than one-third the width of the exit. The first type I exit on each side of the fuselage must be located on the aft portion of passenger compartment unless the configuration of the airplane is such that some other location would afford a more effective means of passenger evacuation. All type I exits are floor-level exits.

Type II: A rectangular opening not less than 20 in. wide by 44 in. high, with corner radii not greater than one-third the width of the exit. Unless type I exits are required, one type II exit on each side of the fuselage must be located in the aft portion of the passenger compartment except where the configuration of the airplane is such that some other location would afford a more effective means of passenger evacuation. Type II exits must be floor-level exits unless located over the wing, in which case they must have a step-up inside the airplane of not more than 10 in. and a step-down outside the airplane of not more than 17 in.

Type III: A rectangular opening not less than 20 in. wide by 36 in. high, with corner radii not greater than one-third the width of the exit, located over the wing with a step-up inside the airplane of not more than 20 in. and a step-down outside the airplane of not more than 27 in.

Type IV: A rectangular opening not less than 19 in. wide by 26 in. high, with corner radii not greater than one-third the width of the exit, located over the wing with a step-up inside the airplane of not more than 29 in. and a step-down outside the airplane of not more than 36 in.

The number of passenger exits required for transport aircraft is determined by the maximum number of passengers which the airplane is certificated to carry. Table 8 · 1 specifies the type and number of exits required for various sizes of aircraft.

When an airplane is equipped to carry 220 or more passengers, it must be equipped with additional exits. The additional exits must provide an effective means of passenger evacuation consistent with the requirements of Table 8 · 1. It is acceptable to install two type IV exits in lieu of each required type III exit.

If it is found that adequate compensating factors exist, as determined by official inspection, it is permissible to increase the passenger seating capacity beyond that shown in Table 8 · 1, except that such increase may in no case exceed 10 passengers.

On airplanes where the vertical location of the wing does not permit the installation of overwing exits, an exit with dimensions not less than those for a type III exit must be installed for each type III or type IV exit required in Table 8 · 1.

Emergency exits must be movable doors or hatches in the external walls of the fuselage and must provide an unobstructed opening to the outside. All emergency exits must be openable from the inside and from the outside of the airplane except that sliding window emergency exits in the flight-crew area need not be openable from the outside if it is found that the proximity of other approved exits makes them convenient and readily accessible to the flight-crew area. The means of opening exits must be simple and obvious and must not require exceptional effort of a person opening them.

Table 8 · 1

Passenger seating capacity	Emergency exits required on each side of the fuselage			
	Type I	*Type II*	*Type III*	*Type IV*
1 to 10, inclusive	. . .	. . .	. . .	1
11 to 19, inclusive	. . .	. . .	1	
20 to 39, inclusive	. . .	1	. . .	1
40 to 59, inclusive	1	. . .	. . .	1
60 to 79, inclusive	1	. . .	1	
80 to 109, inclusive	1	. . .	1	1
110 to 139, inclusive	2	. . .	1	
140 to 179, inclusive	2	. . .	2	
180 to 219, inclusive	2	2		

Means must be provided for locking each emergency exit and for safeguarding against opening in flight either inadvertently by persons or as a result of mechanical failure. Means must also be provided for a direct visual inspection of the locking mechanism by crew members to ascertain whether all emergency exits for which the initial opening movement is outward are fully locked.

Provisions must be made to minimize the possibility of jamming of emergency exits as a result of fuselage deformation in a minor crash landing.

For all landplane emergency exits other than exits located over the wing which are more than 6 ft from the ground with the airplane on the ground and the landing gear extended, approved means must be provided to assist the occupants in descending to the ground.

All passenger emergency exits, their means of access, and their means of opening must be marked conspicuously. The identity and location of emergency exits must be recognizable from a distance equal to the width of the cabin. The location of the emergency-exit operating handle and the instructions for opening must be marked on or adjacent to the emergency exit and must be readable from a distance of 30 in.

A source or sources of light, with an energy

supply independent of the main lighting system, must be installed to illuminate all passenger emergency-exit markings. Such lights must be designed to function automatically in a crash landing and shall also be operable manually.

All emergency exits which are required to be openable from the outside and their means of opening must be marked on the outside of the airplane for guidance of rescue personnel.

Passageways between individual compartments of the passenger area and passageways leading to type I and type II emergency exits must be unobstructed and must be not less than 20 in. wide. Adjacent to emergency exits where assisting means for ground access are required, there shall be sufficient additional space to allow a crew member to assist in the evacuation of passengers without reduction in the unobstructed width of the passageway to such exit.

Access must be provided from the main aisle to all type III and type IV exits, and such access must not be obstructed by seats, berths, or other protrusions to an extent which would reduce the effectiveness of the exit, except that minor obstructions are permissible if it is found that compensating factors are present to maintain the effectiveness of the exit. If it is necessary to pass through a doorway to reach any required emergency exit from any seat in the passenger cabin, the door must be provided with a means to latch it in the open position. A suitable placard stating that the door is to be latched in the open position during takeoff and landing must be installed.

The main passenger aisle at any point between seats must not be less than 15 in. wide up to a height above the floor of 25 in. and not less than 20 in. wide above that height.

For airplanes having a maximum passenger seating capacity of 19 or less, the aisle widths must not be less than 12 in. wide up to a height above the floor of 25 in. and not less than 20 in. above that height.

Figure 8·44 Conventional landing-gear arrangement.

Figure 8·45 Tricycle landing-gear arrangement.

Figure 8·46 Tandem landing gear on the B-52 bomber.

LANDING GEAR

In any study of aircraft structures it is necessary to consider the landing gear, its construction, its arrangement, and the methods by which it is attached to the aircraft structure. The method of attachment to the aircraft structure is important because of the need for transmitting landing loads to the aircraft without overstressing portions of the aircraft structure.

Types of landing gear

Landing gear may be classified as either **fixed** or **retractable,** and it may also be classified according to arrangement on the aircraft. In this case we may say that the two principal arrangements are **conventional** and **tricycle.** The **conventional** arrangement utilizes a tail wheel, and the tail of the aircraft is low when the airplane is on the ground. A conventional arrangement is shown in Fig. 8·44.

The tricycle landing-gear arrangement employs a nose wheel, and the aircraft is nearly in a level position when it is on the ground. An airplane with tricycle gear is shown in Fig. 8·45. Almost all aircraft being manufactured today are designed with tricycle gear, so we may say that the tricycle gear is more "conventional" than the old conventional gear (tail-wheel type).

An unusual arrangement of the landing gear is used on the B-52 bomber. This is called the **tandem** configuration, since the main landing-gear assemblies are arranged in tandem at the bottom of the fuselage. The airplane is prevented from tipping by means of small "outrigger" wheels and struts located near the wing tips. A B-52 with tandem gear is shown in Fig. 8·46.

Shock-absorbing methods

Various methods have been used to absorb landing shocks including rubber shock cord, stacks of rubber disks, coil springs, spring and hydraulic piston (spring-oleo) combinations, flexible spring steel struts, and air-oleo combinations. For many years the rubber shock cord was used on light planes, and many such planes are still in operation.

An unconventional but effective landing gear was developed by the Cessna Aircraft Company and installed only in their light planes manufactured immediately after World War II. This was a flexible-steel-strut gear. Each strut for this gear consists of a tapered strip of strong alloy steel tempered to provide flexibility and elasticity. The strut arrangement is extremely simple and requires practically no service or maintenance. The large end of each strut is bolted into the main forward fuselage structure where the fuselage members are designed with extra strength to absorb landing shocks. The brake and axle assemblies are bolted to the small end of the strut.

The most popular type of shock-absorbing system for both large and small aircraft is the air-oleo strut in the landing gear. The strut consists of an outer cylinder, an inner cylinder (lower strut), a metering piston with an orifice, and a metering pin. The operation is such that, when the airplane lands, the oil in the lower portion of the strut is forced upward through the orifice in the metering piston. The size of the orifice is decreased by the metering pin as the strut is compressed. The compression of the strut, causing the oil to move through the orifice to the upper part of the strut, brings about the compression of the air in the strut. The result is that the first shock of landing is cushioned by the oleo section of the strut and the load of the airplane during taxiing is carried by the compressed air in the strut. One of the main landing-gear struts and the four-wheel gear of a DC-8 airliner are shown in Fig. 8·47. This gear is designed to caster, or swivel, so that the airplane will turn more easily. A simplified cross-sectional drawing of the air-oleo strut is shown in Fig. 8·48.

Figure **8·47** *Main gear unit for the DC-8 airliner.*

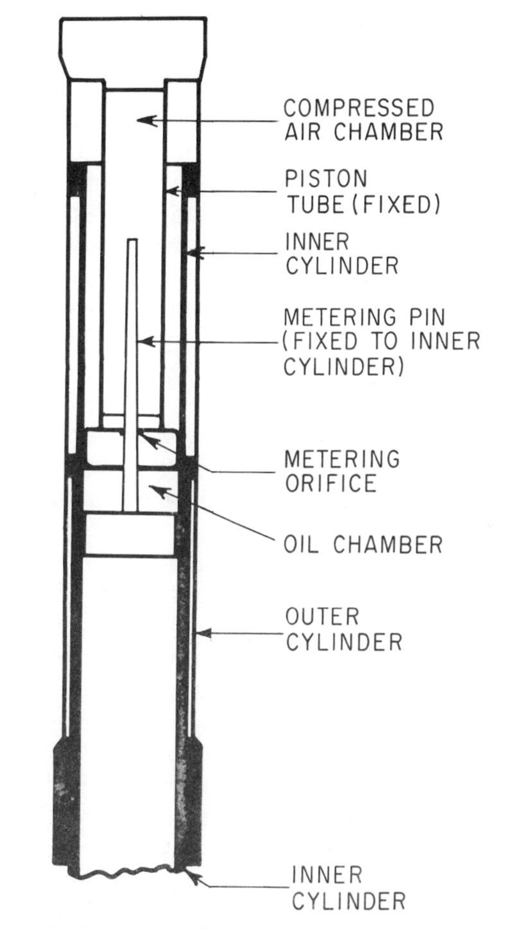

Figure **8·48** *Simplified drawing of an air-oleo strut.*

Retracting systems

Retractable landing gear may be retracted manually, electrically, or hydraulically. The main struts of retractable landing gear are mounted on trunnions and bearings so they can easily be swung upward into the fuselage or wing. The retracting mechanism may be a jackscrew arrangement, an electric-motor-operated screw or gear system, or a hydraulic actuating cylinder connected to suitable linking devices.

Requirements for landing gear

Before a particular landing-gear configuration can be approved for a civil airplane, it must be tested in accordance with specifications established by the FAA. It must be shown that the shock-absorbing system will absorb the energy developed by the airplane in dropping at 12 ft per sec at maximum approved landing weight without failure, assuming that the wing lift is not greater than the airplane weight. The complete airplane must be drop-tested to prove that no structural failure will occur anywhere in the aircraft as the result of landing under the conditions specified.

The landing-gear retracting mechanism, wheel well doors, and supporting structure must be designed for the loads occurring in the flight conditions when the gear is in the retracted position and for the combination of friction, inertia, brake torque, and air loads occurring during retraction and extension at any air speed up to 1.6 times stalling speed *Vs* with flaps in the approach position and the aircraft at design landing weight. The landing gear, the retracting mechanism, and the airplane structure including wheel well doors must be designed to withstand the flight loads occurring with the landing gear in the extended position at any speed up to 0.67 times cruising speed *Vc*, unless other means are provided to decelerate the airplane in flight at this speed.

Landing-gear doors, their operating mechanism, and their supporting structure must be designed for the conditions of air speed and load factor mentioned above, and in addition they must be designed for the yawing maneuvers prescribed for the airplane.

A positive means must be provided for the purpose of maintaining the landing gear in the extended position and to prevent the retraction of the gear when the airplane is on the ground. Retraction is usually prevented by incorporating one or more safety switches in the landing-gear electrical circuit. These switches prevent actuation of the landing-gear retraction control when any weight is on the gear.

Emergency means for extending the landing gear must be provided, so that the landing gear can be extended in the event of any reasonably probable failure in the normal retraction system. In any case, the emergency system must provide for the failure of any single source of hydraulic, electric, or equivalent energy supply. Proper functioning of the landing-gear retracting mechanism must be demonstrated by operational tests.

When an airplane is equipped with retractable landing gear, a suitable means must be provided for indicating to the pilot when the landing gear is secured in either the extended or retracted position. In addition, landplanes must be provided with an aural warning device which will function continuously when all throttles are closed if the gear is not extended and locked. If a manual shutoff is provided for the warning device, it must be installed in such a manner that reopening the throttles will reset the warning system.

The landing-gear control knob for transport airplanes must be shaped like a small wheel and tire, must be located forward of the throttles, and must be easily operable by both the pilot and copilot.

SEAPLANE HULLS AND AIRCRAFT FLOATS

Hulls

A **seaplane hull** is that portion of a flying boat which furnishes buoyancy when in contact with the surface of the water. It contains accommodations for the crew and passengers, usually combining the functions of both float and fuselage.

The hull ties together the functional units of the airplane; hence it has all the loads that are imposed by those units, such as landing gear, cargo, tail assembly, and wing. The fuselage and hull airplane loads are identical except for the landing condition. When the attachment of the landing gear is to the fuselage, it causes the landing loads to be concentrated on the fuselage near the attachment point, whereas the landing loads in a seaplane hull are distributed over a larger area.

A hull is more difficult to design and construct than a fuselage because a hull must be watertight and able to resist corrosion. The choice of the material and finish largely determines the amount of corrosion. Rivet spacing for watertight joints is substantially closer than required for structural strength, and this requirement also applies to the spacing of spot welds. Drain holes should be located at stringers, transverse frames, and other members so that water will drain to the low point without being trapped in pockets at inaccessible points. Adequate inspection openings must be provided. When the bottom of a hull is curved in transverse section, there may be high loads acting inward at the chine (intersection of the bottom with the sides) between frames on account of the tension in the bottom plating.

Water operation imposes severe loads. For this reason, the effect of sharp impacts and racking (stretching) loads must be considered. Particular attention is paid to fittings and, in twin-float seaplanes, to members and trusses carrying unsymmetrical loads. Provision must be made for the effects of striking floating objects.

The hulls of boat seaplanes and amphibians must be divided into watertight compartments in accordance with the following requirements: (1) In seaplanes of 5,000-lb maximum authorized weight or more the compartments must be so arranged that, with any two compartments flooded, the hull and auxiliary floats (and tires, if used) will retain sufficient buoyancy to support the gross weight of the aircraft in fresh water. (2) In seaplanes of 1,500- to 5,000-lb maximum authorized weight the compartments must be so arranged that, with any one compartment flooded, the hull and auxiliary floats (and tires, if used) will retain sufficient buoyancy to support the maximum authorized weight of the aircraft in fresh water. (3) In seaplanes of less than 1,500-lb maximum authorized weight watertight subdivision of the hull is not required. (4) Bulkheads may have watertight doors for the purpose of communication between compartments.

Auxiliary floats must be so arranged that, when completely submerged in fresh water, they will provide a righting moment which is at least 1.5 times the upsetting moment caused by the aircraft being tilted. A greater degree of stability may be required in the case of large flying boats, depending on the height of the center of gravity above the water level, the area and location of wings and tail surfaces, and other consideration.

Floats

A **float** is a completely enclosed watertight structure attached to an aircraft to give it buoyancy and stability when in contact with water. An **inboard stabilizing float** is a stabilizing float placed relatively close to the main float or hull. An **outboard** (or **wing-tip**) **stabilizing float** is a stabilizing float placed relatively far out from the main float or hull, usually at or very near the tip of the wing. A **single float** is a single central float fitted under an aircraft and usually requiring two stabilizing floats to give adequate stability and complete the float system. A **stabilizing** (or **side**) **float** is a float used in addition to a single float or hull and intended to provide lateral stability while the seaplane is at rest on the water. A **float system** is the complete arrangement of permanent floats, used to give buoyancy and stability to a seaplane while it is at rest on the water and to provide hydrodynamic lift while it is taking off.

The general practice in the design and construction of both hulls and floats is well established. The comments already made regarding hull construction generally apply to float construction.

The main seaplane floats must have a buoyancy in excess of that required to support the gross weight of the airplane in fresh water as follows: (1) 80 per cent in the case of single floats and (2) 90 per cent in the case of double floats.

Main seaplane floats for use on aircraft of 2,500-lb or more maximum authorized weight must contain at least five watertight compartments of approximately equal volume. Main seaplane floats for use on aircraft of less than 2,500-lb maximum authorized weight must contain at least four such compartments.

POWERPLANT NACELLES AND MOUNTS

Nacelles

In the broad sense of the term, a **nacelle** is an enclosed shelter for a powerplant or for personnel. However, the word usually refers to an **engine nacelle.** In construction, nacelles somewhat resemble fuselages. A nacelle may be an integral part of the primary structure, or it may be built as a completely separate unit and installed above, below, or as a part of the wing of multiengine airplanes.

As defined by the NASA a nacelle is a streamlined structure, housing, or compartment on an aircraft, as the housing for an engine. As pointed out in the previous paragraph, a nacelle may also be used to house the crew or special equipment.

An engine nacelle for a modern light airplane

Figure 8 · 49 Engine nacelle for an all-metal light twin airplane.

Figure 8·50 Nacelle for a jet airliner.

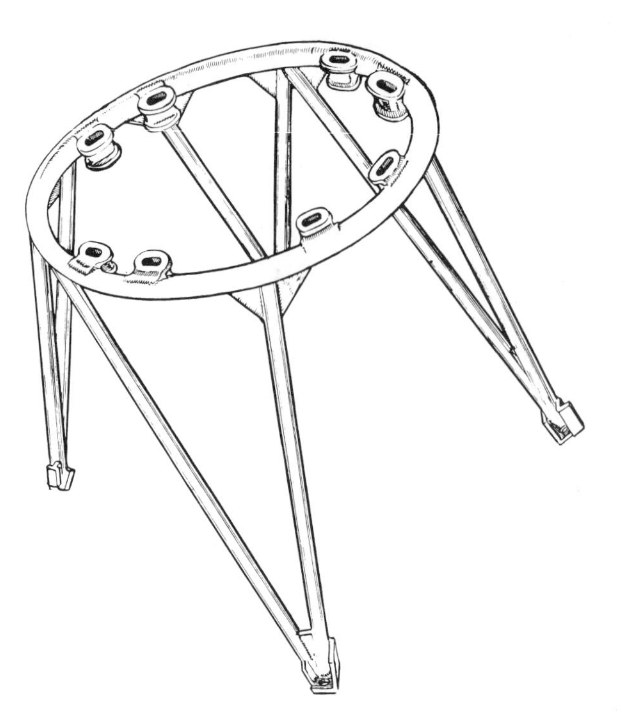

Figure 8·51 Engine mount for a radial engine.

is shown in Fig. 8·49. It will be observed that this nacelle is securely attached to and streamlined with the wing. The wing structure at this point is reinforced to carry the extra weight and thrust of the engine.

A nacelle for a jet airliner is shown in Fig. 8·50. This nacelle is also referred to as a "pod," and as can be seen in the photograph, it is mounted on a strut which extends into the wing. The wing is reinforced at the points where the engine struts are attached.

Engine mounts

An **engine mount** is a frame which supports the engine and holds it to the fuselage or nacelle. It may be made of formed sheet metal, welded steel tubing, or some other suitable material. Engine mounts vary widely in appearance and construction, although the basic features of construction are similar and well standardized. They should be designed so that the engine and its accessories are accessible for inspection and maintenance. Engine mounts for reciprocating engines are often built as individual units which can be detached easily and quickly from the supporting structure. In many of the large transport aircraft, the engine mount, the engine, and its accessories are removed and replaced as a single, complete power-unit assembly. This makes maintenance and overhaul simpler as well as shortening the time required for engine change.

The mounting of jet engines has been simplified to the extent that an engine change can be accomplished very quickly. The liquid lines, electrical cables, and control linkages are all provided with quick-disconnect joints, thus making it possible to uncouple all connections in a matter of minutes. The engine is mounted to the strut with three or four large bolts which can be removed quickly and easily.

Figure 8·51 shows an engine mount for a radial engine. This is a welded, heat-treated steel structure which is attached to the fuselage at four points. The mount for a small opposed engine for a light airplane is shown in Fig. 8·52. This mount is also a welded steel structure designed to be attached to the forward end of the fuselage.

Propeller-driven airplanes are usually equipped with engine mounts constructed of welded alloy-steel tubing or of aluminum-alloy sheet or plate. Forgings of alloy steel or aluminum alloy are

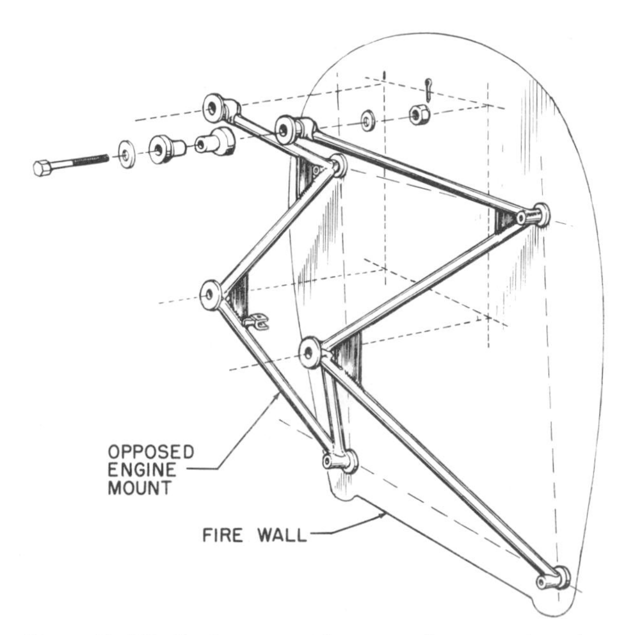

Figure 8·52 Engine mount for a small opposed engine.

often used for highly stressed fittings. Light airplanes often have fittings fabricated from steel plate and welded to the engine mount. At a point where a rigid connection is made between fittings, they are accurately machined.

The vibrations which originate in reciprocating engines are transmitted through the engine mount to the airplane structure; hence mounts for such engines must be arranged with some sort of rubber or synthetic rubber bushings between the engine and mount attaching structure for damping these vibrations. These bushings are often a part of the engine-mounting bracket and may be installed on the engine at the factory. The maximum vibration absorption is obtained when the mounting bolts are tightened so that the engine can move within reasonable limits in a torsional (rotating) direction but is restrained from any fore-and-aft movement. The torsional motion is then damped by the restraining action of the pads or cushions and the friction of the metal surfaces held by the bolts. If these bolts are too tight, the mount tends to vibrate with the engine, which is obviously undesirable. For this reason, mechanics should always consult the manufacturer's handbook when tightening such bolts.

Dynamic suspension is a method of mounting an engine so that the engine-propeller unit is effectively supported at its CG by means of rubber-mounted links with pin ends which lie with their axes intersecting at the CG. The engine then acts as though it were supported on a universal joint at the CG. In the ordinary engine mount, many of the motions and forces are transmitted to the aircraft. With dynamic suspension, many of the vibrations and forces are stopped before they reach the fuselage.

The engine mounting for a light twin-engine airplane is shown in Fig. 8·53. This mount is constructed of formed sheet metal, and the complete mounting structure forms the bottom of the engine nacelle. The structure shown is designed for the Cessna 310 airplane, and it provides a good indication of the mounting arrangement and shock-absorbing devices.

Cracked, bent, or broken members of engine mounts are very dangerous. They must be repaired or replaced by competent technicians, who are authorized to perform this work, before the airplane may be flown again. During the inspection procedure, special care should be given to finding cracks. They are most likely to occur at welded joints or at corners and bends in sheet-metal structures. Small cracks are difficult to find through a protective coating, especially if the structure is dirty. When the protective coatings of steel surfaces of an airplane are damaged, they should be retouched promptly to prevent rusting.

We have already mentioned the importance of properly tightening the mounting bolts. If not tightened enough, the mounting clamps and bolts will allow the mount to move, thus wearing the

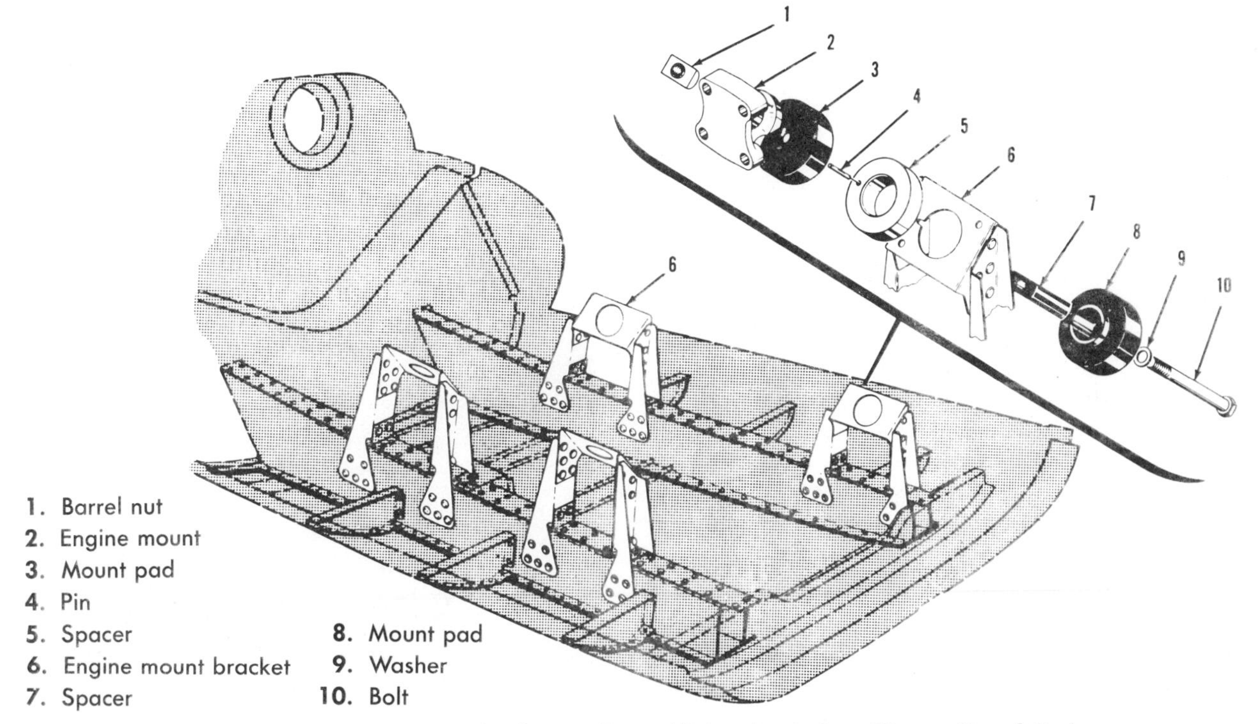

Figure **8·53** *Engine mounting for an all-metal light twin airplane (Cessna Aircraft Co.).*

holes and setting up vibration. If the bolts are tightened too much, the shock-absorbing characteristics of the pads or cushions may be seriously reduced.

Firewalls

All engines, auxiliary power units, fuel-burning heaters, and other combustion equipment which are intended for operation in flight as well as the combustion, turbine, and tail-pipe sections of turbine engines must be isolated from the remainder of the airplane by means of firewalls, shrouds, or other equivalent means.

Firewalls and shrouds must be constructed in such a manner that no hazardous quantity of air, fluids, or flame can pass from the compartment to other portions of the airplane. All openings in the firewall or shroud must be sealed with close-fitting fireproof grommets, bushings, or firewall fittings. Firewalls and shrouds must be constructed of fireproof material and be protected against corrosion.

Cowling and fairings

Cowling and fairings are generally similar, but they differ in detail and to some extent in function. **Cowling** usually consists of detachable sections for covering portions of the airplane, such as engines, mounts, and other parts where ease of access is important. Cowling affords protection and also aids in streamlining the area covered.

Fairing is used principally to streamline a portion of an airplane, although it may protect some small piece of equipment or merely improve the appearance. Fairing units may be composed of several small sections or may be stamped or formed into one large section. The sections may be removable and attached in the same manner as cowling, but usually fairing sections are bolted, screwed, or otherwise permanently attached in place.

All cowling around the powerplant and on the engine side of the firewall must be made of fireproof material and arranged so that any accumulation of dirt, waste, or fuel can be observed without complete removal of the cowling. It should be constructed and supported so as to make it capable of resisting all vibration, inertia, and air loads to which it would be subjected in operation.

Cowling must fit tightly to the firewall, but openings may be provided if the airplane surface within 15 in. thereof is protected with metal or other suitable fireproofing material. It must be suitably drained in all attitudes of flight and on the ground, with separate drains provided for the parts of the fuel system liable to leakage. All such drains must be so located as to prevent fuel or oil from dripping onto the exhaust manifold or any parts of the aircraft and permeating any material of a cellular nature.

A transport airplane must be so designed that, in the event of fire originating in the engine power or accessory sections, the probability is extremely remote for fire to enter either through openings or by burning through external skin into any other zone of the nacelle where such fire could create additional hazards. If the airplane is provided with a retractable landing gear, this provision shall apply with the landing gear retracted. Fireproof materials must be used for all nacelle skin areas which might be subjected to flame in the event of a fire originating in the engine power or accessory sections.

Engine cowling usually consist of formed sheet-metal sections attached with quick-fastening devices or screws, depending upon the necessity for easy access to a particular area. Figure 8·54 illustrates a typical cowling arrangement for a single-engine airplane. The cowling completely encloses the engine except for the inlet areas and outlet area for cooling air.

Cowling sections should normally be of a size and weight convenient for one man to carry. When they are removed for inspection and maintenance work, they should be stored in numbered racks corresponding to numbers placed either

Figure 8·54 Typical cowling arrangement for a single-engine airplane.

temporarily or permanently on the cowling sections so that they can be replaced in the proper order.

Cowling and fairing should be handled with care so that they will not be bent or broken. Long strips of large sections are sometimes not rigid enough to support their own weight. Small parts, made of light-gage material, are easily damaged during maintenance work. The finish must be unmarred; otherwise it should be refinished. Chafing strips, made of either fabric or fiber, may be used between pieces of installed cowling. These strips require renewing if they are worn to the point where metal parts rub together. Attachment devices are inspected to be sure that they function easily and securely. When they become badly worn or loose, they should be replaced.

Cowling fasteners

Cowling may be attached to the aircraft by various types of fasteners including quick-attaching fasteners and screws or bolts. Flush-type Dzus fasteners, such as the one shown in Fig. 8·55, are used on some airplanes to attach cowling sections along the edges and at reinforced points. When the spiraling slot in the nose of the Dzus fastener stud engages the spring wire anchor, the tension holds the cowling firmly against the support. Some manufacturers set the anchor wire in such a position that the slot in the top will be parallel to the edge of the metal section when the stud is locked, thus making it easy to detect any unlocked fasteners during a visual inspection of the airplane. Other manufacturers set the anchor wire in such a position that the slots in the tops of all the fasteners are parallel to each other, although they are not necessarily parallel to the edge of the metal section.

The Camloc fastener, shown assembled in

Figure **8·55** *A Dzus fastener.*

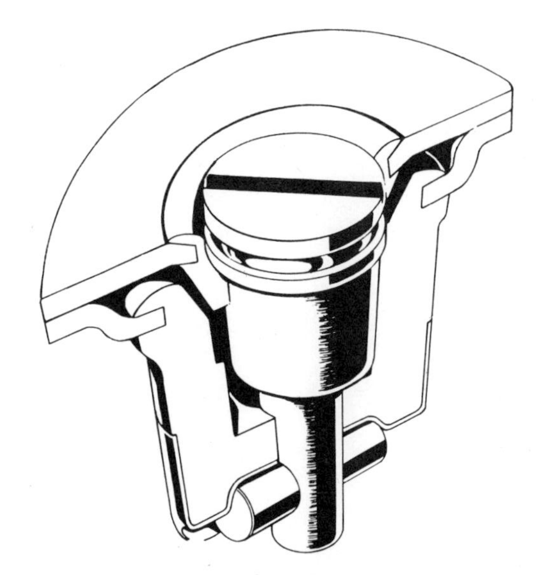

Figure **8·56** *A Camloc fastener.*

Fig. 8·56 and disassembled in Fig. 8·57, is another of the modern quick-acting patented cowling fasteners. Figure 8·57 emphasizes the cam collar, grommet, cross pin, spring cup, stud, and spring, showing the simplicity of design and construction. Patented quick-acting fasteners are being developed constantly, not only for fastening cowling but for a multitude of other tasks where the installation and removal of parts must be done quickly, simply, and inexpensively.

CONTROL SYSTEMS

In the consideration of the structural features of aircraft it is essential that we consider some of

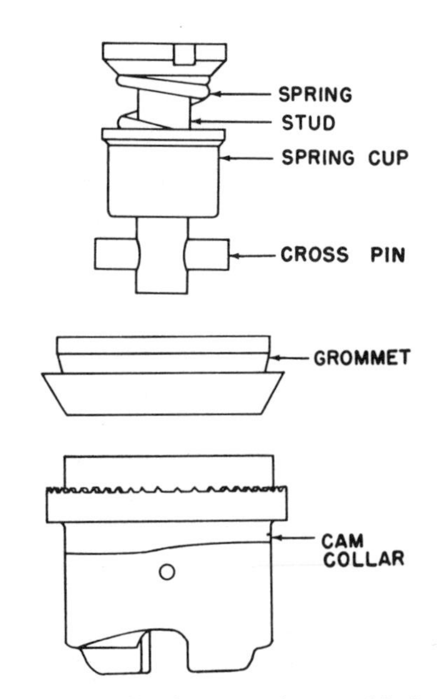

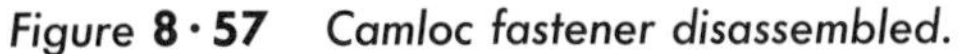

Figure **8·57** *Camloc fastener disassembled.*

Figure **8·58** *Approved shapes for control knobs.*

the requirements for controls and control systems, especially for aircraft in the transport category. The control knobs for the various systems to be controlled from the cockpit must be distinctive in shape so the pilot will know by feel as well as sight the identity of each control lever. The shapes of the control knobs must be made to conform to those illustrated in Fig. 8·58.

All controls and control systems must operate with ease, smoothness, and positiveness appropriate to their function. The elements of the flight-control system must incorporate design features or must be distinctively and permanently marked to minimize the possibility of incorrect assembly, which could result in malfunctioning of the control system.

Tab controls

Tab-control systems must be such that disconnection or failure of any element at speeds up to cruising speed cannot jeopardize the safety of flight. An adjustable stabilizer must incorporate means to permit, after the occurrence of any reasonably probable single failure of the actuating system, such adjustment as would be necessary for continued safety of the flight.

Power-boosted systems

When a power-boost or power-operated control system is used, an alternate system must be immediately available so that any single failure in the power portion of the system will not preclude continued safe flight and landing. The alternate system may be a duplicate power portion or a manually operated mechanical system. The power portion must include the power source, and such items as valves, lines, and actuators. The failure of mechanical parts and the jamming of power cylinders need not be considered if such failure and jamming are believed to be extremely remote.

Both the primary system and the alternate systems must be operable in the event of a single-engine failure. For airplanes with more than two engines, at least one system must be operable in the event of failure of any two engines. It must be shown by analysis that, in the event of loss of power on all engines, the airplane is not uncontrollable.

Trim controls and systems

Trim controls must be designed to safeguard against inadvertent or abrupt operation. Each trim control must operate in the plane and with the sense of motion of the airplane. Thus, if it is desired to cause the airplane to roll toward the right, the trim-control wheel should be rotated to the right. In simpler terms, the trim-control knob or wheel should turn in the same direction as it is desired to turn the airplane. Means must be provided adjacent to the trim control to indicate the direction of the control movement relative to the airplane motion. Means must also be provided to indicate the position of the trim device with respect to the range of adjustment. The indicating means must be clearly visible.

Trim devices must be capable of continued normal operation in case any one connecting or transmitting element of the primary flight control system fails. All trim-control systems must be designed to prevent creeping in flight. Trim tab controls must be irreversible, unless the tab is appropriately balanced and shown to be free from flutter. Where an irreversible tab-control system is employed, the portion from the tab to the attachment of the irreversible unit to the airplane structure must be rigid.

Wing-flap systems

Wing-flap controls must operate in a manner to permit the flight crew to place the flaps in all the required takeoff, en-route, approach, and landing positions and to maintain these positions thereafter without further attention on the part of the crew, except for flap movement produced by an automatic flap-positioning or load-limiting device. The wing-flap control must be located and designed to render improbable its inadvertent operation.

The rate of motion of the wing flap must be such as to obtain satisfactory flight and performance characteristics under steady or changing conditions of airspeed, engine power, and airplane attitude. The wing-flap control must be designed to retract the flaps from the fully extended position during steady flight at maximum continuous engine power at all speeds below design flap speed plus 10 mph ($V_f + 10$).

Wing-flap systems must be provided with indicators to show all positions of the flaps. The flaps must be interconnected to provide for symmetrical operation unless the airplane is demonstrated to have safe flight characteristics while the flaps are retracted on one side and extended on the other. Means must be provided to ensure against hazardous unsymmetrical operation of the wing flaps in case of any reasonably possible failure.

Control operating systems

Control systems must be provided with stops which (1) positively limit the range of motion of the control surfaces; (2) are so located in the system that wear, slackness, or take-up adjustments will not affect adversely the control characteristics of the airplane; and (3) are capable of withstanding the loads corresponding with the design conditions for the system.

Control systems must be provided with locks to prevent damage which might be caused by gusts when the airplane is not in flight. If the lock prevents normal operation of the controls, it must be designed to disengage automatically when the pilot operates the controls in the normal manner or it must limit the operation of the controls to the extent that the pilot receives unmistakable warning at the start of takeoff. The locks must be so designed that they cannot be inadvertently engaged while the airplane is in flight.

All details of control systems must be designed and installed to prevent jamming, chafing, and interference from cargo, passengers, and loose objects. Precautionary measures must be provided in the cockpit to prevent the entry of foreign objects into places where they may jam the control systems. Cables and tubes in the control systems must be so arranged that they will not slap together or against parts of the airplane.

Control cables, fittings, turnbuckles, splices, and pulleys must be of an approved type. Cables smaller than ⅛ in. diameter must not be used in the aileron, elevator, or rudder systems. The design of cable systems must be such that there will be no hazardous change in cable tension throughout the range of travel under operating conditions and temperature variations. For this purpose, constant-tension devices are often installed in cable systems.

Pulley types and sizes must correspond to the cables used and must lie in the plane passing through the cable within such limits that the cable does not rub against the pulley flange.

All pulleys and sprockets must be provided with closely fitted guards to prevent the cables and chains being displaced or fouled. Fair-leads must be so installed that they do not cause a change in direction of more than 3°. Clevis pins retained only by cotter pins must not be used in the control system. Turnbuckles attached to parts having angular motion must be installed to prevent positively any binding throughout the range of travel. Turnbuckles must be safetied in accordance with the drawing of Fig. 8 · 59.

Provision for visual inspection must be made at all fair-leads, pulleys, terminals, and turnbuckles. This is essential because cable failure may first be detected at or near such points.

Manufactured cable systems are normally pro-

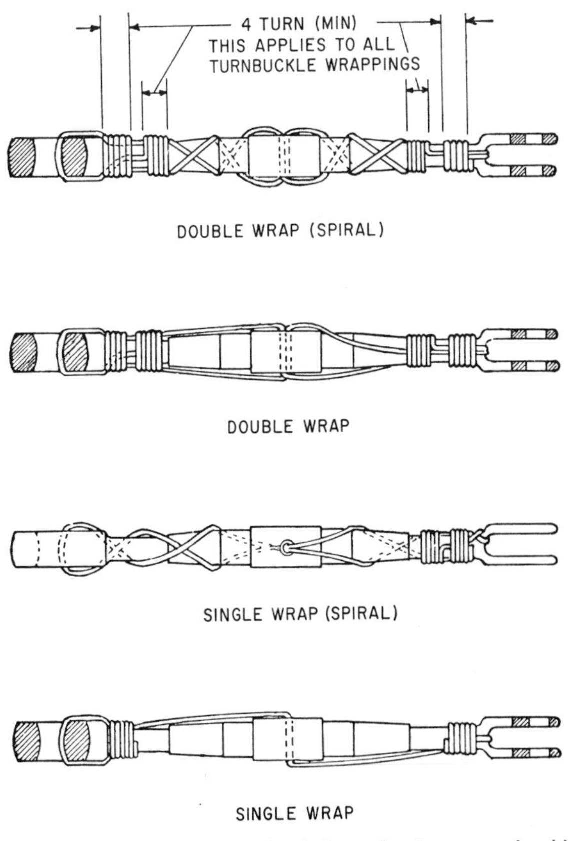

Figure **8 · 59** *Proper methods for safetying a turnbuckle (FAA).*

vided with **swaged** fittings. A swaged fitting is attached with a special tool or machine which compresses (swages) the sleeve or barrel of the fitting into the cable, thus making an extremely strong connection between the cable and the fitting. Swaged fittings are inspected by using a gage to determine that the sleeve of the fitting is shrunk to a given dimension.

When a swaging machine is not available, cable fittings may be attached by using the five-tuck woven splice provided that such a splice is not used where more than 75 per cent of the cable strength is required.

The five-tuck woven splice is made by wrapping the cable around a bushing or thimble and then interweaving the strands of the free end into the cable of the standing part. The splice may be used with either 7 by 19 extra flexible steel cable or 7 by 7 flexible steel cable.

FURNISHINGS AND SAFETY EQUIPMENT

Seats

A wide variety of seat designs have been made for aircraft of the various categories. Seats for light aircraft usually consist of a light metal framework covered with sponge rubber or some other type of resilient padding over which is laid a woven fabric or plastic cover. Seats for airliners are much more elaborate than those for light aircraft (see Fig. 8·40). These seats usually have a metal structure with mechanisms for adjusting the angle of the seat back for reclining. Adjustable footrests are usually provided and are often attached to the seats. The seats are well padded and upholstered to provide a maximum of comfort for the passengers. Plastics and fiber glass are coming into use for the construction of seats which are light in weight but also strong and durable.

All seats, berths, and their supporting structure must be designed for occupant weight of 170 lb with due account taken of the maximum load factors, inertia forces, and reactions among occupant, seat, and safety belt or harness corresponding to all relevant flight- and ground-load conditions, including specified emergency-landing conditions. Seats or chairs, even though adjustable, in open or closed airplanes must be securely fastened in place, whether or not the safety-belt load is transmitted through the seat.

Suitable hand grips or rails must be provided along the aisles of transport airplanes to enable passengers or crew members to steady themselves while using the aisles during moderately rough air flights. Any projecting object likely to cause injury to persons seated or moving about the airplane in normal flight must be adequately padded.

The seats of airplanes of the normal, utility, acrobatic, and restricted categories must be designed for a passenger weight of 170 lb (190 lb with parachute for the acrobatic and utility categories) and the maximum load factors corresponding to all specified flight- and ground-load conditions, including emergency conditions. All such seats must be available to accommodate passengers. Pilot seats for these categories as well as for the transport category must be designed for the reactions resulting from the application of the pilot forces to the primary flight controls.

Safety belts

All seats in an airplane which may be occupied during takeoff or landing must be equipped with approved safety (seat) belts. The requirements for safety belts are set forth in Technical Standard Order C22d, issued by the FAA. New models of safety belts manufactured for installation on civil aircraft on or after Nov. 30, 1960, must meet the standards of National Aircraft Standards Specification (NAS) 802, with certain exceptions. Any safety belt meeting all the requirements of NAS802 may be approved for use.

The principal difference between the requirements of TSO C22d and NAS802 is in the strength of the safety-belt assembly. TSO C22d states that the safety-belt strength need be only 1,500 lb for a single-person belt and 3,000 lb for a two-person belt. NAS802 requires 3,000 and 6,000 lb, respectively. Any safety belt meeting the requirements of TSO C22d may be used on civil aircraft.

Safety belts must be designed so as to be easily adjustable. Each belt must be at least 1 15/16 in. wide and equipped with a quick-release mechanism designed so that it cannot be released accidently.

A safety belt may be approved for one person or for two adjacent persons, depending upon its strength. A belt for one person must be capable of withstanding a load of 1,500 lb applied in alignment with the anchored belt. The quick-release mechanism must be capable of withstanding this load without undue distortion and must be easily releasable under a load simulating a person hanging on the belt.

A safety belt approved for two adjacent persons must be capable of withstanding a load of 3,000 lb applied in alignment with the anchored belt. The quick-release mechanism must be easily releasable as described previously. After a test under extreme load, the release mechanism must be releasable with a pull of not more than 45 lb.

The strength of a safety belt is determined by

a test as specified in NAS802. The static testing of the belt and its attachments must be accomplished under conditions simulating the belt pulling against a human body.

Each half of an approved safety-belt assembly must have legibly and permanently marked on or attached to it a name plate or identification label with the following information: (1) manufacturer's name and address, (2) equipment name or type or model designation, (3) serial number and/or date of manufacture, and (4) applicable TSO or NAS number.

When a safety belt is installed, it must be inspected to ascertain that webbing, buckles, straps, seams, etc., are in good condition; that the attachments are secure; that it is adjusted correctly; and that the release operates properly. This inspection is repeated at regular intervals. All safety belts must be given a regular strength test. Each type is tested while its web and leather parts, if any, are adjusted to the greatest length.

Before takeoff the pilot is responsible for seeing that all belts are properly fastened and that each person understands the method of releasing them. In airline passenger service, this duty is usually delegated to the stewardess or hostess.

Signs which read "No Smoking" and "Fasten Seat Belts" are prescribed by Federal regulations for airplanes in airline passenger service. Whenever a signal or sign of this type is used to indicate to passengers the time when the safety belts should be fastened, such sign or signal must be located in a conspicuous place and so arranged that it can be operated from the seat of either the first or second pilot.

In all cases, safety belts must be of a type certificated in accordance with Civil Air Regulations. They must be so attached that no part of the anchorage will fail at a lower load than that specified for emergency conditions. Provisions must be made at all seats and berths for the installation of belts or harness necessary to meet emergency conditions.

Torn or otherwise damaged safety-belt webbing should not be repaired but should be replaced. In case replacement of webbing or hardware is attempted, the parts should be obtained from the original manufacturer of the belt and stitched with thread of the manufacturer's specifications. The stitch pattern should be identical with the original, and the number of threads per inch should be equal to the number used by the manufacturer.

Oxygen systems

All pressurized transport aircraft approved for extremely high altitude flights must be equipped with adequate emergency oxygen systems even though cabin altitude must not exceed 8,000 ft. The oxygen system installed must be free from hazards in itself, in its method of operation, and in its effect upon other components of the airplane. Means must be provided to enable the crew to determine readily during flight the quantity of oxygen available in each source of supply. For pressurized airplanes certificated for operation at flight altitudes above 40,000 ft, oxygen flow rate and equipment must be approved by the FAA.

Individual oxygen-dispensing units must be provided for each occupant for whom supplemental oxygen is required to be furnished. All such units must be designed to cover the nose and mouth and must be equipped with a suitable means for retaining the unit in position on the face. Oxygen masks are often held in place by means of elastic bands which are placed around the head. Flight-crew masks for supplemental oxygen must provide for the use of communications equipment such as microphones.

For airplanes certificated to operate at altitudes up to and including 25,000 ft, there must be available and within reach of each flight-crew member an oxygen-supply terminal and unit of oxygen-dispensing equipment to provide for the immediate use of oxygen by such crew member. For all other occupants the supply terminals and dispensing equipment must be located so as to permit the use of oxygen as required.

For airplanes certificated to operate above 25,000-ft flight altitude, an oxygen-dispensing unit must be immediately available to each occupant wherever seated. In addition, for airplanes certificated to fly above 30,000 ft, the dispensing units providing the required oxygen flow rate must be automatically presented to the occupants. In some airliners the oxygen masks are stored in small compartments above the heads of the passengers, and in case of depressurization of the cabin the masks drop to a position in front of each person's face. The installation of individual oxygen-dispensing equipment for passengers is shown in Fig. 8·60. The equipment is automatically released if the cabin is suddenly depressurized, or it may be released by pressing a button. (In Fig. 8·60 the passenger is pressing a light switch.) The use of the oxygen units is illustrated in Fig. 8·61. In other airplanes, the oxygen mask is stored in the back of each seat. If decompression occurs, the masks pop out into the laps of the passengers.

To ensure that sufficient oxygen-dispensing units and outlets are available for all occupants, the total number installed exceeds the number of

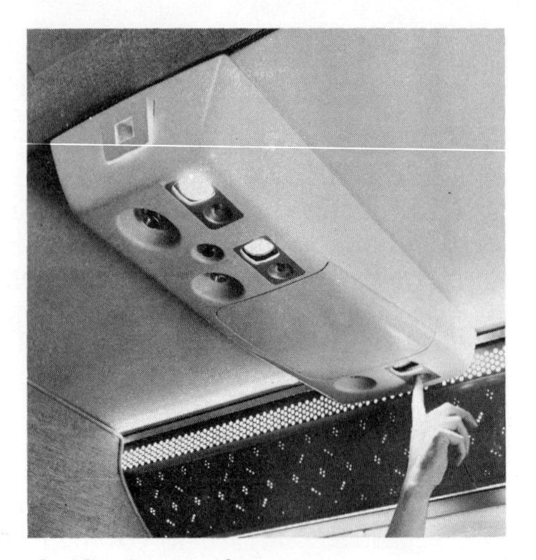

Figure 8·60 Stowage for emergency oxygen equipment in a jet airliner.

Figure 8·61 Using emergency oxygen equipment.

seats by at least 10 per cent with the extra units being as uniformly distributed throughout the cabin as practicable.

Crew members on duty are provided with demand equipment. An oxygen-dispensing unit connected to an oxygen-supply terminal must be immediately available to each flight-crew member when seated at his station. Not less than two outlets and dispensing units are located in each washroom and in each lavatory if separate from the washroom. Portable oxygen equipment must be immediately available for each cabin attendant.

Oxygen equipment and lines must not be located in any designated fire zone and shall be protected from heat which may be generated in or escape from any designated fire zone. Such lines and equipment must be so installed that escaping oxygen cannot cause ignition of accumulations of grease, fluids, or vapors which are likely to be present in normal operation or as a result of failure or malfunction of any system.

The details of oxygen-system performance, including required flow rates for various conditions, are specified in pertinent sections of the Civil Air Regulations.

Fire protection

Because of the possibility of fire occurring in certain areas and compartments of transport airplanes, adequate fire protection must be provided. Fire protection includes the use of fire-resistant materials in construction, the installation of fire-extinguishing systems, the provision of hand fire extinguishers for the use of crew members, the provision of protective breathing equipment for the use of crew members in fighting fires, the installation of fire warning systems, and the fireproofing of compartments where fires are most likely to occur.

All compartments occupied or used by the crew or passengers must be constructed of materials which are not less than flash resistant. The wall and ceiling linings, the covering of all upholstering, the floors, and the furnishings must be flame resistant. Compartments where smoking is to be permitted must be equipped with ashtrays of the self-contained type which are completely removable. All other compartments must be placarded against smoking.

All receptacles for used towels, papers, and waste must be made of fire-resistant material and must have covers or other provisions for containing possible fires.

From one to four hand fire extinguishers must be provided depending upon the passenger capacity of the airplane. The fire extinguishers must be of a type suitable for the class of fires which may be encountered in any particular area.

Cargo and baggage compartments must include no controls, wiring, lines, equipment, or accessories the damage or failure of which would affect the safe operation of the airplane unless such items are shielded, isolated, or otherwise protected so that they cannot be damaged by movement of the cargo in the compartment and so that any breakage or failure of such item will not create a fire hazard.

Provision must be made to prevent cargo or baggage from interfering with the functioning of the fire-protective features of the compartment. All materials used in the construction of cargo or baggage compartments, including tie-down equipment, must be flame resistant. Sources of heat within the compartment must be shielded and insulated to prevent ignition of the cargo.

The areas in the engine nacelle, around auxiliary power units, and around fuel-burning heaters are designated as fire zones because of the possibility of fire occurring as the result of leaking fuel and the proximity of heat which may cause ignition of the fuel or other flammable liquid. Fire-extinguisher systems must be provided to serve all such designated zones. If engine power sections are adequately isolated from the rest of the airplane and meet other provisions of the Civil Air Regulations, fire-extinguishing systems need not be provided for the power sections but must be provided for fire zones.

Quick-acting fire or overheat detectors of an approved type must be provided in all designated fire zones and in the combustion, turbine, and tailpipe sections of turbine-engine installations, and they must be sufficient in number and location to assure prompt detection of fire in such zones and sections.

Numerous detailed requirements for fire protection are given in pertinent Civil Air Regulations. Only the principal requirements are described in this section.

STRUCTURES FOR MISSILES

Although detailed structural information concerning operational or experimental missiles and space vehicles is often classified as secret or confidential and the information is not released to the public, there are a number of general details which are known.

The fuselage or "body" sections of small-diameter missiles are often constructed as simple tubes of metal with no additional structure except the attachments for the engines, instrumentation, and control systems. Such missiles as the Sidewinder, Sparrow, Hound Dog, and Hawk are all of very simple construction as far as the main body of the missile is concerned.

A number of the larger missiles have been constructed in a manner similar to that previously described for metal aircraft. The bodies of these missiles have structure of frames and stringers covered with a stressed skin. These structures are riveted together with flush rivets to provide a smooth surface. The Regulus and Snark missiles, among others, were constructed in this manner.

Structure of the Atlas missile

As an example of a rather unconventional missile structure, we shall describe briefly the Atlas Intercontinental Ballistic Missile (ICBM) manufactured by General Dynamics/Astronautics and shown in Fig. 8·62.

In the development of any long-range missile, where a maximum of performance is desired, every ounce of weight must be considered. In an ICBM missile, each pound of weight saved allows more than a mile of extra payload range. It can readily be seen then that the missile structure must be made as light as possible.

In the case of the Atlas, the weight is about 130 tons at takeoff and 90 per cent of the weight is fuel. Thus, the greater part of the structure is required to carry the enormous quantity of fuel. If the weight of the fuel-carrying structure can be reduced by only ½ ton, more than a thousand miles is added to the range of the payload.

The main structure of the Atlas missile is a tough, lightweight, stainless-steel (AISI grade 301) tank with skin thinner than a dime. The tank, 10 ft in diameter and about 60 ft in length, has no internal framework, but it maintains its shape by virtue of internal pressure, much as a football does. Although the thickest steel in the tank is 0.04 in. and some of it is much thinner, the entire wall sections meet a specification for minimum tensile strength of 200,000 psi. Note that this does not mean that the tank can sustain pressures of 200,000 psi but that the tensile strength of the steel is 200,000 psi cross-sectional area.

The special cold-rolled austenitic steel required to fulfill the requirements of strength and weight for the Atlas was developed through the cooperation of the steel industry and Convair (now General Dynamics/Astronautics). Special welding techniques and equipment were also perfected by the welding industry for the fabrication of the tanks.

The steel for the Atlas tank is manufactured in rolls about 36 in. in width. The steel is cut into strips which are butt-welded together to form bands. The welds are reinforced with underlying strips of stainless steel spot-welded on each side butt weld. The circular bands are lap-welded to similar bands to form the large tube for the tank. During the construction process the tank is held in shape by means of temporary support rings.

When the tank is complete and bulkheads are

welded on each end, it is pressurized and the supporting rings are removed. During handling in the factory, transportation, and erection on a firing pad, pressures of less than 10 psi are required in the tank. During flight, pressures of more than 10 psi are used to provide a "head" for propellant flow to the rocket engines. This pressure, of course, supports the structure while it is providing propellant pressure.

The tank of the Atlas missile is separated into two sections by a single stainless-steel bulkhead, thus providing a forward tank for liquid oxygen and an aft tank for fuel.

On the assembly line, the rocket engines and their associated plumbing, the hydraulic system, and the pneumatic system are attached to the rear of the Atlas tank. The guidance system, autopilot, tracking system, electrical system, range safety system, telemetry and propellant-utilization systems are installed in pods along the sides of the missile. Some of these features can be seen in the three-view drawing of Fig. 8·63. A photograph of the Atlas on the launching pad is shown in Fig. 8·64.

SUPERSONIC JET BOMBER

The North American B-70 Valkyrie, shown in Fig. 8·65, is a triple-sonic bomber, and because of this, it has created a need for new aircraft materials and methods of fabrication.

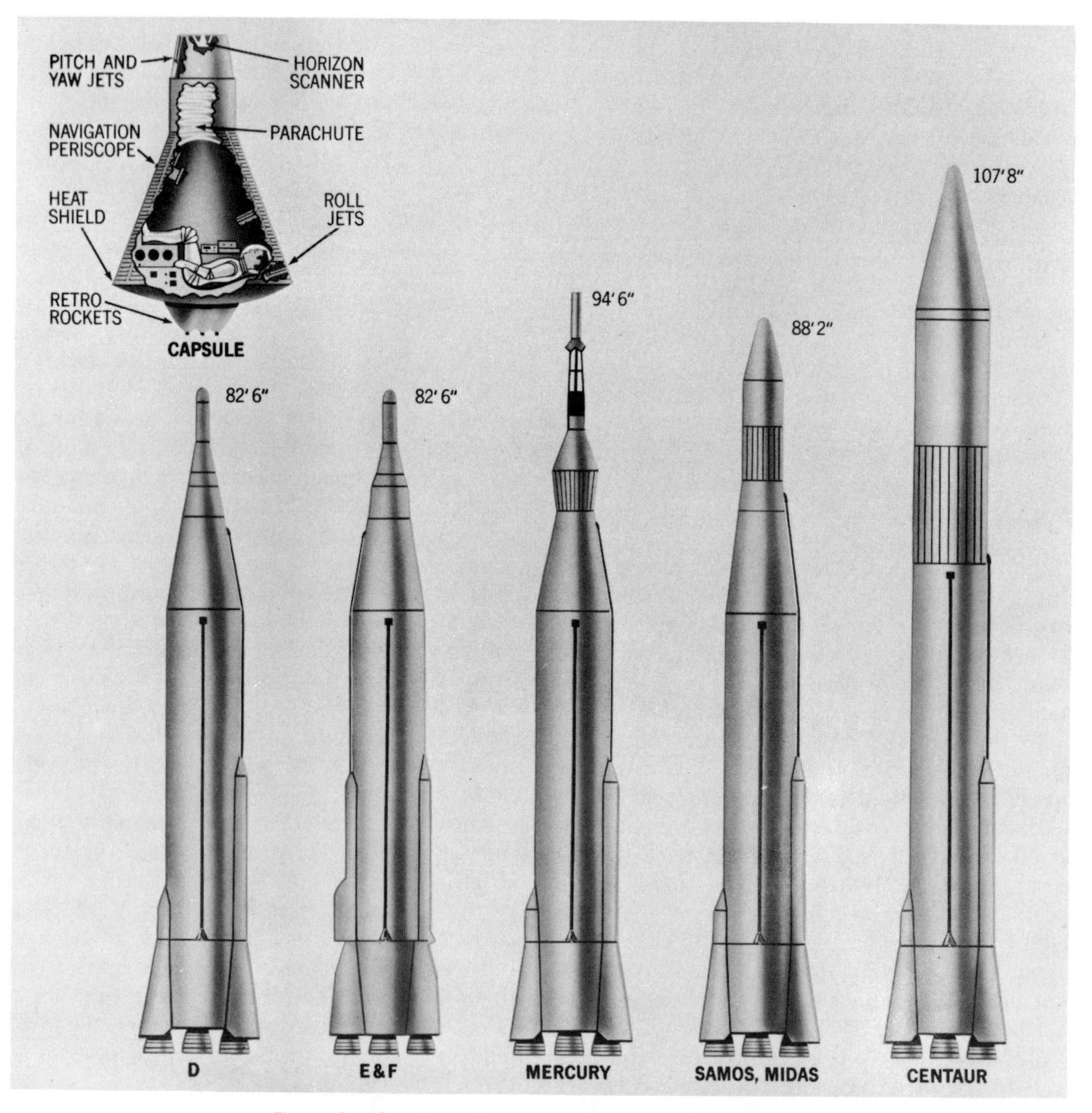

Figure **8·62** *The Atlas Intercontinental Ballistic Missile.*

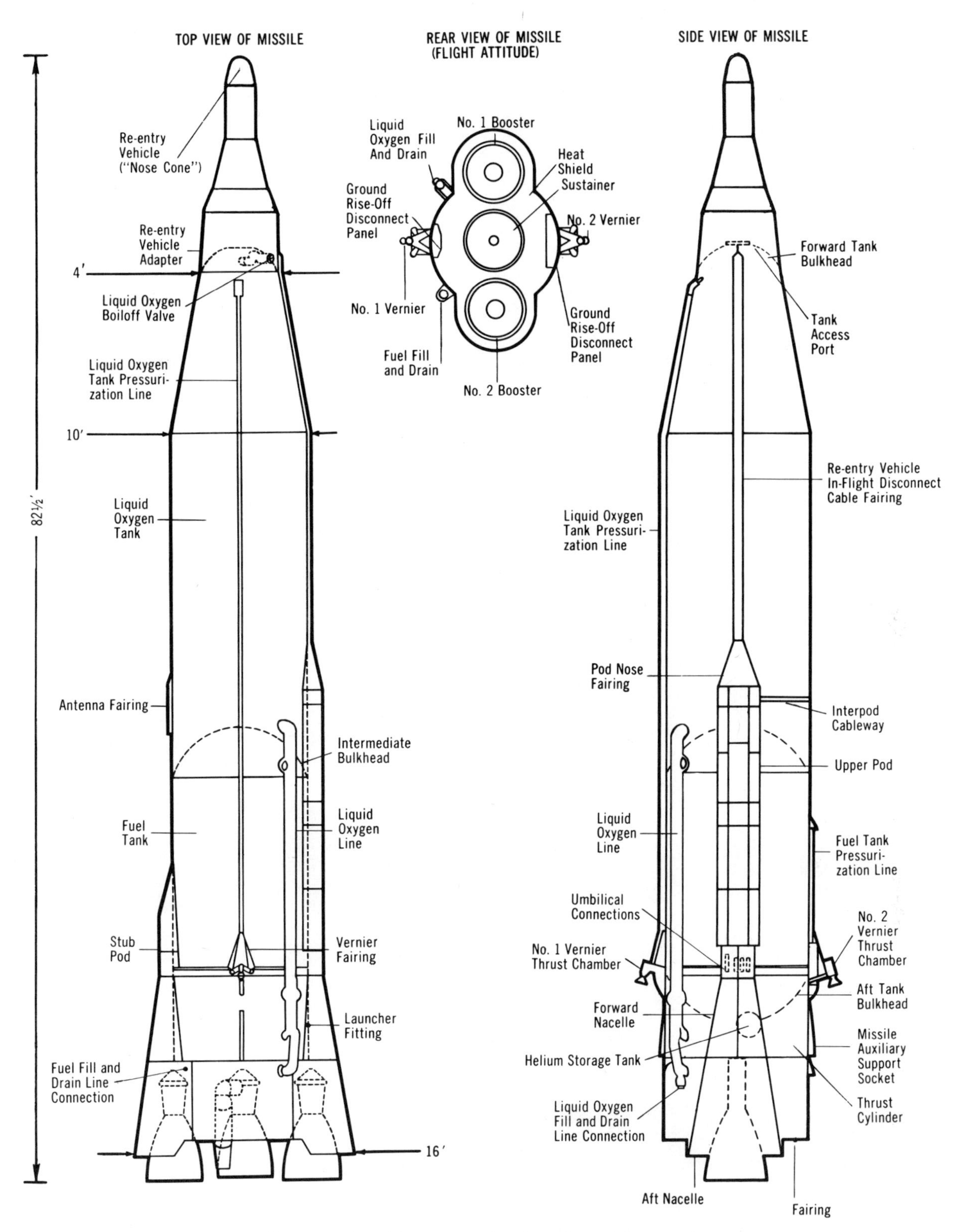

Figure **8·63** *Three-view drawing of the Atlas missile.*

Due to the 600° plus skin temperatures developed during flight at more than 2,000 mph, the conventional aluminum-alloy skin will not suffice but will warp and lose its strength.

No readily obtainable material except steel offers the necessary resistance to high temperature which is required for the B-70 bomber. On the other hand, steel, because of its weight, would seem to be out of the question. The weight problem has been solved, however, by the "honeycomb" technique which has been used to an increasing degree over the past few years. For

Figure **8 · 64** *The Atlas missile on the launching pad.*

Figure **8 · 65** *The North American B-70 Valkyrie supersonic bomber.*

the B-70, sheets of stainless steel as thin as paper were used to sandwich a steel core built in tiny cells like a bee's honeycomb. When properly brazed, the material is almost as strong as a solid slab of steel and many times lighter. In addition, the honeycomb provides excellent insulation for the interior of the airplane.

It is readily understandable that many new machines, devices, and techniques have had to be developed in order to form and braze the complex shapes required for the outer surface of the B-70. Furthermore, after the honeycomb panels are manufactured, it is necessary to join them to other panels to build the complete structure. In conventional airplanes this is done by riveting. For the steel honeycomb panels in the B-70, however, machine fusion welding is employed.

Another new application of brazing is employed in the plumbing for the hydraulic system. Because of the high pressures (4,000 psi) used in the hydraulic system, high-strength AM350 stainless steel is used for the tubing. The sections of steel tubing are joined by induction brazing with specially designed sleeves. This method not only provides the strength required but also saves over 1,000 lb of weight for each airplane.

REVIEW QUESTIONS

1. Name the major parts of an airplane.
2. Name the principal components of an airplane wing.
3. What is an *extrusion?*
4. Name three types of fuselages classified according to the method by which stresses are transmitted to the structure.
5. What is the load-carrying part of a monocoque fuselage?
6. What is a "fail-safe" feature?
7. Describe the construction of an all-metal fuselage.
8. How is a wing sealed so it can be used to carry fuel?
9. Discuss the importance of proper wing design and construction.
10. Describe the construction of a typical stabilizer.
11. What is the requirement for *stops* in connection with a movable control surface?
12. Under what condition may clevis pins be used as hinge pins for movable control surfaces?
13. What is the requirement for separate elevators?
14. What is the principal requirement for the location of propellers on large propeller-driven aircraft?
15. To what extent may water leakage be permitted into the cockpit of a commercial airliner?
16. Discuss the requirements for pilots' seats.
17. Describe the installation of windows in a pressurized cabin.
18. List the requirements for the passenger compartment of a large commercial airliner.
19. What emergency exits are required for a commercial airliner?
20. Describe a tricycle landing gear.
21. Explain the operation of an air-oleo landing-gear strut.
22. Describe the safety features of a retracting landing-gear installation.
23. What are some of the problems encountered with the use of floats on an airplane?
24. Of what materials are engine mounts usually made?
25. Describe the engine mounting and "pod" for a jet airliner.
26. Discuss the necessity for firewalls.
27. What safety characteristics should be possessed by the material used for engine cowlings?
28. Describe fire-protection methods for engine compartments.
29. What are the general requirements for all controls and control systems?
30. Why is it necessary that wing flaps be designed to operate symmetrically?
31. Under what conditions are oxygen systems required for transport-type aircraft?
32. What is the total number of oxygen-dispensing units required for a high-altitude transport-type airplane?
33. Discuss fire-protection details required for the passenger compartments of aircraft.
34. How do missile fuselages compare with aircraft fuselages?
35. Describe a unique feature of the Atlas missile structure.

CHAPTER 9

Hydraulics and Pneumatics

In the chapter on the laws of physics the basic laws relating to hydraulics were explained. In an aircraft or missile hydraulic system a liquid flowing through tubing is used to transmit force from a pump to the point where force is to be applied. Although **fluid** and **liquid** do not mean the same thing, it is the custom among aircraft mechanics, engineers, and pilots to use the two words interchangeably.

The fact that hydraulic fluid (or any liquid) is, for all practical purposes, incompressible makes it a convenient medium for transmitting force from one point to another. Before the use of hydraulics came into being, force or power was transmitted by means of belts, shafts, push-pull rods, and gear trains. These methods are still used when the distance involved is small. However, over longer distances hydraulics has made it possible to do many things not possible by the other methods.

The **compressibility** of a fluid is its ability to occupy a smaller space, or volume, than it did before it was compressed. Under compression, it tends to return to its original volume, and in doing this it exerts an outward force in all directions. If a pressure of 100 psi is applied to a quantity of water, the volume decreases only about three ten-thousandths of the original volume. Other liquids behave in a similar manner; hence for practical purposes it is said that **liquids are incompressible.**

The **thermal expansion** of a liquid is the increase in volume produced by an increase of temperature. All liquids do not behave alike when the temperature is increased. For example, most oils expand more than water when they are heated. In an aircraft or missile hydraulic system there is usually some provision for compensating for the thermal expansion in order to avoid bursting a line or otherwise damaging parts of the system.

As previously explained, the **density** of any substance is its weight per unit of volume. The density of water, for example, is approximately 62.4 lb per cu ft. This may be compared with the density of iron, which is about 491 lb per cu ft, or the density of gold, which is about 1,204.3 lb per cu ft (avoirdupois pound). The specific gravity of a substance is the weight of a certain volume of that substance compared with the weight of the same volume of pure water. The specific gravity of water is given as 1, and all other substances are compared with water. For example, the specific gravity of kerosene is 0.8 because it weighs about 50 lb per cu ft, which is eight-tenths the weight of an equal volume of pure water.

FLUIDITY AND VISCOSITY

When the word **fluidity** is used with reference to either liquids or gases, it means the ability of the fluid to change shape in response to a force. If water is poured from a square container into a round container, the water adapts itself to the shape of the round container. Some liquids, such as tar and heavy oils, are slower in changing their shapes than other liquids such as water. The liquids used in airplane and missile hydraulic systems are generally either light mineral oils or synthetic fluids which have a high resistance to either heat or cold. These fluids must all readily conform to the shape of the tubes and units through which they pass.

Viscosity is that property of a fluid which makes it resistant to flow. It may also be considered its tendency to stick to surfaces and resist relative motion by a shearing stress within itself. A heavy, slow-flowing liquid has a high viscosity, while a light, fast-flowing liquid has a low viscosity. The viscosity of a liquid is often affected by its temperature. Every automobile driver knows that it is difficult to start an automobile engine during extremely cold weather because of the increased viscosity of the lubricating oil in the engine. Variations of temperature affect some hydraulic fluids in the same manner; hence it has been necessary to develop special fluids for missiles, spacecraft, and other flying vehicles which may be subjected to extremely cold temperatures.

TRANSMISSION OF PRESSURE IN LIQUIDS

As previously explained, **Pascal's law** states that a liquid under pressure in a closed container transmits pressure undiminished to all parts of the enclosing wall. For example, if a bottle with a neck having a cross-sectional area of 1 sq in. is filled with water and a force of 1 lb is exerted on a cork driven into the neck of the bottle, the total force exerted on the inner surface of the bottle will equal the number of square inches of inner surface multiplied by 1 lb. Thus if a force of 1 lb is exerted on the cork and the inner surface area is 50 sq in., the total force exerted against the inner surface of the bottle is 50 lb.

Pascal's principle is demonstrated in Fig. 9·1. Cylinder *A* is connected by a tube to cylinder *B*. Piston 1 in cylinder *A* has a cross-sectional area of 1 sq in. Piston 2 in cylinder *B* has a cross-sectional area of 10 sq in. When 1 lb of force exerts a pressure of 1 lb per sq in. (1 lb times 1 sq in.) in cylinder 1, all the liquid the walls and the bottoms of the cylinders together with the interior of the tube and the undersurfaces of the pistons are subjected to the same pressure. In this manner, the undersurface of piston 2 is subjected to a pressure of 1 psi, and since the area of piston 2 is 10 sq in., the total force exerted on piston 2 is 10×1 or 10 lb.

The mechanical advantage gained by use of pistons of different sizes must be made up in

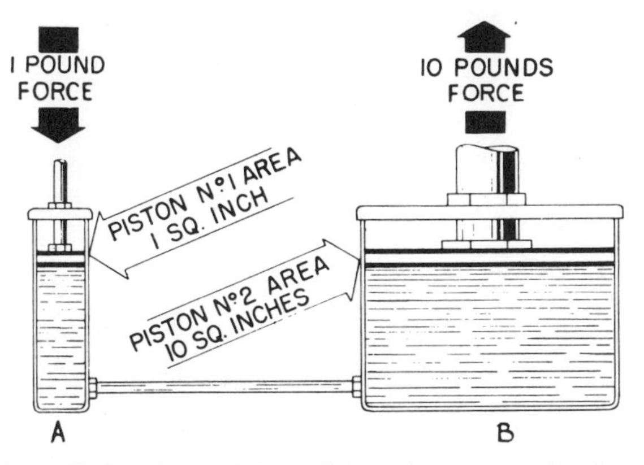

Figure 9·1 Transmission of force by means of hydraulic fluid.

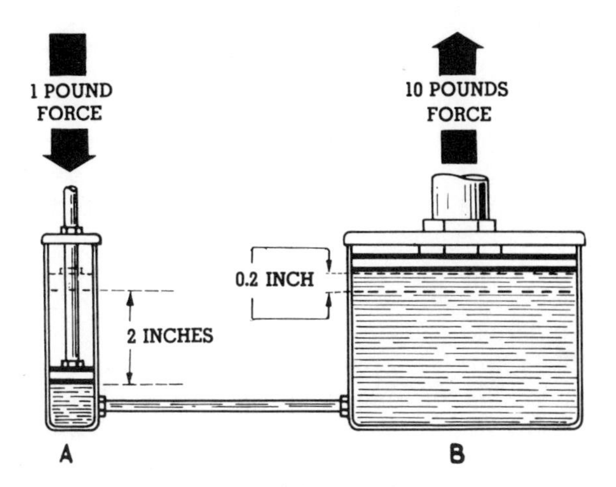

Figure 9·2 Decrease of distance for increase of force.

some manner because energy cannot be created or destroyed. It can only be changed in form. Figure 9·2 shows the result of moving piston 1. As the piston moves downward in cylinder *A* under an applied force of 1 lb, the fluid flows into cylinder *B* and moves piston 2 upward. Since the area of piston 2 is ten times the area of piston 1, piston 2 moves one-tenth the distance that piston 1 moves. For example, when piston 1 moves downward 2 in., piston 2 moves upward one-tenth that distance or 0.2 in. Likewise, the rate of movement of piston 2 is one-tenth that of piston 1 because piston 2 moves 0.2 in. in the same time that piston 1 moves 2 in. For this reason the gain in force is obtained at the expense of distance and speed.

The reason that piston 2 moves more slowly and a shorter distance than piston 1 is easily understood when we consider that it is a **volume** of fluid that moves a piston. It is readily seen that a certain volume of fluid is moved from piston 1 to piston 2. Obviously, when this volume is spread over an area ten times that which it previously occupied, the depth or thickness of the fluid must be reduced in proportion.

MECHANICAL ADVANTAGE

As explained, a **mechanical advantage in force** can be obtained only at the expense of distance, and a mechanical advantage in **distance** can be obtained only at the expense of force. The amount of **work** accomplished is equal to the product of the force applied to a body multiplied by the distance through which the body is moved, provided that the displacement is in the direction of the force. Thus, if a body weighing 20 lb is lifted 10 ft, 20×10 or 200 ft-lb of work is accomplished. Since the mechanical advantage is equal to the resistance overcome divided by the force expended, it is obvious that the theoretical mechanical advantage obtained in Fig. 9·2 is 10. However, the actual mechanical advantage is less than 10 because a fluid flowing through a tube encounters resistance and there is friction when a piston slides along the walls of a cylinder. Therefore, in reality, it is necessary to apply a force slightly greater than 1 lb to piston 1 in cylinder A in order to exert 10 lb of force on piston 2 in cylinder B.

This principle of mechanical advantage, sometimes called **gearing up,** makes it possible to use a small initial force for actuating mechanisms that require a far greater force. Small hydraulic pumps can deliver enough power by this means to operate the relatively heavy landing gear, wing flaps, actuators, and other units on large aircraft and missiles.

The formula for force developed in a hydraulic system is

$$F = PA$$

where F = force, lb
P = pressure, psi
A = area, sq in.

For example, if a pressure of 500 psi is applied to a piston having an area of 12 sq in., the force developed is 6,000 lb.

In a hydraulic system the fluid confined in the tubing is used to transmit the pressure from one location to another, and the pressure is the same at both ends of the tubing as a slight amount of friction is disregarded. This is true even though there may be many bends in the tubing and the tubing may be of considerable length.

When the tubing is connected to a cylinder whose area is greater than that of the tubing and a piston is inserted in the cylinder, the force applied at the end of the tubing may be increased. The fluid flow in the tubing may be rapid, but when it flows into the larger area of the cylinder, the movement becomes comparatively slow.

A BASIC HYDRAULIC SYSTEM

The pump and actuating cylinder

One of the primary requirements for a hydraulic system is, of course, a method for applying pressure to the fluid. This is the pump, which may be hand operated, foot operated, or power operated. Figure 9·3 shows two units connected by a tube. The unit on the left is the pump, marked with the letter A, and the unit on the right is the actuating cylinder, marked with the letter B. In the illustration there is hydraulic fluid to the left of piston C in the hand pump and below piston D in the actuating cylinder. Also, the tube connecting the two units is filled with fluid.

When piston C in the hand pump moves to the left in the illustration, it forces the fluid to flow into the lower part of the actuating cylinder. The fluid is incompressible; hence piston D is forced upward, carrying the piston rod with it and compressing the spring. When the pressure exerted by thc hand pump is released, the compressed spring in the actuating cylinder returns piston D to its original position. When it does this, the fluid is forced back to the hand-pump cylinder and piston C returns to its original position also.

The very simple system described above is similar to hydraulic-brake systems used on both automobiles and small airplanes. The hand pump represents the master cylinder operated by the brake pedal, and the actuating cylinder represents the wheel cylinder which moves the brake shoes within the brake drum.

One of the principal limitations of the system just described is that the piston D can be moved only a short distance because the pump cylinder is smaller than the actuating cylinder. If it is

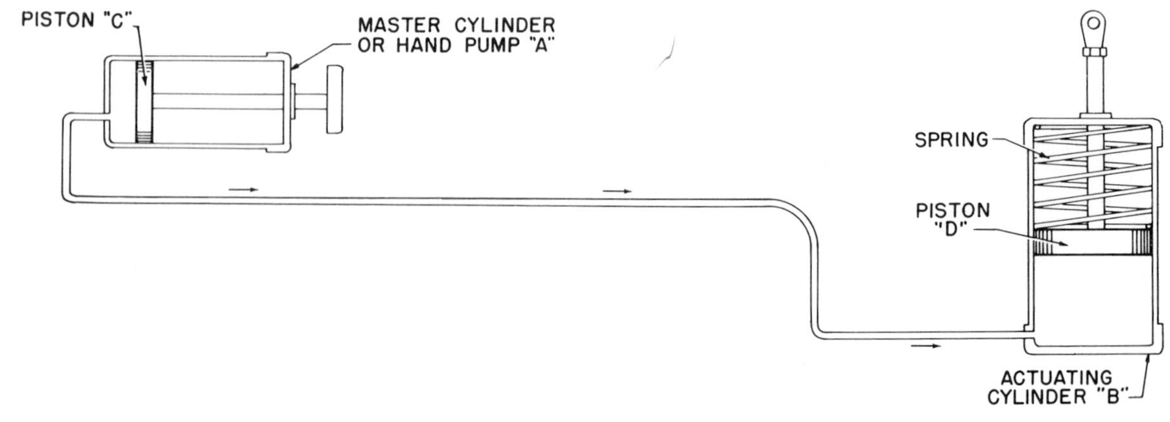

Figure **9·3** *Basic hydraulic system.*

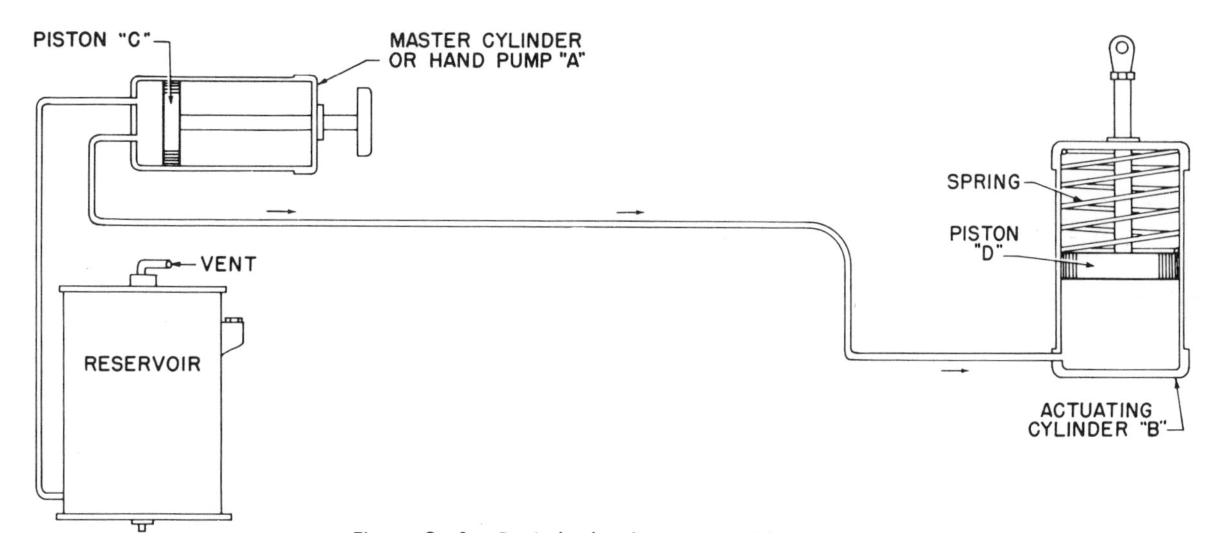

Figure **9·4** *Basic hydraulic system with reservoir.*

necessary to move the actuating cylinder a greater distance than can be accomplished with one stroke of the pump, then it is necessary to have a source of additional fluid.

The reservoir

Reservoirs are used with almost all hydraulic systems. A reservoir stores the supply of fluid for the hydraulic system and must be of sufficient capacity to operate the system and to supply reserve fluid for an emergency. In addition to supplying the operating requirements of the system, the reservoir replenishes fluid lost through leakage and serves as an expansion chamber to receive excess fluid forced out of the system by temperature expansion. At the reservoir, the fluid is purged of air bubbles brought into the system at various other locations.

In Fig. 9·4 a reservoir has been added to the basic hydraulic system. Note that it is attached so that the fluid can flow between the reservoir and the pump. This reservoir is vented to the atmosphere so that air can enter or leave. In this system it will be observed that no action can take place at the actuating cylinder because fluid will flow in and out of the reservoir rather than to the actuating cylinder. It is necessary, therefore, that we include check valves to direct the fluid in one direction only.

Check valves

A **check valve** is a device so constructed that fluid can flow through it in one direction but not in the other. In the diagram of Fig. 9·5 we have added two check valves to overcome the problem presented in the system of Fig. 9·4. In Fig. 9·5 as we draw the pump piston *C* toward the right end of the cylinder *A*, the hydraulic fluid flows from the reservoir into the pump cylinder. Then when we move the piston back toward the left, check valve *H* prevents the fluid from returning to the reservoir, thereby causing all the fluid

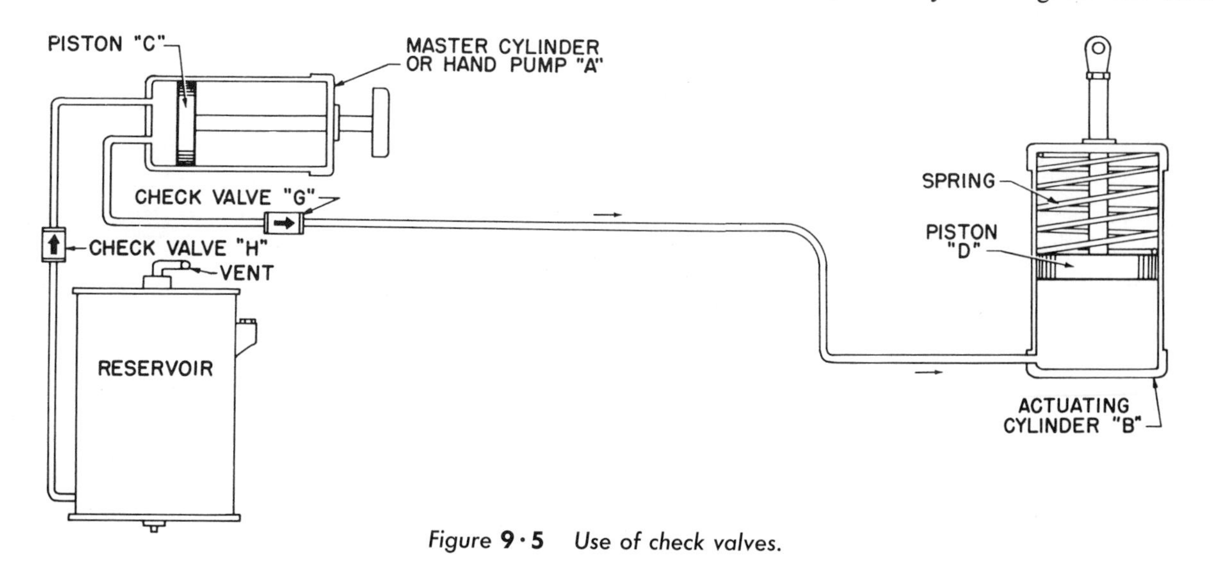

Figure **9·5** *Use of check valves.*

to flow through check valve *G* to the actuating cylinder. In this manner, the piston of the actuating cylinder can be made to travel its entire distance or it can be made to stop at any desired position. The system now provides for the full extension of the piston rod. However, the addition of the check valves makes it impossible for the spring in the actuating cylinder to return piston *D* to the retracted position, since check valve *G* holds the fluid in the actuating cylinder. We see then that some device is still needed to make the system operate effectively.

Selector valve and return line

A **selector valve** is a device by means of which the flow of fluid can be directed in any of several directions. Figure 9·6 shows the basic hydraulic system with a selector valve added. In this case, the selector valve is being used to control the flow of fluid to and from the actuating cylinder. When the selector valve is turned to the position shown by the solid lines, it permits the fluid to enter the bottom part of the actuating cylinder and to extend the piston rod. When the selector valve is turned to the position shown by the dotted lines, the fluid is returning to the reservoir through the **return line** by the action of the compressed spring in the actuating cylinder. Note that the selector valve in Fig. 9·6 is a **two-way valve,** often described as a **two-port selector valve.**

Four-way selector valve

In the system of Fig. 9·6 the actuating cylinder can apply appreciable force only in one direction. If the cylinder is connected to a mechanism which requires force in both directions, the system must have a valving system which permits the application of hydraulic pressure to either side of the piston in the actuating cylinder. For this purpose we use a **four-way** or **four-port** valve installed as shown in the system of Fig. 9·7.

The operation of the hand pump with the selector valve in the desired position permits hydraulic fluid under pressure to act on either side of the actuating cylinder piston, thus extending or retracting the piston rod attached to the piston. When the selector valve is in the position shown by the solid lines, the pump forces fluid to the bottom of the actuating cylinder. The fluid above the piston is forced out through port *E*, through the line *F*, through the selector valve, through the return line, and then into the reservoir.

If the selector valve is turned to the position shown by the dotted lines, the reverse action takes place. The fluid enters the actuating cylinder through port *E*, and the fluid in the bottom of the cylinder passes through the selector valve and back to the reservoir. In this manner hydraulic pressure is available at either side of the piston in the actuating cylinder and no spring is required.

Selector valves are usually provided with a neutral or "off" position. Thus, if the valve in Fig. 9·7 is turned 45°, or halfway between the two operating positions, the internal passages will not be in line with the ports and the flow of fluid is stopped.

Before proceeding further, it is important to understand that the area of the upper surface of piston *D* in the actuating cylinder is smaller than the area of the lower surface because the piston rod is attached to the upper surface. For this reason, if the same pressure is applied to either side of the piston, less force is developed on the

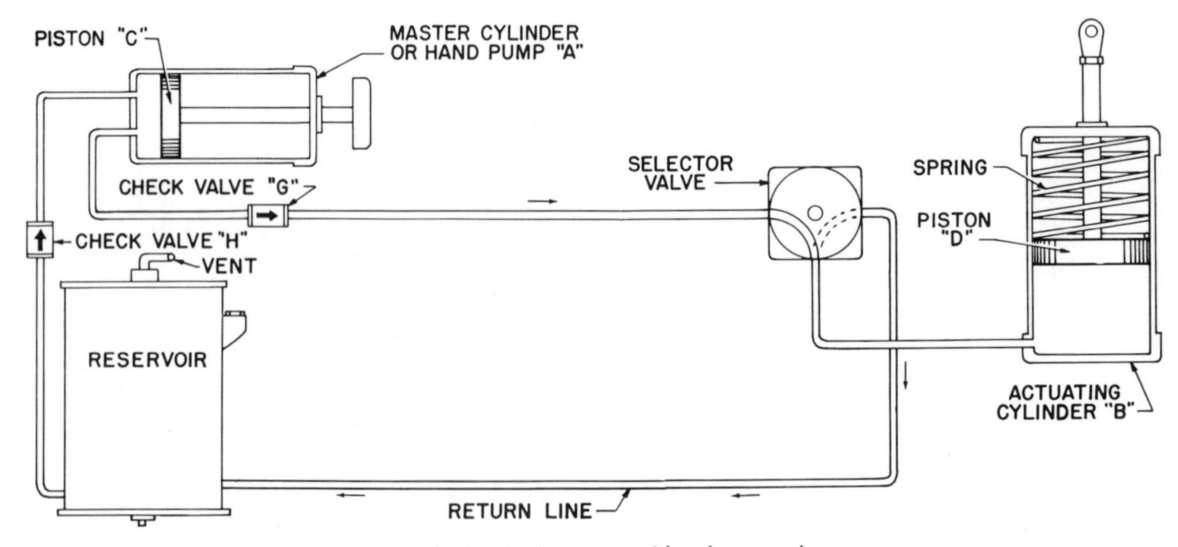

Figure **9·6** *Basic system with selector valve.*

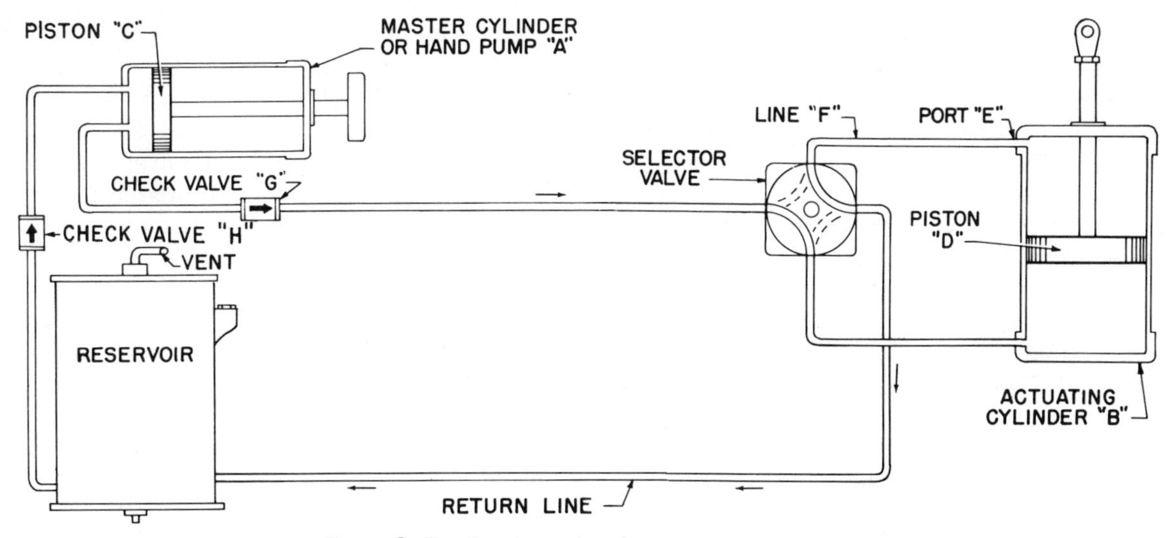

Figure 9·7 System with a four-way selector valve.

side to which the piston rod is attached, and the amount of fluid entering or leaving on the side where the piston rod is attached has a smaller volume than the volume entering or leaving on the other side.

Power pump and relief valve

The diagram in Fig. 9·8 shows the basic hydraulic system with a power pump, a system relief valve, and a check valve *J* added to the previous equipment. When only a hand pump is available, the amount of hydraulic fluid delivered during each stroke of the hand pump is comparatively small. The operation of the landing gear or any other mechanism having large actuating cylinders would therefore require considerable time and effort on the part of the pilot or some other person in the airplane. The installation of a power pump eliminates this disadvantage. Also, since missiles and spacecraft do not as yet operate with human pilots, it is necessary to use power systems in these vehicles.

In Fig. 9·8 the addition of the power pump enables the pilot to move the mechanism merely by placing the selector valve in the desired position and starting the pump. If the pump is engine driven, a pressure regulator will be incorporated in the system to bypass the pump pressure except when the system is operating.

To avoid the danger of excessive pressure building up in the system, a **relief valve** is installed. A relief valve is a valve that opens whenever the pressure exceeds a certain value and returns the fluid to the reservoir. In a system which does not have a pressure regulator, the relief valve will open whenever the power pump is operating and the selector valve is in the neutral position. It will also open when the actuating cylinder has reached

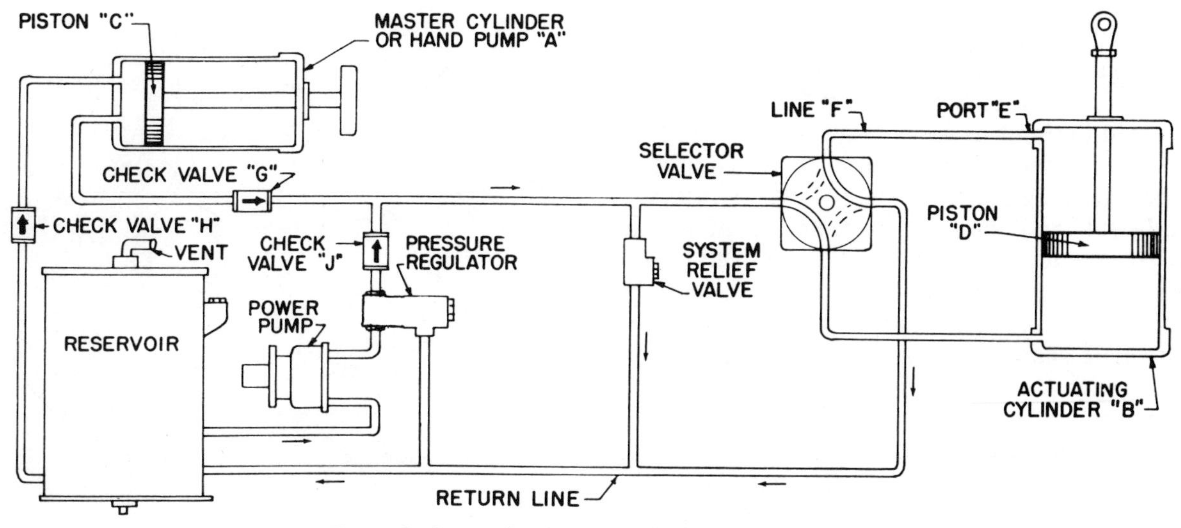

Figure 9·8 Hydraulic system with a power pump.

the limit of its travel. It is important to understand that the system relief valve is installed between the pressure line and the return line.

There is an important difference between a system relief valve and a pressure regulator. The relief valve relieves pressure only above a certain value, whereas the pressure regulator maintains a given pressure range in the system. The relief valve is set for a higher pressure than that of the pressure regulator.

The system illustrated in Fig. 9•8 would be impractical if check valve *J* were not present. The hand pump, retained for emergency operation in case the power pump should fail, would be useless, since the output of the hand pump would turn the power pump backward and return the fluid to the reservoir. To prevent this, check valve *J* is installed between the power pump and the pressure line.

In addition to its use during emergencies, the hand pump is also useful for testing purposes when it is not convenient to operate the power system. In aircraft systems, the power pump may be electrically driven or it may be operated by the airplane engine through accessory drive gears. Large airplanes may have one or more engine-driven pumps for the primary source of power and in addition may use an electrically driven power pump for emergency and auxiliary purposes.

HYDRAULIC SYSTEM COMPONENTS

Hydraulic power pumps

There is a variety of types of pumps used for the production of hydraulic pressure. The type selected for any particular system is determined by the design engineers, who choose the pump characteristics best suited for a particular application. The pump used for a specific system must be capable of delivering the required volume of hydraulic fluid at a pressure sufficiently high to operate the unit or units of the system under all load conditions. For example, it is required to raise a landing gear consisting of two main wheels and struts and one nose wheel and strut, and the main gear requires a force of 1,000 lb to raise it into the locked position. Furthermore, it is required that the operation be complete in 5 sec. The main gear-actuating cylinder is 2 in. in diameter and has a stroke of 18 in., full range. If we apply 400 psi hydraulic pressure to the cylinder, we find that it will produce a force of about 1,257 lb. This is adequate to raise the main gear. The volume of fluid required to move the main gear cylinder through its complete range is found to be about 57 cu in. If we assume that the nose gear cylinder has a volume equal to one-half that of the main gear cylinder, the nose gear cylinder will require 28.5 cu in. of fluid for full-range operation. Since there are two main gear cylinders, the total volume of fluid required for landing-gear retraction is 57 + 57 + 28.5 or 142.5 cu in. We see then that the hydraulic pump must supply not less than 142 cu in. of fluid in 5 sec at a pressure of nearly 400 psi to operate the gear satisfactorily. This volume amounts to about 7.8 gpm.

The **gear-type** pump, often used in low-pressure hydraulic systems, is illustrated in Fig. 9•9. It consists of two meshed gears that revolve in a housing. Note that in the drawing the clearance between the teeth as they mesh and between the teeth and the housing is very small. This close tolerance is provided to assure that very little fluid will leak back as the pump operates. In the drawing, the driving gear is marked 1, the driven gear is marked 2, the "in" port is marked 3, and the "out" port is marked 4.

The inport is connected to the reservoir, and the outport is connected to the pressure line. The driving gear is attached to a drive shaft that extends from the housing, with seals or cups to prevent leakage around the drive shaft. The drive shaft is splined into an engine accessory drive.

When the driving gear turns counterclockwise, it turns the driven gear in a clockwise direction, as indicated by the arrows on the gears in the illustration. As the teeth pass the edge of the inport, fluid is trapped between the teeth and the housing and is then carried around the housing to the outport. As the teeth of the driving gear mesh with the teeth of the driven gear, the fluid

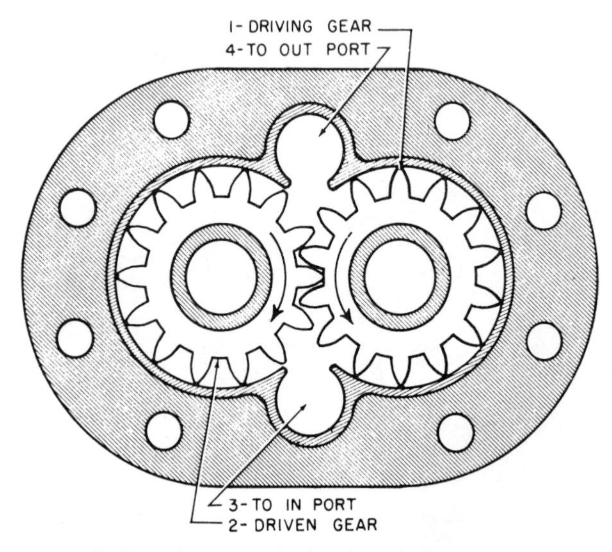

Figure 9•9 Gear-type hydraulic pump.

between the teeth is displaced and is forced out of the "out" port and into the pressure line.

A **gerotor-type** hydraulic pump is illustrated in Fig. 9 · 10. It operates according to the same basic principles as the gear-type pump, but it has a different arrangement of gears. The pump consists essentially of a housing which contains a liner and an internal-gear rotor, which has five wide, flat teeth; a spur driving gear, which has four narrow teeth; and the pump head, which has two crescent-shaped openings. The internal-gear rotor fits snugly inside the liner. The drive gear is keyed to the drive shaft, and it is mounted off center inside the internal-gear rotor in such a manner that only one tooth is completely engaged with the internal gear at any one time. When the drive gear turns, it turns the rotor because the two gears are meshed.

One crescent-shaped opening is connected to the inport, and the other crescent-shaped opening is connected to the outport. When the spur driving gear turns in a counterclockwise direction, the internal-gear rotor is driven in the same direction. Hydraulic fluid enters the inport and passes through the crescent-shaped opening in the head, filling the space created by the separation of the teeth. As the rotation takes place, the space between the gear teeth and the rotor teeth is decreased and the fluid is squeezed through the other crescent-shaped opening in the head and thence to the outport and the pressure line.

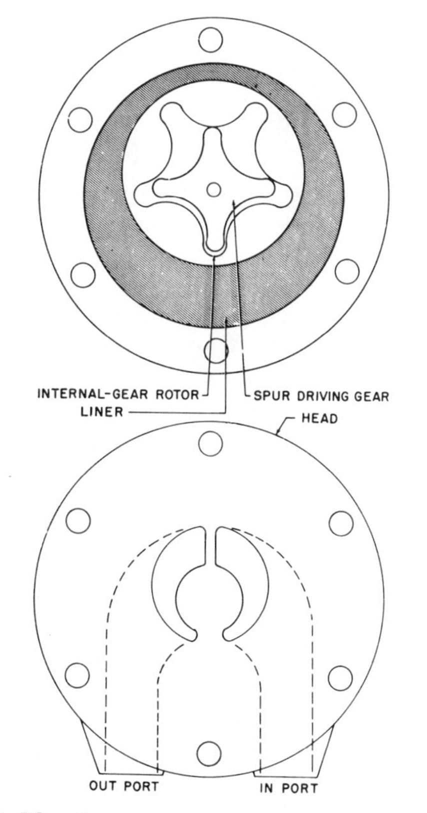

Figure **9 · 10** *Gerotor-type pump.*

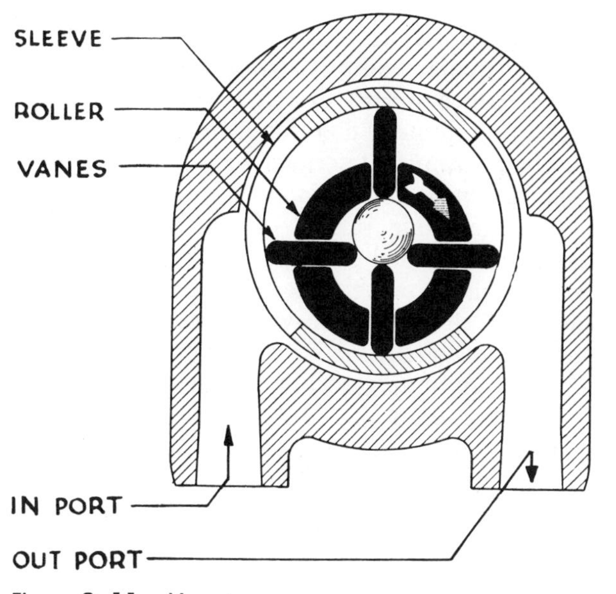

Figure **9 · 11** *Vane-type pump.*

Figure 9 · 11 is an illustration of a low-pressure **vane-type** pump. It consists of a housing containing a steel sleeve with an off-center bore, four vanes or blades, a hollow steel rotor, and a coupling to turn the rotor.

The blades, which are mounted in the rotor, together with the rotor divide the bore of the sleeve into four sections. These four sections vary in volume as the rotor turns, because the rotor is mounted off center in the bore of the sleeve.

As the rotor turns, each section, in turn, passes a point where its volume is at a minimum value, and then the volume increases gradually during one-half of a revolution. During this time while the volume of the section is increasing, the section is connected to the inport through a slot in the sleeve; hence the hydraulic fluid flows into the section.

As the rotor turns during the second half of the revolution, the volume of the section gradually decreases and at the same time the section is connected to the outport through another slot in the sleeve, thus forcing the hydraulic fluid out through the outport into the pressure line. This action is based in part upon the principle of the incompressibility of liquids.

The vane-type pump is not commonly used in aircraft hydraulic systems because pressure impulses during fluid delivery cause a severe vibration in the tubes attached to the pump. The pump is of interest, however, because it may be encountered in some systems and it is often used in fuel systems.

A **piston-type** hydraulic pump often used for

high-pressure systems is illustrated in Fig. 9 · 12. This particular pump is a **constant-displacement** pump, which means that it will always deliver the same volume of fluid for each revolution. The pumps previously described were also essentially constant-displacement pumps.

A rather wide variety of piston-type pumps has been designed for the operation of hydraulic systems; however, the basic principle is the same for all types. The variations are found in such details as the methods by which the pistons are caused to reciprocate within the cylinders.

The pump in the illustration consists of a cylinder block and a piston-and-drive assembly contained in a housing. A head, containing the inlet port and the outlet port, is attached to one end of the housing. The cylinder block contains seven cylinders equally spaced from the center. The piston-and-drive assembly carries the connecting rods, thus permitting the connecting rod and piston to move in relation to each other and to the drive-shaft face.

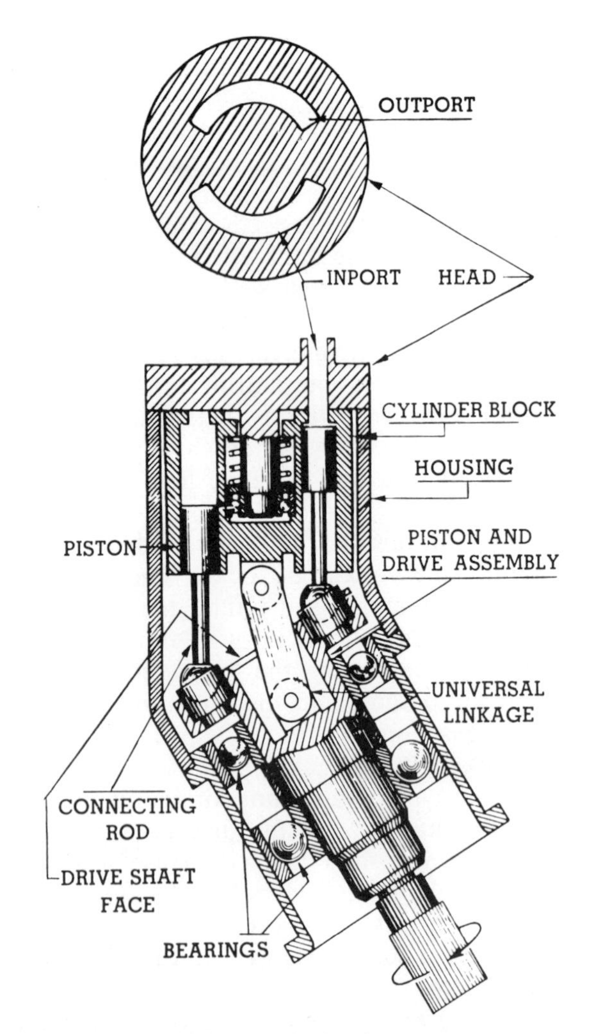

Figure **9 · 12** *Piston-type hydraulic pump.*

When the piston-and-drive assembly and the cylinder block are placed together, each piston is inserted in a corresponding cylinder bore of the cylinder block. When these are installed in the housing, an angle exists between the cylinder block and the drive-shaft face. The piston-and-drive assembly is rotated by an external power source, such as an engine accessory drive. The cylinder block is forced to rotate at the same speed as the drive-and-piston assembly because of the double universal-drive linkage connecting them. The angle existing between the cylinder block and the drive-shaft face causes the pistons to reciprocate within the cylinders, thereby drawing hydraulic fluid from the reservoir and pumping it to the system.

In the bottom of the main housing is a port that serves as a drain. A cup-type seal prevents the leakage of fluid around the drive shaft. When the drive shaft rotates, it rotates the universal-drive linkage, which is basically a rigid drive shaft having a flexible coupling at both ends. This universal-drive linkage rotates the cylinder barrel.

During one-half of a revolution of the cylinder barrel, a given cylinder moves away from the face of the drive, thus causing the piston to move away from the top of the cylinder. During this part of the cycle the cylinder is connected to the inport through a passage in the head. As the piston moves down toward the bottom of the cylinder, hydraulic fluid flows into the cylinder. After the cylinder passes the bottom-dead-center position, it is connected to the outport by means of a passage in the head. During the last half of the revolution the cylinder moves closer to the face of the drive shaft and therefore moves toward the top of the cylinder. The hydraulic fluid that filled the cylinder during the first half of the cycle is now forced out of the outport. Three cylinders are always connected to the inport, and three cylinders are always connected to the outport. One cylinder is not connected to either port. Whenever one cylinder stops pumping, another cylinder begins to pump. In this manner the flow of hydraulic fluid is made constant.

Figure 9 · 13 is a functional drawing of a seven-piston pump. A careful study of this drawing will make the operation clear. Figure 9 · 13 provides additional views of the pump shown in Fig. 9 · 12.

The **variable-displacement** or **variable-volume** pump obtains its name from the fact that such a pump incorporates a mechanism which automatically increases the volume of the fluid flow when actuating units are in operation and which decreases the volume of fluid flow when the actuating units are at rest, thus maintaining a constant preadjusted system pressure.

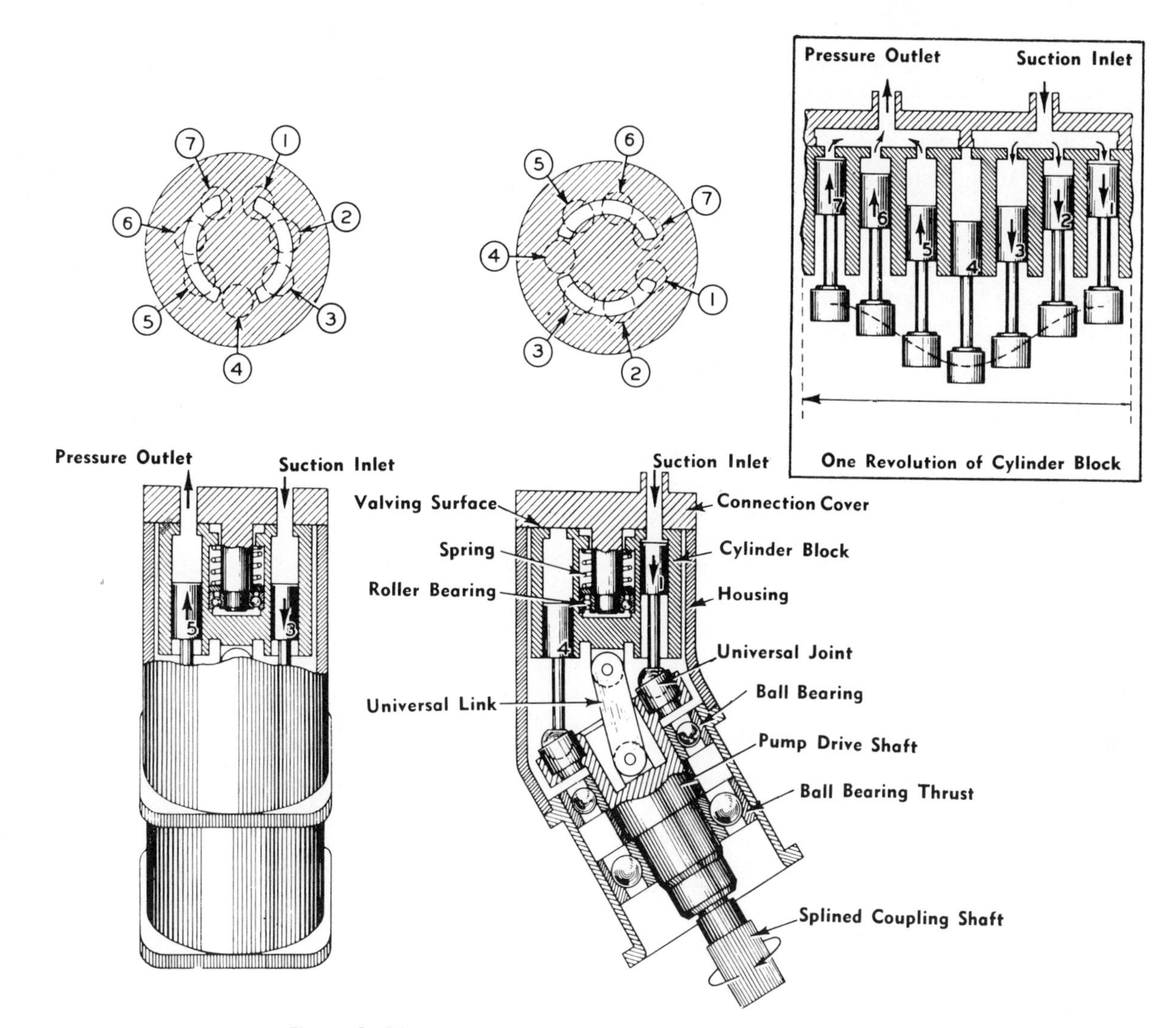

Figure **9·13** *Functional drawing of a seven-piston-type pump.*

One form of the variable-displacement type of pump is similar to the piston-type power pump in its basic design. It should be remembered that in the piston-type power pump the piston is attached to the face of the drive shaft by its connecting rod; hence it must always remain the same distance from the drive shaft. Also, the delivery of fluid to the system is dependent upon the angle between the drive-shaft face and the cylinder block.

The variable-displacement pump, which resembles the piston-type pump, provides a means for varying the angle between the drive-shaft face and the cylinder block, thus varying the length of the pumping stroke. This, in turn, determines the volume of fluid discharged to the system.

In order to accomplish this result, the cylinder block is mounted on a yoke that allows it to turn in relation to the face of the drive shaft. The degree to which the cylinder block turns is governed by a pressure-control device. When the pressure drops, the pressure-control device immediately increases the angle between the drive-shaft face and the cylinder block. When no demands are made on the pump, the pressure-control device decreases the angle between the cylinder block and the face of the drive shaft to a degree sufficient to keep the desired system pressure.

Regardless of variations in details of design, the major forms of the variable-delivery pump rely upon the pumping action of a piston reciprocating within a cylinder and also upon some method (integral with the pump) for increasing or decreasing the length of the stroke to meet the variations of the demands of the hydraulic system.

Hand pumps

Most aircraft hydraulic systems contain a **hand pump** which is used primarily as an emergency means of operating hydraulic units when the power pump fails and secondarily to build pressure in the system for ground testing the hydraulic system when it is not practicable to use the engine-driven power pump.

All hydraulic hand pumps are manually operated, reciprocating, piston-type pumps. They may be divided into two general groups: (1) **single-acting** hand pumps and (2) **double-acting** hand pumps. Single-action pumps have one pressure stroke for each two strokes of the handle. Double-acting pumps have two pressure strokes for each two strokes of the operating handle.

A typical single-acting hydraulic hand pump has a cylinder, a piston, an operating handle, and two check valves. An inport is connected to the reservoir, and an outport is connected to the pressure line or manifold. When the piston is moved toward the operating handle by that handle, the fluid flows from the reservoir through a check valve into the pump. When the piston is moved away from the side on which the operating handle is mounted, the first check valve closes and a second check valve opens. The fluid in the pump is then forced out through the outport and into the pressure line. As stated before, two strokes of the operating handle produce one pressure stroke.

The principle of the single-action hand pump is illustrated in Fig. 9·14. Note that, when the operating handle is pulled back from the cylinder, the piston moves toward the right. This action causes the inlet check valve to open and permit fluid to flow into the pump cylinder. Then when the operating handle is moved toward the cylinder, the piston forces the fluid out through the outlet check valve and into the pressure line. The check valves are held in the closed position by means of coiled springs when there is no fluid flow.

A diagram illustrating the principle of a double-action hand pump is shown in Fig. 9·15. This pump incorporates four check valves. Valves 1 and 2 are inlet valves, and valves 3 and 4 are outlet valves. When the handle is moved to

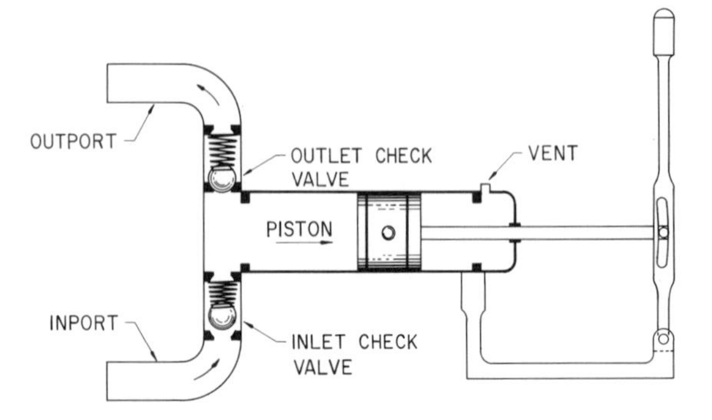

Figure **9·14** *Single-action hand pump.*

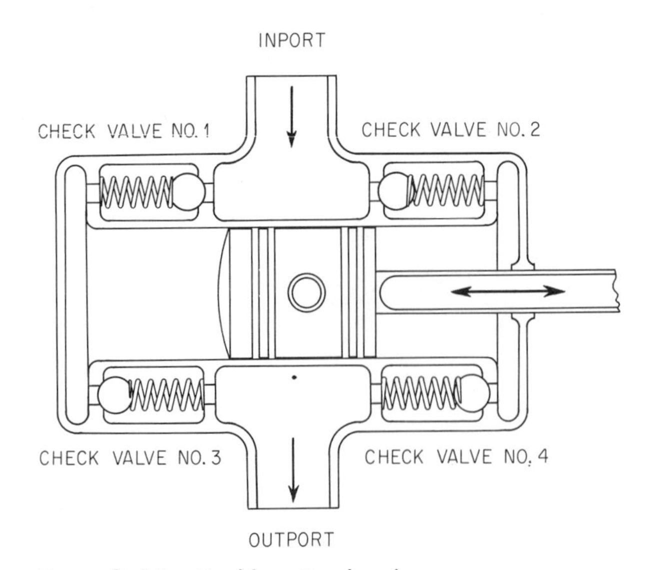

Figure **9·15** *Double-action hand pump.*

the right, check valve 1 opens and check valve 2 closes. This permits fluid to flow from the reservoir through valve 1 into the left end of the cylinder. At the same time check valve 4 is open and check valve 3 is closed. Fluid then flows out of the right end of the cylinder, through check valve 4 and to the outport. When the handle is moved to the left, all the check valves reverse their respective positions. Fluid then flows in through check valve 2 and out through check valve 3. Thus, for each stroke of the piston there is a discharge of fluid from the outport.

Figure 9·16 is a drawing of another type of double-acting pump called a **piston-displacement** hand pump. It consists of a cylinder, a spool-shaped piston with two built-in check valves (1 and 2), an operating handle, and two other check valves (3 and 4). The fluid flows from the reservoir to the middle of the spool-shaped piston. When the piston is moved toward the right in the drawing, check valve 1 is closed and fluid under pressure is forced out of check valve 4 into the system. While this is happening, check valve 3 is held closed by the pressure and its spring and fluid from the reservoir flows to check valve 2 and fills the end of the cylinder at the left in the drawing. When the piston is moved toward the left, check valve 2 is closed and fluid is forced out of check valve 3 into the pressure line. At the same time, check valve 4 is closed and fluid flows into the right end of the cylinder through check valve 1. This action shows that this is a double-acting pump.

Another form of double-acting hand pump is the **piston-rod-displacement** type, illustrated in Fig. 9·17. This pump consists of a cylinder, a piston containing a built-in check valve *A*,

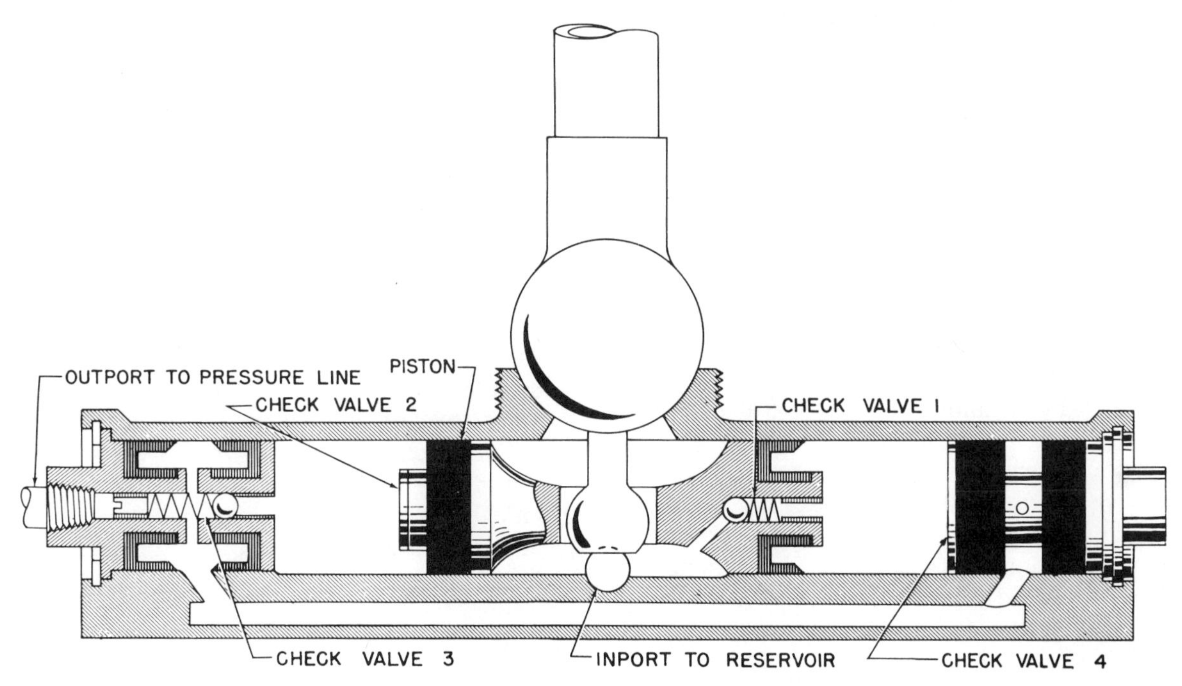

Figure 9·16 Piston-displacement hand pump.

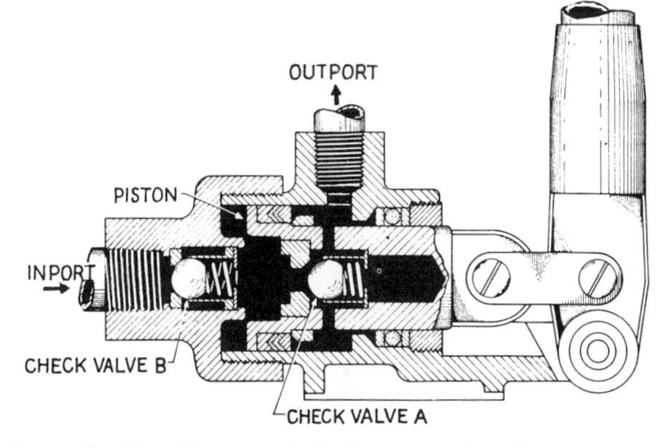

Figure 9·17 Piston-rod-displacement hand pump.

a large piston rod, an operating handle, and a check valve *B*. In some pumps of this type there is a one-way seal on the piston instead of the internal check valve, but Fig. 9·17 shows the usual construction with an internal check valve.

When the piston in Fig. 9·17 moves toward the right in the illustration, check valve *A* is closed and check valve *B* is opened. Fluid from the reservoir flows into the pump. When the piston is moved to the left, check valve *B* is closed. The pressure established in the fluid then opens check valve *A* and allows fluid to be admitted behind the piston. There is now room enough for only a part of the incoming fluid; hence the remainder of the fluid is forced into the pressure line. If the piston is once more moved toward the right in the drawing, check valve *A* is closed. The fluid behind the piston is then forced out through the outport to the pressure line. At the same time, fluid from the reservoir flows into the cylinder through check valve *B*. Since this is merely another form of double-acting pump, two pressure strokes are delivered by the pump for each two strokes of the handle.

Actuating cylinders

The purpose of an actuating cylinder is to transform energy in the form of fluid flow under pressure into mechanical force, or action, to perform work. It is used to impart linear motion to some mechanism.

The cylinder of an actuating unit is mounted so that either the piston rod or the cylinder itself is attached to the movable unit by a mechanical linkage, the other end being secured to the main structure of the vehicle or machine in which it is installed.

Some actuating cylinders are called **jacks,** and others are called **struts,** but these are only examples of the loose terminology that has crept into the subject of hydraulics, just as hydraulic liquid is called a **fluid.** For the sake of clarity, the term **actuating cylinder** is used in this text to mean a unit which receives fluid from the selector valve and which is connected to some movable part of a mechanism for the purpose of producing linear motion.

A typical actuating cylinder consists fundamentally of a cylinder, of one or more pistons and piston rods, and of the necessary seals to prevent the escape of hydraulic fluid. Most hydraulic actuating cylinders are **double-acting;** that is, fluid under pressure can be applied to either side of the piston to provide movement in either direction. However, **single-acting** actuating cylinders, which provide force and movement in only one direction, are sometimes used to actuate brakes, and they have been used on military airplanes to charge the guns.

Actuating cylinders vary in length and diameter, depending upon the length of the stroke desired and the force required to move the attached unit throughout the entire range of operation. For example, a landing-gear actuating cylinder may be required to develop a force of 10,000 lb or more, and the piston rod may be required to extend 20 in. or more.

The diameter of the cylinder, which determines the cross-sectional area of the piston, depends on the force desired. If the pressure in the system is 1,000 psi and it is desired to produce a force of 10,000 lb, the piston will have to have a cross-sectional area of 10 sq in. On the other hand, if the system pressure is 2,000 psi and a force of 10,000 lb is required, the cross-sectional area will have to be only 5 sq in. Obviously, there are many factors involved in the size of an actuating cylinder, one of them being a design where the cylinder is designed to operate a landing-gear lock. In this case the piston travel may be 2 in. or less and the cross-sectional area may be correspondingly small.

Figure 9·18 illustrates a **single-port, single-acting** actuating cylinder. Fluid under pressure enters the port shown at the left in the drawing and forces the piston toward the right, that is, toward the opposite end of the cylinder against the force of the spring. The spring returns the piston to its original position after the desired linear movement has been completed and fluid under pressure is no longer acting against the piston.

Figure 9·19 is an illustration of a **two-port, double-acting** actuating cylinder. Fluid under pressure enters the port at the left in the drawing, forces the piston to the opposite end of the cylinder, and causes the mechanism attached to the rod, shown at the right of the drawing, to move. At the same time, the fluid in front of the piston is forced out of the port at the right and back to the reservoir. When fluid under pressure is directed into the right-hand port, the piston and the mechanism move in the opposite direction. Fluid ahead of the piston is then forced out of the port at the left, and it returns to the reservoir. Since the actuating cylinder is double-acting, a mechanism can be moved in either direction by means of a selector valve.

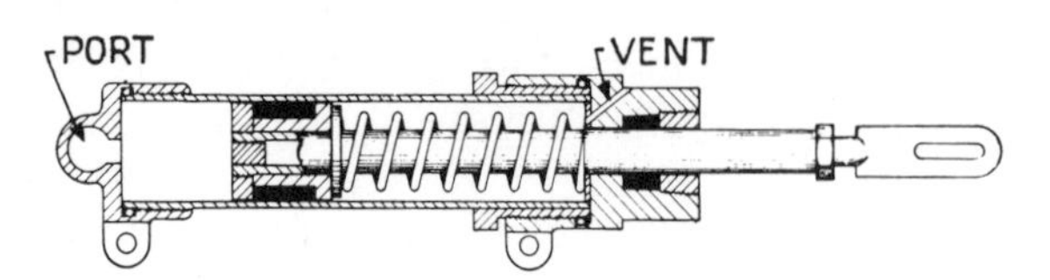

Figure **9·18** *Single-port, single-acting actuating cylinder.*

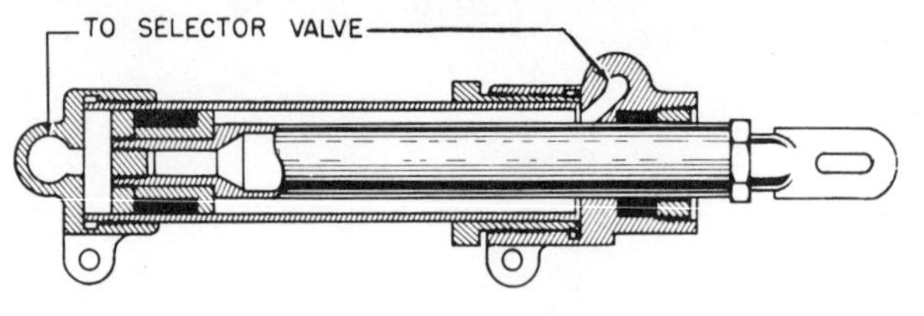

Figure **9·19** *Two-port, double-acting actuating cylinder.*

A cutaway photograph of a special actuating cylinder is shown in Fig. 9·20. This actuator is designed to operate one of the flight controls in a high-speed jet fighter aircraft. The actuator is provided with a hydromechanical servomechanism by which the pilot's effort is converted to hydraulic power to move the control surface. This mechanism is shown in the top view of Fig. 9·20. The actuator is also provided with an electrical servomechanism through which the autopilot operates the control. The electrohydraulic mechanism is shown in the bottom view. The dual-piston arrangement of the actuator cylinder is also shown in the bottom view.

Reservoirs and filters

A reservoir, as indicated previously, is a tank in which hydraulic fluid is stored for the system. It is usually located at the highest point in the system so the force of gravity will keep the pumps supplied with fluid. Some reservoirs are pressurized, however, and it is not necessary that such reservoirs be placed in the highest point in the system. The shape of reservoirs may vary, but the best shape from the purely hydraulic point of view is a vertical cylinder. Welded aluminum-alloy sheet has been widely used for reservoirs; however, magnesium and stainless steel have been found to be satisfactory for many installations. Most reservoirs are mounted on padded supports and are held in place by padded straps.

Figure 9·21 is a schematic drawing of a reservoir. The foaming space, height when full, fluid level when the airplane is on the ground, filler, return line, engine-pump line, land-pump line, and space occupied by the reserve supply for the hand pump are all indicated on the drawing.

Figure 9·22 is another drawing of a hydraulic reservoir showing features not indicated in Fig. 9·21. Note the vent at the top, the sight gage on

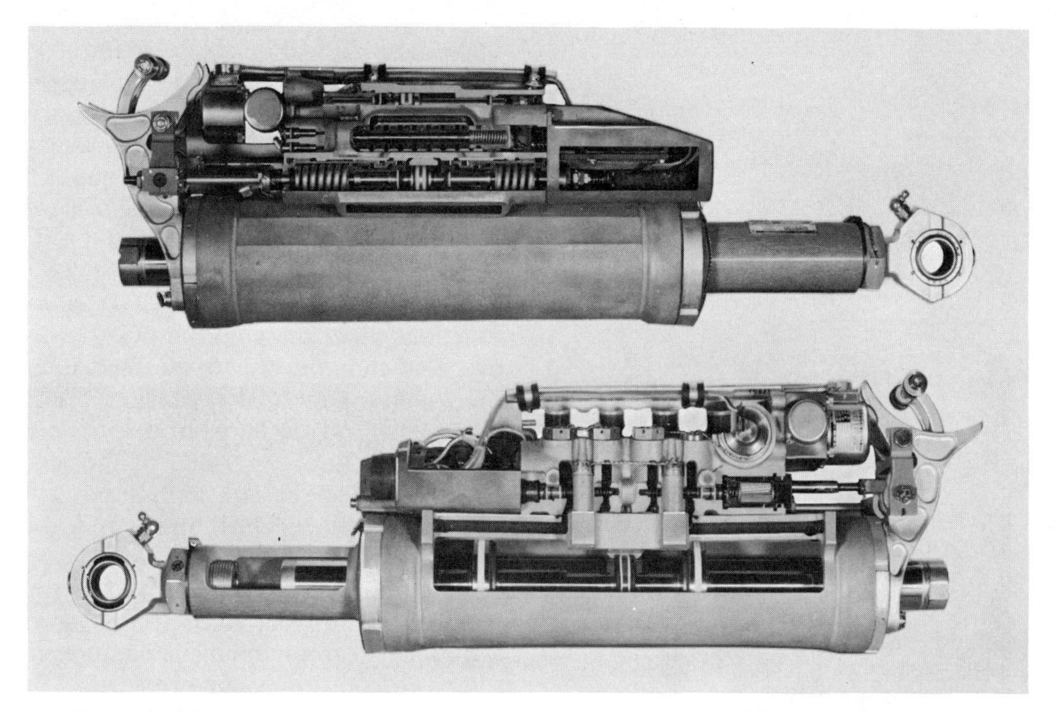

Figure 9·20 Cutaway views of a servo-operated actuating cylinder. (Weston Hydraulics Division of Borg-Warner Corp.)

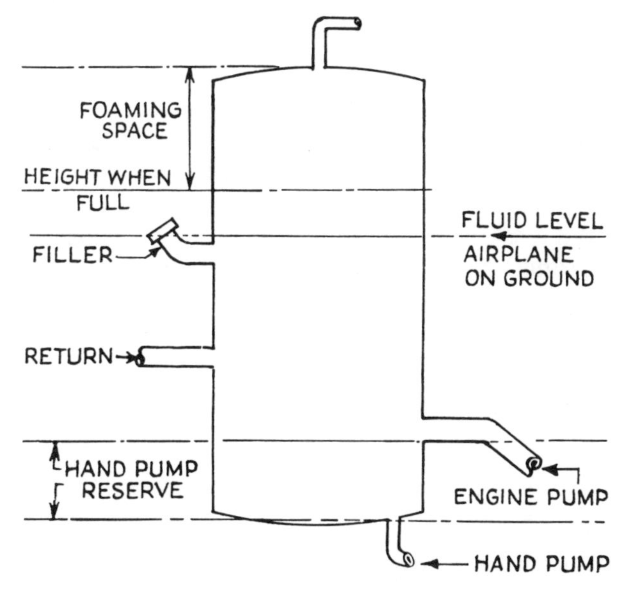

Figure 9·21 Schematic drawing of a hydraulic reservoir.

the side, the filler opening, the return-line connection, the location of the filter screen and the standpipe, and the connections to the power pump and the hand pump.

All nonpressurized reservoirs are vented to the atmosphere so that the reservoir can "breathe" as the fluid level varies; that is, when the fluid level rises, the air is forced out, and when the fluid level falls, the air at atmospheric pressure flows into the reservoir and occupies the space above the fluid. Also, the vent makes it possible for any air that has entered the hydraulic system to find a means of escape. If the reservoir is installed in an airplane which may be expected to engage in inverted flight, a check valve is placed in the vent line to prevent the loss of fluid while the airplane is upside down.

The reservoir is filled with the correct type and grade of hydraulic fluid through the filler neck until the proper level is reached. The level is usually shown on a sight gage in or on the side of the reservoir; however, it may be indicated by a quantity gage.

The reservoir usually has a sediment trap and a drain. A filter screen may be located in the filler neck or in the reservoir itself. These features make it easier to keep the fluid free from impurities.

On the reservoir shown in Fig. 9·22 there are two outlets. One of these is for supplying fluid to the hand pump, and the other for supplying the power pump. The power-pump outlet is connected to the standpipe, and the hand-pump outlet is connected to the bottom of the reservoir. Since the entrance to the standpipe for the fluid in the reservoir is higher than the hand-pump connection, the power pump can draw only that fluid which is above the top of the standpipe, thus leaving the lower portion of the fluid for the use of the hand pump if there is a leak in the system or some other emergency requiring a supply to the hand pump. Some tanks have been made without standpipes, but their power-pump outlets are

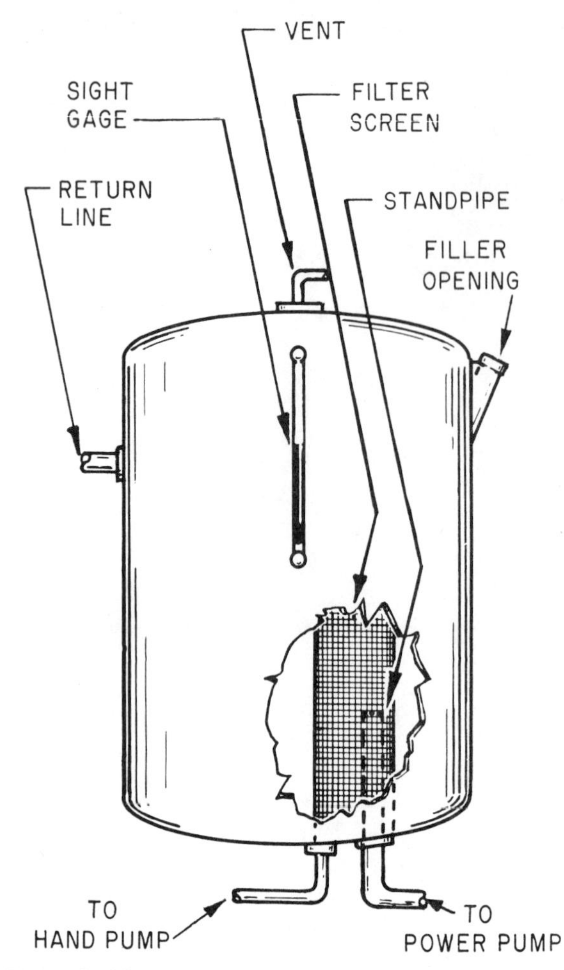

Figure **9·22** *A complete hydraulic reservoir.*

always higher than the hand-pump outlet (see Fig. 9·21).

The return line to a reservoir is usually connected at such an angle that fluid is given a swirling or rotary motion. This reduces turbulence and tends to prevent the air from mixing with the fluid.

A placard, which is usually a metal plate, is mounted on the reservoir and is marked with detailed information concerning the reservoir and the fluid with which it is to be filled.

In addition to a sight gage for determining the level of the fluid within the reservoir, other methods may also be used. One method is to use a dipstick similar to that used on automobile engines to measure the quantity of lubricating oil in the crankcase.

Another method for determining the quantity of fluid in the reservoir is to install a **liquidometer** or some similar device which electrically transmits indications of fluid level to a calibrated indicator located on or near the pilot's instrument panel.

The capacity of a hydraulic reservoir must be such that fluid will be available for all conditions of operation. The capacity for any particular system is determined by the engineers during design of the system. Some reservoirs, such as those used in missile systems, may be quite small, containing only a few cubic inches of fluid. Others, used in large airplanes, may contain 15 gal or more of fluid.

The hydraulic reservoir serves a number of functions other than storing fluid. It serves as an overflow chamber for excess fluid forced out of the system by thermal expansion, piston-rod displacement, and discharge from the accumulators; it provides for the purging of the air from the fluid; and it serves as a settling basin where impurities can be collected and removed through a sediment trap and filter.

Reservoirs may be pressurized in a number of ways. One method, used in jet aircraft, is to introduce air from an engine compressor into the reservoir, controlling the pressure by means of a pressure-regulating device. The principal purpose of pressurization is to ensure a positive flow of fluid to the engine-driven pump during high-altitude flights. The atmospheric pressure at high altitudes may be so low that fluid pressure to the pump is insufficient to maintain operation.

Another method for pressurizing a reservoir is the use of an air injector. Figure 9·23 is a drawing illustrating the principle of the venturi-type air injector. This fitting is installed in a return line to the reservoir, and fluid under pressure is passed through it. An air line connected into the fitting as shown permits air to enter the fluid line. It will be remembered that according to Bernoulli's

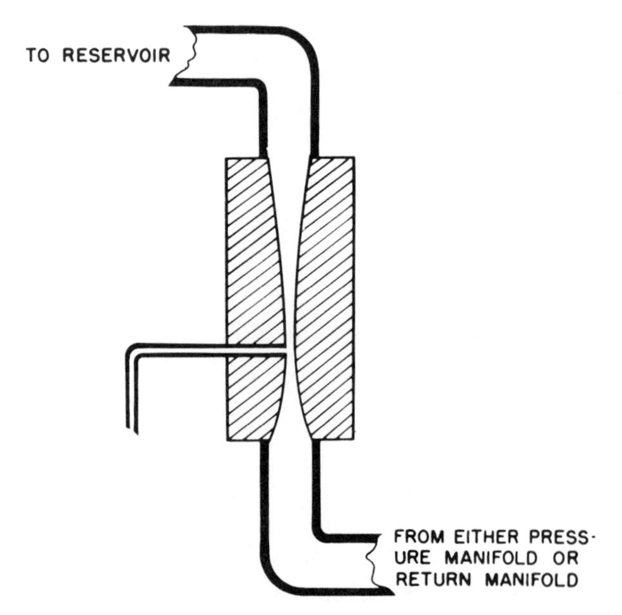

Figure **9·23** *Principle of venturi-type air injector.*

principle an increase of fluid velocity will cause a decrease in pressure. In the venturi shown the fluid velocity is increased because of the decreased cross-sectional area in the throat of the venturi. This results in a pressure decrease, thus causing air to be injected into the fluid. The air entering the fluid is carried to the reservoir, where it is trapped, thus causing an increase in pressure in the reservoir. Excess pressure is passed off through a pressure-relief valve in the reservoir vent line.

A **filter** is often included in a reservoir, and there is usually a filter in the return line also. The filter is a screening or straining device used to clean the hydraulic fluid and prevent foreign particles and contaminating substances from remaining in the system. The importance of clean fluid can be understood when it is known that clearances within some hydraulic pumps and actuators are measured in millionths of an inch. With such close tolerances a very minute particle could interfere with proper operation.

The hydraulic fluid holds in suspension tiny particles of metal that are deposited during the normal wear of selector valves, pump, actuators, etc. Such minute particles of metal may injure the units and parts through which they pass if they are not removed by a filter.

Filters may consist of extremely fine screens, micronic elements made of fibrous material or sintered metal, or a stack of disks placed very close together. Fluid is caused to flow through the filtering material, where it leaves all particles large enough to cause trouble in the system. Figure 9·24 is an exploded view of a standard micronic filter. The nomenclature of the parts is as follows: (1) head, (2) safety wire, (3) piston, (4) spring, (5) spring guide, (6) plug gasket, (7) plug, (8) filter element, (9) safety wire, (10) case or housing, and (11) case gasket.

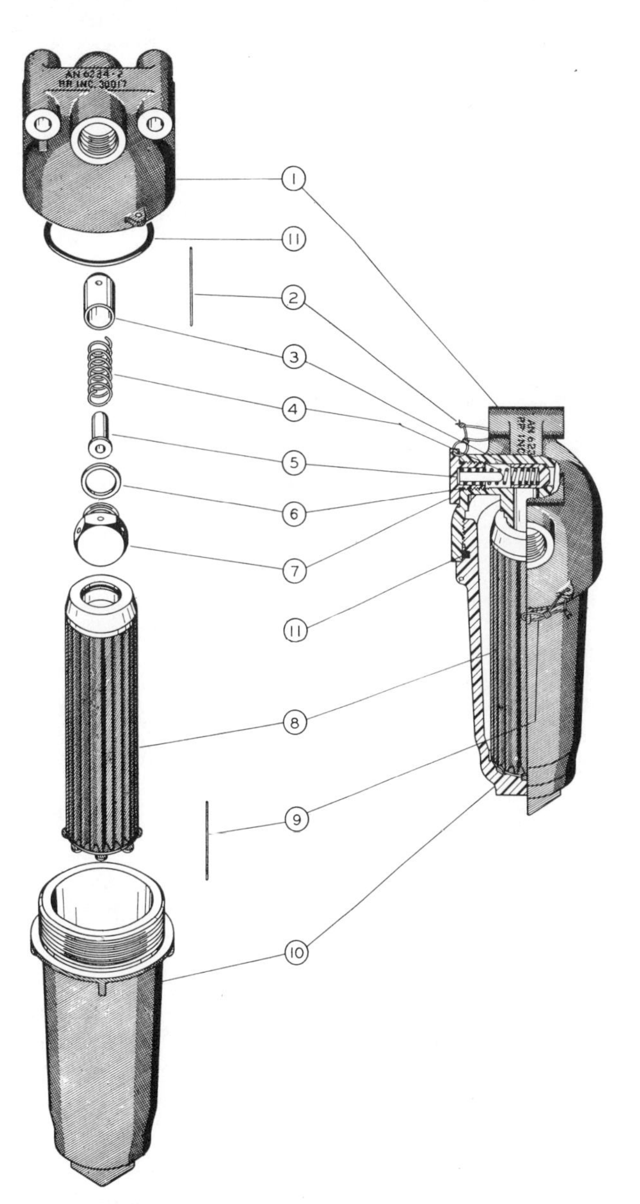

*Figure **9·24** Exploded view of a micronic filter.*

Accumulators

An **accumulator** is a device designed to store hydraulic fluid at working pressure and also to absorb pressure surges which may occur in the system. A more detailed explanation of the functions may be given as follows: (1) to maintain the pressure in the pressure manifold by storing energy in the form of fluid under pressure, thereby supplementing the work of the power pump when it is under peak load; (2) to supply a limited amount of fluid under pressure to actuating units when the power pump fails to operate, the exact amount depending upon the number and size of the accumulators in the system; (3) to dampen the pressure surges which may be caused by the pulsating fluid delivery from the power pump; (4) to absorb fluid shocks, such as those which occur when the pressure regulator seals the pressure manifold and directs the fluid to the reservoir; and (5) to prevent the too frequent cut-in and cut-out of a pressure regulator.

A typical diaphragm-type accumulator is shown in Fig. 9·25. This illustration is a view of a Vickers steel accumulator cut away to show interior details. The accumulator consists of two steel hemispheres threaded together to form a sphere with a synthetic-rubber diaphragm sealed in at the junctions of the two parts. The diaphragm seals the chambers so no fluid or air can leak from one chamber to the other. When the accumulator is placed in operation, the air chamber is charged with air or gas at a predetermined pressure, depending upon the design pressure of the system. The air charge is about one-third of system pres-

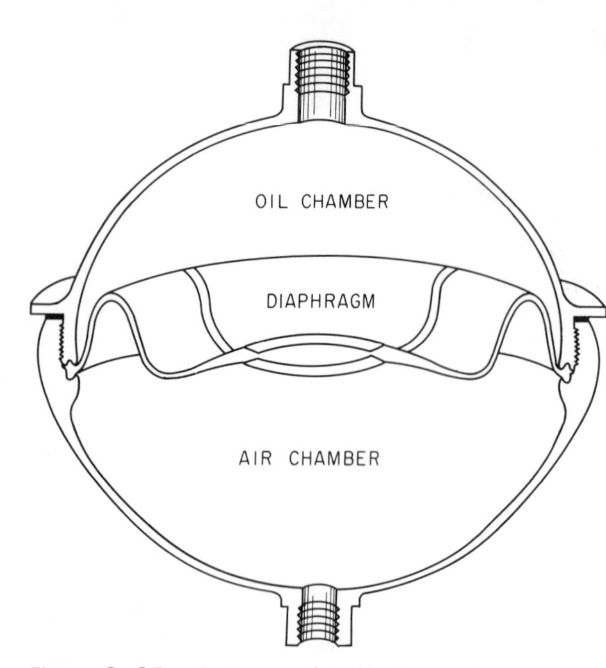

Figure **9·25** *Cutaway of a diaphragm-type accumulator.*

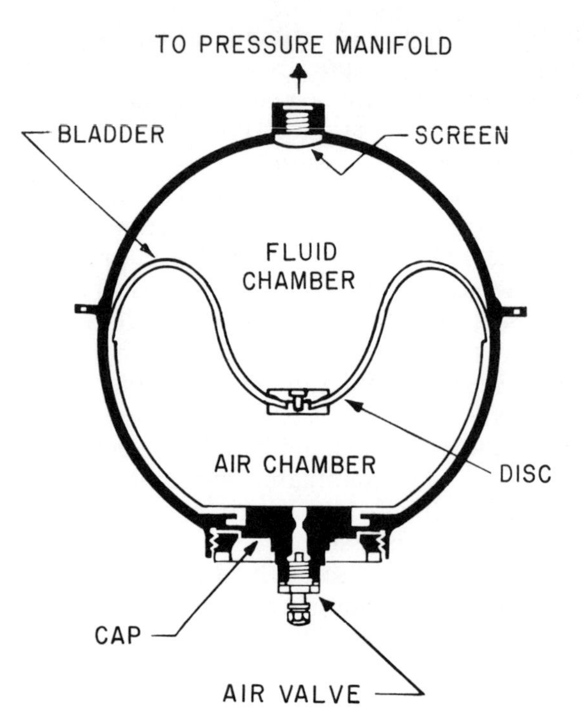

Figure **9·26** *Bladder-type accumulator.*

sure. The air or gas completely fills the chamber and forces the diaphragm to lie snugly against the inner surface of the fluid chamber. As soon as fluid pressure is developed greater than the precharge in the accumulator, the diaphragm begins to move back toward the center of the accumulator. As fluid pressure is increased, the air chamber becomes smaller and the fluid volume becomes greater. The pressures of the air and the fluid always remain equal, so there is no pressure-induced stress on the diaphragm.

During operation of the hydraulic system, the air pressure will force fluid into the system whenever system pressure falls below accumulator pressure. This provides a reserve supply of fluid under pressure to be used as needed.

Another type of accumulator is the **bladder type** illustrated in Fig. 9·26. It is constructed in a manner similar to the diaphragm accumulator except that it is usually made as a single sphere instead of being two hemispheres. A spherical synthetic-rubber bladder takes the place of the diaphragm to form the air chamber and the fluid chamber. The bladder is installed through the lower port and is sealed to the port by means of the cap. The top port of the sphere is connected to the hydraulic-pressure system. When the accumulator contains no fluid and the air charge is released, the bladder is approximately the same size as the accumulator shell; hence the bladder is not stretched by air pressure.

The metal disk located in the center of the bladder prevents the bladder from extruding through the upper port when the fluid is drained from the system. The operation of this bladder-type accumulator is identical with that of the diaphragm-type accumulator.

An accumulator which has found wide acceptance because of its compact construction is the piston type shown in Fig. 9·27. One of the early accumulators was a piston type. However, there was difficulty in obtaining an adequate seal between the air and fluid chambers. This resulted in the escape of air into the fluid and its interference with smooth, positive action.

The accumulator shown in Fig. 9·27 is manu-

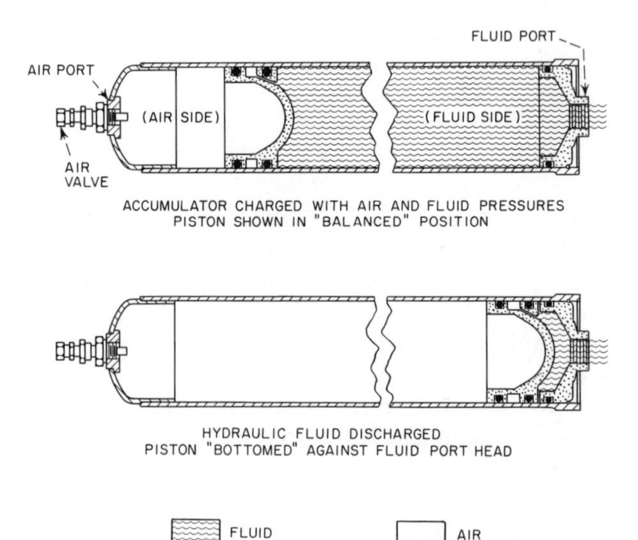

Figure **9·27** *Piston-type accumulator.*

factured by the Bendix Corporation. This accumulator consists of a cylinder with an air connection and valve at one end and a fluid connection at the other. Inside the cylinder is a floating piston which is fitted with O-ring seals. This piston effectively divides the cylinder into two chambers and prevents any leakage of fluid or air between the chambers. This type of accumulator is in common use on jet transports because its small diameter does not require much space.

For operation, the accumulator is charged with air to approximately one-third system pressure with no fluid in the cylinder. As soon as the hydraulic pump starts, fluid pressure builds up rapidly. The fluid forces the accumulator piston to move against the air pressure and compress the air as in the diaphragm- or bladder-type accumulators. When the system pressure is at maximum, the air volume is approximately one-half the fluid volume.

Check valves

As explained previously, the function of a **check valve** is to permit the free flow of fluid in one direction and to prevent flow in the opposite direction. Figure 9·28 is a drawing of a simple ball check valve. Check valves are placed in a number of locations in a hydraulic system where it is necessary to restrict fluid flow to one direction. Check valves are used to trap fluid pressure in some parts of the system in order to prevent the loss of fluid if a line ruptures or a unit fails. A check valve is used in the power-pump line to prevent fluid pressure from backing up into the pump when the pump is not working and also in the accumulator charging line to prevent accumulator pressure from flowing out through the charging line.

The checking device of the check valve shown in Fig. 9·28 is a ball, but it could be a cone, a button, or an object of some other shape. Regardless of its shape, it is ground to fit the seat snugly in order to prevent the leakage of fluid. A light spring holds the checking device on its seat. Fluid entering port *A* unseats the ball and then flows out through port *B*. As soon as fluid has ceased to flow, the spring pushes the ball back on its seat, thus trapping the fluid that has flowed to port *B* and preventing its return to port *A*.

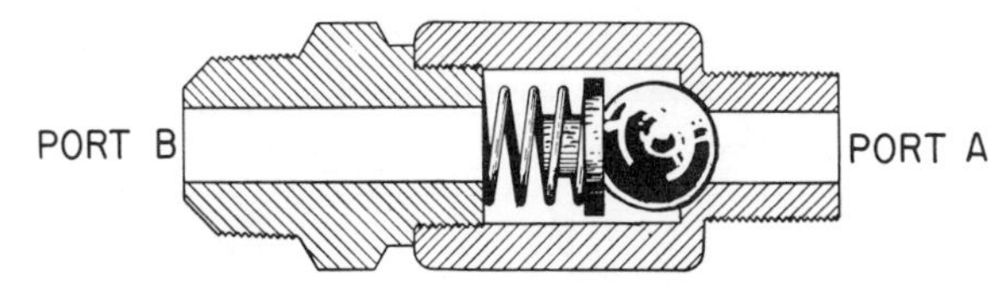

Figure **9·28** *A ball check valve.*

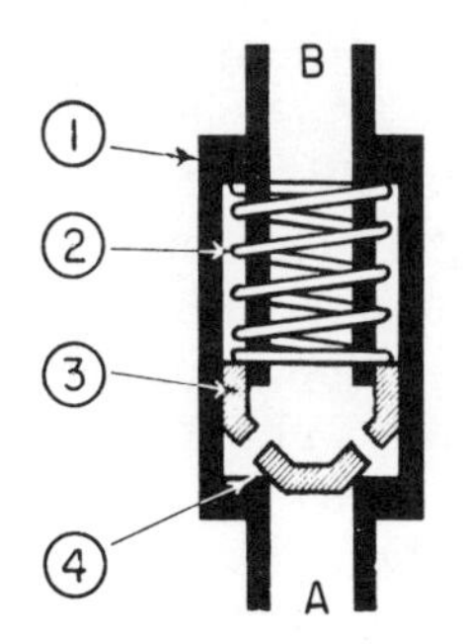

Figure **9·29** *A cone-type check valve.*

Figure 9·29 is a **cone-type** check valve. It consists of a valve body 1, spring 2, cone check 3, and a valve seat 4. The spring holds the cone check against its seat. The restriction of flow from *A* to *B* is very slight because the spring exerts very little pressure on the cone. Flow from *B* to *A* is restricted completely because pressure exerted against the cone by fluid entering at *B* seats the cone firmly and prevents the passage of fluid from *B* to *A*.

Selector valves

In order to operate a hydraulic system as desired, it is necessary that valves be installed which can be used to direct hydraulic pressure in the proper direction to any particular unit or units. As previously explained valves used for this purpose are called **selector valves.** Selector valves are made in a variety of configurations, three of the most commonly used being the **rotor-type valve,** the **piston-type valve,** and the **poppet-type valve.** The operation of a typical four-port rotor valve is shown in Fig. 9·30. In the diagram of position 1 the selector valve sends fluid out of port *A* to the actuating cylinder. We shall assume that the cylinder extends. In position 2 all ports of the valve are closed and no action is taking place. We call this the neutral position. In position 3 we see that fluid is flowing out of port *B* and into port *A*, and the actuating cylinder retracts.

In the diagrams the letter *P* indicates the pres-

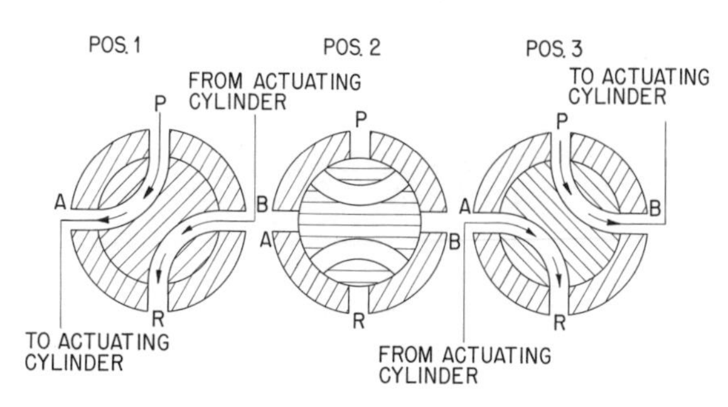

Figure **9·30** *A four-port rotor valve.*

sure manifold connection and *R* indicates the return line to the reservoir.

The rotor-type valve is very simple in operation, but it is often troublesome because a perfect fluid seal around the rotor is difficult to maintain. For this reason we find piston-type and poppet-type valves more commonly used, especially in high-pressure systems.

A simplified hydraulic system showing the use of a rotor-type selector valve is shown in Fig. 9·31. Fluid from the reservoir is pumped through the check valve, relief valve, and pressure regulator and to the selector valve. The position of the selector valve determines the direction of fluid flow to and from the actuating cylinder. The cylinder can be made to move in either direction as desired by placing the selector valve handle in the appropriate position.

A **poppet-type** selector valve is shown in Fig. 9·32. This valve consists of a housing, a camshaft attached to an operating handle, and a series of spring-loaded poppets. The housing consists of a port leading to the return line, a port connected to the pressure line, and two actuating-cylinder ports. In the illustration, the two interior poppets are marked with the letters *A* and *B* and the two exterior poppets are marked with the letters *C* and *D*. The cams on the shaft operate alternate poppets together.

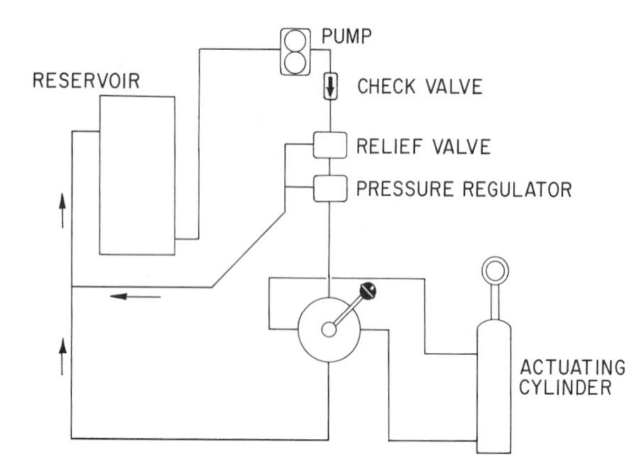

Figure **9·31** *Simple hydraulic system with rotor valve.*

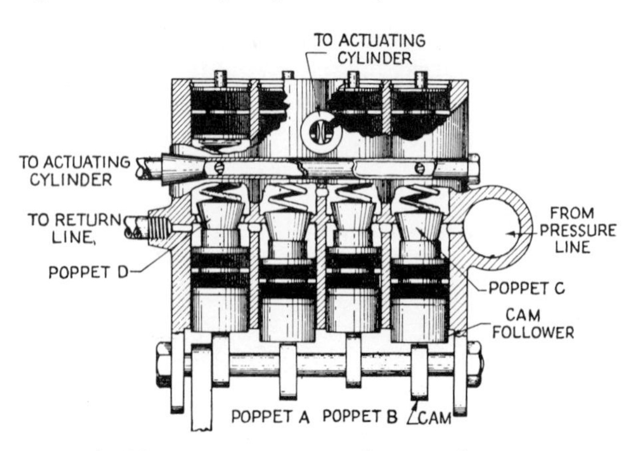

Figure **9·32** *A poppet-type selector valve.*

When the selector valve is in the position shown in Fig. 9·32, poppets *A* and *C* are held in the closed position by springs but poppets *B* and *D* are held open by the cams. When hydraulic fluid under pressure enters the pressure port, it flows by poppet *B* and then out of the actuating-cylinder port to the actuating cylinder. Fluid flows from the other actuating-cylinder port, around poppet *D*, and out the return line to the reservoir.

When the handle is moved to the opposite position, the flow of fluid is reversed and the mechanism attached to the actuating cylinder is moved in the opposite direction. Moving the operating handle in the opposite direction rotates the camshaft, and then poppets *A* and *C* are held open by cams while poppets *B* and *D* are held closed by springs. Since the flow is reversed, the mechanism moves in the opposite direction. If the handle is moved to the neutral position, all poppets are seated and all flow stops.

The **piston-type** selector valve, also called a **slide valve,** is illustrated in Fig. 9·33. It usually consists of a housing containing four ports and a hollow spool-shaped piston that has drilled passages connecting the hollow portion to each end of the housing.

Figure 9·33 shows three views of this type of valve. In the upper view, fluid enters the pressure port 1 and flows around the cutaway part of

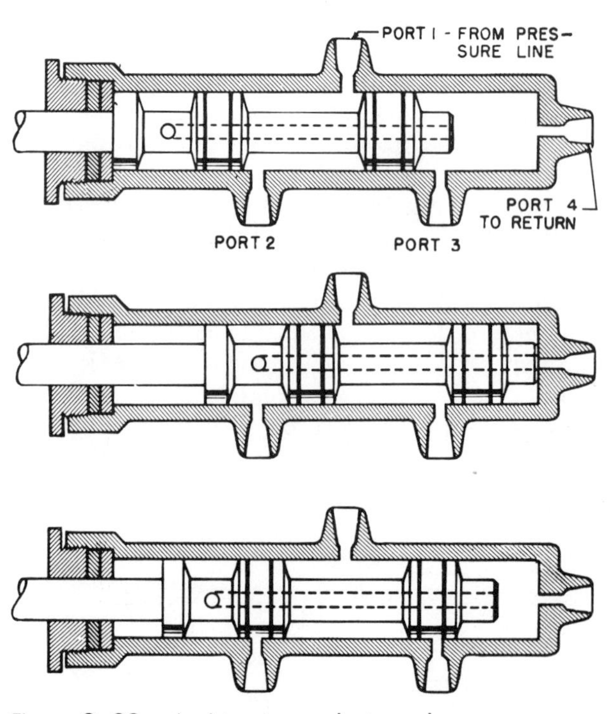

Figure **9·33** *A piston-type selector valve.*

the piston and out port 2 to the actuating cylinder. Fluid from the opposite end of the actuating cylinder flows into port 3 and out through the return port 4 to the reservoir.

When the piston moves to the position shown in the middle view of Fig. 9·33, the flow of fluid to and from the actuating cylinder is reversed. Fluid under pressure enters port 1 and flows out port 3 to the actuating cylinder. Fluid from the opposite end of the cylinder flows in port 2, through the hollow piston, and out port 4 to the reservoir.

If the piston is moved to the position shown in the lower view of Fig. 9·33, both actuating-cylinder ports are closed and the valve is then in the neutral position.

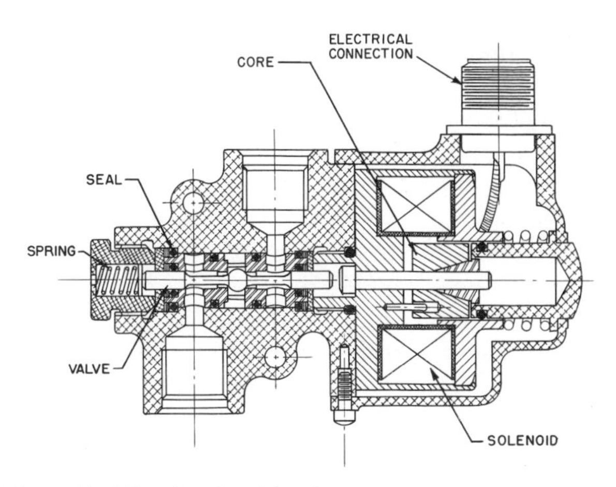

Figure **9·34** *A solenoid valve.*

Solenoid selector valve

A coil of wire has the properties of a magnet when a current is flowing through it. Because of this, coils are frequently used to operate various mechanisms. If a soft iron core is placed in the field of a current-carrying coil, the core will be magnetized and will be drawn toward the center of the coil, thus forming an electromagnet.

A **solenoid** is an electromagnet with a movable core or without any core. The present practice among electricians is to call an electromagnetic device having a movable core a solenoid.

Usually a solenoid is made with a split core. One part of the core is permanently fixed inside the coil, and the other part is free to move. The two sections of the core are normally held apart by a spring, but when the coil is energized, the fixed core has a polarity opposite to that of the adjacent face of the movable core; hence the movable core is attracted to the fixed core. This imparts motion through a connecting rod to the mechanical linkage.

The chief advantage of a solenoid is that it can be placed anywhere in an airplane or missile and it can be controlled by switches or relays. In an unmanned space vehicle, solenoids are controlled by relays which, in turn, receive their energy from electronic circuits. The use of solenoids is limited to operations where only a small amount of movement is required, but they have a greater range of movement than a fixed-core electromagnet.

Some of the common uses for solenoids are the operation of switches, circuit breakers, valves, and other mechanisms. A **solenoid valve,** illustrated in Fig. 9·34, is a valve operated by a solenoid. One end of the valve is attached to the armature (the movable part of the core). Thus, the valve can be opened when the current flows and closed when the current flow stops, or it can be designed to be open when the current is off and closed with the current on.

Solenoid valves are employed when it is desired either to locate the valves close to the actuating cylinders or to avoid the plumbing that is necessary if the valves are located where they can be manually operated. The solenoid method of remote control also offers advantages in savings of weight and space. This makes the method particularly valuable for missile and spacecraft applications. Since missiles and spacecraft are controlled almost entirely by electronic signals, it is quite apparent that the solenoid valve for hydraulic control in such vehicles is essential.

Installation and maintenance problems are reduced with solenoid valves because it is easier to install or replace an electric wire than either tubing or mechanical devices.

The disadvantage of the solenoid-valve system is the necessity of having some method for engaging the selector valves in case of an electrical failure. Generally, on airplanes, this is accomplished by locating the selector valves in places accessible to some member of the crew and by providing a means of mechanically engaging the valves. On the other hand, if the electric system of the airplane is adequately equipped, there may be alternate paths for the electricity to take in the event of failure.

Limit switches are sometimes connected in series with the control switch and each pair of solenoid valves. The purpose of a limit switch is to stop the supply of power to a moving unit, such as a landing gear, when the unit reaches either the extended or the retracted position.

The pressure regulator

The function of a pressure regulator in a hydraulic system is to keep the pressure of the system within a predetermined range. There is usually a difference of several hundred pounds between the maximum pressure and the minimum pressure needed for satisfactory operation. At the same time that the pressure regulator is controlling the pressure range of the system, it also should relieve the pump of most of its load. This greatly increases the lift of the pump.

In general, it may be stated that a pressure regulator serves both as a pump-unloading valve and as a pressure-limiting valve. When the pressure in the pressure section of the system is below a certain value, the pressure regulator will permit the pump to supply pressure to the system. When the pressure reaches the predetermined maximum value, the pressure regulator bypasses the pump output back to the reservoir and traps the stored pressure in the pressure section of the system.

Figure 9·35 illustrates a simple **balanced-type** pressure regulator. It consists of a housing which has three ports, marked with the letters *A*, *B*, and *C* in the drawing; a spring-loaded piston to which a pin is attached; and two ball-type check valves, lettered *D* and *E* in the drawing. Notice that check valve *E* is located in a bypass line between ports *A* and *B*.

When the pressure regulator is in the operating position shown in the illustration, the check valve *D* is seated, the piston is held down by the spring, and fluid from the power pump flows to the system through the external line and the check valve *E*. Check valve *D* is held on its seat by pressure. The same pressure is transmitted through port *B*

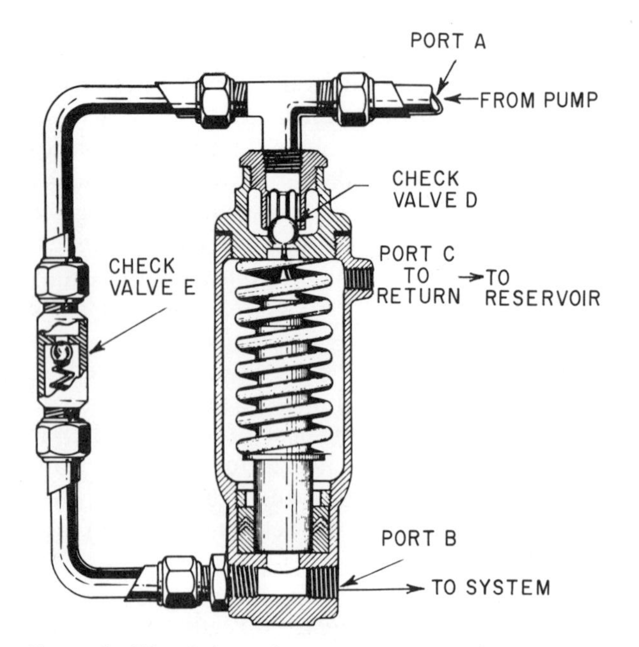

Figure 9·35 Balanced-type pressure regulator.

and acts on the bottom of the piston, exerting a force that tends to move the piston up and open the check valve *D*.

To illustrate the operation of this pressure regulator, a set of values and sizes must be assumed. It may be assumed, for example, that the ball seat (check valve *D*) has an area of ⅓ sq in., the piston has an area of 1 sq in., and the large spring exerts a force of 2,000 lb downward on the piston to hold it sealed against the bottom valve seat. If pressure in the main system is 2,000 psi, the force holding the ball (check valve *D*) down is equal to one-third system pressure plus the force of the spring. This makes a total force of approximately 667 lb plus 2,000 lb, or 2,667 lb. Since the force acting upon the piston is 2,000 lb, we can see that the ball valve remains seated.

If the pressure of the main system increases to 2,700 psi, the force downward on the ball check valve will be $\frac{1}{3} \times 2{,}700$, or 900 lb, plus 2,000 lb, which gives a total of 2,900 lb. The force acting upward is 2,700 lb, so check valve *D* remains closed.

If the system pressure increases to 3,000 psi, the downward pressure on check valve *D* will be 1,000 lb plus 2,000 lb, or a total of 3,000 lb. Since the system pressure is now 3,000 psi, the upward force on the piston is 3,000 lb, so the valve is balanced. Any further increase of pressure will make the upward force greater than the downward force on check valve *D*, and the valve will open. The piston moves up, and the pin unseats the ball. This places the valve in the position illustrated in Fig. 9·36.

When check valve *D* opens, check valve *E* closes and traps the pressure on the bottom of the piston and in the main system. Normally this pressure will be stored in an accumulator. The trapped pressure keeps the regulator open and permits the pump to operate without a load. This is because check valve *D* is off its seat and the force of the spring is the only force tending to close the valve. Since the system pressure is over 3,000 psi, the force of the piston pushing upward is much greater than the downward force and the check valve *D* must remain open. This condition will continue until system pressure is expended and falls below 2,000 psi. The large spring will then force the piston to move downward and withdraw the pin which has held check valve *D* off its seat. Valve *D* is then closed, and pressure will again build up to above 3,000 psi.

A **spool-type** pressure regulator or unloading valve is illustrated in Figs. 9·37 and 9·38. This regulator is designed for use in a system with one or more accumulators to store fluid under pres-

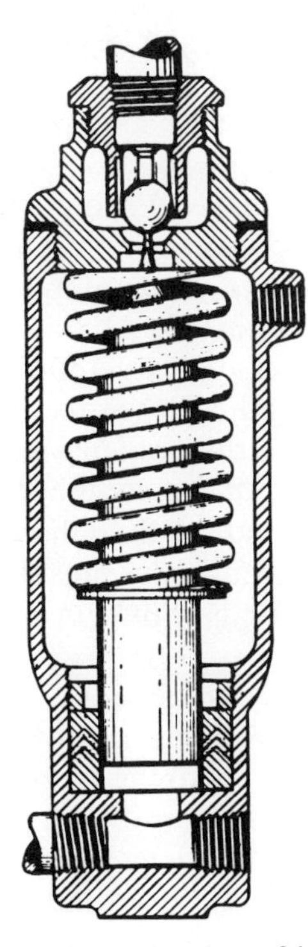

Figure 9·36 Operating position of balanced pressure regulator.

sure. In Fig. 9·37 the illustration shows four external ports in the regulator housing. These are marked *A*, *B*, *C*, and *D*. Port *A* is connected to the power pump, port *B* is connected to the pressure manifold, and ports *C* and *D* are connected to the return line. Port *C* is the main return line from the regulator, and port *D* is an auxiliary drain line used to pass off the fluid used for the operation of the directional spool.

The three spools or spool valves in the regulator are called the **pilot spool,** the **unloading spool,** and the **directional spool.** The direction of the fluid flow through the drilled passages in the regulator is determined by the positions of these spools.

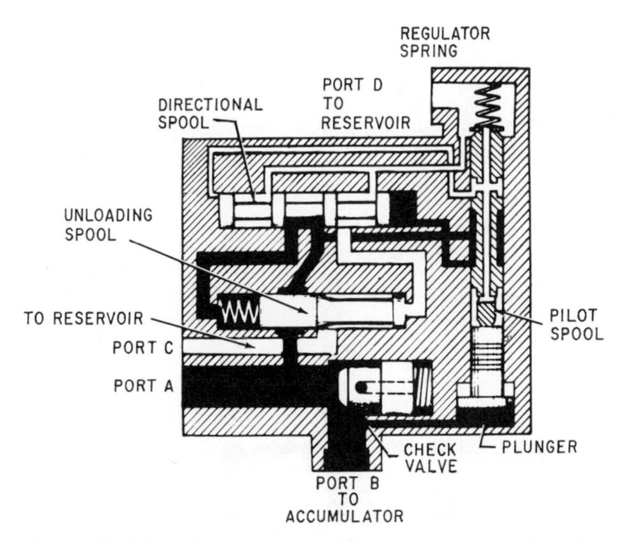

Figure 9·37 Spool-type pressure regulator charging accumulator.

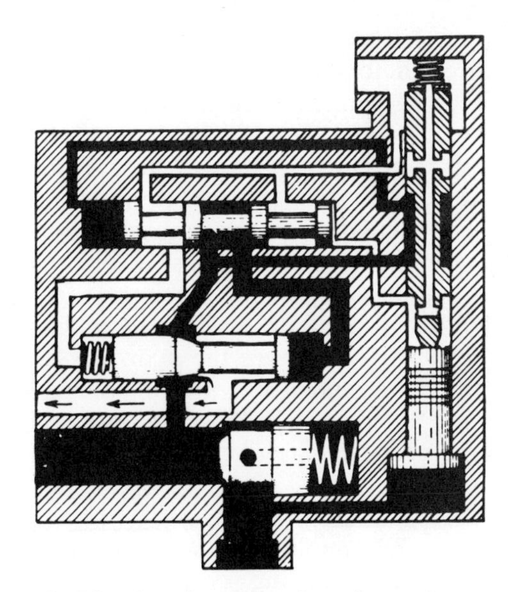

Figure 9·38 Spool-type regulator bypassing.

When the pressure regulator is in the position shown in Fig 9·37, the regulator is "kicked in" and fluid from the power pump is sent through the open check valve to the accumulator. As the pressure builds up, it exerts a force. The pressure travels around the unloading spool and is directed against the right end of the directional spool as long as the pilot spool is held down by the regulator spring. Since this pressure is directed against the right end of the directional spool, it holds the spool toward the left. As long as the directional spool remains in this position, the pressure is directed against the left end of the unloading spool, thus holding that spool toward the right and preventing the fluid from the power pump from reaching port *C*. When the system pressure becomes great enough to overcome the force of the regulator spring, the pilot spool is forced up and the parts are then in the positions shown in Fig. 9·38.

The shoulders on the pilot spool, when forced up, direct the pressure to the passage that leads to the left end of the directional spool and connects the right end of the directional spool to the return port through the hollow pilot spool.

Next, the pressure moves the directional spool to the right. The shoulders on this spool direct the pressure through internal passages to the right end of the unloading spool and connect the left end of the unloading spool to the return line. The unloading spool moves to the left so that ports *A* and C are connected. The output of the pump is then directed to the reservoir, and the pump is unloaded. The pressure regulator is now "kicked out."

At this time the check valve closes and traps pressure in the system and on the end of the pilot spool. The regulator remains in this position until the pressure in the system drops. If some mechanism is hydraulically operated, the pressure holding the pilot spool up will decrease and the regulator spring will force the pilot spool down. The directional spool and the unloading spool are moved to the position shown in Fig. 9·37, and the cycle is repeated.

The relief valve

Figure 9·39 is an illustration of a **system relief valve.** A separate drawing is provided for each of two positions. The numbers refer to the following parts: (1) pressure discharge port, (2) valve, (3) chamber, (4) metering clearance, (5) pressure inlet port, (6) valve seat, (7) spring, (8) cap, (9) spring guide, and (10) reservoir return port.

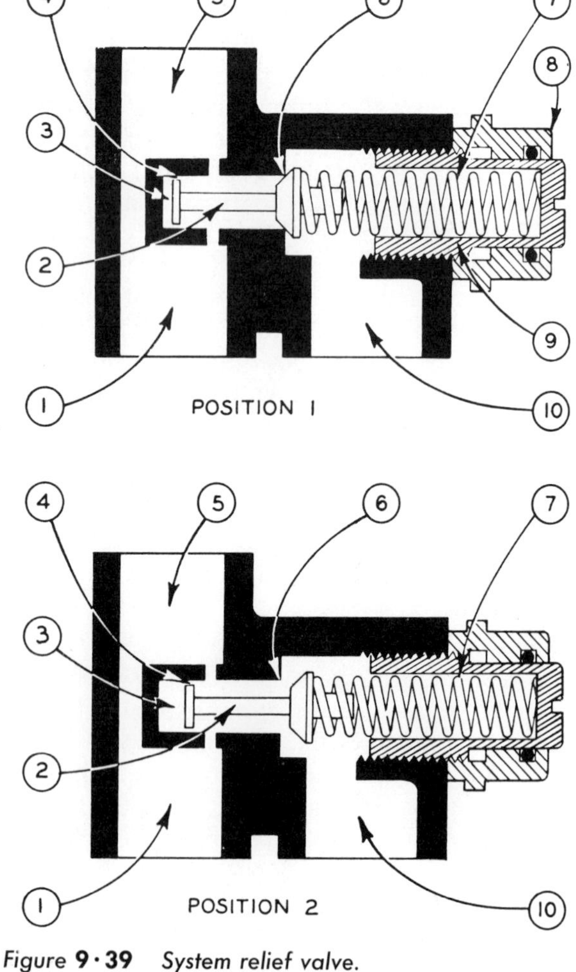

Figure 9·39 System relief valve.

This valve can be used in any location where it is desired to limit the pressure of the system or a part of the system to a certain maximum value, usually 150 to 250 psi above system pressure.

Position 1 of Fig. 9·39 shows the positions of the valve parts when the hydraulic-line pressure does not exceed the maximum value for which the spring 7 is adjusted. At this time the main poppet at 6 is on its seat and fluid is flowing through ports 1 and 5. When the pressure at 1, 5, and 3 builds up to the predetermined maximum, the fluid pressure in the chamber 3 forces valve 2 off its seat 6 so that the fluid discharges past the valve seat and through the port 10 to the return line. This condition is shown in position 2 of the illustration.

As valve 2 moves to the right, the fluid pressure in chamber 3 drops below the line pressure. However, as valve 2 moves to the right and the poppet comes off the seat 6, the effective pressure area of the poppet increases. Therefore, a reduction in pressure in chamber 3 does not cause the valve to close again immediately. The design of the poppet valve also improves the surge characteristics of the relief valve. Sudden pressure surges will not unseat the valve because fluid must pass through the restricted passage 4 to enter the chamber 3 to force the poppet valve to the right. The clearance 4 of the drawing is exaggerated to make the picture easier to understand.

Another type of relief valve is shown in Fig. 9·40. This drawing illustrates an in-the-line relief valve with the parts shown as they are under normal operating pressures. The fluid under pump pressure enters the valve through port A and discharges through port B. The tension of the spring prevents the fluid from escaping from port A to the return port past the piston. The tension of the spring is adjusted by screwing the cone seat in or out of the housing.

When the hydraulic line pressure exceeds the maximum value for which the spring is adjusted, the fluid under pressure forces the piston from its

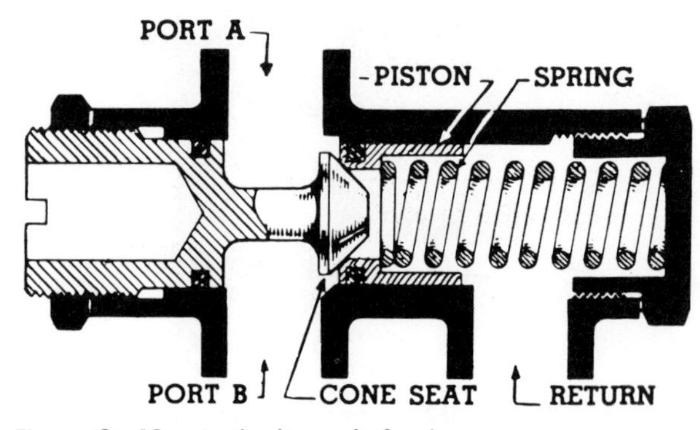

Figure 9·40 In-the-line relief valve.

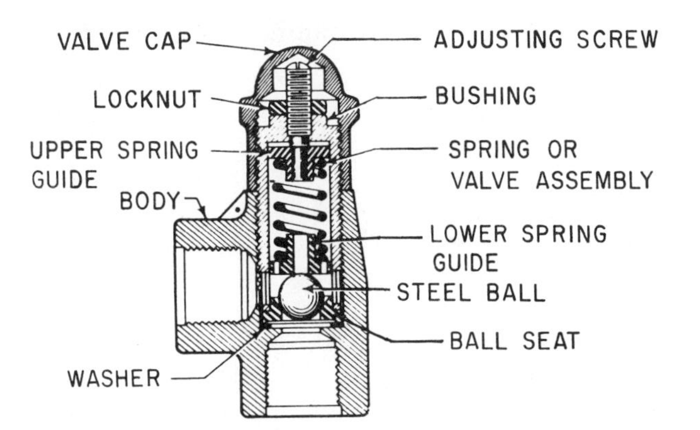

Figure **9·41** *Bypass relief valve.*

cone seat against the tension of the spring. This allows the fluid to escape past the valve seat to the reservoir return port. The fluid continues to discharge through the return port until the line pressure reduces enough to allow the spring to reseat the piston.

The relief valves described in the foregoing paragraphs are designed to be installed in the main line of a hydraulic system. There are relief valves, however, which are designed for installation in bypass lines connected between pressure lines and return lines. One such valve is illustrated in Fig. 9·41. The relief valve shown has a highly polished, hardened steel ball that is held on the valve seat by the pressure of a steel spring. The spring is held between two guides in the form of metal disks having integral bosses which slip inside the spring ends. One of these spring guides bears on the ball, while the other receives the adjusting screw in the upper end of the relief valve. An aluminum-alloy dust cap encloses the adjusting screw. The aluminum-alloy housing has two ports: an inlet port and outlet port.

Figure 9·42 is a simplified diagram which can be used to explain the operation of the valve shown in Fig. 9·41. In the diagram of Fig. 9·42 the system pressure is connected at port *A*. Port *A* is connected to the return line. The ball check valve 4, held on its seat by the spring 2, prevents the flow of fluid from *A* to *B*. The tension of the spring can be increased or decreased by turning the adjustment screw 1. The spring tension is adjusted so that when the pressure *A* reaches a predetermined value, valve 4 is lifted off its seat against spring tension. This allows the fluid to flow from *A* through *B* to the return line, thus preventing a pressure increase at *A*. The fluid continues to flow through the valve until the pressure at *A* reduces enough to allow the spring to reseat the ball. The parts numbered in Fig. 9·42 are as follows: (1) adjustment screw, (2) spring, (3) valve body, and (4) ball check valve.

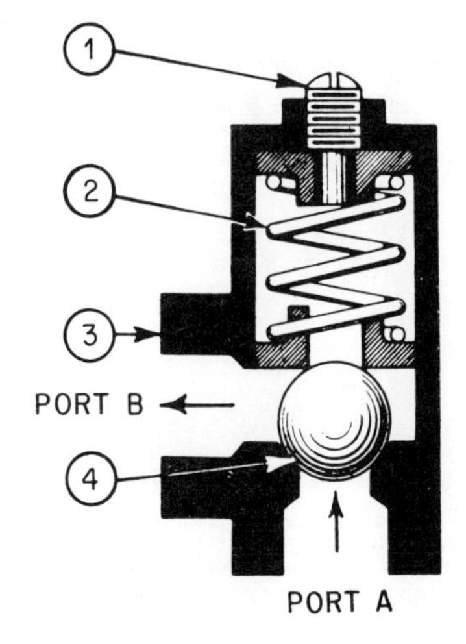

Figure **9·42** *Relief-valve operation.*

Restrictors

A **restrictor** is a device incorporated in a hydraulic system to limit the flow of fluid in certain parts of the system. It usually consists of a unit having a small opening or **orifice** through which the fluid must flow. Restrictors are often used to reduce the speed at which a mechanism is moved by the hydraulic force.

Figure 9·43 is a drawing of a simple orifice restrictor. This restrictor is merely a fitting which contains a small passage and which has threaded ends to which tube fittings can be attached. When fluid enters the restrictor, the rate of flow is limited because of the small orifice through which it must flow. This unit can be placed in a line leading to an actuating cylinder to slow the rate of movement of the piston.

Figure 9·44 is a drawing of a **variable restrictor.** In this drawing there are two horizontal ports and a vertical adjustable needle valve. The size of the restricting passage through which fluid must flow can be adjusted by screwing the needle valve in or out. The fact that the passage can be varied in size is the feature that distinguished the variable restrictor from a simple orifice restrictor.

Figure 9·45 is a drawing of an **orifice check valve,** which is a special type of restrictor designed to restrict the flow of fluid in one direction only. Valves such as this are used in lines connect-

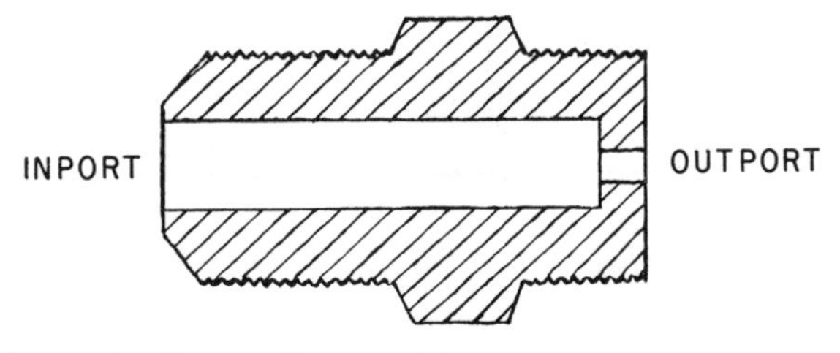

Figure **9·43** *Orifice restrictor.*

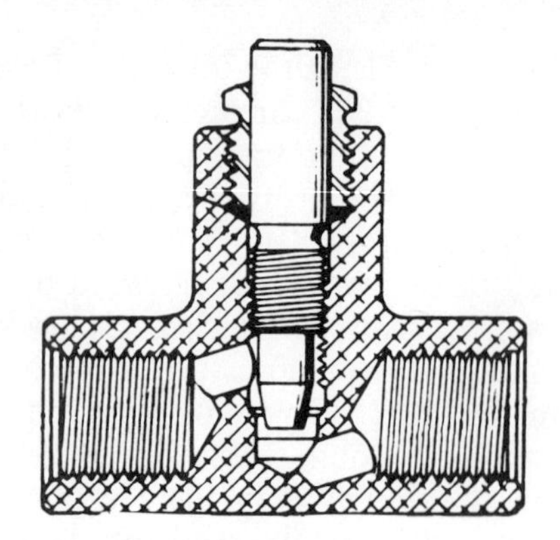

Figure 9·44 Variable restrictor.

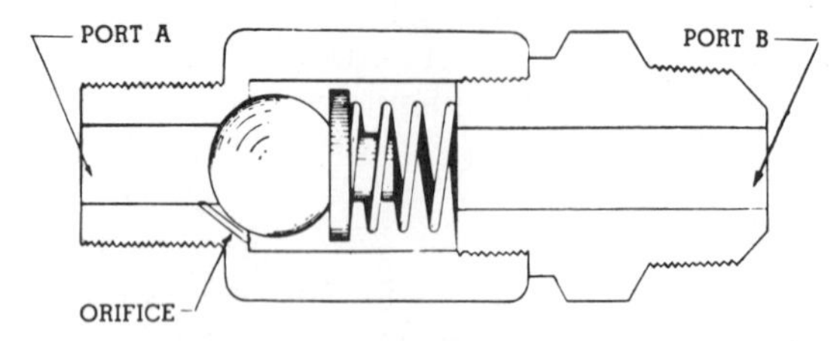

Figure 9·45 Orifice restrictor.

ing selector valves to actuating units for the operation of flaps, landing gear, etc., to reduce the rate of movement in one direction only. This is particularly important in the landing-gear section of a system. In this case the orifice check valve is placed in the "up" line because this is the line through which fluid returns to the reservoir when the landing gear is lowered. The orifice limits the return flow of fluid, thus slowing the movement of the gear to the down position. If this were not done, the weight of the gear plus the force of the hydraulic fluid would cause the gear to drop at a high rate, which would probably cause structural damage.

The orifice check valve is essentially a simple check valve with a small passage drilled through its seat, as shown in the illustration. Fluid entering port *A* pushes the ball off its seat and flows out through port *B*. In the opposite direction, fluid entering port *B* holds the ball firmly on its seat but a small amount of the fluid passes through the orifice and leaves through port *A*, thus slowing the rate of flow. In the **cone-type orifice check valve,** the passage is generally drilled through the cone instead of being drilled through the seat.

Shuttle valve

The purpose of a **shuttle valve** is either to direct hydraulic fluid automatically from the normal source of supply or from an emergency source of supply to the actuating cylinder or to direct air from the emergency source to the actuating cylinder. The shuttle valve can be used in the down line of a landing-gear system or in the pressure line of a power-brake system. Figure 9·46 is a drawing of a shuttle valve shown in the position for normal operation. Fluid from the selector valve flows through port *B* and out port *C* to the actuating cylinder. The shuttle valve is held in the position illustrated by means of the spring and also by fluid pressure. When the normal supply of fluid is lost, there is no fluid pressure at port *B*. The emergency air supply, when released by a control, enters port *A* and moves the shuttle valve to the left (in the drawing), thus blocking port *B* and opening a passage to the line leading to the actuating cylinder through port *C*. Notice that there are three external ports, two of which are inlet ports and the third being an outlet port.

Figure 9·47 illustrates the operation of a shuttle valve in the emergency operation. The selector valve has been placed in the "down" position to provide a return path for fluid from the actuating cylinder. Fluid under pressure from the emergency source enters the shuttle valve through port *A* and forces the valve to the left to close port *B* and open port *C* to the emergency line. Fluid then flows from the emergency supply through

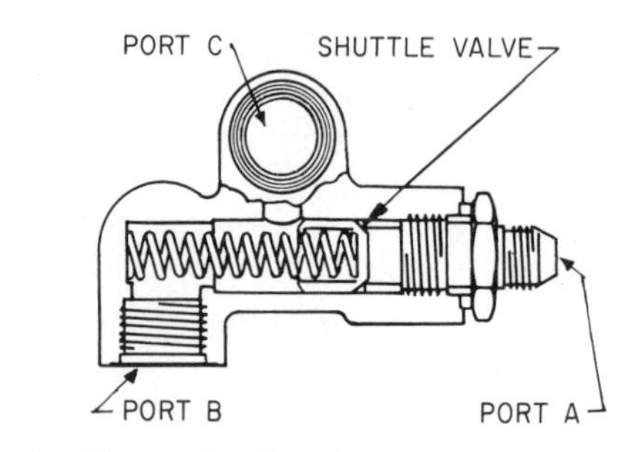

Figure 9·46 A shuttle valve.

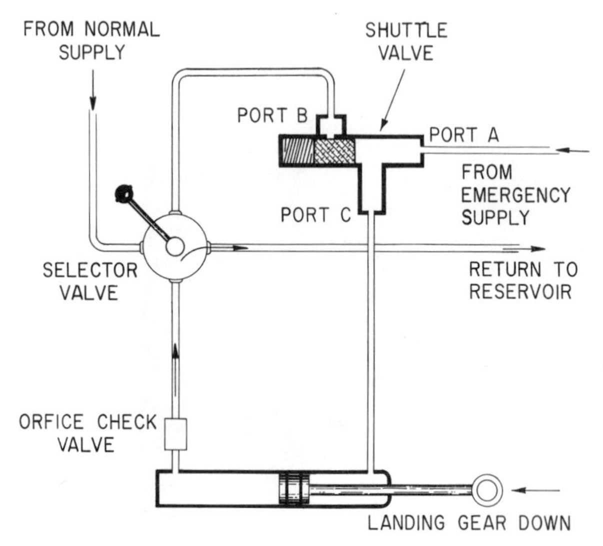

Figure 9·47 Emergency operation of the shuttle valve.

port C to the down side of the actuating cylinder, thus lowering the landing gear.

The hydraulic fuse

The **hydraulic fuse,** shown in Fig. 9·48, is a device designed to seal off a broken hydraulic line and prevent excessive loss of fluid. It will permit normal flow in a line, but if the flow increases above an established level, the valve in the fuse closes the line and prevents further flow.

Referring to the illustration, fluid enters the fuse through the passage at the right and flows between the outer case and the inner cylinder. It then passes through cutouts in the left end of the inner cylinder and out through the center opening. At the right end of the inner cylinder is a metering orifice which permits a small amount of fluid to enter the cylinder behind the poppet valve. During normal operation the pressure of this fluid is approximately the same as the pressure on the opposite side of this poppet; hence there is no movement of this poppet. As fluid flow increases, the pressure differential across the poppet also increases. If this differential becomes excessive, the poppet will move to the left and close the exit port of the fuse, thus stopping the fluid flow. The fuse will remain closed only as long as a substantial pressure differential exists. If the pressure differential decreases to a certain predetermined level, the spring will unseat the poppet and permit normal flow to resume.

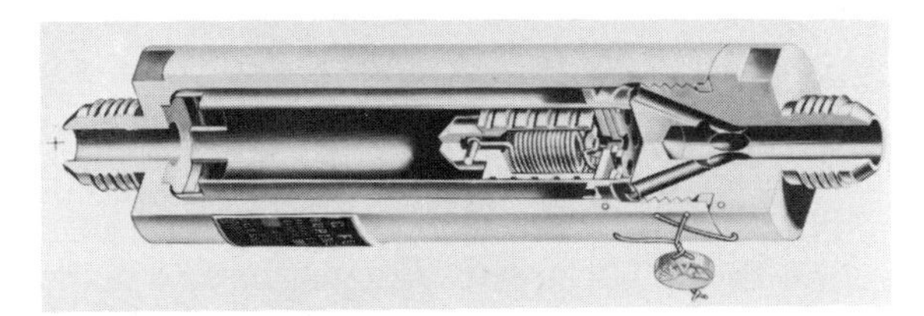

Figure 9·48 Hydraulic fuse.

HYDRAULIC SYSTEM

A complete hydraulic system for an airplane is shown in Fig. 9·49. This diagram is not designed for any particular system, but it serves to show how the components of a system are connected together and interrelated in an operating system. All the components shown in this system have been discussed in this chapter with the exception of the brake valves and brake cylinders. The brake valves are merely metering valves which port fluid pressure to the brake cylinders when the brake pedals are pressed and return the fluid to the return line when the brake pedals are released. The brake cylinders are small actuating cylinders which may take a variety of forms in brakes of different design.

The student should study each component of this system and determine why it is placed in the particular position shown. Observe, for example, that the system relief valve is placed relatively near the power pump. In case of an excessive pressure buildup the relief valve opens and routes the fluid to the return line.

The positions of the check valves, orifice valve,

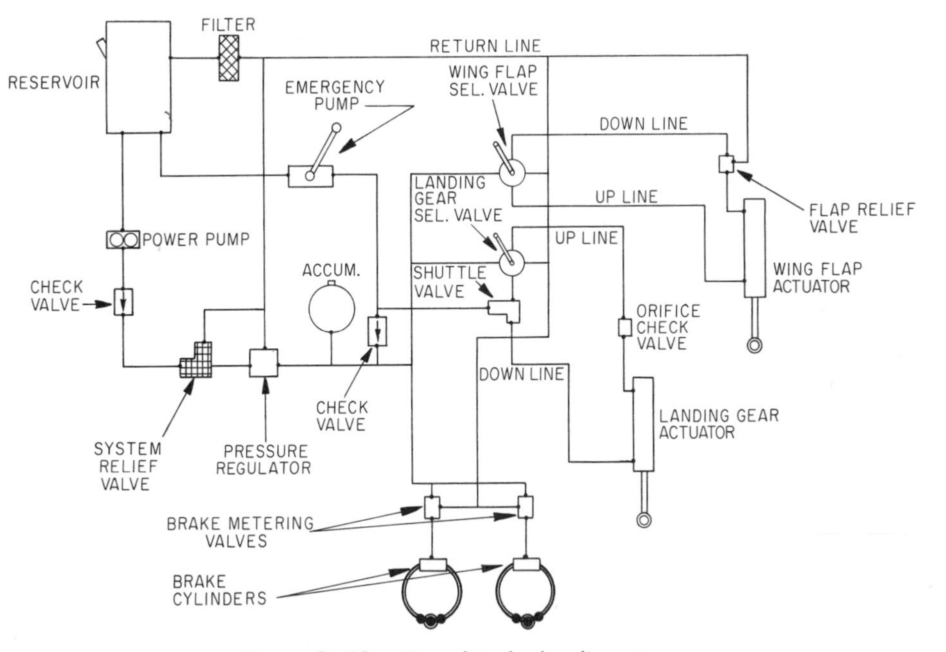

Figure 9·49 Complete hydraulic system.

and shuttle valve are all most important if they are to function as desired. Note also that the flap relief valve is in the flap "down" line to prevent the flaps from being lowered when the airspeed is too great.

PNEUMATIC SYSTEMS

Uses of pneumatic systems

Air under pressure can be used for the actuation of mechanical units in a manner similar to the use of hydraulic fluid under pressure. The one important difference is that air is compressible; hence it is not so easy to control as fluid. Among the advantages of a pneumatic system are less weight, no fire hazard, a cleaner system, and no requirement to return air to a reservoir. When these and other advantages outweigh the disadvantages, air is used as an actuating medium.

In modern jet airliners, air under low pressure (40 psi) is used for many purposes. The jet-engine compressors provide an abundance of compressed air which can be bled off and routed through air ducts to any part of the airplane. The principal uses of compressed air in a jet airplane are air conditioning, pressurization, and anti-icing. For the air-conditioning and pressurization systems, the air from the jet engines is often used to drive a turbine which, in turn, drives another compressor to provide the air for cabin pressurization. The reason for this roundabout method of obtaining compressed air for the cabin is that the bleed air from the engine compressor may contain oil fumes, water, or other contaminants which would make it unsuitable for use in the cabin. The air for thermal anti-icing of the wings and empennage surfaces can be taken directly from the engine compressors.

In some pneumatic systems, the air for cabin pressurization is taken directly from the engine compressors; however, the air used for air conditioning and cabin heating is cooled by air taken from outside the airplane and passed through a heat exchanger. The compressed air from the engines passes through the radiatorlike heat exchangers and is cooled to the required temperature for use in the airplane. Since the compressed air from the engines may reach a temperature of over 600°F, this air transmits a large amount of heat to the heat-exchanger tubes.

High-pressure pneumatic actuating systems are used on some airplanes to operate wing flaps, landing gear, and brakes. Such systems are found on the British Dove and Heron. In the United States this is not a common practice, however, and it will be found that most airplanes have either hydraulic or electric actuating systems for these units.

Pneumatic system for a jet airliner

To provide a general understanding of a typical pneumatic system in a modern airplane, we shall describe briefly the pneumatic system for the Boeing 720 jet airliner. The pneumatic system of this airplane supplies high-temperature low-pressure compressed air for cabin air conditioning, pressurization, wing anti-icing, and engine starting.

A schematic diagram of the pneumatic system is shown in Fig. 9·50. From this diagram it will be noted that turbocompressors are located on top of engines 2 and 3. These turbocompressors furnish the main supply of air for the air-conditioning system and cabin pressurization. An alternate or supplemental air supply is obtained by bleeding air from the intermediate compressor case of each of the four engines. Either this engine bleed air can be used to supply the wing thermal anti-icing system manifold, or it can be used in an emergency to supply the cabin pressurization system. Shutoff valves in the ducting control the flow of air as required.

The turbocompressor is an integral turbine and compressor unit. The turbine is driven by high-pressure air taken from the sixteenth stage of the engine. It is delivered to the compressor turbine section through a pressure regulator and a shutoff valve. The turbine drives the coaxial compressor which receives fresh air from an inlet on top of the engine nacelle. The compressed air from the turbocompressor flows past a surge valve outlet and through a check valve to the wing leading-edge pneumatic manifold. A low-pressure pneumatic duct for the engine starter ties into the pneumatic manifold at each engine.

The left- and right-wing manifolds are connected across the fuselage by a crossover pneumatic duct. This duct contains the valves necessary to isolate each wing manifold, deliver high-temperature compressed air to the air-conditioning system, and receive air from a pneumatic ground supply. A swing check valve is located outboard of each wing isolation valve to balance the pressure between the wing pneumatic manifold and the air-conditioning distribution bay when the wing isolation valve is closed. A pressure takeoff from the crossover pneumatic duct provides an indication of duct pressure through an electric servo system.

Each turbocompressor is self-regulated by means of controls designed to provide a constant mass airflow at any cruising altitude of the air-

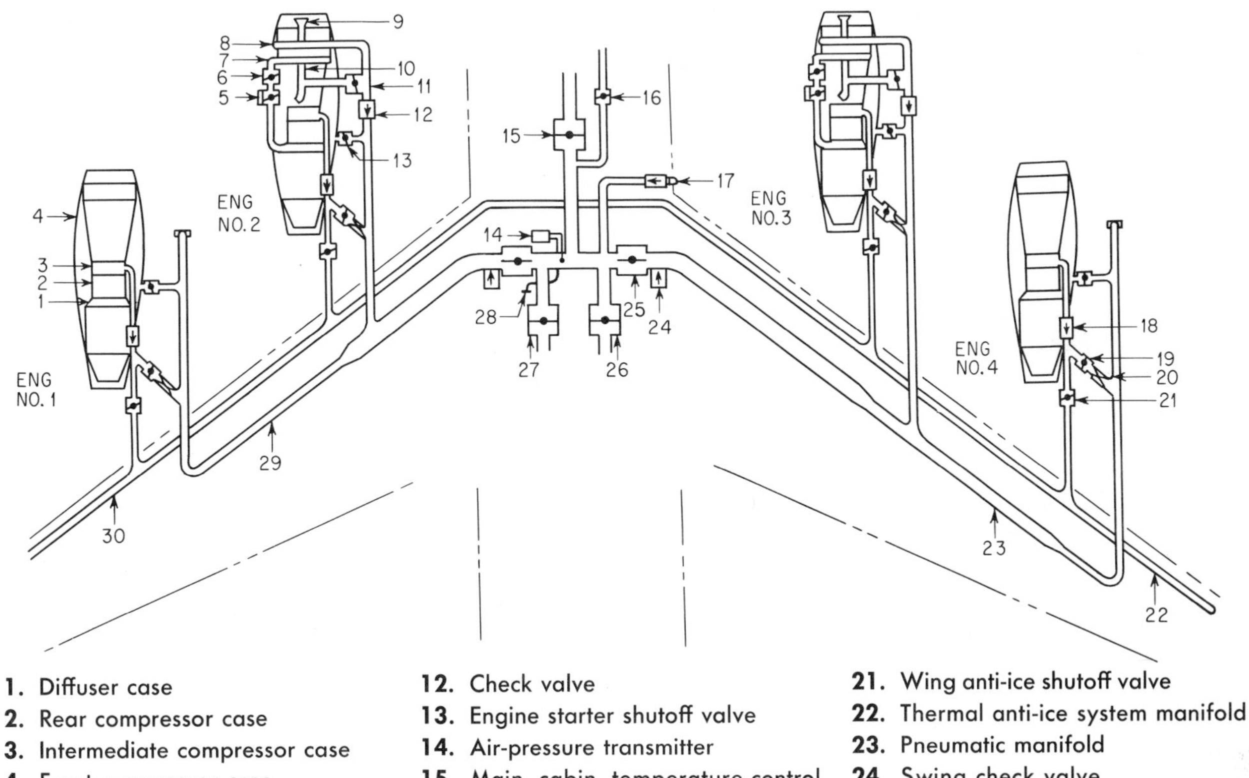

1. Diffuser case
2. Rear compressor case
3. Intermediate compressor case
4. Front compressor case
5. Pressure regulator
6. Shutoff valve
7. Turbine
8. Compressor
9. Air inlet
10. Turbine and surge bleed exhaust duct
11. Compressor surge valve
12. Check valve
13. Engine starter shutoff valve
14. Air-pressure transmitter
15. Main cabin temperature-control valve
16. Control cabin temperature-control valve
17. Ground-air connection and check valve
18. Check valve
19. Alternate air source shutoff valve
20. Venturi (flow limiter)
21. Wing anti-ice shutoff valve
22. Thermal anti-ice system manifold
23. Pneumatic manifold
24. Swing check valve
25. Wing isolation valve
26. Right air-conditioning pack shutoff valve
27. Left air-conditioning pack shutoff valve
28. Ambient-air sensing fitting
29. Pneumatic manifold
30. Thermal anti-ice system manifold

Figure **9-50** *Pneumatic system for Boeing 720 airliner.*

plane. The turbocompressor consists primarily of a radial inward-flow turbine wheel with an integral shaft and a centrifugal compressor impeller. The high-pressure air from the engine compressor drives the turbine which is mounted on the shaft with the turbocompressor. Also driven by the turbine shaft is an oil-pump assembly which consists of a spur-gear oil pump, a centrifugal oil pump, and a tachometer generator. The spur-gear oil pump supplies lubricating oil to the rotating assembly and oil under pressure to a separate hydraulic control system. The hydraulic control system actuates a variable-area nozzle at the inlet to the turbine wheel and a surge valve in the compressor outlet duct. An electrically selected pneumatic control system actuates the shutoff valve and the differential pressure regulator in the turbine inlet duct.

A main housing assembly provides the mounting facilities for the turbine torus (case), the compressor scroll, and the hydraulic and pneumatic controls. On the right side of the turbocompressor assembly are the oil filler neck, ground-start electromagnetic valve, compressor surge bleed control assembly, and the main electrical connector. On the left side are the oil filter assembly, minimum oil pressure switch, and bearing overtemperature switch electrical connection.

An oil sump beneath the main housing assembly serves as an oil reservoir and mounting base for the unit. A dipstick in the oil filler neck is marked LEFT WING FULL and RIGHT WING FULL to allow for the difference in oil-level readings due to wing dihedral. An oil-drain plug is fitted in each end of the sump to allow for any difference in mounting of the unit. The oil-draining plugs are magnetic to collect any ferrous metal particles which may be present in the oil. The oil sump is vented to atmosphere through an overboard vent line.

In addition to the functions already described,

the pneumatic system can be employed to drive small, high-speed turbines for the operation of hydraulic pumps, generators, and other emergency units.

REVIEW QUESTIONS

1. What is the principal advantage of a hydraulic system?
2. Why is liquid said to be incompressible?
3. Define *fluidity.*
4. Explain *viscosity.*
5. What does *Pascal's law* state?
6. Explain how mechanical advantage is obtained in a simple hydraulic system.
7. Give the formula for the force developed by a hydraulic piston.
8. What are the functions of the reservoir in a hydraulic system?
9. Explain the operation of a check valve.
10. Describe the function of a selector valve.
11. Why is a relief valve necessary in a power-operated hydraulic system?
12. Explain the operation of gear-type and vane-type pumps.
13. Describe a multipiston hydraulic pump.
14. How is variable delivery obtained in a piston-type pump?
15. What is the primary purpose of a hand pump in a hydraulic system?
16. Describe an actuating cylinder.
17. Explain the importance of a suitable filter in a hydraulic system.
18. Explain the purpose of an accumulator, and describe three types.
19. Explain the operation of a poppet valve.
20. How can a selector valve be made to operate electrically?
21. What is the difference between a relief valve and a pressure regulator?
22. Explain the operation of a pressure regulator.
23. Why is a restrictor sometimes used in a hydraulic actuating system?
24. Explain the operation of a shuttle valve.
25. Compare the operation of a hydraulic system with that of a pneumatic system.
26. For what purposes are pneumatic systems used in modern aircraft?
27. Give two sources of pneumatic pressure in a jet airliner.

CHAPTER 10

Plumbing for Aerospace Vehicles

USES OF TUBING IN AEROSPACE VEHICLES

All aerospace vehicles, regardless of size, depend upon tubing of various sizes and types to carry on vital functions of operation. Among the systems requiring the use of tubing are fuel systems, hydraulic systems, oil systems, oxygen systems, fire-extinguishing systems, water-injection systems, and others. For aircraft, the most vital functions are the supplying of fuel and oil to the engine. Failure of either the fuel system or oil system is likely to cause disastrous results; hence the installation of plumbing for these systems must be of the highest quality.

Every airplane must have certain basic instruments. Many of these instruments require the installation of tubing for their operation. The material of the tubing may be aluminum alloy, copper, or stainless steel, and in many cases rubber or synthetic rubber is used for hoses in such systems.

Airplanes and missiles employing hydraulic systems require tubing for the transmission of hydraulic power from pumps to valves and thence to operating devices. Many hydraulic systems require fluid pressures of 3,000 psi or more, and some operate with pressures as high as 5,000 psi. Low-pressure systems utilize aluminum-alloy tubing, and high-pressure (3,000 psi or more) systems usually employ stainless-steel tubing in the high-pressure sections of the system.

Tubing is often used in aircraft for electrical conduit. This means that it is used to shield and protect electrical wiring. In this capacity it protects the wiring from wear and damage and also serves to reduce electromagnetic emanations from the wiring.

PLUMBING MATERIALS

Even though copper tubing is still used for some installations, it is common practice to use aluminum alloy and stainless steel for most systems. The aluminum-alloy tubing is generally made of alloys such as 1100-H14, 3003-H14, and 5052-0. As mentioned previously, these materials are used for low-pressure systems.

The stainless-steel (corrosion-resistant) tubing used for high-pressure systems is of the 18-8 chrome-nickel type. Steel tubing should also be used for exposed hydraulic brake lines on the landing gear to resist damage due to rocks and other material which may be thrown against it during operation. Inasmuch as stainless steel is much stronger than aluminum, the tubing can have a lighter wall, thus compensating for the greater weight of the steel.

In general, the material of the fittings is determined by the material of the tubing; hence aluminum-alloy fittings are used with aluminum-alloy tubing, steel fittings are used with steel tubing, and brass or bronze fittings are used with copper tubing. Fittings for the ends of flexible hose are made of aluminum or steel, depending upon the pressure requirements.

SERVICEABILITY

A properly designed and constructed system composed of tubes and fittings will operate over a long period of time without failure. There are many factors which contribute to the serviceability of such a system, and these must be carefully considered. If the parts in a system are subjected to excessive vibration or flexing, the mechanical stresses produced tend to bend or stretch the tubing and also cause crystallization. Eventually, the tubing or fittings become cracked and the system develops leaks which often result in complete failure.

In the maintenance of tubing, the technician must pay particular attention to the radii or bends in tubing, the alignment of tubing and fittings, and the attachment of tubing to the structure of the vehicle.

It is of the utmost importance that damaged parts be replaced with the proper material. Specifications for parts can be obtained from manufacturers' maintenance manuals, and, if these are not available, the technician can duplicate the part to be replaced. The parts of a system are designed to withstand the maximum pressures encountered in operation and to meet all other operating requirements. It is the technician's responsibility to see that the standards set by the manufacturer are rigidly followed.

Figure **10·1** *Flexible conduit.*

ELECTRICAL CONDUITS

Although the use of open electrical wiring is often quite successful, there are areas where conduit is used to provide protection and electromagnetic shielding. Conduit will minimize the possibility of a cable fault which would result in loss of the electrical system and will protect the cable from detrimental substances such as hydraulic fluid or gasoline and from abrasion which might be caused by moving aircraft elements within the aircraft.

Conduit should not be located where operating or maintenance personnel would use it as a handhold or footstep. The material of conduits is light in weight and can be easily bent or otherwise damaged. It should be adequately supported to prevent chafing against the structure and to avoid stressing the end fittings. Drain holes should be drilled at low points to allow the drainage of any accumulated moisture.

Rigid conduits consist of semisoft aluminum or aluminum-alloy tubing such as 1100-H14 (pure aluminum) and 5052-0. Magnesium is used sometimes because of its light weight.

Rigid conduit stock is available in 10- or 12-ft lengths with various wall thicknesses and diameters. When the sizes of rigid conduit stock are referred to, the outside diameter of the tubing is specified. Since conduit tubing is not subjected to internal-pressure stresses, the wall thickness is less than for tubing used in systems operating under the pressures of fluids or gases.

Installations with small-bend radii and which are subject to flexing and vibration require flexible conduit (see Fig. 10·1). Flexible conduit is more expensive and heavier than rigid conduit, but its use is justified in many instances. Flexible conduit is made from an interlocking type of aluminum tubing over which plated copper braid has been woven for additional protection. The copper braid is plated with tin to facilitate soldering. It can be procured in any desired length and inside diameters up to 2 in. In the selection of conduit size for a specific cable bundle application, it is common practice to allow for ease in maintenance and possible future circuit expansion by using a conduit inner diameter about 25 per cent larger than the maximum diameter of the cable bundle. Large conduit sizes should be avoided, since simultaneous damage to many cables is possible and maintenance becomes difficult.

Great care should be taken in the installation of fittings to conduit because these areas present the only possible point for cable abrasion inside the conduit. The fittings should be applied in such a manner that a smooth surface comes in contact with the cable within. The conduit should be adequately supported by clamps along the conduit run.

HOSES AND HOSE CONNECTIONS

Because of the need for flexibility in many areas of aerospace vehicle construction, it is often necessary to employ hose instead of rigid tubing for the transmission of fluids and gases under pressure. Specifications for hose to be used in aerospace vehicle systems are given in the Air Force–Navy Aeronautical Design Standard (AND) 10340. This specification covers hoses for fuel, oil, hydraulic, pneumatic, and other systems.

A non-self-sealing, flame-resistant, and aromatic resistant hose for fuel, oil, water, and alcohol systems is covered by MIL-H-8794. It is marked with a yellow double dot and dash code, specification number, size, quarter of the year, and the year of manufacture along the length of the hose. Another hose used frequently where flame resistance is not required is the MIL-H-6000 hose. This hose is also covered under AN-H-35 specification. It is marked with a broken red stripe and a white stripe. The size, date of manufacture in quarter of the year and year, and the specification numbers are also marked on the hose. This hose is also suitable for fuel, oil, water, and alcohol. Other hose specifications such as MIL-H-7938 and MIL-H-5593 may also be used for most applications. The technician should make sure that the hose he uses in any particular system is suitable for the purpose intended and that he uses the proper fittings for making hose connections. Typical hose for aircraft use is illustrated in Fig. 10·2.

VENTILATOR AND HOT-AIR DUCTS

Ventilator and hot-air heater ducts are made from a variety of materials. Among these materials are a lightweight asbestos fabric impregnated with synthetic rubber and having a spiral body wire, plastic-impregnated glass fiber, aluminum, and stainless steel. The type of material used and the attachments employed for connecting sections are determined by the temperatures and pressures under which the duct must operate. For high-pressure and high-temperature air, large-diameter, thin-walled stainless steel is used. For medium temperatures and pressures, aluminum tubing may be used.

In the replacement of ducting in a particular aircraft the technician should use a manufactured part or should construct the part of the same material used in the original installation. The manufacturer's maintenance manual usually specifies the material to be used for a particular part.

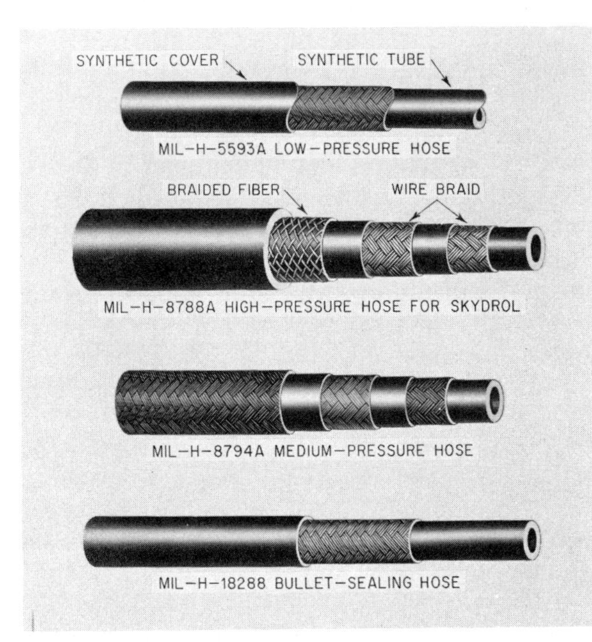

Figure **10·2** *Hose for aircraft and missile plumbing.*

FITTINGS

Tubes and pipes are connected to other tubes and pipes or to units of an installation by **fittings.** These fittings are made in many shapes and styles, and each is designed to fulfill certain requirements.

Many fittings used in the past have become obsolete because better types have been developed. The AC fittings have been replaced by the AN fittings. Some of the older-type fittings are still in use in airplanes, and it is essential that the mechanic recognize each type. This is particularly important because AC and AN fittings cannot be used together successfully.

An AC fitting and an AN fitting for similar installations are illustrated in Fig. 10·3. Observe carefully the spaces on each side of the thread on the flare side of the AN fitting. There are no such spaces on the AC fitting; hence this provides a ready means for identification. Other differences between the AN and AC fittings include the number of threads per inch and the sleeve design. The AC fitting has serrations on the hex face.

A more recent designation for fittings is the MS (Military Standard) number. These designations cover a number of special tubing and hose fittings including flareless fittings for tubing. The design of fittings is also covered by AND standards AND10056 through AND10064.

In general, only two types of threads are provided on AN fittings. These are **tube threads** and **pipe threads,** both of which may be either external (male) or internal (female). Tube threads on a given fitting are uniform in diameter, while pipe threads are tapered. Where pipe threads are used, the seal is provided by the threads and a sealing compound. With tube threads, the fitting is sealed

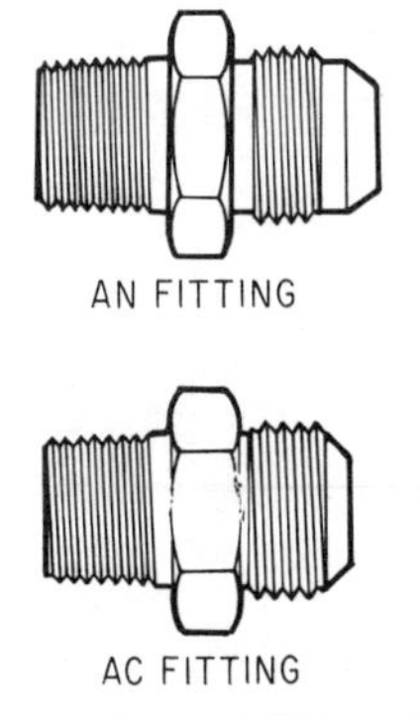

Figure **10·3** *Comparison of AN and AC fittings.*

where the flared portion of the tube fits against a cone seat in the fitting. Tube threads and pipe threads are illustrated in Fig. 10·4.

Fittings commonly used are variously classified as tube fittings, universal and bulkhead fittings, universal fittings, hose fittings, and pipe fittings.

Typical AN tube fittings are shown in Fig. 10·5. These fittings are identified by AN numbers which indicate the design of the fitting and not the size. The size is determined by a "dash number" with the fitting number. The following numbers identify typical tube fittings:

AN815 Union, flared tube
AN816 Nipple, flared tube and pipe thread
AN817 Nut, sleeve, coupling
AN818 Nut, coupling
AN819 Sleeve, coupling
AN821 Elbow, flared tube, 90°
AN822 Elbow, flared tube and pipe thread, 90°
AN823 Elbow, flared tube and pipe thread, 45°
AN824 Tee, flared tube
AN825 Tee, flared tube with pipe thread on side
AN827 Cross, flared tube

It is often necessary to pass fuel, oil, or other lines through the metal structures of an airplane. This requires a type of fitting with a long body and provisions for securing the fitting to the bulkhead. Fittings for this purpose are shown in Fig. 10·6 and are called **universal and bulkhead fittings.**

When a fitting of this type is installed, it is necessary to drill a hole through the bulkhead

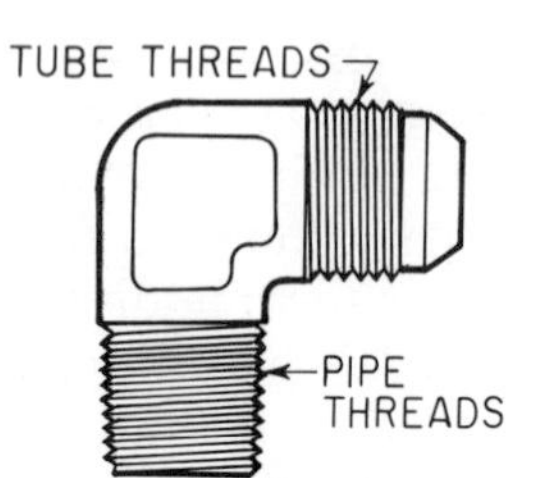

Figure **10.4** *Tube threads and pipe threads.*

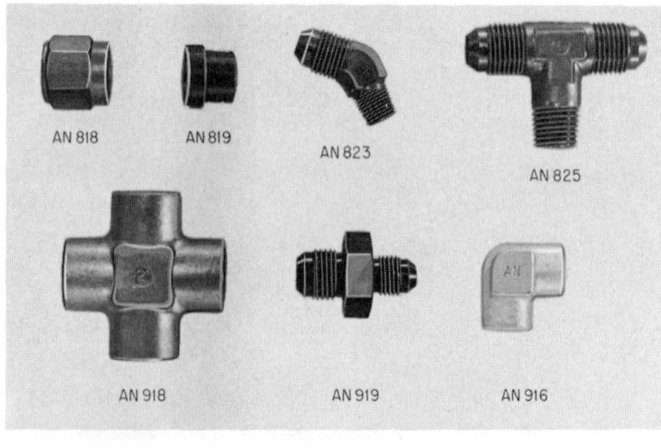

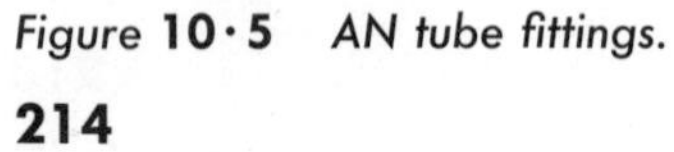

Figure **10·5** *AN tube fittings.*

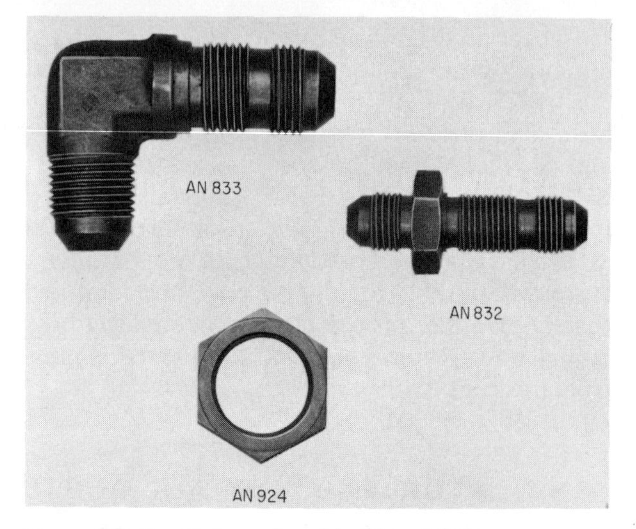

Figure **10·6** *Universal and bulkhead fittings.*

which will accommodate the body of the fitting. After the fitting is installed in the hole, a flat nut is screwed on the inner threads. This nut compresses the bulkhead between itself and the shoulder on the body of the fitting, thus holding the fitting firmly in place. Typical fittings of the bulkhead and universal type are identified by the following AN numbers:

AN832 Union, flared tube, bulkhead and universal
AN833 Elbow, flared tube, bulkhead and universal, 90°
AN834 Tee, flared tube, bulkhead and universal
AN924 Nut, lock, bulkhead and universal

Universal fittings are used in special installations where a certain degree of flexibility is required. They are used in connection with either stationary or moving units. When used with moving units, such as hydraulic actuating cylinders, they are sometimes called "banjo" fittings. A complete universal assembly includes a bolt (AN775), which has longitudinal and transverse passages, and a fitting which the bolt holds in place. Soft metal "crush" washers (gaskets) are placed under the head of the bolt and between the fitting and the unit to which it is attached. Serrations on the clamping surfaces provide a satisfactory seal of the joints.

Universal fittings or couplings permit the connection of a section of tubing at any angle of rotation about the bolt center and often replace the pipe fittings formerly used.

Figure 10·7 illustrates typical universal fittings. These fittings are identified by the following AN numbers:

AN775 Bolt, universal fitting
AN776 Elbow, universal, 90°
AN778 Elbow, universal, 45°

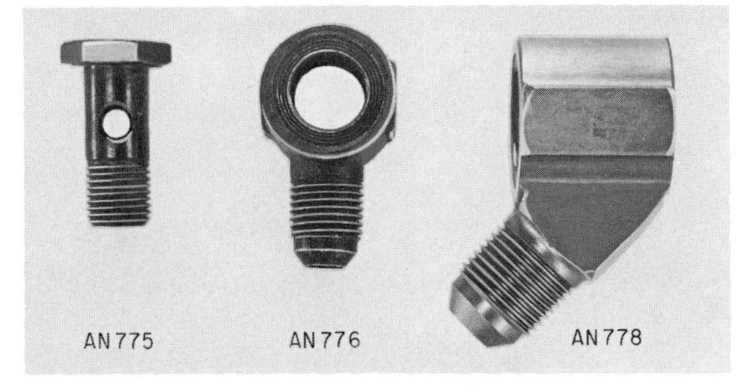

Figure **10·7** *Universal fittings.*

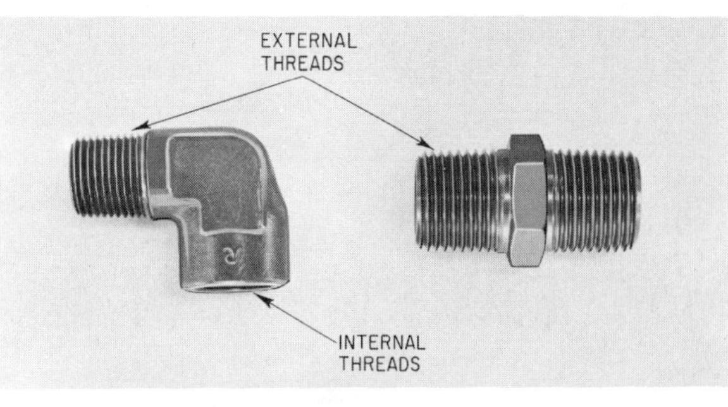

Figure **10·9** *AN pipe fittings.*

Hose fittings are used where it is required to connect hose to units of a system or where hose is joined to tubing. Some of these fittings are provided with a beaded end over which hose can be clamped. The other portion of the fitting may have another beaded end. The type of fitting equipped with the beaded end is not used in modern plumbing systems for aircraft and missiles but has been replaced by hose ends which are permanently attached as a part of hose sections. Typical of such hose and fitting assemblies are those shown in Fig. 10·8.

Pipe fittings have a close resemblance to commercial plumbing used in the water and gas systems of buildings. Such fittings have pipe threads only and cannot be connected directly to flared tube fittings or to hose. If it is necessary to make such a connection, the proper type of adapter must be used.

The nature of a pipe thread should be clearly understood. First, the size of the thread tapers so that the fit becomes tighter as the fitting is tightened. Second, the size of a pipe thread is designated by the inside diameter of the pipe on which the thread is cut. A ⅛-in. pipe thread is actually about 5⁄16 in. in diameter, and a ½-in. pipe thread is actually ¾ in. in diameter. These peculiarities must be remembered in ordering pipe fittings. Third, it is important to use a good antiseize and sealing compound when joining pipe fittings.

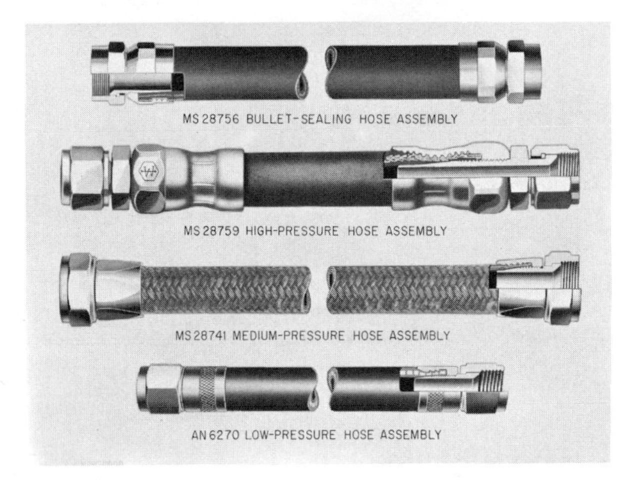

Figure **10·8** *Fluid hose and fittings.*

Standard AN pipe fittings are illustrated in Fig. 10·9. One of the fittings shown has both external and internal pipe threads as indicated.

Fittings used in aircraft or missiles are usually made of brass, bronze, aluminum alloy, or stainless steel. Visual identification of the material of a fitting is provided by the color of the material in the case of brass or bronze and by a dye in the case of aluminum or stainless steel.

FLARELESS TUBE FITTINGS

Flareless tube fittings are not covered by AN specifications but have been assigned MS numbers from MS21900 to MS21918. These fittings are so constructed that it is not necessary to use flared tubing in order to form a perfect fluid seal. Instead, a special sleeve is installed with the fitting. This sleeve incorporates a cutting edge which seizes and grooves the tubing as the fitting is tightened, thus producing a fluidtight seal. The flareless tube fitting therefore eliminates all flaring, threading, welding, and soldering in connection with tube fittings.

The flareless tube fitting consists of three units: a body, a sleeve, and a nut. There are also special parts for close couplings and reducer couplings.

The body of the flareless tube fitting has a counterbored shoulder against which the end of the tube rests. This counterbore has a cone angle of about 24° which, on assembly, causes the cutting edge of the sleeve to cut into the outside of the tubing. Further tightening of the nut forces the sleeve to form the tight seal mentioned above. The nut also engages the bevel of the sleeve, causing it to grip the tube and provide additional support. The pilot edge of the sleeve limits the depth of the cut and thereby prevents any closing of the tube. A cutaway illustration of the MS flareless tube fitting is shown in Fig. 10·10.

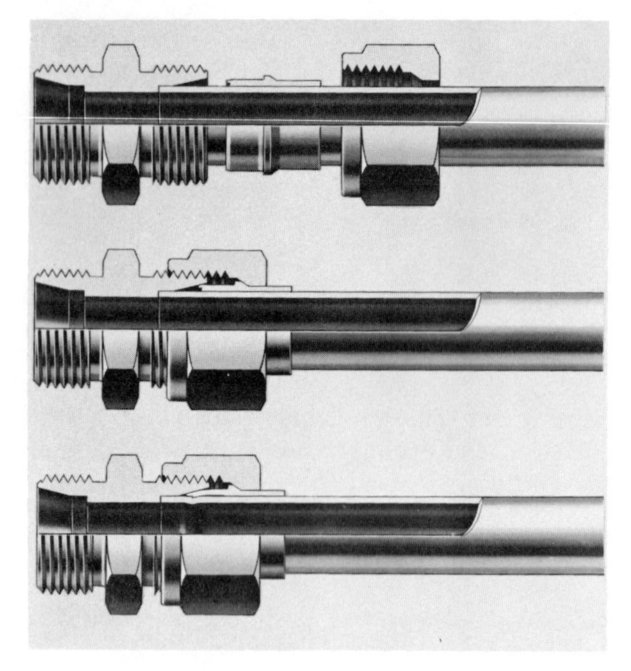

Figure 10·10 Flareless tube fitting.

FABRICATION OF TUBING

Field repairs

Most of the plumbing jobs an aircraft technician will be called upon to do are field and emergency repairs and replacements where fabrication equipment may not be available. It is therefore important to consider techniques which can be used without the help of special tools and machinery but for which the well-trained technician will have the equipment in his own tool kit.

When it is necessary to replace a section of tubing, a section of tubing or pipe of the identical material, diameter, and wall thickness must be selected. This section must be straight and round. Small dents, kinks, and flat spots can be removed by putting the tube on a flat wooden surface and hitting it lightly with a wooden paddle while rolling the tube back and forth.

Another method which can be employed to remove dents is illustrated in Fig. 10·11. To remove dents in tubing by this method, it is merely necessary to draw an oval-shaped piece of steel of the correct diameter through the tube. The piece of steel, called a "bullet," is attached to a

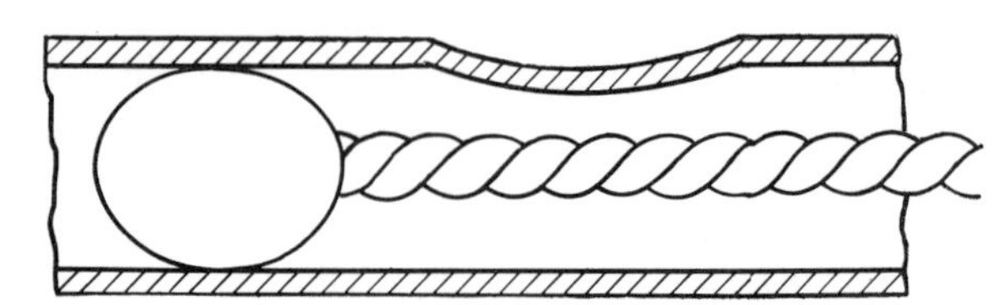

Figure 10·11 Removal of a dent from tubing.

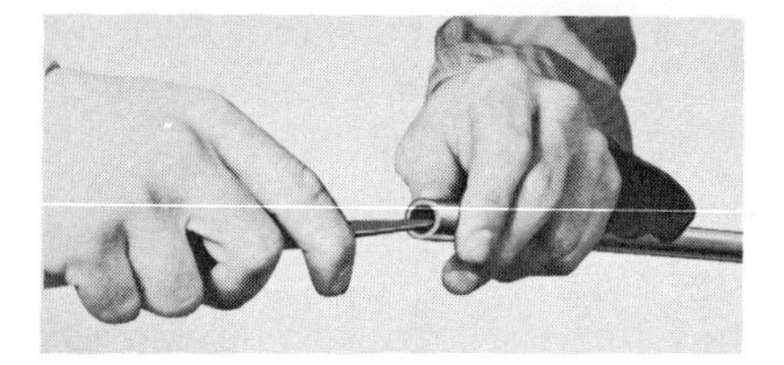

Figure 10·12 Dressing the end of cut tubing.

cable which can be threaded through the tube. The diameter of the bullet should be such that it fits the inside of the tube, and when it is drawn through by means of the cable, it presses the dent out.

Next, the ends of the tube can be cut. It is important to make clean, square cuts. This means that the cuts should be at 90° to the center line of the tubing. A hacksaw with the proper blade (tooth count) can be used to cut the tubing to the required length. It is necessary to consider the difference, if any, of the length required for the tube, pipe, or hose and the length of the line assembly, which includes all or part of the fittings on each end. Since most of the tube ends must be flared later, it is important to have clean, square ends and to remove burrs from the edges, so that the tube ends are smooth and straight. To smooth the inside edge, a reamer, scraper, or knife blade can be used as shown in Fig. 10·12. The outside edge should be dressed with a file, but care must be taken that the ends are not rounded off too much.

When it is desired to cut aluminum or copper tubing or tubing of any other comparatively soft metal, a small tube cutter can be used. A cutter suitable for this purpose is shown in Fig. 10·13. This cutter makes a clean, right-angle cut without leaving burrs or crushing the tube. A hardened

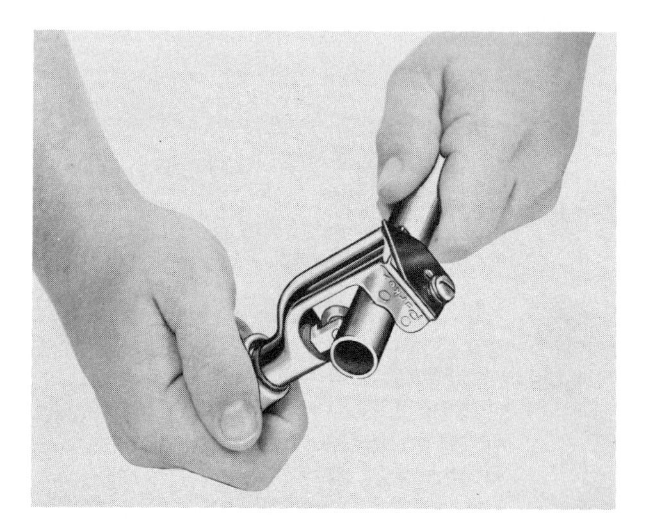

Figure 10·13 A tube cutter.

reamer for cleaning the ends of the tubing is often included as a part of such a cutter. This reamer is used to smooth the inner edge of the cut where the metal is pressed inward a small amount. If the ends of the cut tube are not properly cleaned and smoothed, the flares will be unsatisfactory because any nick, cut, or scratch will be enlarged in the flaring operation.

In addition to the tube cutters mentioned above, special sawing vises are available to make perfect right-angle cuts on the larger sizes of pipe and tubing. Sawing vises have a screw clamp to secure the pipe and a slotted guide for the hacksaw blade.

Used to clean both the inside and outside of cut tube, an inner and outer reamer consists of a steel shell into which a steel cone is fitted. This cone is slotted to make three cutting edges. The tubing is inserted in one end of the tool for inside reaming and in the other end for outside reaming. The three hardened, hollow-ground cutting edges cut in either direction and are self-centering, so that a smooth, uniform edge is formed on the tube end.

Short straight sections of tubing are avoided in the designing of an installation because of the danger of excessive strain when the tube expands or contracts as a result of temperature changes. It is therefore the general practice to make installations with bends in the tubing to absorb the changes in length wherever they may occur.

When a section of tubing is replaced in an aircraft or missile system, the section to be replaced can be used as a pattern. If this is not possible, a piece of welding rod or stiff wire can be used. The wire is bent as required to conform to the shape of the tube section. This results in a considerable saving of time and material. If the pattern material is marked every few inches before it is bent, it will help to determine the length of tubing needed for the replacement. When the pattern is being bent, special attention must be paid to clearances around obstructions and to the alignment of the ends at the point where they connect to the other parts of the installation.

Hand bending

The wall thickness and the outside diameter govern the minimum permissible bend radius for tubing, but it is advisable to make the bends as large as the installation will permit. It is also desirable to make all bends of the same radius in any one line. As a general rule, at least five times the diameter of the tubing should be used as a minimum bend radius, although it is permissible to use a radius as small as three times the diameter of the tubing under some conditions.

Table 10·1

	Torque range for tube nuts, in.-lb		*Minimum bend radii, in.*	
Tube OD, in.	*Aluminum alloy*	*Stainless steel*	*Aluminum alloy*	*Stainless steel*
1/8	...	...	3/8	
3/16	...	30–70	7/16	21/32
1/4	40–65	50–90	9/16	7/8
5/16	60–80	70–120	3/4	1 1/8
3/8	75–125	90–150	15/16	1 5/16
1/2	150–250	155–250	1 1/4	1 3/4
5/8	200–350	300–400	1 1/2	2 3/16
3/4	300–500	430–575	1 3/4	2 5/8
1	500–700	550–750	3	3 1/2
1 1/4	600–900	...	3 3/4	4 3/8

Minimum-bend radii and torque values approved for certificated aircraft tubing installations are given in Table 10·1.

The method for determining the radius of a bend is shown in Fig. 10·14. Observe that the radius of the bend is measured from the center line of the tubing. Correctly bent tubing maintains its circular shape and presents a smooth appearance throughout, without kinks or breaks. Proper and improper bends are shown in Fig. 10·15.

It is very difficult to make satisfactory bends without a support to maintain the circular shape of the tubing. For field and emergency work, several methods are employed to provide this support. One method consists of filling the tube with a substance which will provide an all-around support to prevent deformation of the circular tube and still permit flexibility for the bending operation. Sand, which is easily obtainable, can be used provided it is not coarse and is dry. One end of the tube is closed with a suitable plug. The dry sand is poured in the other end and permitted to pack tightly inside the tube. This can be accomplished by tapping the side of the tube with a wooden paddle while the sand is being poured. The other end of the tube is then plugged.

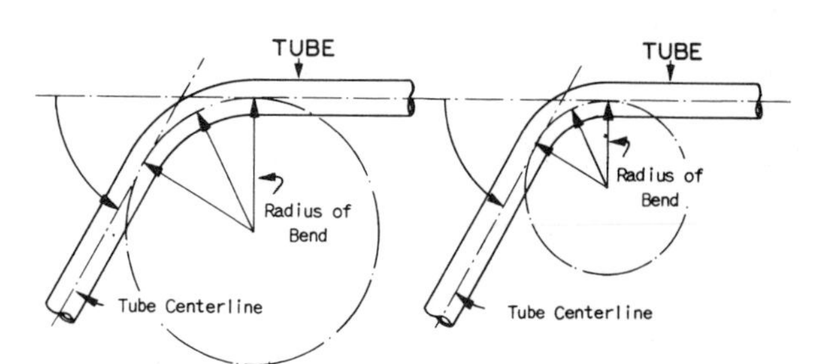

Figure **10·14** *Radius of a tubing bend.*

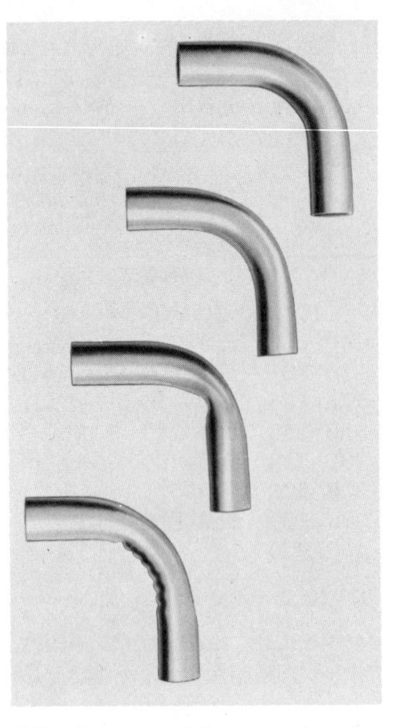

Figure **10·15** *Proper and improper bends.*

For tubing of over 1 in. OD, salt is often used instead of sand. In order to pour freely and to fill the tube completely, both the sand and salt must be perfectly dry. Copper tubing will bend more easily when annealed, that is, softened by heating to a red heat and quenching in cold water. Resin, tar, and lead are sometimes used as a filler for bending, but their use is not recommended, since it is difficult to remove them from the inside of the tubing after bending.

A metallic alloy filler, known by its trade name Cerrobend, and also other eutectic (low-melting-point) materials are often used for tube bending. Cerrobend is a mixture of bismuth, lead, tin, and cadmium and melts readily at 158 to 160°F. Since it expands slightly when solidifying, it makes a tight fit in the tube. In order to prevent adhesion of the Cerrobend to the tube wall, the tube should be coated internally with a light grade of oil before the Cerrobend is poured. The best method to fill the tubing completely and to keep the Cerrobend in a fluid condition is to fill the tubing with boiling water, pour the melted Cerrobend into the tubing, and allow it to displace the water. Water at the boiling point is all that is needed to melt Cerrobend or other similar alloys and to remove them from the tubing after bending. Another metallic alloy with a very low melting point is known as Wood's metal.

Tube bending can also be accomplished by supporting the outside of the tubing instead of the inside. This method requires the use of a spring wire coil, commonly known as a "spring-type tube bender." Cadmium-plated spring wire is coiled into a cylinder, the ID of which is slightly larger than the OD of the tubing for which it is made. The coil is slipped over the tubing to be bent, giving an all-around support to the outer wall. This makes it possible to bend the tubing without causing it to collapse. A complete set of these tube benders consists of six units, one each for ¼-, 5⁄16-, ⅜-, 7⁄16-, ½-, and ⅝-in.-OD tubing.

Though bends in tubing can be made by hand with a filler or spring-type tube bender, a smooth job will result only if time and trouble are spent to make a wooden form block as shown in Fig. 10·16. A suitable piece of hardwood is cut in the shape of the desired bend radius and degree of bend. A groove to fit the OD of the tube is cut to take the tubing, and the bend is made by forcing the tubing to assume the shape of the form block by applying even pressure. The original tubing or the bend pattern must be compared with the new tubing to assure proper forming. The sections of the tubing between bends should be straight. After all bends are made, the filler material or the tube benders are removed and the tubing is thoroughly cleaned.

Use of bending tools

To bend tubing in shops and factories, the simple hand methods are not adequate. More elaborate equipment will pay for itself by producing faster and more uniform work.

Bending tools are divided into two types: (1) hand tube benders, which require a different bender for each tube OD, and (2) production benders, which can be used for different tube sizes by changing the attachments. Production benders may be either manually or power operated.

The choice of the particular model bender to be used depends upon the size and material of the tubing to be bent, the kind of benders available, and the number of bends to be made. If only one or two bends are to be made for a particular job,

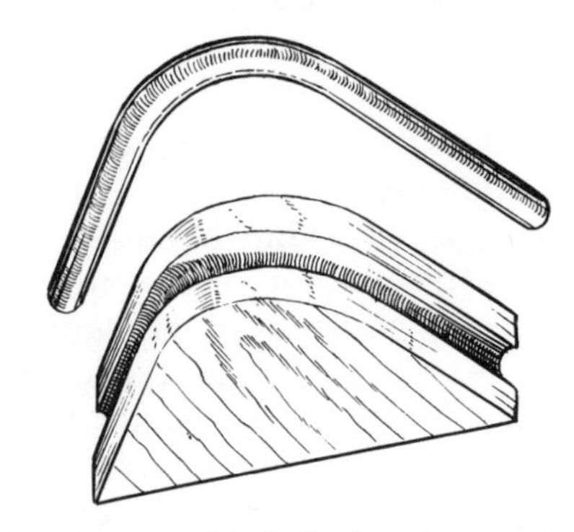

Figure **10·16** *Form block for bending a tube.*

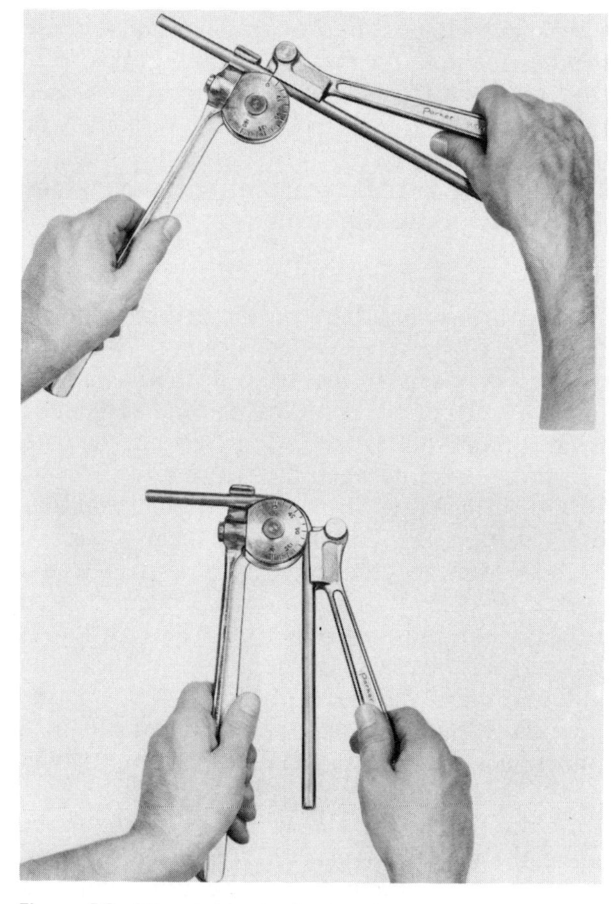

Figure 10·17 A hand tube bender.

it is often more economical to use a hand bender rather than taking the time to set up a production bender.

A typical hand bender is shown in Fig. 10·17. The bender consists of a sheave block and handle with a clip attached and a slide bar with a handle. To insert a piece of tubing to be bent, the slide bar is turned back away from the sheave block. The tubing is placed in the sheave block, and the clip is hooked over the tubing. The slide-bar handle is then rotated so the groove in the slide bar fits over the tubing. Continued rotation of the slide-bar handle makes the bend with the degree of bend determined by the distance of rotation as indicated by the scale on the sheave block.

A hand tube bender may seem like a relatively unimportant tool to an inexperienced technician, but those who have worked in the maintenance of aerospace vehicles realize that many of the important mechanisms in airplanes or missiles are dependent to some degree upon the proper functioning of a complex plumbing system, since the plumbing in aerospace vehicles is the means by which the power for operation is transmitted from the controlling unit to the mechanism to be operated.

The hand tube bender is a vital means of installing and maintaining the many systems in which tubing plays a vital part. Fuel, lubricating oil, and other liquids and also a variety of gases are carried from supply tanks to various operating mechanisms. In an airplane, wing flaps, cowl flaps, retractable landing gear, dive brakes, power-boosted controls, propeller pitch-changing mechanisms, flight instruments, and various other mechanisms may be operated hydraulically through a plumbing system. For the maintenance of these systems, the hand tube bender is found to be a most useful tool.

Production tube bender

Although the aerospace maintenance technician may not be required to operate production tube bending equipment frequently, it is well to have an understanding of such equipment. The production equipment utilizes the same principles as those for the hand bender; that is, the tubing is supported on the outside by suitable blocks designed to accommodate the various sizes of tubes.

The bending mechanism of a typical production bender is shown in Fig. 10·18. The bending mechanism consists of a radius block, a clamp block, and a sliding block. The clamping block secures the tubing at the point of the bend to the radius block. The clamp block and the sliding block are adjusted for position by means of vise mechanisms.

When a section of tubing is to be bent, it is placed in the bender as shown in Fig. 10·19. The radius block is chosen for the radius desired and the diameter of the tubing to be bent. The clamp block is grooved to fit the tubing, and when the clamp block vise is tightened, the tubing is

Figure 10·18 Bending mechanism of a production bender.

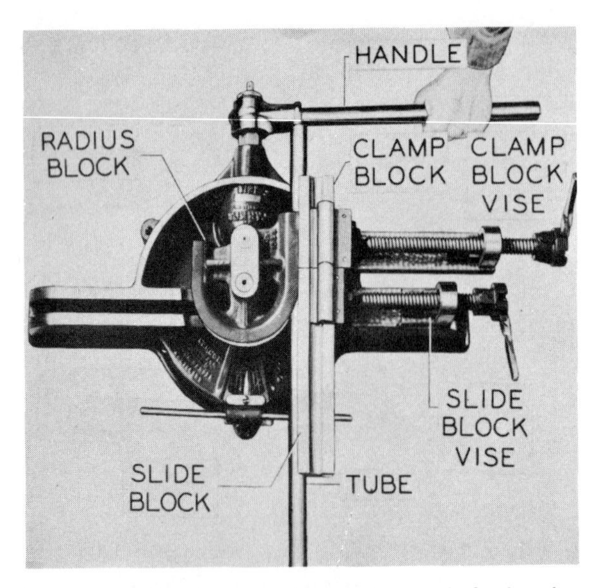

Figure **10·19** *Tubing in the bender ready for bending.*

held firmly against the radius block. The slide block vise is also tightened to bear against the tubing. When the handle is turned, the radius block and clamp block together rotate, draw the tubing around, and produce the bend. The slide block holds the tubing in shape as the bend is made.

If tubing is to be bent with a radius less than standard, or if the tubing wall is thinner than standard, it is necessary to use a mandrel inside the tubing. The mandrel is mounted on a rod of sufficient length to accommodate the length of tubing to be bent. The rod is secured by an adjustable mount on the bender bench. The mandrel is positioned in the tubing at the point where the sliding block bears against the radius block. As the tubing is drawn around the radius block, the mandrel supports it from the inside as shown in the simplified drawing of Fig. 10·20.

The production tube bender is provided with a scale to indicate the degree of bend completed. This makes it possible to produce an accurate bend as required for the installation. In the operation of the tube bender it is important to see that all parts are clean and not scratched or nicked; that the radius block, clamp block, and sliding block are of the correct sizes; and that the vises are correctly adjusted.

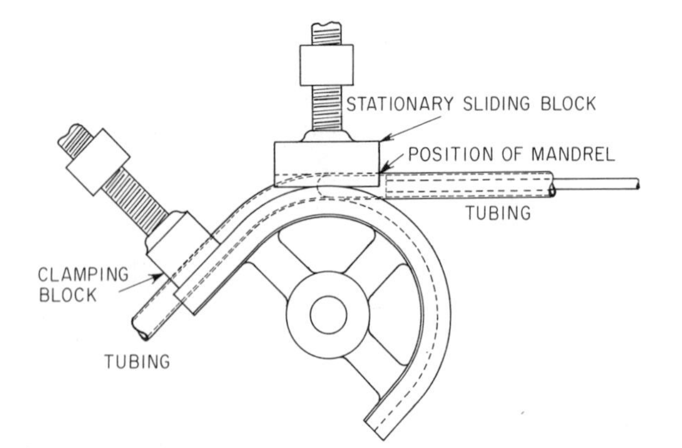

Figure **10·20** *Position of the mandrel for tube bending.*

Flaring

The purpose of a flare on the end of a tube is twofold. First, it provides a flange which is gripped between the sleeve or flare nut and the body of a fitting. This prevents the end of the tube from slipping out of the fitting. Second, the flare acts as a gasket between the sleeve and the cone of the fitting, thus providing a tight seal. It is obvious that the flare must be nearly perfect, because minute cracks or irregularities would permit leakage at the junction. The flare must be neither too long nor too short. A flare which is too long will bear against the threads of the fitting and may cause damage to both the flare and the threads. A tight seal cannot usually be obtained under such conditions. Maximum and minimum flare lengths are shown in Fig. 10·21.

Before flaring the end of a tube, it should be remembered that a part of the fitting, in most cases sleeves (if required) and nuts, must be slipped on the tubing, since it is impossible to install them after the flare is formed.

It is not possible to make a satisfactory flare without the aid of a good tool. Several types of flaring tools are available at reasonable cost, but the technician must make sure that the tool selected will produce a suitable flare without damaging the tubing.

The simplest tool is a piece of steel rod with a ball on each end. It can be used in combination with the flare of the fitting sleeve or nut, but it takes considerable skill and practice to produce a flare with this tool.

A practical hand flaring tool (see Fig. 10·22) consists of parallel bars between which are mounted blocks with holes of various sizes drilled between the blocks. The blocks are split at the holes so they can be separated for the insertion

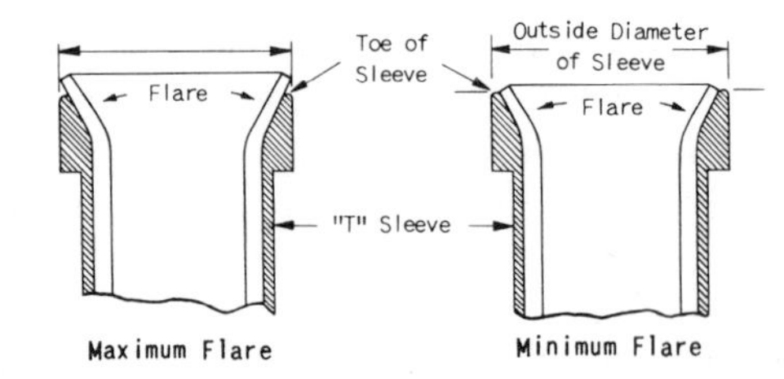

Figure **10·21** *Maximum and minimum flare lengths.*

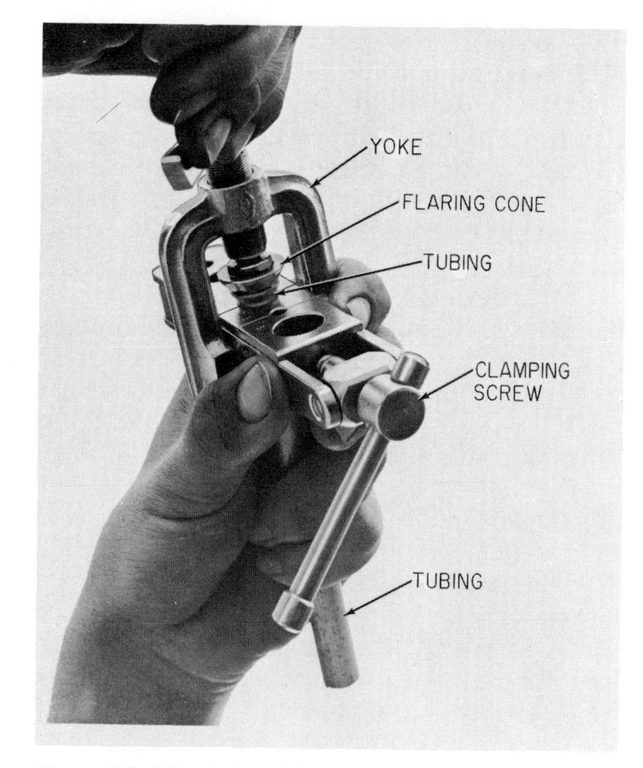

Figure **10·22** *A hand flaring tool.*

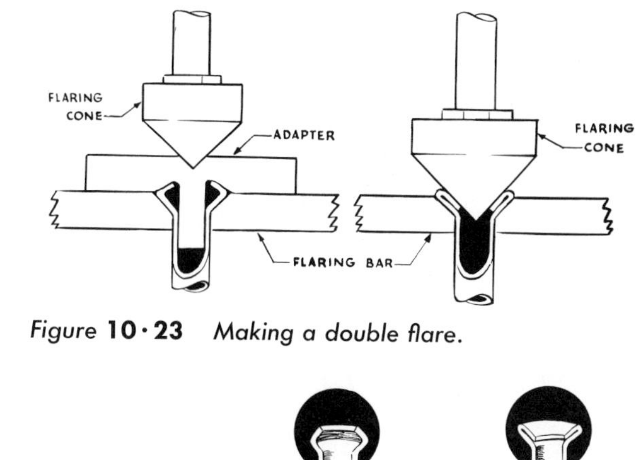

Figure **10·23** *Making a double flare.*

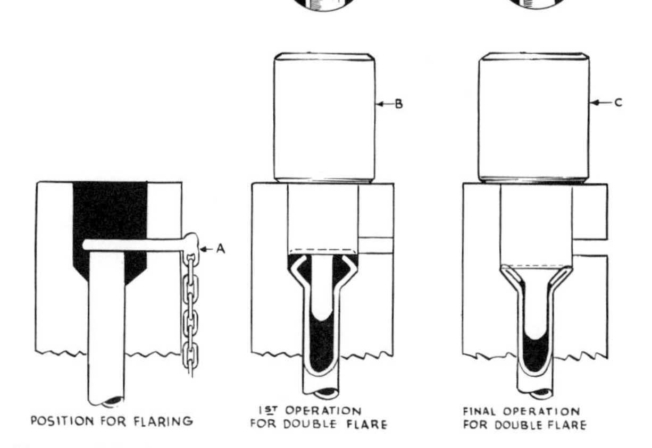

Figure **10·24** *Tools for making a double flare. (A) Limit pin; (B) set pin no. 1; (C) set pin no. 2.*

of tubing. The holes between the blocks are drilled with a diameter slightly less than the outside diameter of the tubing so they will grip the tubing firmly when the clamping screw is tightened. A yoke which carries the flaring cone slides over the entire assembly as shown in Fig. 10·22.

To produce a flare with this tool, the clamping screw at the end of the tool is loosened so tubing can be inserted through the correct-sized hole. About ¼ in. of the tubing is extended above the clamping blocks. The clamping screw is then tightened to hold the tubing in place. Next, the yoke with the 37° flaring cone is slid over the tool and positioned so the cone is directly over the end of the tubing. When the flaring-cone screw is turned, the cone is forced into the end of the tubing until the flare is formed.

Difficulties and failures with single flares have been overcome by making a double flare. This requires only slight addition to or alteration of the flaring tools. The use of an adapter will make most of the flaring tools suitable for double flaring. Making a double flare with an adapter is shown in Fig. 10·23.

A set of tools especially designed for making double flares is shown in Fig. 10·24. A steel block is bored through for the OD of a tube and counterbored from the other end to the diameter of a flaring pin. The counterbore ends in the correct angle for the flare. A limit pin *A* ensures sufficient stock for the double flaring operation. The block with the tube inserted is clamped in a vise and the pin *B* is inserted. This pin has a pilot of the diameter of the tubing ID and concave on its lower surface. The pin is driven until its shoulder seats on the block. The concave lower surface will force the tubing to bell against the flare die and inward at the tube end. Pin *B* is then removed, and the set pin *C* is inserted and driven to complete the flare. This pin also has a shoulder to limit its distance.

In the tube-fabricating departments of large maintenance shops and factories, power machines are generally used for flaring tubing for standard AN fittings. If flareless fittings are employed, it is not necessary to flare the tubing.

Tube beading

Even though flexible hose sections in modern installations are almost always made with manufactured hose fittings, there are times when it becomes necessary to join sections of hose to tubing without the use of such fittings. When this is done, it is necessary to bead the tubing if the diameter is more than ⅜ in. OD.

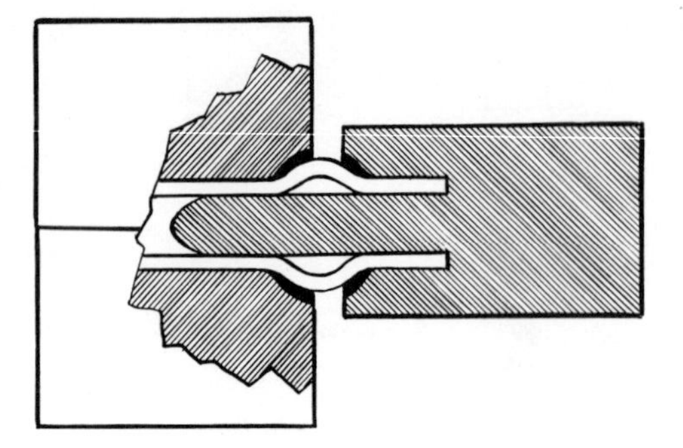

Figure **10·25** *A hand-made beading tool.*

A hand beading tool can be made as shown in Fig. 10·25. This tool consists of a split block bored to a size which will clamp the tubing tightly when the block is secured in a vise. A pin die is made with a pilot to fit the ID of the tubing to be beaded. Both the die and the block are made with a curved cavity to accommodate the bead as it is formed. The bead is formed by driving or pressing the die over the end of the tubing as shown in the illustration.

A manufactured hand beading tool consists of a body which carries a hardened bushing for the inner beading rollers and a guide for a slide block which carries two rolls that size the outer section of the bead. An adjusting screw whose end is enclosed in the slide block is mounted in the body. Stop nuts are placed on this screw for limiting the length of the bead.

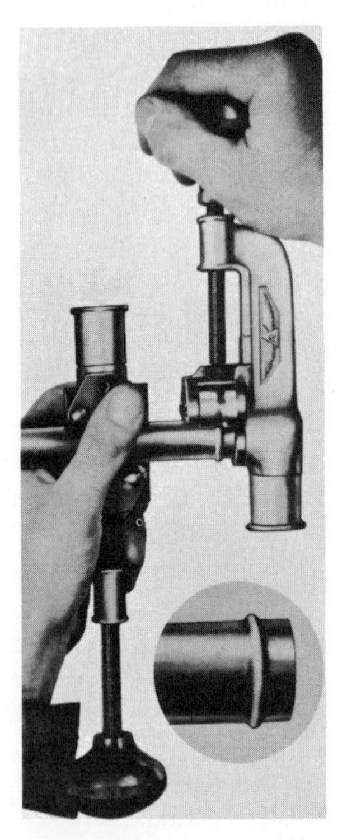

Figure **10·26** *Using the beading tool.*

To make a bead with the tool, the tubing is placed over the inner roller after being lubricated. The roller must be of the size to accommodate the tube being beaded. The tube end is placed against the face of the hardened bushing to locate the bead in the correct position. The slide block is adjusted to contact the outer rollers against the tube.

The tube clamp assembly is then attached to the tube. This assembly is similar to the beading tool except that a synthetic rubber block is used instead of rollers on the slide block, and a similar block assembly is rigidly mounted in the body. When the slide block is adjusted against the tube, the friction of the clamp is sufficient to hold the tube while the bead is formed. By holding the clamp assembly in the left hand and turning the beading assembly with the right hand, one can make a bead in a few seconds. This operation is shown in Fig. 10·26. Pressure is applied to the bead-forming roller by means of the hand screw while the tool is being turned.

PLUMBING INSTALLATION

Installation of tubing

The proper functioning of the many fluid and gas systems in aerospace vehicles depends to a large extent on the proper installation and servicing of the tubing, hose, and piping used in the systems. The initial installation is usually performed by a manufacturer and undergoes a rigid inspection at the time of assembly. In the field it is the duty of the technician to inspect, troubleshoot, and repair the systems.

One of the important steps before lines are installed is the lubrication of the fittings. Lubrication is not essential to all types of fittings, but it **must** be applied to some, and it is a good practice for others. In the application of lubricant, it is important that none of the lubricant enter the tubing unless the lubricant is the same material which will be flowing in the system. This applies particularly to hydraulic fluids. In general, no lubricant should be applied to the starting threads and it should be used sparingly on the rest of the fittings. Figure 10·27 shows the points of lubrication for typical fittings. The following general rules apply:

Lubricate nuts and fittings on the **outside** of the sleeve and on the male threads of the fittings except for the starting threads.

Lubricate B nuts and fittings on the outside of the flare, and lubricate the female threads of B nuts except for the starting threads.

For fittings on oxygen lines, a petroleum base

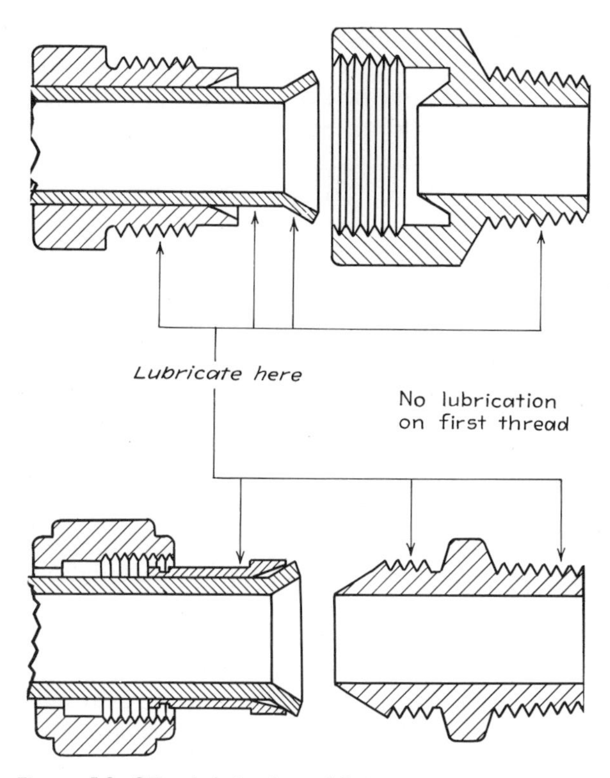

Figure 10·27 Lubrication of fittings.

or oily lubricant may not be used. For fittings of oxygen systems, a special lubricant must be used. A lubricant conforming to AN-C-86 or to the pertinent military specification may be used.

For hot-gas and hot-air line fittings, AN-VV-C-566 or an equivalent material is suitable.

Several lubricants are used on hydraulic fittings including the fluid to be used in the system. Straight threads of brass or steel may be left dry or may be lubricated with the fluid. If the threads are in aluminum alloy, petrolatum (petroleum jelly) may be used.

For pipe threads, the lubricant must be of a type which is not soluble in the fluid being carried in the system. If a petroleum-base lubricant is used on pipe fittings in a fuel system carrying gasoline or jet fuel, the lubricant will be dissolved and a leak will develop. It must be remembered that the lubricant used with a pipe fitting must also serve as a seal and fill the space at the roots of the threads.

Before tubing assemblies are installed, a final inspection should be made. Flares and sleeves must be concentric and free of cracks. The tubing must not be appreciably dented or scratched. Each assembly must be in initial alignment with the fitting to which it is to be attached. **A fitting or assembly must never be forced into position.** A section that must be forced to line up is under initial stress and may fail in operation.

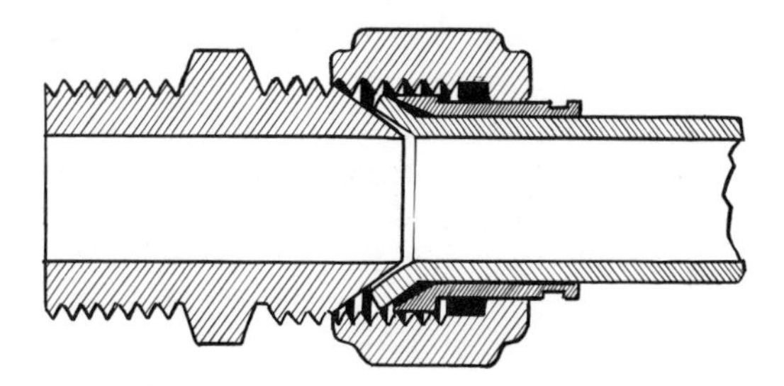

Figure 10·28 Position of fitting part for assembly.

Tubing should be pushed against the fitting snugly and squarely before starting to turn the coupling nut. This is illustrated in Fig. 10·28. The tubing should not be drawn up to the fitting by tightening the nut because the flare may be easily turned off. To make sure that a snug fit is effected, all nuts should be started by hand. Tubing installed in an airplane must not be used as a footrest or as a ladder, and lamp cords and other weights should not be suspended from it. The most important of all operations for tubing installation is that of tightening or torquing the nuts. The most common mistake is to overtighten the nuts in order to ensure a leak-free union in a pressure system. Overtightening causes damage to the flare and often results in line failure in flight. Correct torque values are given in Table 10·1.

Improper tightening effects are illustrated in Fig. 10·29 as compared with nuts which are

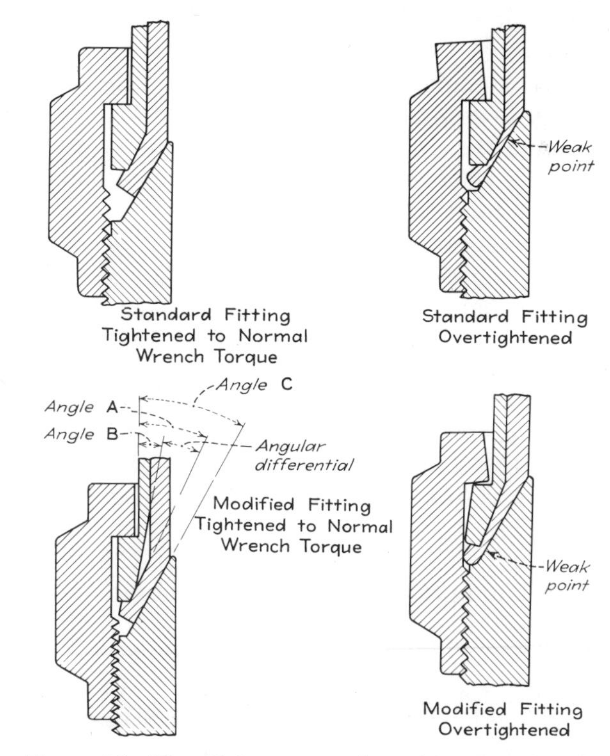

Figure 10·29 Fittings properly and improperly tightened.

properly tightened. These drawings also show that there is an angular difference between the sleeve and the flare on the AN-type fitting.

To obtain correct torque values when tubing sections are installed and the couplings tightened, it is desirable to use a torque wrench. Special wrenches for fittings are available, and some of these are constructed with snap releases so they automatically release when the proper torque is attained.

Installing rigid conduit

Since rigid conduits are made from a semisoft material, their support is of major importance. Single conduits are supported by clamps, while groups of conduits are arranged in supporting blocks. The metal clamps are either plain or lined with rubber, synthetic rubber, or plastic material. Special care is required when the clamps are tightened in order to prevent damage to the tubing. The conduit should be fingertight in the clamp. The insertion of an aluminum-alloy washer between the clamp tabs is permissible to prevent overtightening. Support clamps are specially designed for each group of conduits. They are made from material which is impervious to gasoline, oil, hydraulic fluid, and most other liquids. Holes, corresponding to the number and diameters of the conduits for which the block is made, are in general located along the center line of the block. The block is cut along the center line to permit insertion of the conduits and the installation of a tinned copper strip for bonding. A similar bonding strip is incorporated in the lined clamps to ensure good contact. The inside of the plain metal clamps must be free of paint or other coating so that good electrical contact will exist between the clamp and the conduit.

Flexible conduits are installed in a manner similar to that for rigid conduit except that additional support for the area under a clamp or support block should be provided to prevent damage to the conduit. Since flexible conduit is used where movement of the installation is unavoidable, too rigid a support will defeat its purpose. The outside metallic braid of flexible conduits is tinned to facilitate soldering of bonding braids. An aluminum-alloy washer under the head of the bonding screw will make a good contact and preserve the copper braid.

Installation of hose

In the few cases where a plain hose is used to provide a flexible joint between two sections of tubing, the ends of the tubing must be beaded. Clamps should not be overtightened because of the danger of damaging the hose. A good practice is to tighten the clamp fingertight plus one-fourth turn. It must be emphasized that plain hose and clamps must not be used where the fluid in the system is under pressure. In this case flexible-hose assemblies of an approved type must be employed.

The installation of flexible-hose assemblies requires that the hose be of a length which will not be subjected to tension. The hose section should be of sufficient length to provide about 5 to 8 per cent slack. The hose should be installed without twisting by keeping the white line on the hose straight. The coupling nuts for flexible-hose assemblies should be torqued to the correct value as specified by the manufacturer. Bends in the hose should not have a radius less than twelve times the ID of the hose for normal installations.

Inspection and maintenance of plumbing systems

Lines and fittings should be inspected carefully at regular intervals for leaks, damage, loose mountings, cracks, scratches, dents, and other damage. Flexible lines should be checked for cracks, cuts, abrasions, soft spots, and any other indication of deterioration. Parts with defects should be either replaced or repaired. A damaged metal line should be replaced in its entirety if the damage is extensive. If the damage is localized, it is permissible to cut out the damaged section and insert a new section with approved fittings. Care must be taken that no foreign material enters the line during the repair operation. When soft aluminum tubing utilizing flare fittings is replaced, a double flare should be used on all tubing of ⅜ in. OD or smaller.

The following defects are not acceptable for metal lines:

1. Cracked flare.
2. Scratches or nicks greater in depth than 10 per cent of the tube wall thickness or in the heel of a bend. Such cracks or nicks may be repaired by burnishing with hand tools.
3. Severe die marks, seams, or splits.
4. A dent of more than 20 per cent of the tube diameter or in the heel of a bend.

When it is necessary to replace flexible-hose assemblies, the replacement part should be of the same length and type as the original. If reusable fittings are employed on the section being removed, the fittings may be attached to a new section of approved hose of the correct length. The installation of the fittings should be per-

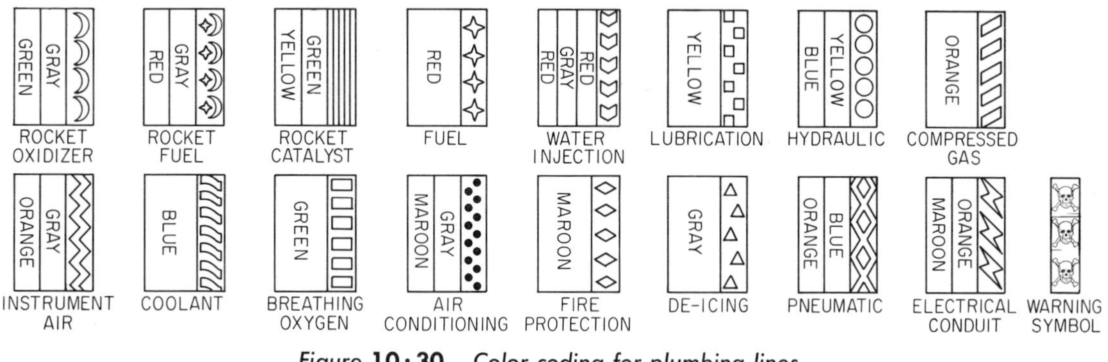

Figure **10·30** *Color coding for plumbing lines.*

formed in accordance with the manufacturer's directions and with the proper tools.

Fuel lines should be of a size adequate to carry not less than double the maximum flow required for takeoff power. Fuel lines should not have vertical bends or humps which may trap vapor. There should be a continuous "up" or "down" slope in such lines. The lines must be so supported and installed that there is no possibility of structural loads being imposed upon them.

Where copper lines are installed, it is required that such lines be annealed from time to time to prevent hardening and cracking. This is accomplished by heating the line to a red heat and then quenching in cold water. Aluminum lines should never be annealed except under accurately controlled conditions in a heat-treating oven. Field annealing with a torch is likely to produce an uneven hardness and may also result in intergranular corrosion.

Color code for plumbing lines

Color codes for aircraft and missile plumbing lines are established by AND10375. These codings replace the plain color system used prior to August, 1949. Because of fading of the colors and the fact that the color perception of some persons is not sufficiently acute, the plain colors were found to be subject to misinterpretation under adverse conditions. For this reason the new color coding was established together with black-and-white symbols.

Figure 10·30 shows the coding for various systems in an airplane or missile. In practice the coding bands are colored as indicated in the illustration. The symbols are black against a white background. For tubing in which extreme pressures exist or tubing which carries poisonous or corrosive liquids, an additional symbol band is used. This symbol is a black skull and crossbones on a white background.

REVIEW QUESTIONS

1. Name six systems in aircraft or missiles which may require the use of plumbing.
2. What materials are used to carry fluids in the systems for aircraft and missiles?
3. Why is tubing or conduit used for electrical wiring?
4. How can you determine that a particular hose is suitable for use in an aerospace vehicle system?
5. What types of fittings are used to connect tubing in plumbing systems for aerospace vehicles?
6. Explain the nature of pipe threads.
7. Why is a sealer required with pipe fittings?
8. Describe a flareless tube fitting.
9. What is the proper method for cutting tubing?
10. How can a satisfactory bend be made in tubing?
11. What is the correct torque for a ⅜-in. aluminum-alloy fitting?
12. Give the minimum bend radius for ½-in. stainless-steel tubing.
13. What type of flares may be used for aircraft tubing?
14. What are the precautions required in the connecting of tubing fittings?
15. What should you look for in the inspection of plumbing?
16. What type of tubing should be annealed at overhaul periods?
17. How can the various plumbing systems be identified?
18. What type of tubing and fittings should be used for high-pressure systems?

CHAPTER 11

Weight and Balance

INTRODUCTION

In the early days of aviation a pilot could fly "by the seat of his pants" and any man with a few tools could take the role of an aircraft mechanic. Decisions were made by intuition and hunches and by trial and error. If a procedure did not result in the loss of life and destruction of an airplane, it was assumed to be correct and was followed until some event occurred which proved it wrong. Today, orderly procedures based on knowledge and understanding are followed, with the result that flight operations and maintenance procedures are carried out in a safe and efficient manner.

The proper loading and balancing of an airplane today are performed according to exact rules and specifications. Weight and balance calculations must be prepared whenever aircraft are altered, whether such alterations involve adding or removing equipment or making structural changes in an airplane. Calculations must also be made when loading aircraft, regardless of whether the airplane is large or small. The constantly changing conditions of modern aircraft operation present more and more complex combinations of cargo, crew, fuel, passengers, and baggage. The necessity for obtaining the utmost efficiency from any flight has emphasized the need for a precise system control over the weight and balance of all airplanes.

Improper loading reduces the efficiency of an airplane from the viewpoint of ceiling, maneuverability, rate of climb, and speed. This is the least of the harm that it can cause. The greatest danger is that the improper loading may cause the destruction of life and property, even before the flight is well started, because of the stresses imposed upon the aircraft structure or because of altered flying characteristics of the airplane.

EFFECTS OF IMPROPER LOADING

Overloading

If an airplane is overloaded, any one or all of the following conditions may exist:

1. Reduced maneuverability
2. Longer takeoff run
3. Lower angle of climb
4. Lower rate of climb
5. Lower ceiling
6. Increased fuel consumption for any given speed, shown by a decrease in miles per gallon
7. Increased wear on tires
8. Reduced factors of safety for the airplane structure during rough air or takeoffs from poor fields
9. Increase in stalling speed
10. Change in the flight characteristics of the airplane which can lead to accidents
11. Increased landing speed
12. Increased angle of glide

The foregoing conditions are not presented in the order of their undesirability because a condition that is extremely dangerous under one set of conditions may be comparatively unimportant under another. It is particularly hazardous when a pilot is flying an airplane which is loaded above the weight at which he normally flies the airplane. There is an increased possibility of stalling the airplane on takeoff and again just before he lands. Either event could be disastrous.

Too much weight forward

When too much weight is toward the forward part of the airplane, the center of gravity is shifted forward and any one of the following conditions may exist or they may occur in combinations at the same time:

1. Increased fuel consumption
2. Increased power for any given speed

3. Increased tendency to dive, especially with power off
4. Increased difficulty in raising the nose of the airplane when landing
5. Increased oscillation tendency
6. Increased stresses on the nose wheel
7. Increased danger during flap operation
8. Development of dangerous spin characteristics
9. Decrease in stability
10. Directional unstability on the ground because of the manner of using brakes
11. Increased danger if the tail assembly is damaged
12. Danger of going into a dive when power is cut off for landing

A study of the above-listed conditions will reveal that most of them could lead to an accident with a resulting loss of life and destruction of the airplane.

Too much weight to the rear

When too much weight is toward the tail of the airplane, any one of the following conditions may exist or they may occur in combination:

1. Decreased flying speed
2. Decreased range
3. Increased strain on the pilot during instrument flight
4. Increased danger of stall
5. Dangerous spin characteristics
6. Reduction of long-range optimum speed
7. Poor stability
8. Increased danger if tail assembly is damaged
9. Poor landing characteristics

FUNDAMENTAL PRINCIPLES

Introduction

In a previous chapter we discussed laws of physics, and included in these discussions were **specific gravity** and **balance** together with explanations of levers. These principles form the basis for computing weight and balance data for an airplane and will be reviewed briefly at this point.

Force of gravity

Every body of matter in the universe attracts every other body with a certain force that is called gravitation. The term **gravity** is used to refer to the force that tends to draw all bodies toward the center of the earth. The weight of a body is the resultant of all gravitational forces acting on the body.

Center of gravity

Every particle of an object is acted on by the force of gravity. However, in every object there is one point at which a single force, equal in magnitude to the weight of the object and directed upward, can keep the body at rest, that is, can keep it in balance and prevent it from falling. This point is known as the **center of gravity.**

The CG might be defined as the point at which all the weight of a body can be considered concentrated. Thus, the CG of a perfectly round ball would be the exact center of the ball provided that the ball were made of the same material throughout and that there were no air or gas pockets inside (see Fig. 11·1). The CG of a uniform ring would be at the center of the ring but would not be at any point in the ring itself (see Fig. 11·2). The CG of a cube of solid material would be equidistant from the eight corners as shown in Fig. 11·3.

In airplanes, ease of control and maneuverability depend partly on the location of the CG.

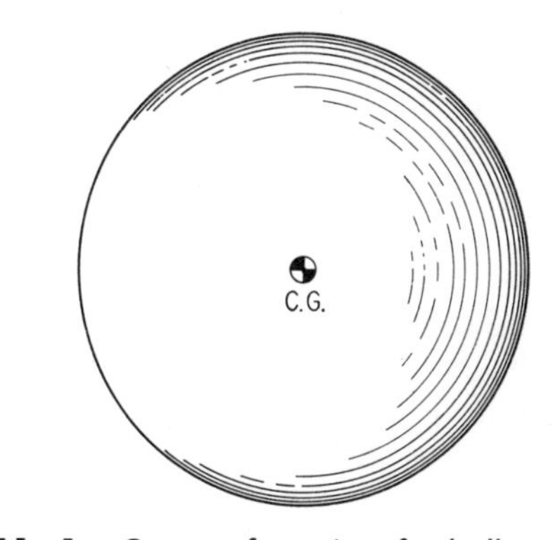

Figure **11·1** *Center of gravity of a ball.*

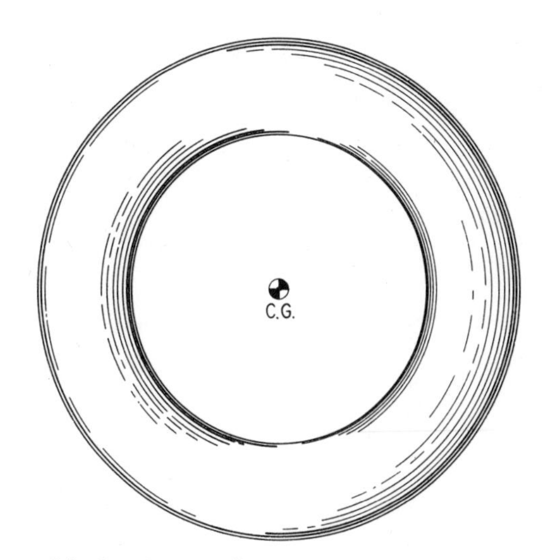

Figure **11·2** *Center of gravity of a ring.*

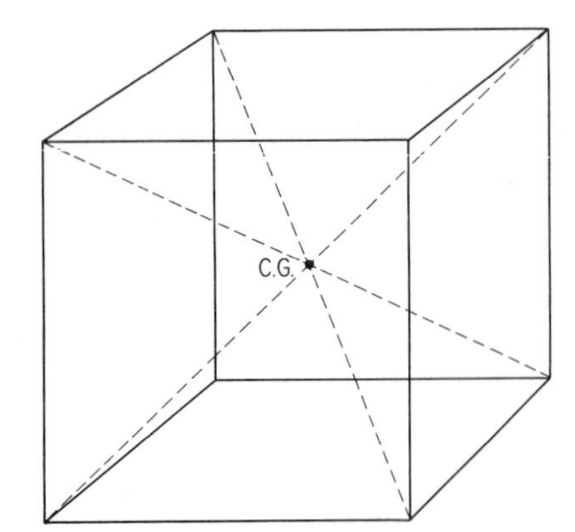

Figure **11 · 3** *Center of gravity of a cube.*

Location of the CG

Since the CG of a body is that point at which its weight can be considered to be concentrated, the CG of a freely suspended body will always be vertically beneath the point of support when the body is supported at a single point. To locate the CG, therefore, it is necessary only to determine the point of intersection of vertical lines drawn downward from two separate points of support employed onc at a time. This is demonstrated in Fig. 11 · 4, which shows a flat, square sheet of material lettered *A*, *B*, *C*, and *D* at its four corners, suspended first from point *B* and then from point *C*. The lines drawn vertically downward from the point of suspension in each case intersect at the CG.

The CG of an irregular body can be determined in the same way. If an irregular object, such as the one shown in Fig. 11 · 5, is suspended from a point *P* in such a manner that it can turn freely about the point of suspension, it will come to rest with its CG directly below the point of suspension *P*. If a plumb line is dropped from the same point of suspension, the CG of the object will coincide with some point along the plumb line; a line drawn along the plumb line passes through this point. If the object is suspended from another point, which we shall call *A*, and another line is drawn in the direction indicated by the plumb line, the intersection of the two lines will be at the CG. In order to verify the results, the operation can be repeated, this time with the object suspended from another point, called *B*. No matter how many times the process is repeated, the lines should pass through the CG; hence it is evident that the CG of the object lies at the point of intersection of these lines of suspension. Therefore, any object behaves as if all its weight were concentrated at its CG.

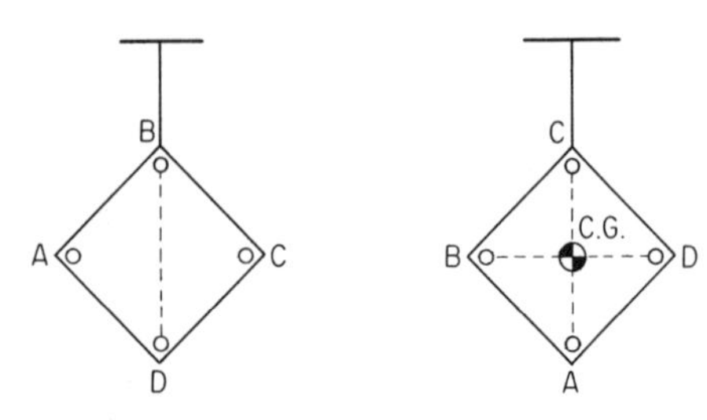

Figure **11 · 4** *Location of the CG.*

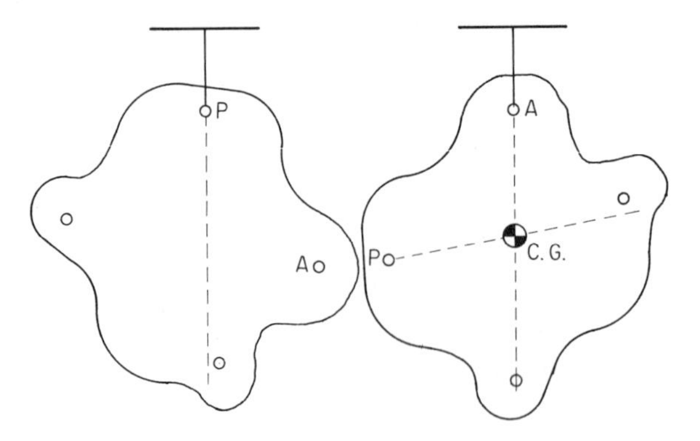

Figure **11 · 5** *Locating CG in an irregular body.*

Practical CG of an airplane

If an airplane is not too heavy and can be equipped with suspension loops as in *A* and *B* of Fig. 11 · 6, the CG of the airplane can be determined easily by the trial method. This actually is a duplication of the process explained in the previous paragraph and illustrated in Fig. 11 · 5. If we suspend the airplane at point 1 and draw a vertical line downward from the point of suspension, then repeat the process with the airplane suspended from point 2, we shall find an intersection of the extended lines which will be at the CG as shown in *C* of Fig. 11 · 6. The foregoing is not the method normally used for locating the CG for an airplane, but it gives a demonstration of what can be done and illustrates one of the basic principles of weight and balance.

The general law of the lever

In the chapter on the laws of physics we explained the law of levers; however, it will be repeated briefly here to show how it relates to the weight and balance of an airplane.

Wrenches, crowbars, and scissors are levers used to gain mechanical advantage, that is, to gain force at the expense of distance or to gain distance at the expense of force. A lever, in general, is essentially a rigid rod free to turn about a point called the **fulcrum.** There are three types of levers, but in the study of weight and balance we are principally interested in the type known as a **first-class lever.** This type has the fulcrum between the applied effort and the resistance (see Fig. 11 · 7).

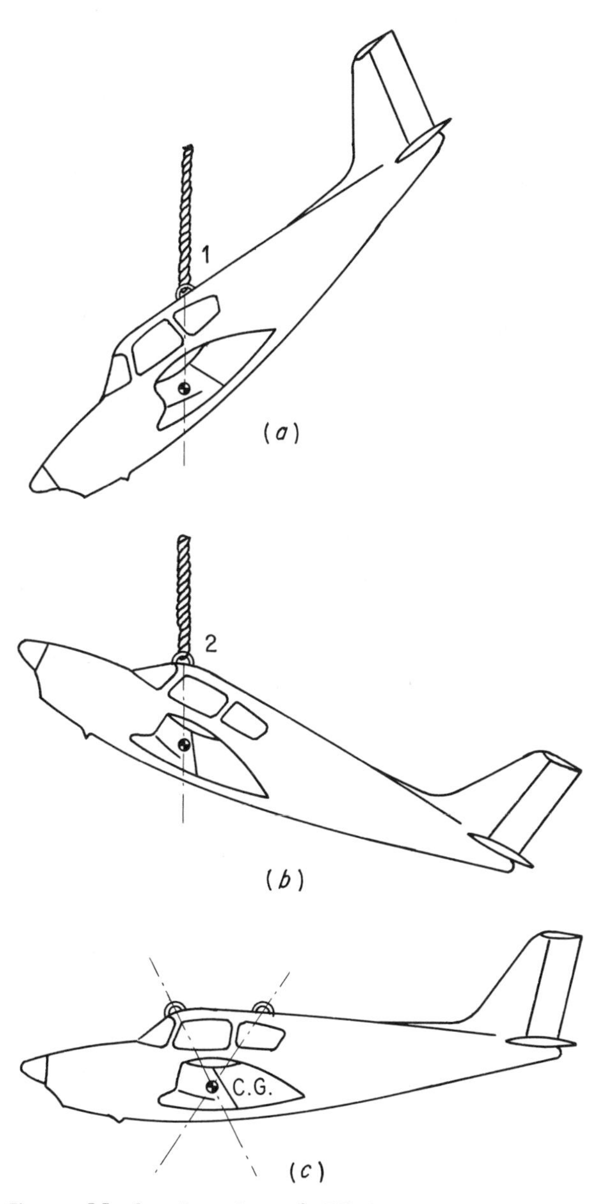

Figure 11 · 6 Location of CG in an airplane, trial method.

In the accompanying illustration, the fulcrum is marked *F*, the applied effort is *E*, and the resistance is *R*. If the resistance *R* equals 10 lb and it is 2 in. from the fulcrum *F*, and if the effort *E* is applied 10 in. from the fulcrum, it will be found that an effort of 2 lb will balance the resistance *R*. In other words, when a lever is balanced, the product of the effort and its lever arm (distance from the fulcrum) equals the product of the resistance and its lever arm.

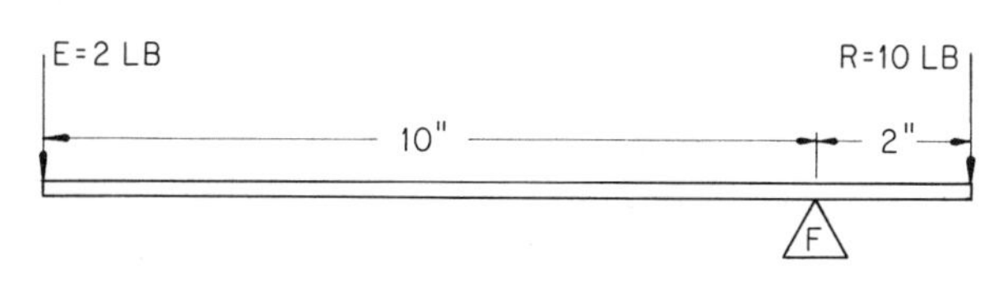

Figure 11 · 7 First-class lever.

The product of a force and its lever arm is called the **moment** of the force.

The general law of the lever is stated as follows: **If a lever is in balance, the sum of the moments tending to turn the lever in one direction about an axis equals the sum of the moments tending to turn it in the opposite direction.** Therefore, if the lever is in balance, and if several different efforts are applied to the lever, the sum of the moments of resistance will equal the sum of the moments of effort.

Moment of a force and equilibrium

The tendency of a force to produce rotation around a given axis is called the **moment of the force** with respect to that axis.

The amount and direction of the moment of a force depend upon the direction of the force and upon its distance from the axis. The perpendicular distance from the axis to the line of the force is called the **moment arm,** and the moment is measured by the product of the force and the moment arm. Thus, a force of 10 lb acting at a distance of 2 ft from the axis exerts a turning moment of 20 ft-lb.

In order to avoid confusion between moments tending to produce rotation in opposite directions, those tending to produce a clockwise rotation are called positive and those tending to produce counterclockwise rotation are called negative.

If the sum of the positive or clockwise moments equals the sum of the negative or counterclockwise moments, there will be no rotation. This is usually expressed in the form $\Sigma M = 0$. Σ is the Greek letter sigma, and ΣM means the sum of all the moments M, both positive and negative.

In the diagram of Fig. 11 · 8 is shown a moment diagram with moments about the point A. M_1 acts in a counterclockwise direction, with a force of 1 lb at a distance of 3 ft; hence the value of M_1 is -3 ft-lb. M_2 acts in a counterclockwise direction, with a force of 2 lb at a distance of 2 ft, thus producing a moment of -4 ft-lb. M_3 acting in a counterclockwise direction with a force of 1 lb at a distance of 1 ft produces a moment of -1 ft-lb. M_4 acts in a clockwise direction, with a force of 4 lb at 2 ft, which makes a moment of $+8$ ft-lb. $-3 - 4 - 1 + 8 = 0$.

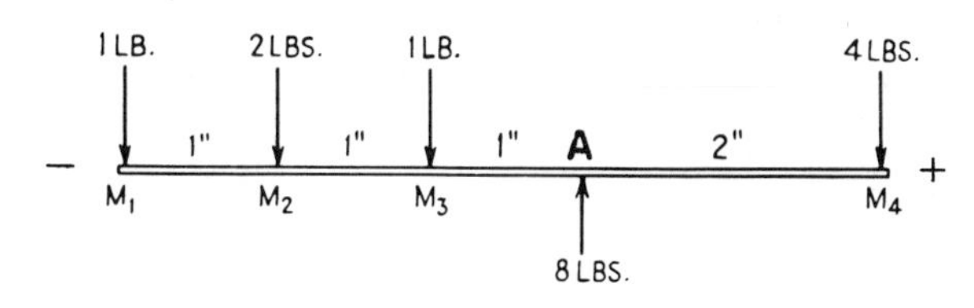

Figure 11 · 8 Moment diagram.

The sum of the negative moments is equal to the positive moment; hence there is a condition of **equilibrium** and there is no rotation about the point *A*.

There is a total force of 8 lb acting downward, and unless the axis is supported by an upward force of 8 lb, there will be downward movement but no rotation. The condition of complete equilibrium requires that there be no rotation and no translation (movement of the axis).

The purpose of this explanation is to show why an airplane must be designed, loaded, and operated with a constant regard for balance in order to permit it to fly safely with the minimum amount of energy required for propulsion and the minimum amount of energy expended by the pilot in the control of the airplane. When the necessary conditions of aircraft balance are not met, the pilot has difficulty in controlling the airplane even under normal flight operations. Under adverse conditions, improper balance can cause the airplane to crash.

BALANCE FOR AIRCRAFT AND MISSILES

Principles of balance

The fundamental theory of weight and balance is very simple. It is merely the principle of the first-class lever and is easily demonstrated by means of an old-fashioned steelyard scale shown in Fig. 11·9. The scale shown is in a state of equilibrium when it rests on the fulcrum in a horizontal position. The weight is directly dependent on its distance from the fulcrum, and for equilibrium the weight must be distributed so that the turning effect is the same on one side of the fulcrum as it is on the other. A heavy weight near the fulcrum has the same effect as a lighter weight farther from the fulcrum.

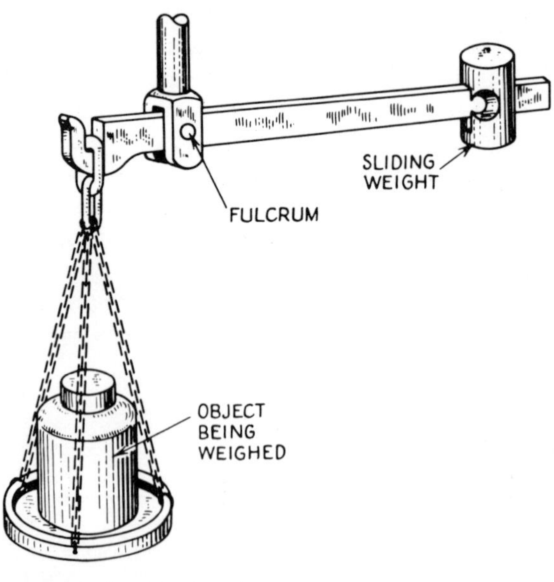

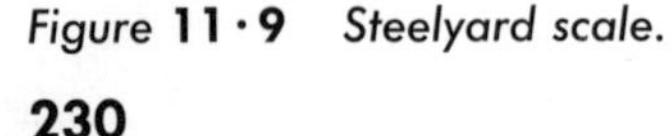
Figure 11·9 Steelyard scale.

Center-of-gravity range and limits

The steelyard scale is in balance only when the horizontal CG is at the fulcrum. However, an airplane can be balanced in flight anywhere within certain specified forward and aft limits if the pilot operates the trim tabs or elevators to exert an aerodynamic force sufficient to overcome any static unbalance. Center-of-gravity locations outside the specified limits will cause unsatisfactory or even dangerous flight characteristics. The allowable variation of CG location is called the **CG range** and is carefully determined by the engineers who design an airplane and by engineering flight tests. The CG range usually extends forward and rearward from a point about one-third the chord of the wing back of the leading edge, provided that the wing has no sweepback. The exact location is always shown in the aircraft specifications or the Type Certificate Data Sheet. Heavy loads near the wing location are balanced by much lighter loads at or near the nose or tail of the airplane. In the diagram of Fig. 11·10, a load of 5 lb at *A* will be balanced by a load of 1 lb at *B*. This is because the moments of the two loads are equal.

Since the CG limits constitute the range of movement that the airplane CG can have without making the airplane unstable or unsafe to fly, the CG of the loaded airplane must be within these limits at takeoff, in the air, and on landing. In some cases, the takeoff limits and landing limits are not exactly the same, and the differences are given in the specifications for the airplane.

Figure 11·11 shows typical limits for the CG

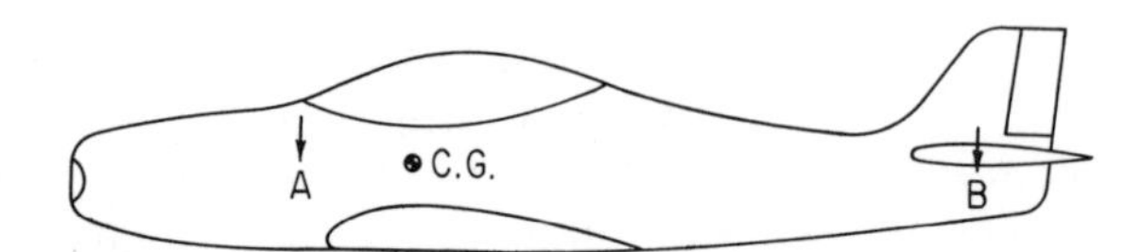

Figure 11·10 Balancing of load.

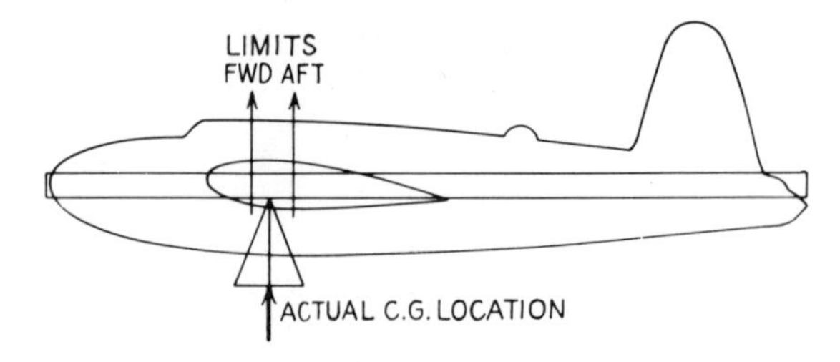

Figure 11·11 Center-of-gravity limits.

location in an airplane. As previously stated, these limits establish the **CG range.** The CG of the airplane must fall within this range if the airplane is to fly safely; that is, it must be to the rear of the forward limit and forward of the aft limit.

Center-of-gravity and balance in an airplane

The CG of an airplane may be defined, for the purpose of balance computations, as an imaginary point about which the nose-heavy (−) moments and tail-heavy (+) moments are exactly equal in magnitude. Thus, the aircraft, if suspended therefrom, would have no tendency to rotate in either direction (nose up or nose down). This condition is illustrated in Fig. 11·12. As stated previously, the weight of the aircraft can be assumed to be concentrated at its CG.

The CG with the useful load installed is allowed to range fore and aft within certain limits which are determined during the flight tests for type certification. These limits are the most forward- and rearward-loaded CG positions at which the aircraft will meet the performance and flight characteristics required by the FAA. These limits may be given in percentage of the mean aerodynamic chord (MAC) or in inches forward or to the rear of the **datum line.** The MAC is the chord of an imaginary airfoil used in aerodynamic computations for the particular airplane under consideration. Technicians, pilots, and maintenance engineers are seldom required actually to determine the MAC, since this is done by the aerodynamicist in the manufacturer's engineering section. The MAC is usually given when it will be required for weight and balance computations; hence the person working on the airplane is expected to have only a general understanding of its meaning. A more detailed discussion of MAC was given in the section on theory of flight.

The datum line

The **datum line,** or simply **datum,** is a plane or line in a plane used as a reference in order to show relative locations of objects. In computations for weight and balance the datum is vertical and is usually at the leading edge of a wing, at the firewall of a single-engine airplane, at the nose of the airplane, at a particular bulkhead, or at some other convenient point. To avoid confusion, the datum noted on the aircraft specifications should be used because all **moment arms** given in the specifications are referred to this line. When weight and balance records are prepared, the location of the datum line should be noted clearly in the record. A typical datum location for a light airplane is shown in Fig. 11·13.

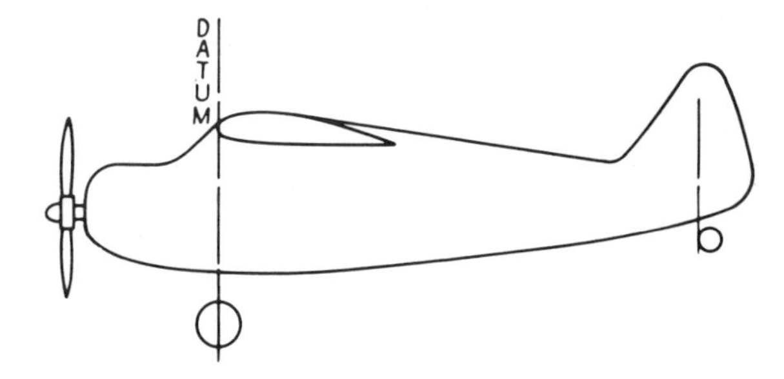

Figure 11·13 Location of typical datum line.

Datum at the nose

The datum line, also called the **reference datum,** is often located at the nose of an airplane because this simplifies computations. It has been pointed out that all clockwise moments are positive and counterclockwise moments are negative. If the datum is located at the nose of the airplane, all moments must be positive because all arms are measured to the rear of the datum and this direction has been given the positive sign. Remember that a tail-heavy moment is positive and a nose-heavy moment is negative. If the airplane were suspended at the nose, it is obvious that the tail would be downward; hence all moments are tail-heavy or positive.

It is very important to determine the exact location of the datum line before starting to solve a weight and balance problem. Figure 11·14 shows an airplane with the datum at the nose.

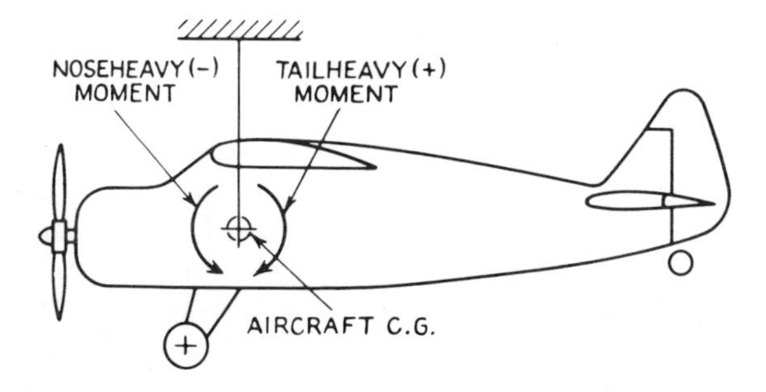

Figure 11·12 Airplane suspended from CG location.

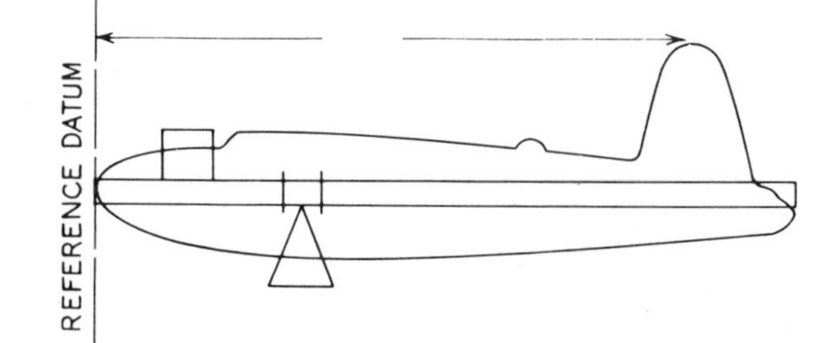

Figure 11·14 Datum line at the nose of an airplane.

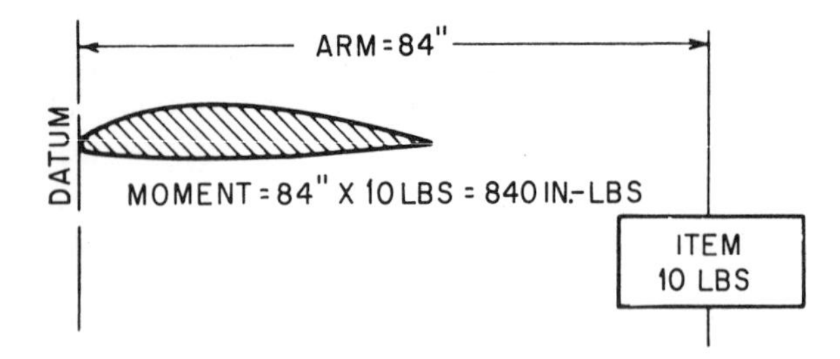

Figure **11 · 15** *Computation of moment.*

When working from this datum all moments are positive.

The moment arm

The **moment arm,** commonly called merely the **arm,** is the horizontal distance in inches to the CG of an item measured aft (plus) or forward (minus) of the datum. If the datum is at the nose of the airplane, all measurements are aft and therefore positive.

On current aircraft specifications the arm of a particular item in the airplane is given (in parenthesis) immediately following its name and weight. When the arm is not given, it must be determined by actual measurement.

Figure 11 · 15 illustrates a situation where the datum is at the leading edge of the wing. The arm in this case is 84 in. An item installed to the rear of the wing, at the end of the arm, weighs 10 lb. The measurement is to the rear of the datum; hence the arm is positive. Since the weight bears downward, it also is positive; hence the moment (arm times weight) is also positive and is equal to +840 in.-lb.

Moment

As previously shown, **moment** is the product of the **weight** and the **arm.** Thus, the moment of an item about the datum is obtained by multiplying the weight of the item by its horizontal distance from the datum.

Moment manifests itself as a tendency to cause rotation of the aircraft about its CG, and it is represented in illustrations by a circular arrow indicating the direction of the rotational tendency (see Fig. 11 · 16).

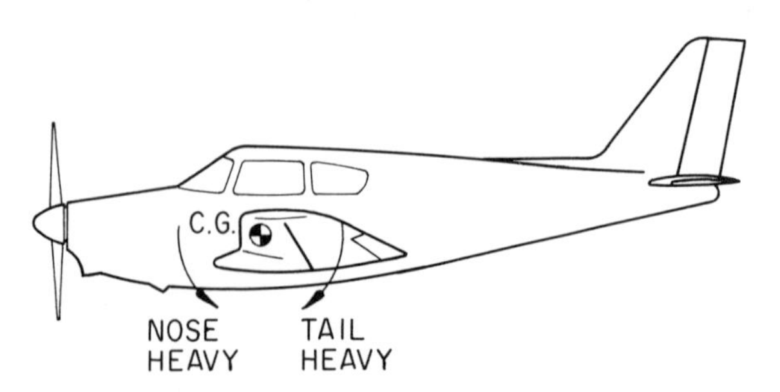

Figure **11 · 16** *Nose-heavy and tail-heavy moments in an airplane.*

To save work, especially with large airplanes, the moment may be divided by some constant, thereby reducing the number of digits with which it is necessary to work. For example, the moment is often divided by 1,000 to obtain an **index unit.** In using an index such as this, however, it is essential that the operator understand the nature of the index unit and make sure that he remembers its origin.

Requirement for weight and balance computation

It is essential that the weight and balance of an airplane or helicopter be kept within certain limits if the aircraft is to be flown safely. To make sure that the aircraft is in safe flying condition, weight and balance computations must be made whenever a repair, alteration, or change of equipment is performed which may affect the weight or balance of the aircraft appreciably. The weight of the aircraft must be such that when loaded it will not exceed the specified maximum, and the CG must remain within the specified limits.

The addition or removal of equipment will obviously affect the empty weight of the aircraft; hence the permissible load is also affected. Each change must therefore be investigated to make sure that the limits of the CG and maximum gross weight have not been exceeded.

Information on which to base the record of weight and balance changes to the aircraft can be obtained from the pertinent aircraft specification, the prescribed aircraft operating limitations, and the latest approved Form ACA337 (major repair and alteration form) which shows the aircraft empty weight and CG.

Weight and balance terminology

Before we can proceed with explanations of the methods for computing weight and balance problems, we must have a good understanding of the words and terms used.

empty weight: The empty weight of an aircraft includes the weight of the airframe, powerplant, required equipment, operating equipment which has a fixed location and is normally carried in the airplane, fuel drained (residual fuel remains in lines and carburetor), oil drained (residual oil remains in lines and in engine), fixed ballast, full engine coolant (for liquid-cooled engines), and any other parts or equipment which are required during flight and are installed in the airplane.

maximum weight: Maximum weight is the maximum authorized takeoff weight of the aircraft and its contents as listed in the pertinent specifications or the Type Certificate Data Sheet for the particular airplane under consideration.

useful load: Useful load is the empty weight subtracted from the maximum authorized takeoff weight for the aircraft. This load includes the pilot, crew if applicable, maximum oil, maximum fuel, passengers, and baggage and/or freight.

weight check: A weight check consists of checking the sum of the weights of all items of useful load against the allowable useful load (maximum weight less empty weight) of the aircraft.

datum: The datum is an imaginary vertical plane or line from which all horizontal measurements are taken for balance with the aircraft in level flight attitude.

arm or moment arm: The arm is the horizontal distance in inches from the datum to the center of gravity of an item. The algebraic sign is plus (+) if measured aft of the datum and minus (−) if measured forward of the datum.

moment: The moment is the product of a weight and its arm. The moment of an item about the datum is obtained by multiplying the weight of the item by its horizontal distance from the datum.

center of gravity: The center of gravity is a point about which the nose-heavy and tail-heavy moments are exactly equal in magnitude. If the airplane were suspended therefrom, it would have no tendency to pitch in either direction. The weight of an aircraft can be assumed to be concentrated at its CG.

empty-weight CG: The empty-weight CG (EWCG) is the center of gravity of an aircraft in its empty condition and is an essential part of the weight and balance record which must be kept with the aircraft file.

empty-weight CG range: The EWCG range is established so that when the EWCG falls within this range, the specification operating CG limits will not be exceeded under standard specification loading conditions. In cases where it is possible to load an airplane in a manner not covered in the aircraft specification or Type Certificate Data Sheet, complete calculations should be accomplished. The EWCG range shown for many light airplanes is listed in the aircraft specifications or Type Certificate Data Sheet to eliminate further calculations by the technician making equipment changes.

operating CG range: The operating CG range is the distance between the forward and rearward limits indicated on the pertinent specifications for the aircraft. These limits are determined as the most forward- and rearward-loaded CG positions at which the aircraft meets the operating requirements of the Civil Air Regulations.

mean aerodynamic chord: The MAC is the length of the mean chord of the wing as established through aerodynamic considerations. For weight and balance purposes it is used to locate the CG range of the aircraft. The location and dimension of the MAC, where used, will be found in the aircraft specification, the Type Certificate Data Sheet, the Flight Manual, or the Aircraft Weight and Balance Record.

weighing point: The weighing points of an airplane are those points by which the airplane is supported at the time it is weighed. Usually the main landing gear and the nose or tail wheel are the weighing points. Sometimes, however, an airplane may have jacking pads from which the weight is taken. In any event, it is essential to define the weighing points clearly in the weight and balance record.

minimum fuel: Minimum fuel for weight and balance purposes is 1/12 gal per maximum-except-takeoff (METO) horsepower and is the maximum amount of fuel which should be used in weight and balance computations when low fuel might adversely affect the most critical balance conditions. To determine the weight of minimum fuel in pounds, divide the METO horsepower by 2. Fuel weight is usually given as 6 lb per gal.

full oil: Full oil is the quantity of oil shown in the aircraft specifications or Type Certificate Data Sheet as the oil capacity for the aircraft under consideration. Full oil should always be used as the quantity of oil when the loaded weight and balance computations are made. Oil weight is usually given as 7.5 lb per gal.

tare: Tare is the weight of the equipment necessary for weighing the airplane (such as chocks, blocks, slings, jacks, etc.), which is included in the scale readings but is not a part of the actual weight of the airplane. Tare must be subtracted from the scale readings in order to obtain the actual weight of the airplane.

leveling means: Leveling means are the reference points used for leveling the aircraft. They may consist of lugs installed at two points on the fuselage so that a straightedge can be placed upon them with a level to provide longitudinal leveling and similar lugs placed athwartship for lateral leveling. Leveling means may also be a longitudinal member of the fuselage which is parallel to the line of flight and is designated for longitudinal leveling and a lateral member suitable for lateral leveling. Typical leveling means are given in a Type Certificate Data Sheet as follows:

Longitudinal: Lugs on left nose wheel door longeron, Sta. 61.5 and 72.5
Lateral: Lugs on rear face of Bulkhead Sta. 44.5 in nose wheel well

The station numbers shown in the foregoing specification indicate the number of inches to the rear of the datum. The datum for this particular airplane is 8 in. forward of the nose of the airplane.

DETERMINATION OF EMPTY-WEIGHT CENTER-OF-GRAVITY LOCATION

Weighing the aircraft

In order to obtain an accurate reading of the aircraft weight, the following procedures should be used:

1. The aircraft should be weighed inside a closed building to avoid errors which may be caused by wind.
2. The aircraft should be free from excessive dirt, grease, moisture, or any other extraneous material before weighing.
3. If the location of the EWCG is to be determined, the airplane should be leveled longitudinally and laterally in accordance with specifications.
4. The accuracy of the scales must be established. This can be done in accordance with instructions provided by the manufacturer of the scales or by testing the scales with calibrated weights. When there is nothing on the scales platform, the reading should be 0.
5. All items of equipment to be installed in the aircraft and included in the certificated empty weight should be in place for weighing. Each item must be in the location which it will occupy during flight as shown in the aircraft equipment list.
6. Unless otherwise noted in the aircraft specification, the oil system should be drained with all drain cocks open. Under these conditions, the amount of oil remaining in the oil tanks, lines, and engine is termed "residual oil," and it should be included in empty weight. It is permissible to weigh the airplane with full oil, but the weight of the oil must be subtracted from the total weight to obtain the empty weight of the aircraft. The moment of the oil must be taken into consideration when the CG location is computed.

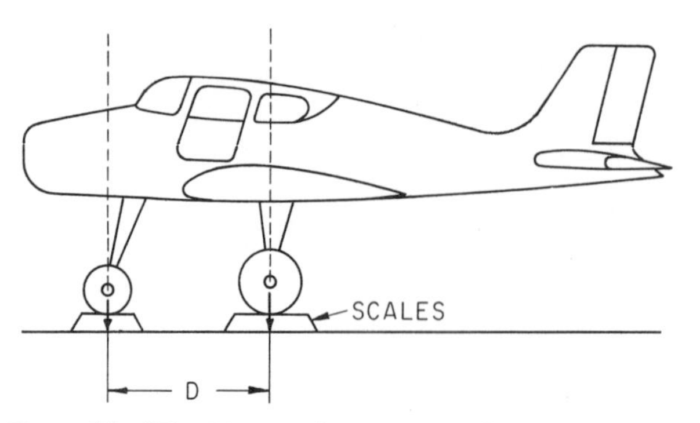

Figure 11 · 17 Distance between weighing points.

7. The fuel should be drained from the airplane unless other instructions are given in the specification. Fuel should be drained with the airplane in the level position to make sure that the tanks are as completely empty as possible. The amount of fuel remaining in the aircraft tanks, lines, and engine is termed "residual fuel," and its weight is included in the empty weight of the aircraft. In special cases the airplane may be weighed with full fuel in the tanks provided that a definite means is available for determining the exact weight of the fuel.
8. The weight of the tare should be recorded, either before or after weighing the airplane, and the tare weight should then be subtracted from the total weight as obtained from the scales.
9. When the airplane is in the level position, the exact horizontal distance between the supporting points must be recorded. This is accomplished as shown in Fig. 11 · 17. The airplane is leveled on the scales, and a mark is made on the floor at the end of the vertical line through the center of the axle of the airplane. The distance D is accurately measured and recorded for use in the weight and balance computation.
10. The weights of the right wheel, left wheel, and the nose or tail wheel must be recorded to provide information needed for the CG determination.

Computing CG location

The fundamental rule for determining the location of the CG for an airplane is: **Divide the total moment of the airplane (taken from a specific reference point) by the total weight of the airplane. The result will be the distance of the CG from the reference point.**

In Fig. 11 · 18 a tricycle-gear airplane is weighed and it is found that the nose-wheel weight is 320 lb, the right-wheel weight is 816 lb, and the left-

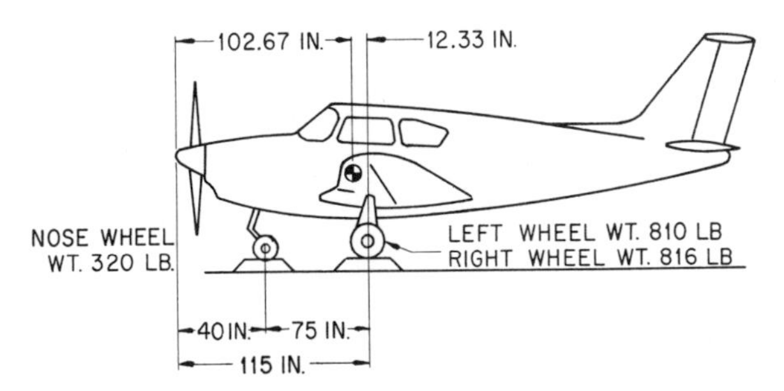

Figure **11·18** *Quantities required for determination of CG location.*

wheel weight is 810 lb. The horizontal distance between the weighing points is 75 in. These data give us all the information we need to find the location of the CG. When blocks are used on the scales, the weight of the blocks must be removed as "tare."

To simplify the computation we establish the center of the main wheels as the reference point from which to determine the moment. This provides a "zero" moment at the main wheels because the arm is zero. The moments and the CG location are then found as shown in Prob. 11·1.

In the foregoing problem it is important to note that we are working from the main-wheel center line (MWCL) as the reference point. Because the nose wheel is forward of the reference point, the arm is negative and the moment of the nose wheel is negative. The arm of the CG is negative because the CG is forward of the reference point (MWCL).

The CG location will always be the same no matter what reference point we use. To demonstrate that this is so, we shall rework the computation for the airplane in Fig. 11·18 and use the nose of the airplane as the reference point. The nose of the airplane is 40 in. forward of the nose-wheel center line and 115 in. forward of the MWCL. Since each weighing point now has an arm, there will also be a moment for each point. We proceed as shown in Prob. 11·2.

We see from the computation that the CG is 102.67 in. aft of the datum line (nose of airplane). This, of course, places it in the same position determined for the previous computation (102.67 + 12.33 = 115, which is the distance in inches from the datum line to the MWCL).

Problem 11·1

Item	*Weight*	×	*Arm*	=	*Moment*
Right wheel	816 lb		0		0
Left wheel	810 lb		0		0
Nose wheel	320 lb		−75		−24,000 in.-lb
	1,946 lb				−24,000 in.-lb

Then $\frac{-24,000}{1,946} = -12.33$ in. (CG dist. fwd of MWCL)

Problem 11·2

Item	*Weight*	×	*Arm*	=	*Moment*
Right wheel	816		+115		+ 93,840
Left wheel	810		+115		+ 93,150
Nose wheel	320		+ 40		+ 12,800
	1,946				+199,790

Then $\frac{+199,790}{1,946} = +102.67$ in.

Use of algebraic signs

In the discussion and examples thus far we have mentioned the use of positive and negative signs for arms and moments. Care must be taken to ensure that the proper sign is applied to each quantity expressed in a weight and balance computation.

The weight of an airplane is always positive (+). Also, the weight of any item **installed** in the airplane is positive. The weight of any item **removed** from the airplane is negative (−).

According to the standard rules of algebra, the product of two positive numbers is positive; the product of two negative numbers is positive; and the product of a positive number and a negative number is negative. This can also be stated: **The product of numbers with like signs is positive; the product of numbers with unlike signs is negative.**

When items of aircraft equipment are added or removed, four combinations are possible. These are as follows:

1. When items are added forward of the datum line, the signs are (+) weight × (−) arm = (−) moment.
2. When items are added to the rear of the datum line, the signs are (+) weight × (+) arm = (+) moment.
3. When items are removed forward of the datum line, the signs are (−) weight × (−) arm = (+) moment.
4. When items are removed to the rear of the datum line, the signs are (−) weight × (+) arm = (−) moment.

A simple diagram will aid in determining the effect of changes in aircraft equipment. In Fig. 11·19 a straight line represents the airplane. The nose of the airplane is shown to the left, this being the conventional method for representing aircraft

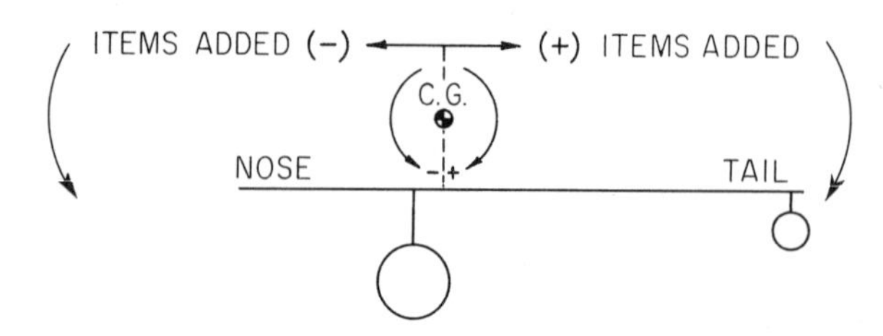

Figure **11 · 19** *Effects of weight changes in an airplane.*

in weight and balance diagrams. Using the CG location as a reference, we note that any item installed forward of the CG will produce a negative moment and will cause the CG to move forward. Items added to the rear of the CG produce a positive moment and move the CG rearward. Items removed in either case will have an effect opposite to that of items installed.

Observe that the curved arrows shown around the CG location indicate the effects of positive and negative moments. Positive moments are clockwise and cause a tail-heavy force, while negative moments are counterclockwise and cause a nose-heavy force.

Computing EWCG for a conventional airplane

Figure 11·20 shows a conventional airplane in position for weighing. We assume that we are weighing the airplane with 2 gal of oil still in the engine and the oil arm is given as −20 in the specification. As shown in the illustration the weights obtained from the scales are as follows: right wheel, 580 lb; left wheel, 585 lb; tail wheel, 130 lb (including tare).

The computation for the EWCG can be arranged as in Prob. 11·3.

Problem 11·3

Item	*Weight*	*Tare*	*Net weight* ×	*Arm* =	*Moment*
Right wheel	580	0	580	0	0
Left wheel	585	0	585	0	0
Tail wheel	130	20	110	+160	+17,600
			1,275		+17,600

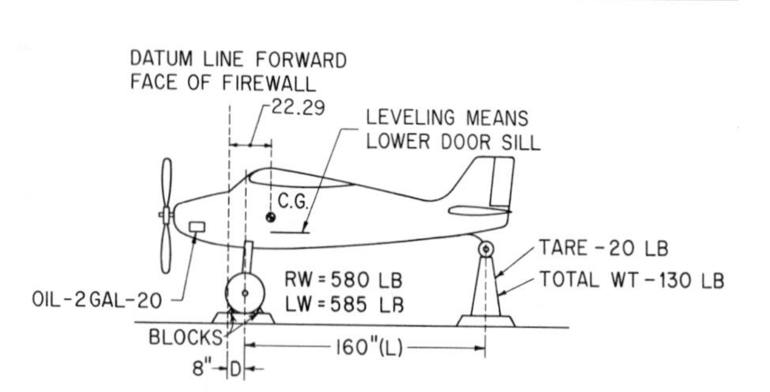

Figure **11 · 20** *Empty-weight CG computation for a conventional airplane.*

As explained previously the CG is equal to the total moment divided by the total weight. Therefore

$$\text{CG} = \frac{17{,}600}{1{,}275} = +13.8 \text{ in. (CG aft of MWCL)}$$

The result obtained in the computation is the CG location to the rear of the reference point, which is the center line of the main landing gear. To obtain the CG from the datum line, we must add the distance from the MWCL to the distance of the datum line from the MWCL. Then 13.8 + 8 = 21.8, which is the distance of the CG from the datum line.

We have not yet completed the EWCG computation, however, because the CG we have obtained includes the weight of the oil which was in the aircraft at the time it was weighed. We must therefore remove the oil by computation to obtain the EWCG (see Prob. 11·4).

Problem 11·4

Item	*Weight* ×	*Arm* =	*Moment*
Airplane	1,275	21.8	+27,795
Oil (removed)	− 15	−20	+ 300
	1,260		+28,095

$$\text{EWCG} = \frac{+28{,}095}{1{,}260} = +22.29 \text{ in. (EWCG location)}$$

EWCG formula

A standard formula is often used for the EWCG computation. This formula is illustrated and explained in Fig. 11·21 taken from Civil Aeronautics Manual 18. In the first diagram the datum is at the nose of the airplane, and since the airplane is of the tricycle-gear type, the CG must be forward of the MWCL. The part of the formula FL/W gives the distance of the CG forward of the MWCL. This distance must then be subtracted from the distance D to find the distance of the CG from the datum.

In the second diagram the airplane is of conventional tail-wheel type, so the CG must be to the rear of the MWCL. With the datum at the nose of the airplane it is necessary to *add* the datum line distance D to the RL/W distance to find the EWCG from the datum line.

In the third diagram, the CG and the MWCL are both forward of the datum line; hence both distances are negative. For this reason the CG distance from the MWCL and the datum dis-

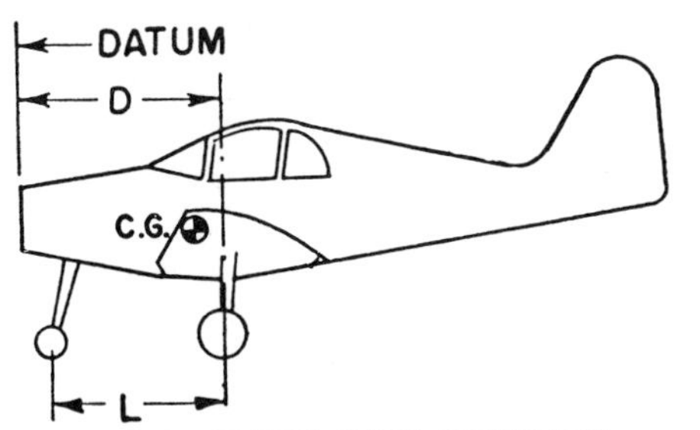

NOSE WHEEL TYPE AIRCRAFT

DATUM LOCATED FORWARD OF THE MAIN WHEELS

$$C.G. = D - \left(\frac{F \times L}{W}\right)$$

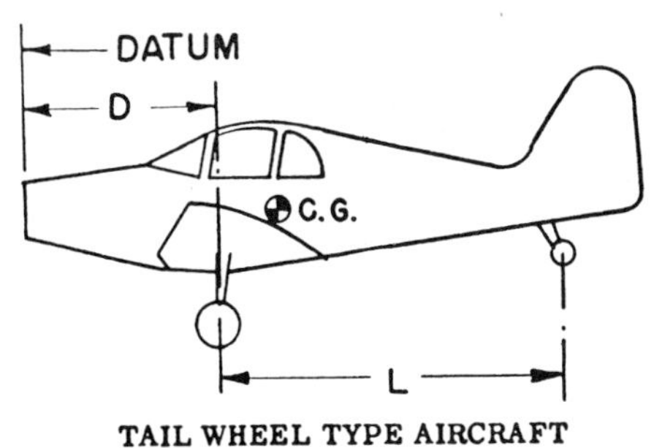

TAIL WHEEL TYPE AIRCRAFT

DATUM LOCATED FORWARD OF THE MAIN WHEELS

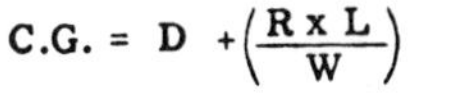

$$C.G. = D + \left(\frac{R \times L}{W}\right)$$

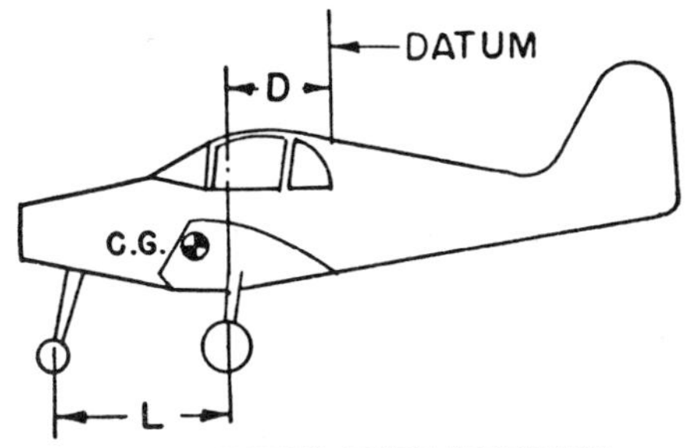

NOSE WHEEL TYPE AIRCRAFT

DATUM LOCATED AFT OF THE MAIN WHEELS

$$C.G. = -\left(D + \frac{F \times L}{W}\right)$$

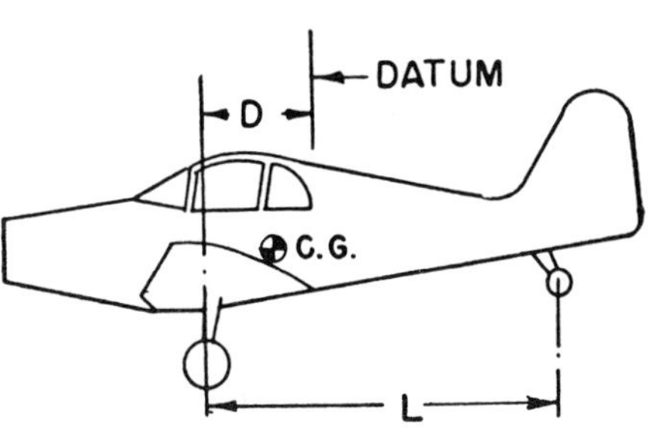

TAIL WHEEL TYPE AIRCRAFT

DATUM LOCATED AFT OF THE MAIN WHEELS

$$C.G. = -D + \left(\frac{R \times L}{W}\right)$$

CG = distance from datum to CG of aircraft
W = weight of aircraft at time of weighing
D = horizontal distance measured from datum to main-wheel weighing point
L = horizontal distance measured from main-wheel weighing point to the nose or tail weighing point
F = weight at nose weighing point
R = weight at tail weighing point

Figure **11·21** *Different arrangements of the formula for EWCG.*

tance from the MWCL are added together and the total is given a negative sign.

The fourth diagram shows a condition where the CG is positive from the MWCL but negative from the datum line. The datum to the MWCL is a negative distance, and the CG from the MWCL is a positive distance. Therefore the EWCG from the datum line will be the difference of the two distances and in this case will carry a negative sign.

Referring back to Fig. 11·20 and disregarding the oil computation, we may solve the problem with the following formula:

$$CG = D + \frac{RL}{W} = 8 + \frac{110 \times 160}{1{,}260}$$
$$= 8 + 13.97 = +21.97 \text{ in.}$$

It will be noted that this answer is slightly less than the original computation, but this is because we did not concern ourselves with the moment of the oil.

For any computation, it is always a good practice to draw a diagram of the airplane (nose to the left) with the weighing points and the datum, and from these it is easy to determine what formula should be used. If the technician has a clear understanding of the principles of weight and balance, he needs no formula but can determine the EWCG as we did in the earlier examples.

LOADING THE AIRPLANE

Extreme forward condition

We have previously explained that every aircraft has an approved CG range within which the CG must lie if the aircraft is to be operated safely. In order to determine whether the loaded CG falls within the approved limits, it is necessary that two computations be made, one for **most forward loading** and one for **most rearward loading.**

To determine the conditions for most forward loading we must examine the aircraft specification or Type Certificate Data Sheet to determine fuel capacity and arm, oil capacity and arm, passengers and arm, and cargo (baggage) and arm. From these we must determine which items will tend to move the CG forward and include maximum quantities of these items in our computation. Since some items may have to be included which tend to move the CG rearward, we must use a minimum of such items.

In examining a Type Certificate Data Sheet for a certain airplane we find that the following specifications are given for weight and balance:

CG range	(+85.1) to (+95.9) at 1,710 lb
	(+87.0) to (+95.9) at 1,900 lb
	(+91.5) to (+95.9) at 2,200 lb
Datum	78.4 in. forward of wing leading edge
Leveling	Two screws left side fuselage below window
Max. weight	2,200 lb
No. of seats	4 (2 at +85.5, 2 at +118)
Max. cargo	100 lb (+142.8)
Fuel capacity	50 gal (+94)
Oil capacity	2 gal (+31.7)

For the CG range we can prepare a chart such as that shown in Fig. 11·22. It will be noted that the values given on the chart agree with the specifications listed.

Assuming that the empty weight of the airplane is 1,075 lb and the EWCG is +84, we can load the airplane to determine whether the forward CG is within limits with maximum forward loading. Remember that we must include only necessary load and load which will tend to move the CG forward.

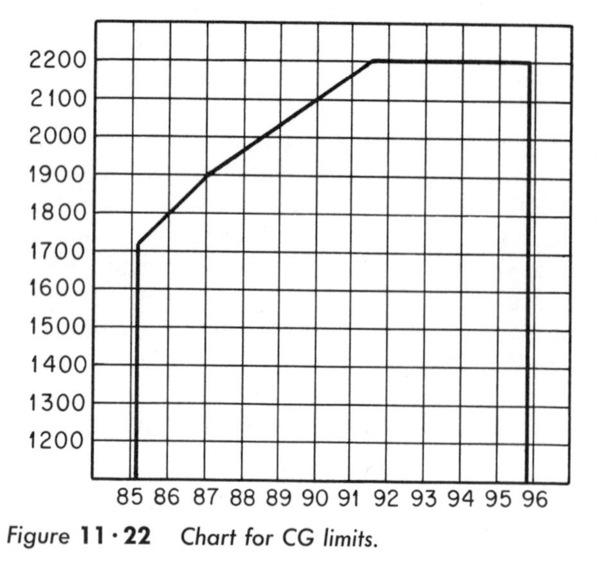

Figure **11·22** *Chart for CG limits.*

The airplane must have a pilot, so we shall load 170 lb at +85.5.

Since the fuel is at +94, which is substantially to the rear of the forward limit, we shall load only minimum fuel. METO (maximum-except-takeoff) power is 150 hp, so 75 lb minimum fuel is required. This we shall load at +94.

The cargo compartment is at +142.8, and any load at this point will move the CG to the rear, so we shall load no cargo.

Full oil is required for the engine, so we must load 15 lb (7.5 lb per gal) of oil at 31.7.

The loading chart will then appear as in Prob. 11·5.

Problem 11·5

Item	*Weight*	×	*Arm*	=	*Moment*
Airplane (empty)	1,075		+84		+90,300
Pilot	170		+85.5		14,535
Fuel	75		+94		7,050
Oil	15		+31.7		475.5
	1,335				112,360.5

Then $\frac{112{,}360.5}{1{,}335} = 84.16$ in. (most forward CG)

Checking the result of the foregoing computation against the CG limits for the airplane, we find that the CG is 0.94 in. forward of the forward CG limit. To correct this condition, the airplane must carry ballast or a certain amount of baggage in the cargo compartment at times when a forward loading could exist or a warning placard must be placed on the panel. The amount of the ballast is easily computed, and the method will be explained later in this chapter.

When making a check of forward CG limit, it must be remembered that we employ maximum weights for all items forward of the forward CG limit and minimum weights for all items to the rear of the forward CG limit. In the foregoing problem all items except the oil are located to the rear of the forward limit; hence minimums were used. Information required for a forward CG check is as follows:

1. Weight, arm, and moment of the empty aircraft
2. Maximum weights, arms, and moments of all items of useful load located ahead of the forward CG limit

3. Minimum weights, arms, and moments of all items of useful load located to the rear of the forward CG limit

Extreme rearward condition

To check an airplane for rearward CG limit, we must use a maximum of all weights to the rear of the CG limit and a minimum of all weights forward of the rearward CG limit. Using the specifications for the same airplane as under consideration in the previous problem, we find that the cargo compartment and the two rear seats are the only items with locations to the rear of the rearward CG limit. The problem is then arranged as in Prob. 11·6.

Problem 11·6

Item	*Weight*	× *Arm*	= *Moment*
Airplane (empty)	1,075	+ 84	+ 90,300
Pilot	170	+ 85.5	+ 14,535
Passengers (2)	340	+118	+ 40,120
Fuel	75	+ 94	+ 7,050
Oil	15	+ 31.7	+ 475.5
Baggage	100	+142.8	+ 14,280
	1,775		+166,760.5

Then $\frac{166{,}760.5}{1{,}775} = 93.9$ in. (rearward CG)

It may be noted that we could have made the CG move slightly more toward the rear by including maximum fuel, since the arm of the fuel is +94. This location is still forward of the rear limit, however, so it could not have moved the CG beyond its rearward limit.

Information required for a rearward CG check is as follows:

1. Weight, arm, and moment of the empty aircraft
2. Maximum weights, arms, and moments of all items of useful load located to the rear of the rearward CG limit
3. Minimum weights, arms, and moments of all items of useful load located forward of the rearward CG limit

Correcting the CG location

In the computation for the forward CG limit of the airplane in the previous problem, it was found that the CG was 0.94 in. forward of the forward CG limit. It is therefore necessary that we find a means for correcting this condition. To start this computation we use the forward CG limit (85.1 in.) as the reference point.

We can correct the CG by adding fixed ballast at a point in the rear of the airplane near the tail, or we can install fixed ballast in the cargo compartment. We can also placard the cargo compartment to the effect that a minimum amount of baggage must be carried under certain conditions. For the purpose of this computation we shall assume that we install fixed ballast in the cargo compartment.

The cargo compartment has an arm of +142.8. Since we are now using the forward CG limit as the reference, we must subtract 85.1 from 142.8 to find the arm of the cargo compartment for this computation. In the diagram of Fig. 11·23 we can see that the arm of the cargo compartment from the new reference point is 57.7 in.

The first step necessary in the computation for the correction of CG location is to determine what moment is necessary to provide the required correction. Since the CG is 0.94 in. forward of the forward limit, the moment necessary for correction is 0.94 × 1,335 (the weight of the forward-loaded airplane). The product is 1,254.9 in.-lb, the required moment.

To determine the weight necessary to provide a moment of 1,254.9 in.-lb with an arm of 57.7 (the arm of the cargo compartment from the forward CG limit), we must divide 1,254.9 by 57.7. The result of this division is 21.7 lb, which is the weight required in the cargo compartment to correct the CG location. We can verify this by working the original computation with 22 lb installed in the cargo compartment (see Prob. 11·7).

Problem 11·7

Item	*Weight*	× *Arm*	= *Moment*
Aircraft (as loaded)	1,335	+ 84.16	+112,360.5
Ballast	22	+142.8	+ 3,141.6
	1,357		+115,502.1

Then $\frac{115{,}502.1}{1{,}357} = 85.1$ in. (forward CG limit)

If the ballast in the foregoing problem had been installed near the tail of the airplane, the weight required would have been less. The requirement was to produce a certain moment (1,254.9 in.-lb),

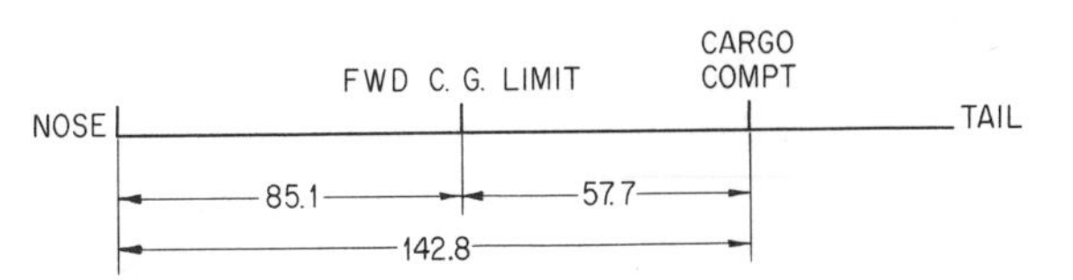

Figure **11·23** *Diagram to show correction computation for forward CG limit.*

and this could have been done by any combination of weight and arm that would produce this moment. Note that the moment was computed from the forward CG limit (85.1). However, after the weight was added to the airplane, we used the original moment of the airplane and cargo compartment.

Baggage reduction

When it is found that the rear CG limit is exceeded, it is often convenient to reduce the baggage for conditions when the airplane loading is to the rear extreme. If the baggage compartment is at +150, a reduction of 20 lb in baggage capacity will provide a negative moment of 3,000 in.-lb. The actual amount of baggage reduction, of course, will depend upon the moment necessary for correction.

ADDING AND REMOVING EQUIPMENT

During the lifetime of many airplanes it is often found desirable to change the type of equipment which is installed. The owner of an airplane may wish to install radio navigation equipment, an autopilot, an auxiliary fuel tank, or various other items to make his airplane more serviceable. In every case of such a change it is necessary to figure the effect on weight and balance. If the change in equipment should move the CG outside the limits, flight in the airplane would not be safe or legal.

Adding equipment

Let us assume that an owner has an airplane with an empty weight of 1,220 lb and an EWCG at +25. He wishes to install some radio equipment weighing 15 lb. In addition to the radio equipment he must install a larger generator in order to provide the additional power required to operate the radio.

The first consideration, of course, is to determine where the items of equipment are to be installed. He then must determine the arm of each item of equipment, and this arm must be measured from the airplane datum line to the CG of the equipment to be installed. It must be pointed out that, if the CG of the item of equipment is not given in the accompanying instructions, the CG must be determined by the person making the installation. This is easily done by balancing the item of equipment at a single point in the position it will assume in the airplane. The balance point should then be marked or recorded for use in the computation.

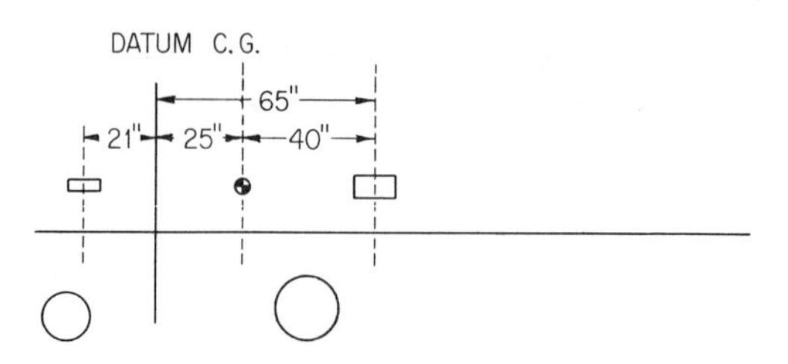

Figure **11 · 24** *Installation of equipment.*

For the purposes of the problem under consideration we shall assume that the radio is installed at +65 and the new generator is installed at −21. These points are shown in the diagram of Fig. 11·24.

In order to install a new generator, the old generator must be removed. The weight and arm of the old generator are given in the aircraft specification as 11 lb (−21.5). The new generator weighs 14 lb, and the arm is found to be −21.

We now have sufficient information to make the computation. We arrange the work as shown in Prob. 11·8.

Problem 11·8

Item	*Weight*	× *Arm*	=	*Moment*
Airplane (empty)	1,220	+25		+30,500
Radio	15	+65	+	975
Generator (removed)	− 11	−21.5	+	236.5
Generator (installed)	+ 14	−21	−	294
New empty weight	1,238			+31,417.5

$$\frac{31{,}417.5}{1{,}238} = +25.38, \text{ the new CG (empty)}$$

From the computation we find that the EWCG of the airplane has moved rearward 0.38 in. as a result of the new installation.

In some aircraft specifications for light airplanes an EWCG range is given, and if the EWCG of the airplane falls within this range, the loaded CG will also be within limits. In many cases, however, there is a wide variation of loaded conditions and an EWCG range becomes useless and will not be found in the specifications.

Removing equipment

In removing equipment from an airplane it is just as necessary to make weight and balance computations as when installing equipment.

Let us assume that the owner of an airplane wishes to remove flares because he finds that they are no longer necessary or required for the type of operation for which he is using the airplane. The airplane weighs 1,300 lb empty (with the flares), and the flares weigh 18 lb. The CG of the airplane as equipped is +78 and the arm of the flares is +145 (see Prob. 11·9).

Problem 11·9

Item	*Weight*	× *Arm*	= *Moment*
Airplane (empty)	1,300	+ 78	+101,400
Flares (removed)	− 18	+145	− 2,610
New empty weight	+1,282		+ 98,790

$$\frac{98{,}790}{1{,}282} = +77.06 \text{ in. (new EWCG)}$$

We observe from the foregoing computation that the removal of the flares caused the EWCG to move forward almost 1 in. It should be remembered that any removal of weight aft of the CG will cause the CG to move forward.

It is often necessary to compensate for changes in equipment by adding or removing ballast, changing the baggage weight allowance, or some other means. If the airplane in the foregoing problem was critical for forward loading before the flares were removed, it would be necessary to correct for the change in CG caused by the removal of the flares. This could be accomplished by installing ballast at a point near the tail of the airplane.

Let us assume that there is a strong structure at +268 near the tail of the airplane where ballast could be installed and that the forward-loaded CG limit is +69. In order to correct for the condition at the forward limit, we use the forward limit (+69) as the reference line for computing the correction (see Fig. 11·25).

$$\text{Distance from forward CG limit to flares} = 145 - 69 = +76$$

$$\text{Moment of removed flares} = -18 \times +76 = -1{,}368$$

$$\text{Distance from forward CG limit to ballast} = 268 - 69 = +199$$

$$\text{Ballast to be installed} = \frac{1{,}368}{199} = 6.87 \text{ lb.}$$

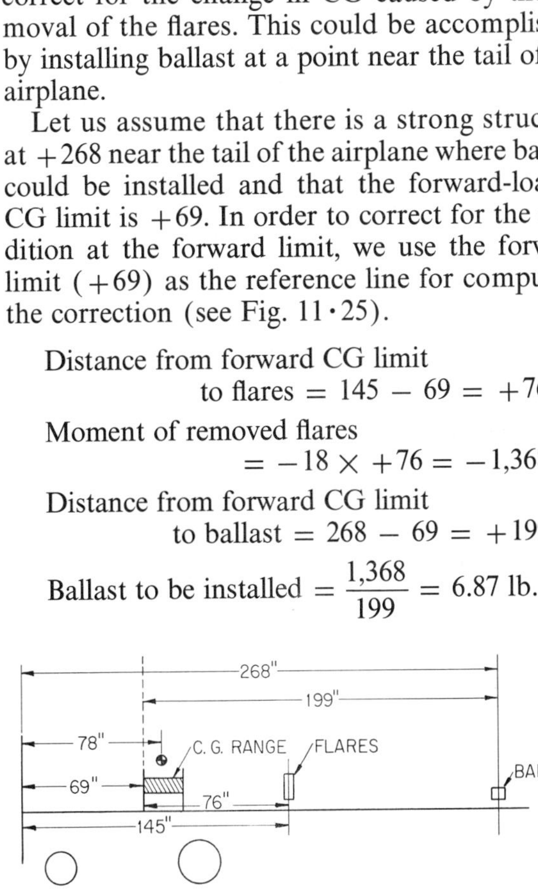

Figure **11·25** *Removal of equipment and correction for CG change.*

This shows that it will require 6.87 lb at +268 to overcome the effect of removing 18 lb at +145. If this amount of ballast is included in the original computation, it will be found that the EWCG is slightly rearward of +78. However, this is satisfactory because the CG will not move forward of the forward CG limit. In practice a weight of 7 lb would probably be installed, and this would assure that sufficient correction had been made.

SIMPLIFIED LOADING METHODS

Center-of-gravity envelope and loading chart

Because of the many possible loading combinations, especially in airplanes where more than two passengers can be carried, methods have been developed whereby the pilot can quickly determine whether the airplane is loaded within limits without going through a long process of computation. One of these methods involves the use of the **CG envelope** and the **loading chart.**

The CG envelope chart is a graph with airplane weight plotted against index units. The index unit is the moment of the airplane divided by 1,000. The envelope is an area on the graph establishing the combinations of weight and index units where the CG of the airplane will be within limits. A typical CG envelope is shown in Fig. 11·26. In this chart it can be seen that there is a satisfactory range of moments for each weight of the airplane. For example, if the airplane is loaded to weigh 1,650 lb, the moment can be from 60,000 to about 76,500 in.-lb or the index units can be from 60 to 76.5. The maximum loaded weight of the airplane is 2,200 lb, and the maximum index number is about 102. If we divide 2,200 into 120 × 1,000, we obtain the rearward CG limit. This limit is established by the line *AB* in the illustration.

In order to make the CG envelope simple to use, the **loading graph** is provided. This graph, illustrated in Fig. 11·27, provides for the loading of passengers, fuel, and baggage. Since passengers are loaded at two separate arms, there are two reference lines for passengers. The chart shown is designed for loading the Cessna 170 airplane. The graph plots load weight against index units. If we wish to determine the moment of any loaded item, we merely follow the weight line to the right until we intersect the position line for the item, then drop straight down to the base line and read the index unit. The index unit multiplied by 1,000 is the moment.

To use the loading graph we proceed as in Prob. 11·10.

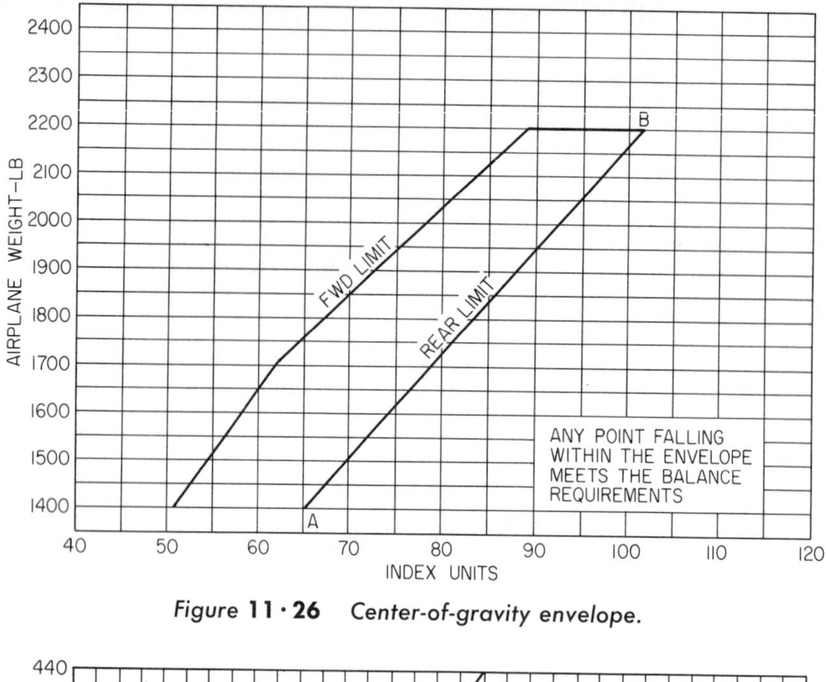

Figure **11 · 26** *Center-of-gravity envelope.*

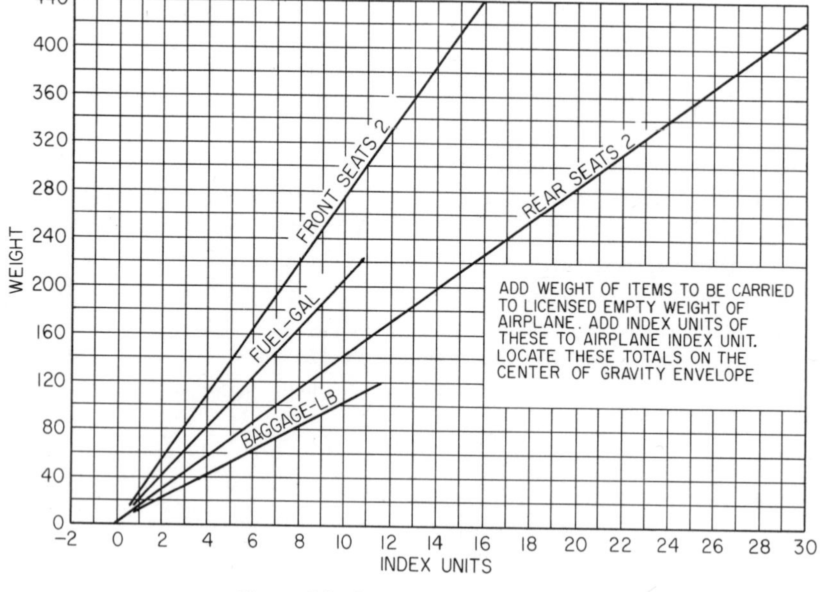

Figure **11 · 27** *Loading graph.*

Problem 11 · 10

Item	*Weight, lb*	*Index units*
Airplane empty weight	1,210	+ 47.1
Oil	15	− 0.3
Pilot and passenger	340	+ 12.2
Passengers (2)	340	+ 23.8
Fuel (maximum), 37 gal	222	+ 10.7
Baggage	70	+ 6.7
	2,197	+100.2

We then apply the weight and index number to the CG envelope of Fig. 11 · 26 and find that the point is within the envelope.

If we wish to operate the airplane with only a pilot, one passenger, and no baggage, the result will be as shown in Prob. 11 · 11.

When these figures are applied to the CG envelope, we find that the CG is still well within limits even though it has moved forward.

When computing the CG or loading for a particular airplane, the technician should consult the approved manual prepared for the airplane by the manufacturer. The basic CG location may be given with this manual, and the method for computing the weight and balance is explained. The charts and graphs used for the airplane CG are also included in the manual.

For large airliners, rather complex loading charts are prepared. In use, however, these charts greatly simplify the loading process. The charts

Problem 11·11

Item	Weight, lb	Index units
Airplane empty weight	1,210	+47.1
Oil	15	− 0.3
Pilot and passenger	340	+12.2
Fuel	222	+10.7
	1,787	+69.7

give the moment arms of the various compartments and fuel tanks and provide an easy method for determining the index of the load in any particular area. The indexes are combined by one of two or three methods, and the CG location found on the chart. In some cases a special slide rule ("slip stick") is designed to add or subtract moments as the airplane is loaded, thus providing a quick method for computation. This special slide rule is called a "load adjuster" and operates on the principle of index units.

REVIEW QUESTIONS

1. List some of the dangers which may exist as a result of overloading an airplane.
2. What undesirable conditions may exist when an airplane is loaded with too much weight forward or to the rear.
3. Define *center of gravity.*
4. Explain *arm* and *moment.*
5. What are the conditions existing when a lever is in balance?
6. If the wings of an airplane have no sweepback, at approximately what point should the CG be with respect to the chord of the wing?
7. What is the purpose of the *datum line?*
8. Define *empty weight* of an aircraft as employed for weight and balance purposes.
9. How is the *useful load* of an airplane determined?
10. Explain the importance of the *EWCG range.*
11. Under what conditions must the MAC of an airplane be taken into consideration in establishing the correct CG location?
12. What is meant by *tare?*
13. How would you determine the *leveling means* for a particular airplane?
14. List the steps necessary for weighing an airplane.
15. In preparing to determine the CG location for a certain light airplane, the following conditions were found:

Right-wheel weight	875 lb
Left-wheel weight	880 lb
Tail-wheel weight	120 lb
Distance, MWCL to TWCL	200 in.
Distance, datum line forward of MWCL	30 in.

Find the CG location relative to the MWCL.
Find the CG location relative to the datum line.

16. Determine the CG location relative to the datum line for a tricycle-gear airplane when the conditions are as follows:

Right-wheel weight	1,200 lb
Left-wheel weight	1,190 lb
Nose-wheel weight	400 lb
Distance of MWCL to nose-wheel CL	85 in.
Distance of datum line forward of MWCL	40 in.

17. Compute the most forward loading conditions for an airplane with the following specifications:

Empty weight	1,200 lb
EWCG	+11.0 in.
CG limits	+9.0 to +17.0
Seats	2 at +16 and 2 at +50
Max. cargo (baggage)	120 lb at +75
Fuel	40 gal at +18
Oil	2 gal at −30
METO hp	160

18. Compute the most rearward loading conditions for the airplane in the previous problem.
19. What correction can be made when an airplane CG is outside the approved limit?
20. The EWCG of an airplane is +25.00, and the empty weight is 1,100 lb. When a 15-lb generator is installed at −21 and a 12-lb battery is installed at −40, what is the new CG location?

CHAPTER 12

Pressure Instruments

INTRODUCTION

Since the beginning of powered flight, the need for instruments of various types has increased continuously until at the present time a very large number of instruments are required in modern aircraft. Instruments on an airplane may be classified according to function in three principal categories. These are (1) the powerplant instruments, (2) the flight and navigational instruments, and (3) the systems instruments. The powerplant instruments provide information concerning the operation of the engines and the powerplant systems. The flight and navigational instruments give the pilot information concerning flight speed, altitude, airplane attitude, heading, rate of ascent or descent, and other indications pertaining to the airplane and its flight path. The systems instruments provide information concerning the hydraulic system and its pressures, the air-conditioning system, the electrical system, and other special systems which may be installed in the airplane.

In the early days of flying the pilot could tell approximately how high he was flying by looking at the horizon or the ground or by comparing the airplane height with the height of other objects, such as mountains, trees, buildings, etc. He could do this because he was unable to get very far off the ground. When airplanes began flying at higher altitudes, in overcast weather, and at greater distances from the home airport, the need for instruments increased. The pilot needed to know exactly how high he was, how fast his airplane was traveling, in what direction the airplane was headed, how fast he was climbing or descending, the attitude of the airplane, how the engine was performing, and numerous other factors. These demands have led to the development of instruments, the prime requisites of which have been sensitivity and dependability plus lightweight construction. The aircraft instruments of today are masterpieces of the designer's art. Even with the extreme conditions of pressure, temperature, velocity, and altitude, modern aircraft instruments continue to function accurately and dependably.

There are two particularly important reasons why the principles of operation and the art of interpreting the readings of instruments used in modern aircraft should be thoroughly understood by the maintenance technician. First, the safety of the airplane, the crew, and the passengers depends on the proper installation and correct operation of the instruments. The powerplant instruments can forewarn the pilot or flight engineer of impending engine failure, and the flight instruments indicate any irregularity of flight attitude or direction. It is the duty of the maintenance technician to check the instruments regularly.

A second reason why the technician must understand the operating principles of instruments is that they provide many indications of impending powerplant or system failure. Just as the physician diagnoses an illness by means of instruments, the maintenance technician can diagnose possible troubles in an aircraft powerplant or system by an understanding of instrument indications. Through a complete analysis of instrument readings which were recorded during flight, the technician can determine what units or systems are not functioning correctly. When a pilot returns from a flight and reports engine trouble, it is the duty of the maintenance technician to determine the cause of the trouble. He can eliminate several possible causes by determining such factors as the altitude at which the airplane had been flying, the temperature of the powerplant concerned, the rpm and the manifold pressure of the powerplant, and the recorded fuel and oil pressure. From his understanding of the instruments and their function, the technician can often determine where the trouble lies. Instruments are useful for troubleshooting regardless of whether the airplane concerned is a small private airplane or a large jet airliner. It is therefore the responsibility of the technician to ensure as far as humanly possible continuous and accurate operation of all instruments.

Instruments are classified according to the means by which they give their indication. In this type of classification we find four main categories: (1) pressure-type instruments, (2) mechanical instruments, (3) gyro instruments, and (4) electrical and electronic instruments. It is our purpose in this chapter to consider the operation of the pressure-type instruments.

BOURDON-TUBE INSTRUMENTS

Bourdon-tube mechanism

Instruments which measure pressures in relatively high-pressure fluid systems are usually operated through the medium of a bourdon tube. Among the indications requiring this type of instrument are hydraulic pressure, engine-oil pressure, oxygen pressure, and any other indication of comparatively high pressures. The bourdon tube is constructed of metal and is oval or flattened in cross-sectional shape, with the tube itself formed into a crescent or part circle. Figure 12 · 1 is a drawing indicating the general construction of a bourdon tube. One of the ends of the tube is open, and the other end is closed. The open end is attached to a casting which is anchored to the case of the instrument, thus making the open end of the tube stationary. The closed end of the tube is free to move and is attached to a series of linkages such as levers and gears. When fluid under pressure enters the open end of the bourdon tube, it causes a pressure against the closed end, and this tends to straighten the tube. The principle involved here is well illustrated by the familiar party novelty—the rolled-up paper

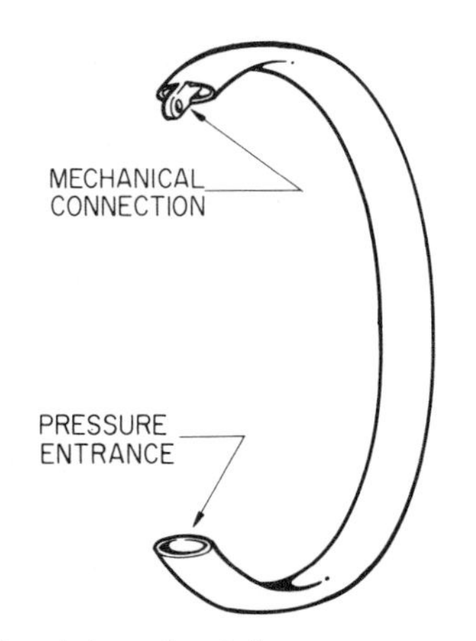

Figure **12 · 1** *A bourdon tube.*

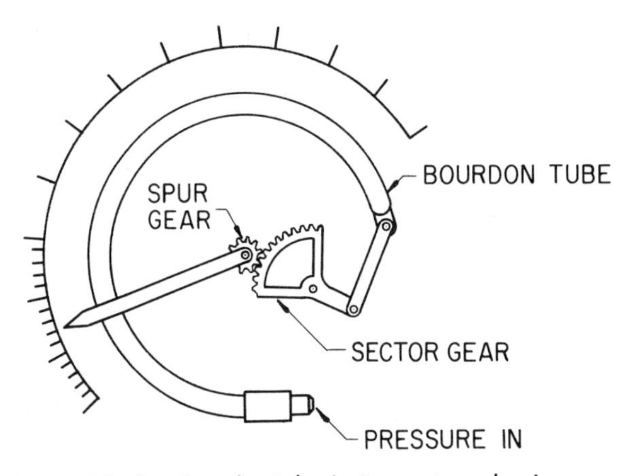

Figure **12 · 2** *Bourdon-tube instrument mechanism.*

tube which uncoils when you blow into it. The pressure on the closed end of the paper causes it to uncoil, and the springs inside cause it to coil up again when the pressure is released. The bourdon tube is constructed of a metal such as spring-tempered brass, bronze, or beryllium copper. These metals have a strong spring effect which causes the bourdon tube to return to its original position when pressure is released.

In Fig. 12 · 2 a simplified diagram of a bourdon-tube instrument mechanism is shown. When pressure enters the bourdon tube, the tube tends to straighten out, and as it does so, it moves the linkage connected to the sector gear. The movement of the sector gear causes the spur gear to rotate, and this in turn moves the indicating needle along the scale to give a reading of the pressure. The indicating needle is mounted on the hand staff, which is rotated by the spur gear. Instruments such as that illustrated are ruggedly constructed, and the maintenance required on them is relatively small.

Vapor-pressure temperature gages

The standard glass-bulb-type thermometer in which mercury or colored alcohol expands from a bulb into a capillary tube to provide the temperature indication is accurate and dependable. However, for the purpose of aircraft use it is impractical because of its construction. Most of the temperatures required during the flight of an airplane must be measured at a point many feet from the pilot's station. Therefore the readings must be transmitted to a point in the airplane where they are easily read by the member of the flight crew concerned.

A thermometer, or temperature indicator, using the bourdon tube is called the vapor-pressure type. Oil temperatures and temperatures of the cooling liquid in liquid-cooled engines are important because they provide vital information concerning the operations of the engine. If the temperature indication is not picked up by an electrical-type indicator, the vapor type can be used. Even though the electrical-type instruments are used extensively in modern aircraft, there are still many smaller airplanes in operation which use the vapor-pressure-type indicator. This indicator utilizes a mechanism as illustrated in Fig. 12·2. The bourdon tube in this case is connected to a temperature bulb by means of a capillary tube. The temperature bulb is designed to be installed in direct contact with oil, water, air, or whatever material is being tested for temperature. Inside the temperature bulb is a highly volatile (easily vaporized) liquid. The liquid expands and contracts with the rise and fall of the temperature. This, in turn, governs the pressure transmitted through the capillary tube to the bourdon tube in the instrument. The pressure in the bourdon tube is created by the influence of heat on the volatile liquid in the temperature bulb. Methyl chloride is commonly used in the bulb, but any liquid which vaporizes easily could be substituted. Methyl ether and sulfur dioxide have been found suitable, but methyl chloride is being produced in larger quantities and meets all the requirements, that is, stability, low freezing point, and purity. Furthermore, methyl chloride does not react to produce corrosion on most metals.

When the capillary tubing is being installed between the temperature instrument and the temperature bulb, care should be taken not to have the tube too long or too short. In practice the temperature bulb, the capillary tubing, and the instrument comprise a sealed unit, thus making it impossible to add to or remove any part of the capillary tubing. If the tube is too long, it must be coiled to take up the excess length and then secured properly with some type of clamping device. It is poor practice to have a tube which will "almost reach," thus requiring that the tube be pulled or stretched when it is connected. If the tube is connected under stress, it is likely to break very soon and render the instrument ineffective. The capillary tube used with temperature instruments usually measures between 0.014 and 0.020 in. ID. If the wall of the tube is fairly thin, it is necessary to provide a protective casing of braided metal, thus lessening the possibility of breakage. This protective braid is usually placed over the capillary tubing by the manufacturer of the instrument. The capillary tube should be carefully routed in the airplane to avoid chafing or rubbing against other lines or members of the airplane. It should be clamped tightly to some rigid member at least every 12 in. The clamp should be lined with a rubber or synthetic-rubber lining to prevent damage to the tube. Where the tube passes through a firewall or bulkhead, a rubber or plastic grommet should be installed to protect the tube.

Oil-pressure gage

All aircraft engines are equipped with oil pumps which furnish oil under pressure to the essential parts of the engine for lubrication purposes. Pressure is usually controlled by a relief valve which opens when the pressure exceeds a specified limit. In order to determine at exactly what pressure this pump is delivering oil to the engine, an oil-pressure gage must be connected between the relief valve and the engine. The oil-pressure gage also provides a method for measuring the pressure while setting the relief valve. During flight it tells the pilot or engineer that oil is circulating properly and under normal pressure or it gives him warning of impending engine failure due to lack of oil, broken lines, oil-pump failure, or burned-out bearings.

The construction of the oil-pressure gage is similar to the bourdon-tube instruments already discussed, with a line filled with oil entering the open end of the bourdon tube. Normally, engine oil is used in the line leading to the instrument, but in cold climates it is sometimes necessary to substitute a lighter oil if the oil-pressure line is very long. When any oil is cold, it is more sluggish and naturally flows through the pressure tube at a slower rate. Therefore a lighter oil in the pressure tube gives instantaneous indications on the gage when the engine is started and also gives a more accurate indication while the oil in the engine is warming up. It may be found necessary to disconnect the line and refill it from the lower end with a light oil quite frequently when operating continuously in cold climates because of the natural tendency of the light oil and the engine oil to mingle. Manufacturers' recommendations should be followed when making any such substitution, but instrument oil and compass oil are generally considered satisfactory for this purpose. The principal difference between oil-pressure gages and most bourdon-tube instruments is that the opening into the bourdon tube is smaller than the rest of the line leading to the engine; that is, the opening is restricted. This restriction is placed in the line for the purpose of obtaining a more steady indication on the gage than would be given if the fluctuations of pressure caused by the oil pump and pressure regulator were permitted to be transmitted directly to the pressure gage. The restriction usually consists of a short fitting, threaded at both ends, with a small hole drilled through it to restrict the flow. One end is inserted in the instrument, and the other end is connected to the tube leading to the engine. These restrictors serve as a protection to the instrument mechanism and also provide for a more accurate indication by preventing pointer fluctuation.

It must be noted here that in cold climates, because of the restriction in the line, it may take several seconds for the oil pressure to show up on the pressure gage after the engine is started. However, the mechanic or technician should be warned against waiting longer than the time specified by the engine manufacturer before shutting off the engine if oil pressure fails to develop.

The instrument dial, or the pressure gage, is graduated in pounds per square inch with a range suited to the engine to which it is connected. The range may be from 0 to 100 psi or as high as 0 to 200 psi or even greater. In any event the range of the instrument must cover the entire operating range of the engine.

Pressure transmitters which eliminate the necessity of filling a line from the instrument to the engine with a light oil have been used on some airplanes. The transmitter is located on the firewall near the engine. It consists of two chambers separated by a flexible diaphragm. A line from the engine enters one chamber, exerting pressure against the diaphragm. Another line leads from the chamber on the other side of the diaphragm to the instrument in the cockpit. This is a small capillary line which is filled with a light oil such as instrument oil or compass oil. Thus the engine oil entering the first chamber expands the diaphragm, which creates a pressure on the light oil in the capillary tube. This pressure is transmitted to the bourdon tube in the instrument in the same manner as discussed in the foregoing description of an oil-pressure gage.

Engine gage unit

A discussion on bourdon-tube instruments would not be complete without a description of the **engine gage unit** used on some airplanes. This instrument is a combination of three engine instruments: the on temperature gage, the oil-pressure gage, and the fuel-pressure gage. The parts of this gage unit are actually three individual bourdon-tube instruments with the necessary lines leading to the back of the instrument case. It is obvious that the purpose of this instrument is to furnish a more economical utilization of the instrument panel space. It also makes it easier for the pilot to read simultaneously all three indi-

Figure **12·3** *An engine gage unit.*

cations relative to the operation of one engine. An engine gage unit is illustrated in Fig. 12·3.

Some engine gage units are made with oil pressure and fuel pressure indicated by means of bourdon-tube mechanisms and temperature indicated electrically. In this case, the temperature-sensing device will probably be a resistance unit which changes resistance as the temperature changes. The mechanism in the instrument will then be a Wheatstone-bridge unit or a ratiometer.

Pressure indications

It will often be noted that pressure readings are followed by the letters **psig** or **psia.** The letters **psig** mean **pounds per square inch, gage.** The letters **psia** mean **pounds per square inch, absolute.** Pounds per square inch, gage, usually indicates pressure above atmospheric pressure. The standard pressure of the atmosphere at sea level is about 14.7 psi or 29.92 in. of mercury (in. Hg). Therefore a reading of 30 psig would be 44.7 psia because 30 lb gage would be 44.7 psi above absolute zero pressure. In any consideration of pressures it is necessary to note whether the pressure is **gage** or **absolute.** A manifold-pressure gage (to be discussed later) reads in inches of mercury absolute. Therefore in its normal static condition when the engine is not running, the gage will read approximately 29.92 in. Hg at sea level. With the engine running, the gage will read below 29.92 or below atmospheric pressure at low rpm.

Diaphragm and bellows instruments

Pressure gages designed to provide readings of comparatively low pressures are usually of the diaphragm or bellows type. In some cases, both a diaphragm and a bellows are used in the same instrument. A drawing of the cross section of a typical instrument diaphragm is shown in Fig. 12·4. The diaphragm consists of two disks of thin metal corrugated concentrically and sealed together at the edges to form a cavity or capsule. The diaphragm in Fig. 12·4 is designed with an opening through one of the disks to admit the pressure to be measured. The opposite side is provided with a bridge which may bear against a rocking shaft lever through which the movement is transmitted to the indicating needle.

In some instruments, such as a simple barometer, the diaphragm is sealed with dry air or an inert gas inside at sea-level atmospheric pressure. Changes in the pressure of the air outside the diaphragm will cause it to expand or contract, thus producing a movement which is converted to a dial reading through the instrument mechanism.

A bellows capsule is illustrated in Fig. 12·5. The bellows is made of thin metal with corrugated sides and formed into a cylindrical capsule as shown. This unit operates in much the same manner as the diaphragm but it provides a greater range of movement.

Figure **12·4** *An instrument diaphragm.*

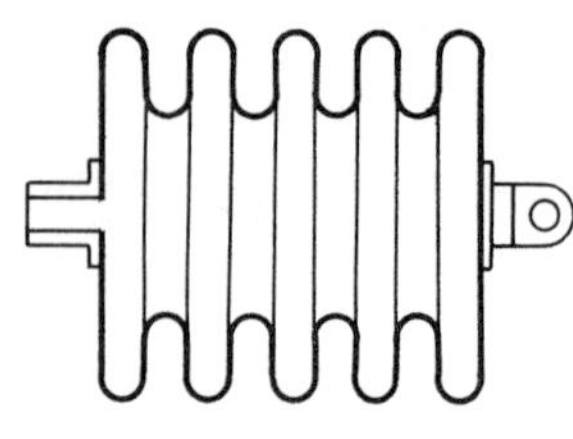

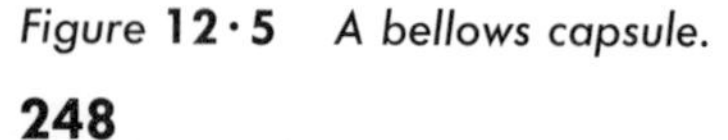

Figure **12·5** *A bellows capsule.*

Figure **12·6** *Fuel-pressure gage for a light airplane.*

Fuel-pressure gage

The importance of the fuel-pressure gage in its relationship to engine operations cannot be overstressed. It gives a clear picture of the status of the fuel system at all times. It provides a constant check on the operation of the fuel pump and the fuel-pressure-relief valve and shows whether fuel is being supplied to the carburetor or the fuel-control unit steadily and at correct operating pressures.

In jet-engine fuel systems a fuel-pressure gage is employed to indicate the pressure of fuel being applied to the fuel nozzles of the engine. This fuel-pressure gage gives an indication only after the power-control lever is advanced during the starting of an engine to indicate that fuel is being applied to the fuel nozzles in the combustion chambers of the engine.

A typical fuel-pressure gage for a light airplane is shown in Fig. 12·6. This gage is a dual type because it is used for an airplane with twin engines. The mechanism of the instrument consists of two bellows capsules joined end to end. One capsule is connected to the fuel-pressure line and the other capsule is vented to ambient pressure in the airplane. The fuel pressure causes the fuel bellows to expand and move toward the air capsule. This movement is transmitted to the indicating needle through conventional linkages.

Airspeed indicator

The **airspeed indicator** is one of the most important instruments of the flight group, and it is listed with the turn-and-bank and rate-of-climb indicators, compass, and sensitive altimeter as the **primary flight group.** Among these, the airspeed indicator, altimeter, and magnetic compass are the absolute minimum requirements for any certificated airplane. If the airplane is to be used for "instrument flying," then the other instruments in the primary group must be included. Instrument flying means that the aircraft is partially or solely controlled through the use of instruments when continual reference to land or water is not possible and must be performed in accordance with **Instrument Flight Rules** (IFR).

Some of the uses of the airspeed indicator are as follows:

1. It gives the pilot a definite indication of the attitude of the airplane with reference to the horizontal flight path. There will always be an increase in airspeed if the nose is down and a decrease in airspeed if the nose is high provided there is no change in throttle setting.
2. It assists the pilot in determining the best throttle setting for most-efficient flying speeds.
3. Indications of airspeed are necessary in estimating or calculating ground speed (speed of the airplane with reference to positions on the ground).
4. Every airplane has certain maximum speeds recommended by the manufacturer, and without the airspeed indicator these limits of design might be exceeded without the pilot's being aware of it. This is particularly true with respect to flap and landing-gear extension speeds.
5. The airspeed indicator shows the correct take-off and landing speeds, and it warns when the airplane is approaching stalling speed. It also indicates angle of attack, because higher speed means lower angle of attack.

The mechanism of an airspeed indicator is shown in Fig. 12·7. It consists of an airtight diaphragm enclosed in an airtight case, with linkages and gears designed to multiply the movement of the diaphragm and provide an indication on the dial of the instrument. The bottom portion of the diaphragm is attached to the instrument case, and

A. Pitot pressure connection
B. Diaphragm
C. Rocking-shaft arm
D. Rocking shaft
E. Hairspring
F. Sector gear

Figure **12·7** *Mechanism of an airspeed indicator.*

the top portion is free to move. Unlike the diaphragm in an aneroid barometer this one is provided with a connection for dynamic pressure from the pitot tube. Impact pressure from the pitot tube entering the diaphragm causes expansion which is transmitted through the multiplying mechanism to the indicating needle. Tubing connects the static side of the pitot head or other static ports to the instrument case, allowing static pressure to enter the case and surround the diaphragm. Thus the instrument actually measures **differential pressure** between the inside of the diaphragm and the inside of the instrument case.

Table 12·1 shows the relationship between airspeed and impact pressure on the pitot head under standard conditions, at sea level.

In level flight, as the speed of the airplane increases, the impact pressure becomes greater but the static pressure remains the same. This causes the diaphragm to expand more and more as the pressure increases inside. When the diaphragm expands, the rocking shaft picks up the motion and transmits it to the sector. The sector turns the pinion which is fastened to the tapered shaft (handstaff). The pointer is pressed onto this tapered shaft and moves around a calibrated dial. The hairspring keeps the linkage taut and causes it to follow the movement of the diaphragm as the airspeed increases or decreases. The dial on the face of the instrument is calibrated in **knots** or **miles per hour.** One knot is a speed of one nautical mile per hour. The nautical mile is 6,080.27 ft, whereas the statute mile is 5,280 ft; hence a speed of 1 knot is equal to almost 1⅐ statute mile per hour. The conversion factor for knots to miles per hour is 1.151553. The knot is now the standard unit of airspeed in aeronautics.

Table 12·1

Airspeed, mph	Ram air pressure	
	in. Hg	*psi*
20	0.0146	0.007
40	0.0582	0.028
60	0.1309	0.064
80	0.2330	0.114
100	0.3646	0.180
120	0.5263	0.258
140	0.7178	0.352
160	0.940	0.462
180	1.193	0.586
200	1.477	0.725
250	2.331	1.145
300	3.397	1.673
350	4.67	2.29
400	6.19	3.04
500	9.97	4.89
600	15.02	7.38

The airspeed indicator is mounted in the instrument panel with the other flight instruments and is usually placed so that the zero is at the top of the instrument. The lines connecting to the rear of the instrument are usually marked *P* and *S* for pressure and static, respectively. The color coding of lines will be explained in another portion of the text, but a word of precaution at this time is in order. Airspeed lines are marked by a **black band,** and static lines are identified by a **black and green band.** When it becomes necessary to remove one line and reinstall another, great care must be taken to see that the new line is color coded. Because of some locations of the pitot mast it is difficult to trace the lines unless they are coded as explained above.

Even though an airspeed indicator may have been perfectly calibrated before installation on an airplane, it may be subject to **installation error,** that is, an error developed as a result of the position of the pitot head on the airplane. Each airplane has flying and aerodynamic characteristics which must be studied before the pitot mast or boom is installed. In spite of the care taken in this installation, an error due to air disturbances still exists. The error is usually in the static pressure source.

Whenever the pitot-static head is changed or when any part of the airspeed system is altered with the possibility of causing an erroneous reading, it becomes necessary to perform an airspeed calibration during flight. Airspeed calibrations are also conducted at any time that the pilot believes that there are discrepancies in the airspeed indications.

Calibration over a **speed course** is the most common method of airspeed calibration. A speed course consists of two ground stations at an accurately known distance apart on level terrain and easily identifiable from the air. The distance should be at least 2 miles for low-speed aircraft and 5 to 10 miles for higher-speed aircraft. The ground stations should be equipped with electronic timing devices to obtain a very precise measurement of speed. However, an observer with a stopwatch can obtain a measurement which is within reasonable limits.

To ensure accurate results, course calibrations should in general not be conducted if the wind speed exceeds approximately 5 mph or if the air is appreciably turbulent. In the case of a crosswind, the airplane should be headed parallel to the course (perpendicular to the marker lines at each end) and allowed to drift. If it is attempted to fly directly along the course by crabbing the airplane, the resultant airspeed will be in error by an amount depending upon the actual airspeed of the airplane and the crosswind velocity.

At least one run in each direction should be made at each of the selected speeds. In each run the altitude and the necessary power settings should be stabilized for a considerable distance before the speed course is entered. Neither power nor altitude should be altered during the particular run. Runs should not be made at an altitude less than 50 ft above the ground. When the "full-throttle" run is conducted, the rpm (revolutions per minute) should not exceed the rated rpm of the engine.

The following data should be observed:

1. The outside air temperature and the average pressure altitude of all runs should be observed and recorded.
2. The indicated airspeed should be recorded at frequent intervals during the run, and the average speed of these recordings taken as the speed of that particular run.
3. The average manifold pressure, tachometer reading, and carburetor air temperature should be observed for each run and recorded as precisely as possible. "Average speed" should be determined as the average of the measured-course ground speed for each direction. Do not average the time intervals.

The **trailing-bomb** method is considered as one of the most reliable means for airspeed calibrations but can be used only at slow speeds. The bomb can be used at any altitude and therefore lends itself readily to calibrations at speeds which should be considered unsafe at the altitudes at which calibration runs are made over a measured course. Also the trailing-bomb method can be used over nearly any terrain and is less dependent on weather conditions.

The airspeed bomb consists of a streamlined mass of heavy metal which has been calibrated in a wind tunnel. The bomb is provided with static ports and is attached to a cable 50 to 100 ft long by which it can be lowered from the airplane. This permits the bomb to be in a location well below the disturbed air adjacent to the airplane.

A length of rubber or plastic tubing transmits the static pressure from the bomb to the instruments in the airplane. The tubing is securely fastened to the cable so it will not vibrate and disturb the pressure indication. At the point where the tube and cable enter the airplane, adequate protection is provided to prevent damage to the tube or cable.

The purpose of the arrangement described above is to provide a static system under ideal conditions so it will be unaffected by disturbed air around the airplane. Obviously the indications on the test indicator can then be compared with the indications of the airspeed indicator in the airplane. The readings are taken at various speeds, ranging from the slowest speed that can be flown without danger of stalling to the highest speed which can be flown without causing the trailing bomb to be pulled into the wake of the airplane. The **wake** is the area of disturbed air which trails somewhat below and behind the airplane. Two or more operators are required, one to take readings on the test indicator and the others to record the indications of the airplane instruments.

After the test runs have been completed, a calibration card is made up by averaging the miles per hour registered on the test indicator and those registered on the airplane instrument. When these speeds are plotted on graph paper, it can be determined what the calibrated airspeed should be for the various indicated airspeeds within the flying limits of the airplane.

To make sure that a trailing-bomb calibration is accurate, it is most important that the bomb and the indicator be checked periodically for accuracy. Also, the test operation should be carried out in accordance with the specifications established for the particular units being used.

An airspeed indicator should be installed in such a manner that it indicates the airspeed at sea level with the maximum practicable accuracy, but the total error must not be more than plus or minus 3 per cent, except that it must not be more than 5 mph. It is considered desirable that the indicator error be within plus or minus 5 mph throughout the speed range, and also, in the interest of safety, it is desirable that any error present be such that the indicator reads high at comparatively high speeds and low at comparatively low speeds.

If flaps are installed on the airplane being calibrated for airspeed accuracy, a separate calibration covering at least five speeds should be made with the flaps extended. If the landing gear is retractable, the calibration with the flaps retracted should be made with the landing gear also retracted and that with the flaps extended should be made with the landing gear also extended.

The immediate results obtained in airspeed calibrations must not be confused with **true air-**

speed or **ground speed.** They represent merely a correction or calibrated airspeed, eliminating errors common to the airspeed system of that particular airplane.

True airspeed and calibrated airspeed would be the same only when the airplane is flying at sea level at standard temperature (59°F or 15°C). **True airspeed** in flight can be determined after the temperature of the air in which the airplane is flying and its pressure altitude above sea level are recorded. When these factors have been determined, true airspeed (TAS) can be found by the following formula:

$$V_t = V_i \frac{T_h + KP_s}{T_s + KP_h}$$

where V_t = true airspeed
V_i = indicated airspeed
T_s = standard temperature (59°F or 15°C)
P_s = standard pressure (29.92 in. Hg or 760 mm Hg)
T_h = air temperature at flight altitude
P_h = air pressure at flight altitude, in. or mm Hg
K = fixed value for changing temperatures to absolute values (459.4 for °F and 273 for °C)

In general it can be assumed that true airspeed can be obtained from indicated airspeed by the addition of approximately 2 per cent for every 1,000 ft of altitude.

Ground speed is the speed of the airplane relative to objects on the ground. If the airplane were flying in perfectly still air, the **true airspeed** and the **ground speed** would be the same. Otherwise, the direction and speed of the wind must be calculated before the ground speed can be determined.

Airspeed–angle-of-attack indicator

The instrument whose dial is shown in Fig. 12·8 is called an **airspeed–angle-of-attack** indicator. Its function is to indicate airspeed, maximum allowable indicated airspeed, and angle of attack.

Indicated airspeed is shown on the dial by means of a pointer driven by a conventional pressure diaphragm. This diaphragm is labeled **Airspeed Diaphragm** in the schematic drawing of Fig. 12·9.

Angle-of-attack information is obtained by reading the indicated airspeed (IAS) pointer against a segment rotating about the periphery of the instrument's dial. This movable segment is positioned, relative to the IAS pointer, by the

Figure **12·8** *Airspeed–angle-of-attack indicator (Kollsman).*

servomechanism which responds to a signal from the **angle-of-attack** sensor. The IAS pointer, therefore, indicates both indicated airspeed and angle of attack, the latter either in degrees or by markers showing maximum L/D ratio, best cruise, approach, over-the-fence, and stall angles. The angle-of-attack sensor provides electrical signals which control the servomechanism driving the angle-of-attack sector on the dial.

The **maximum allowable** pointer indicates "maximum allowable" and/or "never exceed" indicated airspeed. It is actuated by a static pressure diaphragm and mechanism with a special calibration, so that the pointer reads **maximum allowable indicated airspeed** as a function of absolute pressure only. Maximum allowable indicated airspeed increases as altitude increases to about 25,000 ft and then decreases, because it must not be allowed to approach Mach 1 (the speed of sound); that is, the airspeed is "Mach limited" at altitudes above 25,000 ft.

Machmeter

Because many of the modern jet and rocket aircraft fly near the speed of sound and military aircraft fly faster than the speed of sound, it is essential that such aircraft be equipped with an instrument which will compare the speed of the aircraft with the speed of sound. The flight characteristics of these high-speed aircraft change substantially as the speed of sound is approached or passed. These changes are associated with the occurrence of locally supersonic flow and shock

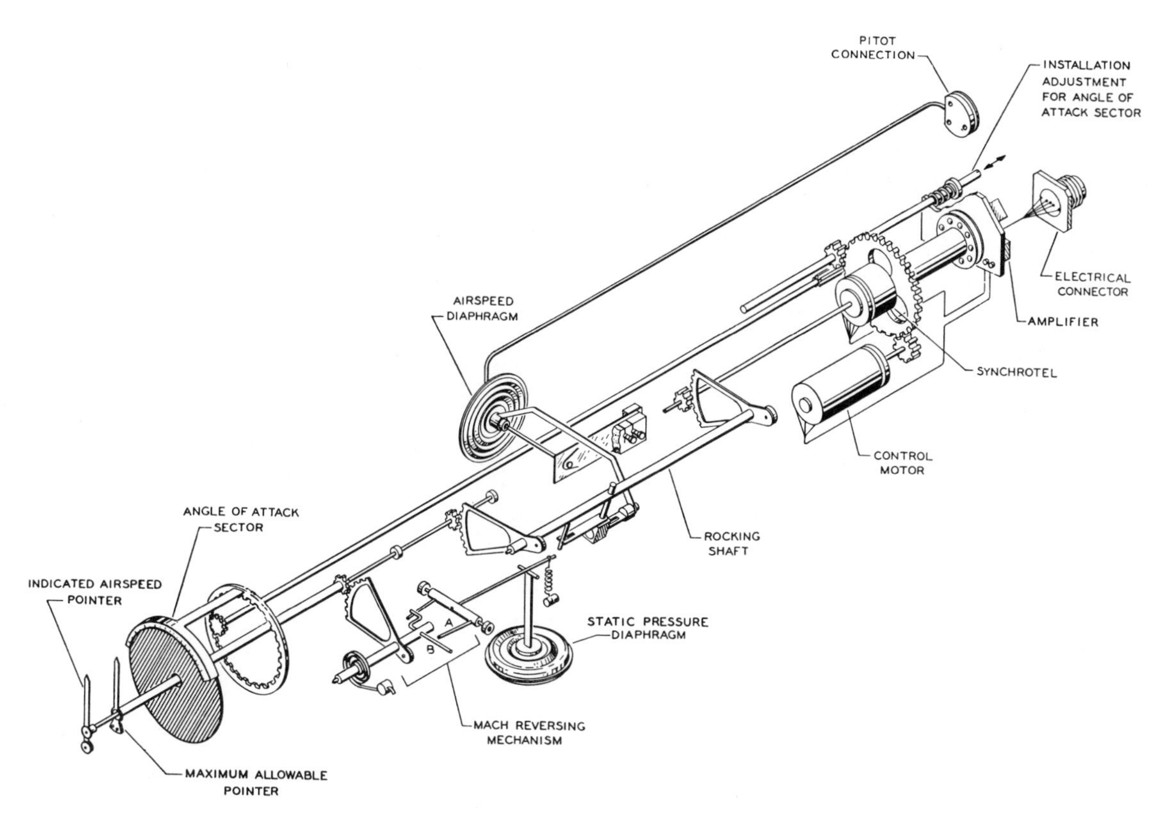

Figure **12·9** *Schematic diagram of airspeed–angle-of-attack indicator (Kollsman).*

waves. The result is that the pilot must substantially change his handling of the aircraft controls and must retrim the airplane to meet the new conditions.

If an airplane is not designed to withstand the violent stresses which are sometimes imposed as a result of shock-wave formation during transonic flight, it may be severely damaged or may even disintegrate. In flying such an airplane the pilot must know when his craft is approaching the speed of sound.

Since the speed of sound varies according to temperature and altitude, it is obvious that an airspeed indicator will not give the pilot an accurate indication of the airplane speed relative to the speed of sound. It has therefore become necessary to use an instrument which gives the airplane speed in proportion to the speed of sound under the atmospheric conditions in which the airplane is flying. The instrument designed to accomplish this is the **Machmeter,** or Mach indicator, and it measures the ratio of TAS to the speed of sound. This ratio is called the **Mach number,** named for the Austrian philosopher of science Ernst Mach (pronounced "mock"), who made the first studies on fast-moving projectiles.

The Machmeter, illustrated in Fig. 12·10*a*, shows the number directly on its dial. For example, the number .7 is read as "Mach point seven," and it means that the airplane is flying at seven-tenths the speed of sound. The number 1.0 is read "Mach one" and means that the speed is equal to the speed of sound.

The Machmeter is similar in construction to an airspeed indicator; however, it includes an additional expanding diaphragm which modifies the magnifying ratio of the mechanism in proportion to altitude. As the altitude of the airplane increases, the altitude diaphragm expands and moves the floating rocking shaft. This movement changes the position of the rocking-shaft lever in relation to the sector lever, thus modifying the movement of the indicating needle to account for the effect of altitude. The arrangement of the diaphragm with respect to the rocking shaft is clearly shown in Fig. 12·10*b*. Observe that expansion of the diaphragm will decrease the proportional movement of the indicating needle.

The ram air pressure is registered through a diaphragm which rotates the rocking shaft as it expands or contracts. Temperature correction is applied through a thermometal fork mounted on the altitude diaphragm.

Altimeter

It is obvious that the altimeter is a most important flight instrument, especially when flying under conditions of poor visibility. The altitude

Figure **12·10** *The Machmeter.*

of an airplane must be known when determining airspeed, for computing engine power, to maintain proper separation of flight paths for aircraft flying in opposite directions, to assure adequate clearance over mountains and other flight obstacles extending upward from the ground, and for instrument flight.

In general, there are two different types of altimeters operating on the barometric principle. One is the **simple altimeter,** and the other is the **sensitive altimeter.** The simple altimeter has a single diaphragm which has been evacuated and sealed and a single pointer which makes one or two revolutions for the full range of the instrument.

The sensitive altimeter is so named because of its sensitivity. The dial of a sensitive altimeter is shown in Fig. 12·11. The longest hand, which has the appearance of the minute hand on a clock, registers 1,000 ft for a complete revolution. The dial is indexed so this hand can easily show differences of 10 ft in altitude. Furthermore, as an average-sized man reads this altimeter at eye level and then places it at his feet and takes another reading, he will note that the large needle has moved approximately one-half space, which indicates a difference of about 5 ft in altitude. The shorter, wider pointer rotates one-tenth the distance of the long hand; hence it registers 10,000 ft for a complete revolution around the dial. Each numbered increment of the dial represents thousands of feet when read from this hand. The small hand and the center dial are arranged to read in increments of 10,000 or 40,000 ft for a complete revolution.

The dial shown in the illustration registers an altitude of about 1,770 ft. If the altimeter were showing 15,770 ft, the small hand in the center would be slightly past the midpoint between the 1 and the 2 on the outer scale; the short, wide hand would be pointing about three-fourths the distance from the 5 to the 6; and the long hand would point to the same position in Fig. 12·11.

The pressure element of the sensitive altimeter consists of two or three diaphragm capsules in series, and there may be either two or three dial pointers. The pointers register hundreds, thousands, or tens of thousands as explained in the preceding paragraphs.

A cutaway diagram of the interior of a Kollsman sensitive altimeter is shown in Fig. 12·12. This instrument utilizes three diaphragm capsules to impart movement to the rocking shaft as changes in altitude occur. The rocking shaft is linked to a sector gear which drives the multiplying mechanism. It will be noted that the rotation of the rocking shaft must be multiplied many times, since the large hand must rotate 50 times to indicate an altitude of 50,000 ft.

An altimeter must be compensated for atmospheric pressure changes if it is to give true indications under all conditions. This compensation

Figure **12·11** *Dial of a sensitive altimeter (Kollsman).*

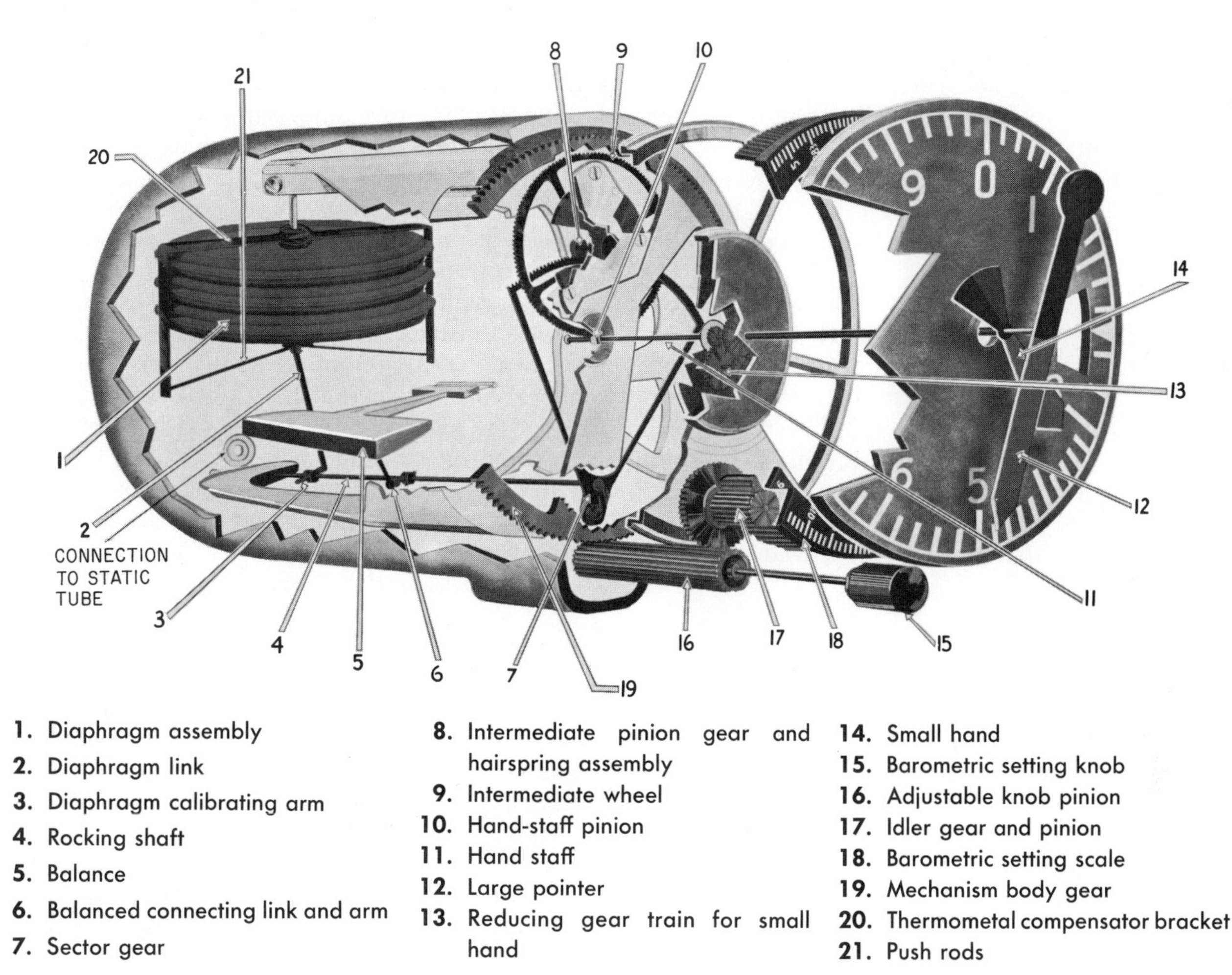

Figure **12·12** *Cutaway diagram of altimeter mechanism.*

must be done by mechanical means by the pilot or another member of the flight crew with the **barometric pressure setting** mechanism in the instrument. The setting device rotates the entire indicator drive mechanism within the case of the instrument and at the same time drives a barometric indicating dial which is visible through a window in the face of the instrument. When the adjusting knob is turned, the altitude dial remains stationary but the drive mechanism and pointers change position.

The reason for changing the barometric setting on an altimeter can be understood when the effect of barometric pressure on the altitude indication is considered. Assume that a certain airport is known to be at sea level with **standard** atmospheric pressure existing on a particular day. Before taking off in an airplane, the pilot sets the barometric scale to 29.92 in. Hg (standard sea-level atmospheric pressure). Then all altimeter pointers point to the zero mark on the altimeter scale. While the airplane is in the air, perhaps 2 hr, the barometric pressure at the airport has dropped rapidly and is only 29.38 in. Hg. The pilot is ready to come in for a landing. If he does not contact the field to obtain the corrected barometric pressure and leaves the altimeter at the setting he made before taking off, the wheels of the airplane will hit the ground when the altimeter registers an altitude of approximately 500 ft.

The correct procedure, therefore, is to contact the field for the corrected existing barometric pressure before coming in for a landing. Upon receipt of the information in the foregoing case, the pilot sets his barometric scale at 29.38 in. Hg. He can now expect the wheels to touch the ground when the altimeter indicates zero feet altitude.

For cross-country flying, the pilot corrects his altimeter to sea-level pressure at each reporting station over which he flies and the dial of the altimeter reads in feet above sea level. When the pilot approaches a field, he radios for the correct local barometric pressure reading and sets his altimeter accordingly. By reference to a map or through information received from the tower, the pilot knows the elevation of the field. When he lands, therefore, his altimeter will read the actual field elevation above sea level.

Temperature compensation is automatically accomplished in the altimeter mechanism. Although the amount of error due to temperature change would normally be small because of the materials used in the construction of the mechanism, this small error is offset by a bimetallic strip which neutralizes any expansion or contraction of the parts.

In a standard instrument panel configuration the altimeter is mounted to the right of the airspeed indicator and gyro horizon. The airspeed indicator is the uppermost instrument at the extreme left of the flight group. Static pressure is supplied to the altimeter from the static-pressure line through a flexible connection. This line must be of sufficient strength to withstand the pressurization of the cabin in any pressurized airplane.

The Bendix compensated altimeter

Because of the high speeds and altitudes at which modern aircraft fly, the altimeters employed in such aircraft must be much more accurate than those used on the older, slower airplanes. To provide an altimeter which will be sufficiently accurate for all conditions of operation, certain corrections and compensations must be made.

First, an accurate altimeter must be corrected for installation or position error. This error applies to a particular airplane. Second, the instrument must have automatic compensation for temperature changes. Third, the changes in static pressure due to changes in Mach number must be compensated. An altimeter designed to make the necessary adjustments for accuracy is the mechanically compensated, pneumatically operated altimeter manufactured by the Pioneer-Central Division of the Bendix Corporation.

The mechanically compensated altimeter operates from the aircraft pitot-static pressure system and consists of a combination of altimeter and machmeter mechanisms (see Fig. 12 · 13*a*). The indicated pressure altitude is sensed by an aneroid, and the Mach number is obtained from the combined motion of the **altitude-sensing aneroids** and a **differential-pressure diaphragm capsule.** Aircraft position error information is applied to a two-dimensional cam and is algebraically added to the indicated pressure altitude by means of a mechanical differential. Thus, correction in feet of altitude is made to the altimeter indication for a given Mach number. This is required because of the change in static pressure at a given altitude for a change in Mach number. True altitude is computed by means of a mechanism actuated by the altitude- and Mach-sensing elements as shown in the illustration.

As the aircraft changes altitude, the two aneroid capsules sense the change in static pressure. Deflection of these capsules is transmitted through the **bimetal units** to the rocking shaft. Hence, as altitude changes, the rocking shaft is caused to rotate.

When the aircraft changes velocity, the ram air pressure on the pitot tube changes, and this pressure differential ΔP is sensed by the **differential-pressure capsule.** The deflection of the capsule is transmitted through a **link** to the **link follower** which rotates a rocking shaft and a sector gear. This gear changes the position of the **altitude-correction cam.** This mechanism is shown in Fig. 12 · 13*b*. The correction applied by the mechanism is proportional to altitude error caused by changes in Mach number and is the input to the **altitude-correction differential.** The differential output is geared to the dials and pointers to read directly in corrected altitude.

Temperature compensation for the altimeter is provided through the operation of the bimetal elements in the linkage between the aneroid capsules and the main rocking shaft. Calibration of the instrument is accomplished by making adjustments of the eccentric attachments between the bimetal units and the rocking-shaft lever arms. The lever arms can also be rotated on the shaft to cause a change in the linkage starting angle.

The **barometric set** mechanism, shown in Fig. 12 · 13*a*, consists of an adjusting knob, gear train, cam, and rotating mechanism assembly. The range of ground-level pressure indications is 28.1 to 31.0 in. Hg with stops incorporated to limit the travel of the barometric counter to the range of desired operation.

Adjustment of the zero setting system is accomplished by unlocking the knob shaft from the front of the instrument by a single screwdriver lock. This allows the pinion to disengage the counter gear train while still engaging the rotating frame assembly. The adjusting knob will then rotate the pointers to the corrected setting.

The three-pointer dial display shown in Fig. 12 · 13*c* consists of two pointers and a disk with a pointer extension indicating 1,000, 10,000, and 100,000 ft of altitude, respectively, for one revolution. An opening in the disk exposes a cross-hatched area, warning that the indication is below 15,000 ft.

If a counter-type readout is more desirable from the human engineering standpoint, it can be provided as an alternate to the three-pointer presentation. This dial is also shown in Fig. 12 · 13*c* and consists of a three-digit counter and a rotating

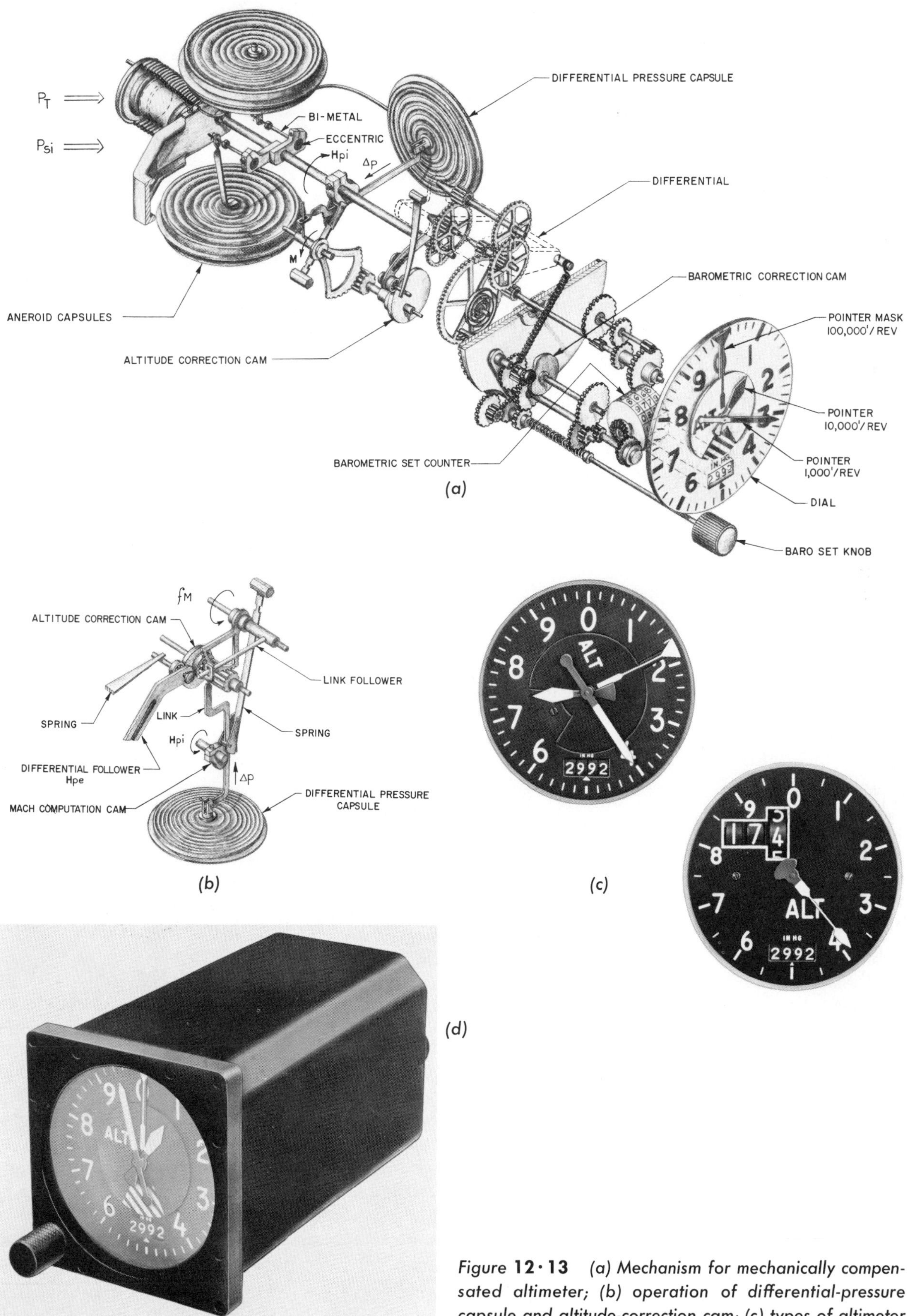

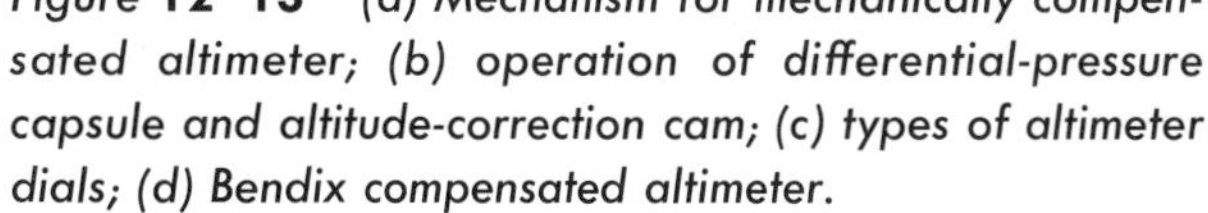

Figure **12·13** *(a) Mechanism for mechanically compensated altimeter; (b) operation of differential-pressure capsule and altitude-correction cam; (c) types of altimeter dials; (d) Bendix compensated altimeter.*

pointer. The two large digits indicate thousands of feet altitude, while the smaller third digit and the pointer indicate hundreds of feet. The small digit rotates continuously with pointer rotation, while the two larger digits index with an intermittent motion. One complete revolution of the pointer indicates 1,000 ft of altitude, thereby providing a sensitive indication of altitude change to the pilot. The dial presentation in the illustration indicates an altitude of 17,390 ft.

Pitot-static tubes

Mention has been made previously of pitot tubes, pitot heads, and static pressure. It is therefore desirable that we describe briefly the function of pitot systems.

Figure 12 · 14 illustrates a pitot head for a standard system on some older airplanes. The purpose of the head is to pick up indications of dynamic (ram) air pressure and static (ambient) air pressure to be transmitted through tubing to the instruments requiring these pressures for operation. The dynamic pressure caused by the movement of the airplane through the air is picked up through port *A* shown in the illustration. This pressure is carried through the head and out tube *D* to the airspeed indicator and Mach number sensing units. The baffle plate *B* helps to prevent water from entering the system. Water that goes by the baffle plate is stopped by the water trap *C*. Water is drained from the head through the drain holes *E* and *F*.

Static pressure is picked up through the holes at *G* and *H* and is carried through the tube *I* to instruments such as the altimeter, vertical-speed indicator, and others requiring static pressure.

The pitot head shown is provided with heaters to prevent the formation of ice. These heaters are shown at *J* and *K*, and the electrical connecting plug is indicated by *L* in the illustration.

On modern jet aircraft and on many light aircraft the dynamic pressure only is picked up by the pitot heads. The heads are mounted on the aircraft where they will provide the most accurate indications of dynamic pressure. The static pressure is obtained through screened ports on the sides of the fuselage.

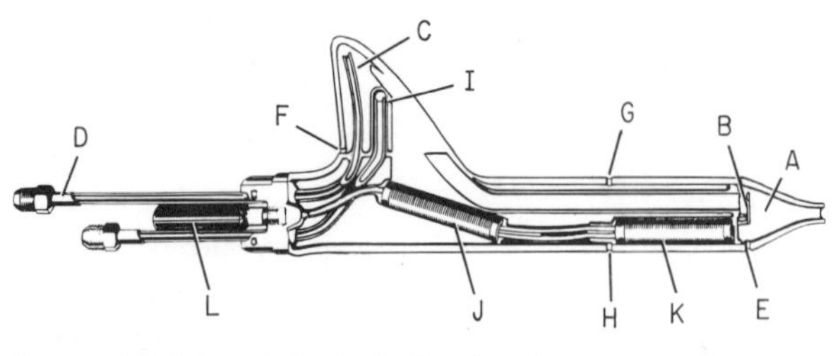

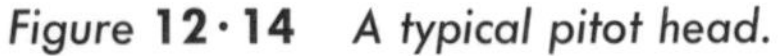

Figure 12 · 14 *A typical pitot head.*

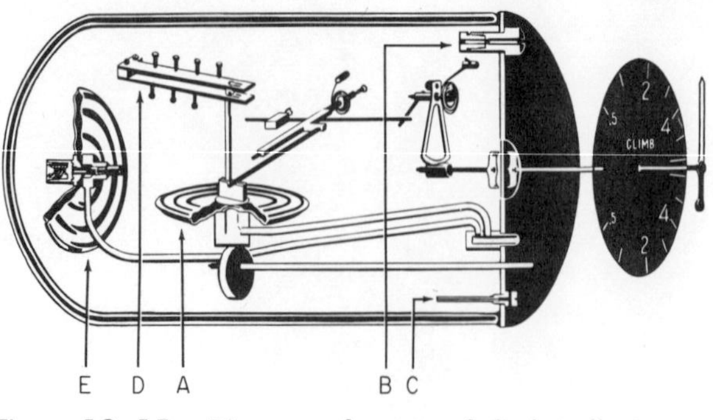

Figure 12 · 15 *Diagram of a rate-of-climb indicator.*

Rate-of-climb indicator

The rate-of-climb indicator illustrated in Fig. 12 · 15 is sometimes called the **vertical-speed indicator,** or for the sake of brevity, it is sometimes referred to as a **climb indicator.** This instrument is valuable in blind flight because it indicates the rate at which the airplane is climbing or descending. Level flight can be maintained by keeping the pointer of the instrument on zero, and any change in altitude is indicated on the dial in **feet per minute.** In this manner it assists the pilot in establishing a rate of climb which is within the prescribed limits of the engine. Likewise when the pilot is coming in for a landing or descending to a lower altitude, the rate of descent can be controlled.

Like the airspeed indicator, the climb indicator is a differential-pressure instrument. It operates from the differential between atmospheric pressure and the pressure of a chamber which is vented to the atmosphere through a small calibrated capillary restriction.

Modern rate-of-climb indicators are "self-contained," with all the necessary mechanism enclosed in the instrument case. However, some of the outside-cell or bottle types are still being used on older aircraft.

The diagram of the rate-of-climb (vertical-speed) indicator illustrated in Fig. 12 · 15 shows the internal mechanism of the instrument. Changes in pressure due to changes in altitude are transmitted quickly through a large tube to the inside of a diaphragm *A* and slowly through an orifice assembly *B* and capillary *C* to the inside of the case. This creates a pressure differential which causes the diaphragm to expand or contract according to the rate of change of altitude. Adjustable restraining springs *D* are provided which control the diaphragm deflection and permit accurate calibration.

The action of the diaphragm is transmitted through a lever and gear system to the pointer. As the plane assumes level flight, the pressures equalize and the pointer returns to zero. An overpressure diaphragm and valve *E* prevent excessive rates of climb or descent from damaging the mechanism.

It is characteristic of the rate-of-climb indicator to lag in its readings; that is, it does not respond instantaneously to changes in rate of climb. This is because it takes a few seconds for the differential pressures to develop after a change in rate of climb takes place. The more modern instruments used in jet transport aircraft have little or no lag.

Temperature changes have a tendency to cause variations in the flow of air through the capillary restrictors in the rate-of-climb instrument. Therefore, manufacturers have devised various methods of compensating the instrument for temperature. Likewise, altitude changes must be compensated for owing to a tendency toward a greater lag when flying at higher altitudes.

Although the rate-of-climb indicator is one of the most sensitive differential-pressure instruments, it is not easily damaged during steep dives or violent maneuvers because of mechanical stops which have been incorporated in the instrument. Climb indicators are made with ranges up to 2,000 ft per min for planes which operate at slow rates of climb or descent and at more than 10,000 ft per min for some of the modern jet planes.

Manifold-pressure gage

The **manifold-pressure gage** is basically a barometer, and it measures atmospheric pressure when the engine is idle. With the engine running, the manifold-pressure gage registers the absolute pressure of the fuel-air mixture in the intake manifold before it enters the engine. The face of a typical manifold-pressure gage is shown in Fig. 12·16.

Figure **12·16** *A manifold-pressure gage.*

The manifold-pressure gage is used primarily on supercharged engines to help the pilot to know how much power is being developed by the engine. A supercharged engine is one which includes a blower system, either in the engine or in the air ducting outside the engine, to force an increased amount of air into the engine. A "naturally aspirated" engine is one which is not supercharged, and it is obvious that the manifold pressure for this type of engine could never be greater than atmospheric pressure. If this type of engine is driving a constant-speed propeller, a manifold-pressure gage is required.

In supercharged engines where the manifold pressure can be controlled, the operator must know the extent of the pressure being developed in the intake manifold just prior to the entrance of the fuel and air mixture into the cylinder. Thus he can avoid excessive pressure at low altitudes, which could result in serious damage to the engine; he is warned of loss of power when flying at high altitudes; and he has a guide for adjusting the throttles and operating within the safe limits of the engine.

The manifold-pressure gage is an absolute-pressure-measuring instrument; that is, it measures pressure in the manifold plus atmospheric pressure or pressure above absolute zero. It is calibrated in inches of mercury absolute, thus measuring the actual pressure existing in the inlet manifold. The diaphragm and mechanism must be completely sealed against the effects of external atmospheric pressure.

There have been two types of manifold-pressure gages in common use, and both types will be encountered from time to time. In the first type, the case is airtight with a tube leading from the case to the point at which the engine manufacturer provides for connecting it to the manifold. If an instrument is being installed with a new engine, there will be a dummy plug at the point where the tube connection is to be made at the engine. The plug must be removed, and a tube fitting installed to provide a connection to the instrument.

The mechanism inside the case consists of an evacuated diaphragm attached to a multiplying mechanism which transmits movement, due to pressure changes within the case, to the pointer on the face of the instrument.

The manifold-pressure gage illustrated in Fig. 12·17 is the dual type which indicates the manifold pressure of two engines by two pointers on the same dial. The full face of this type of instrument is shown in Fig. 12·16.

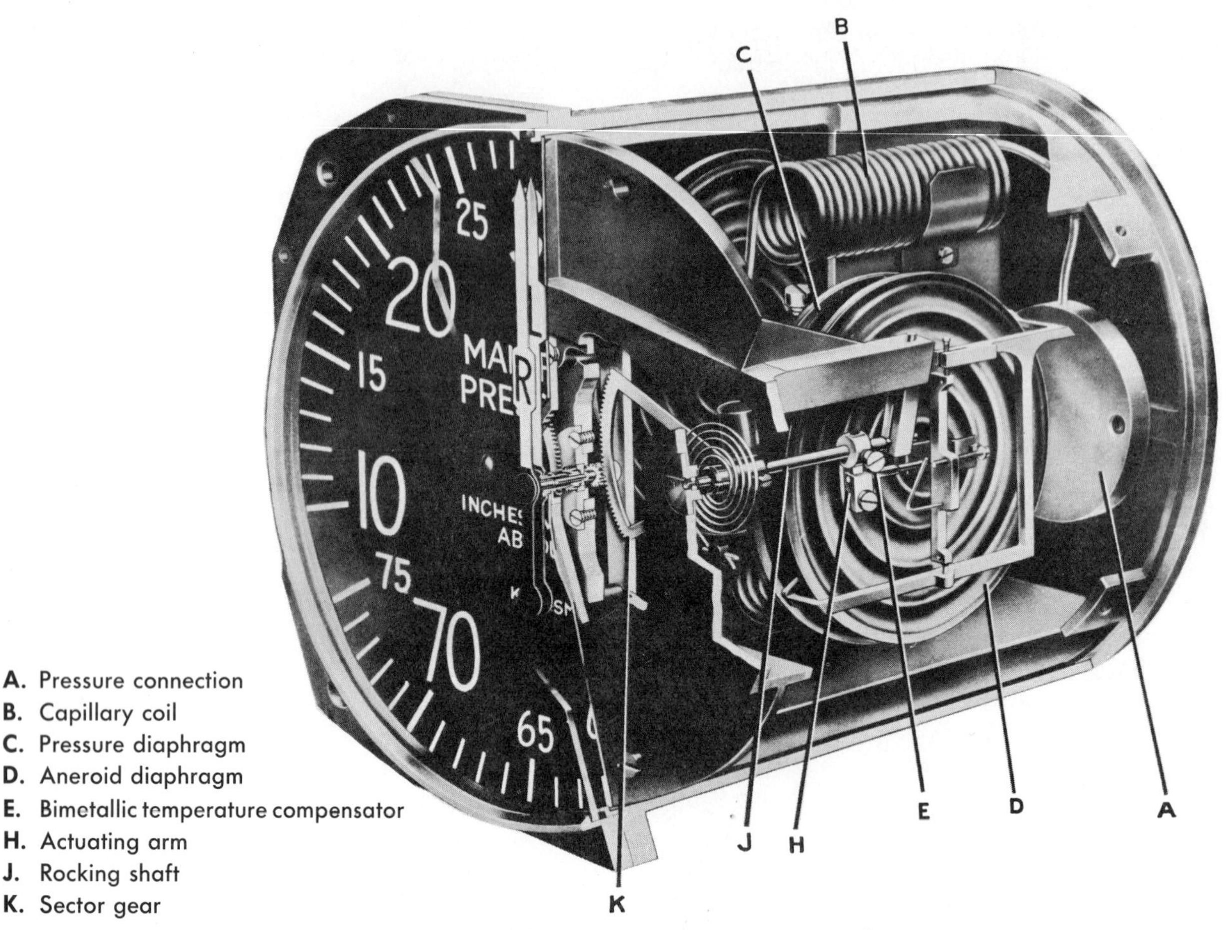

Figure **12·17** *Manifold-pressure-gage mechanism (Kollsman).*

The instrument illustrated in Fig. 12·17 is a direct indicating unit. The manifold pressure is transmitted from the engine through tubing to the connection *A* in the rear of the case. It is then passed through the capillary coil *B* which dampens minor fluctuations and is introduced to the interior of the diaphragm *C*. The nearer diaphragm *D* is an evacuated (aneroid) diaphragm which expands or contracts with altitude changes and compensates for their effects. The bimetallic strip *E* compensates for the effect of temperature changes on the mechanism. As the manifold pressure increases, the diaphragm *C* expands, causing the arm *H* and the rocking shaft *J* to rotate. This, in turn, moves the sector gear *K*, and the movement is transmitted through the spur gear to the pointer. A similar mechanism on the other side of the case actuates the pointer for the second engine.

The manifold-pressure gage should be installed near the tachometer, since these two instruments give the necessary readings for computation of the power output of the engine. The pointer of the gage should be in a vertical position when it is registering sea-level atmospheric pressure; that is, the 30 on the dial should be at the top. As mentioned previously, sea-level pressure is 29.92 in. Hg. A definite check of the zero reading of the manifold-pressure gage is obtained by comparing it with the altimeter on the airplane or with a portable barometer. This must be done when the engine is stopped.

A restriction is customarily placed in the connection at the rear of the instrument to dampen the effect of surges in the engine manifold pressure. Also, on the instrument panel and as close to the instrument as possible, a purge valve is sometimes installed. This valve is for the purpose of drawing out any condensate which may have collected in the line. One recommended procedure for clearing the line is to open the purge valve after the engine has been started and only while it is idling. During idling, the manifold pressure is considerably below atmospheric pressure and will create a strong suction through the line. The purge valve should be held open for about 30 sec, and this will give ample time for the line to be cleared of all moisture. The flow at this time will be from the atmosphere through the purge valve and into the engine. When the valve is closed, the gage should give the correct reading for engine manifold pressure. At idling this should be below 15 in. Hg.

When the engine rpm is increased, the manifold-pressure gage should be watched to see that it increases evenly and in proportion to power output. In the event that it lags or fails to register, the cause can usually be traced to one of the following three discrepancies: (1) The restriction in the instrument case fitting is too small; (2) the tube leading from the engine to the gage is clogged or leaks; (3) the diameter of the tubing is too small in proportion to its length.

Conversely, if the indication is too jumpy and erratic when the engine speed is increased, the restriction in the fitting is probably too large.

During operation of the airplane, the manifold-pressure gage is a prime indicator of engine performance. In an operation manual for a particular aircraft the manufacturer provides information on manifold pressure and rpm to give the pilot an accurate indication of the power being developed by the engine. For example, on a Cessna 310 airplane, when the engine is turning at 2,450 rpm and the manifold pressure is 24 in. Hg at a pressure altitude of 5,000 ft, the engine is developing 77 per cent of maximum brake horsepower (bhp). This is a condition established for maximum cruise power. If the engine is turning at 2,300 rpm under the same conditions, the power output will be 70 per cent of maximum bhp. On an airplane of this type with constant-speed propellers, the rpm of the engine is controlled by a governor which is adjusted by the pilot with the propeller control in the cockpit. Care must be taken that excessive manifold pressure is not used because this will cause high cylinder-head temperatures and danger of detonation. The result may be burned valves, damaged pistons, or complete engine failure. The operator of an airplane should be sure that he understands the correct power settings for all conditions of operation.

Fuel-quantity gage

Although most fuel-quantity gages today are electrically operated, the technician may encounter a pressure-type gage from time to time, and it is well that he understands its operation. A gage of this type is called a **hydrostatic gage** because it utilizes the pressure of the fuel, developed as a result of depth, to indicate fuel quantity.

The hydrostatic fuel-quantity system is operated on the principle that **the pressure exerted by a volume of liquid in a container is proportional to the depth of the liquid.**

This principle can be illustrated by the following simple experiment. Attach a balloon to the top of a bell jar. Holding the jar in a vertical position, immerse the large open end in a container partially filled with water. As the jar is lowered deeper into the water, pressure on the air above the level of the water increases and the balloon inflates. Now holding the jar in one position, add more water to the container. The added pressure of this water in the container forces more air into the balloon, and the inflation of the balloon increases.

An inverted cell, called a **hydrostatic cell,** similar to the bell jar in the foregoing experiment, is installed inside and at the bottom of the fuel tank in such a manner that the open end of the cell is subjected to the fuel pressure at that point. An upright open tube is attached to the cell and leads directly to the diaphragm of the indicator in the cockpit. Thus, when there is fuel in the tank, pressure is transmitted to the airtight diaphragm. The diaphragm and mechanism operate on the same principle as the one described in the airspeed indicator. As the fuel is consumed by the engine, pressure exerted on the bottom of the tank is decreased and the diaphragm in the indicator begins to collapse. The operation of the hydrostatic fuel-quantity-indicator system is illustrated in the diagram of Fig. 12 · 18. It will be observed that the pressure of the fuel in the hydrostatic cell will cause air pressure to be transmitted to the diaphragm in the indicator. The expansion of the diaphragm causes rotation of the rocking shaft and through linkage will move the sector gear. The movement of the sector gear will rotate the pinion and cause the indicating needle to move across the dial.

In order to maintain a correct differential-pressure reading, it is necessary that equal pres-

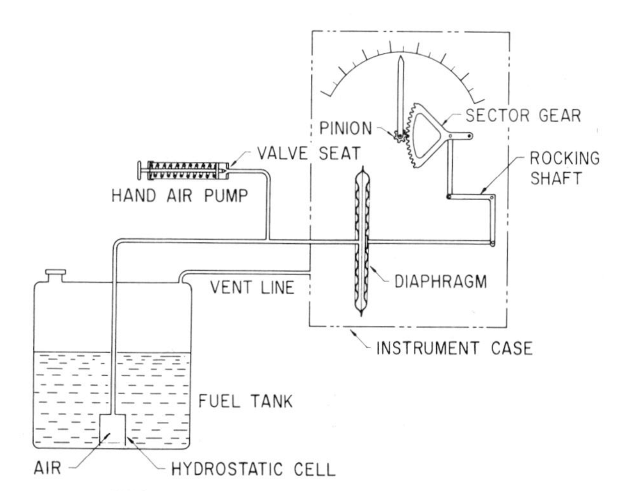

Figure **12 · 18** *Schematic diagram of a hydrostatic fuel-gage system.*

sure exist above the fuel level in the tank and inside the instrument case. This is accomplished by installing a vent line from the instrument case to the top of the fuel tank.

When properly installed, the cell, the upright tube, and the tube connecting them to the diaphragm in the instrument are filled with air. Then if fuel is put into the tank, the air in the cell and upright tube is compressed, allowing liquid partially to fill the hydrostatic cell. However, in order to get a correct reading of the pressure exerted by the fuel in the tank, all liquid must be expelled from the cell. This is accomplished by a small hand pump installed near the fuel-quantity indicator. The hand pump is connected to the pressure line between the tank and the indicator by means of a small tube. The purpose of the hand pump is to pump air into the line in order to force all fuel out of the hydrostatic cell. The pump operation is simple and effective. It is merely necessary to pull the pump handle back and release it. Air is forced into the line and cell, pushing all liquids ahead of it. The unit is spring loaded so that the needle valve inside the pump is held against the valve seat at the end of the pump. No air can escape back through the pump when the valve is seated.

During flight, any changes in air pressure due to changes in altitude or temperature will cause the loss of small quantities of air from the hydrostatic cell. Under such conditions the hand pump should be operated before a reading on the gage is taken. During level or normal flight, continuous and accurate indications can be obtained without the use of the pump.

If the airplane is designed for inverted flying, an important item in the installation of a hydrostatic fuel-quantity system is a check valve in the line leading to the instrument case. This valve automatically closes if the airplane is inverted, thus preventing fuel from flowing out of the tank and into the instrument.

A fuel gage must be calibrated to specify the number of gallons in the particular tank with which it is installed. This is normally done at the factory or prior to installation of the fuel tank. Otherwise, the instrument manufacturer must be furnished with accurate drawings and dimensions of the fuel tank and a table giving the distance in inches from the bottom of the hydrostatic cell to the surface of the fuel for each increment of 1 gal. The length of the tube from the cell to the gage and the tank venting system also must be known.

In order to check the accuracy of the instrument installed in the plane, it is first necessary to empty the fuel tank. The indicator is then checked for **zero** or **empty** reading. A known quantity of fuel is then placed in the tank, in whatever increments are to be measured, and the pointer indication checked after each addition. The airplane should be in normal flying position for this check. The gage is calibrated in gallons or marked **empty** and **full** at the two extremes, with graduations between. For the most accurate results, it is important that the fuel used for calibrations be of the same density as that used in flight.

Suction gages

Suction gages, or **vacuum gages,** are used in airplanes for the purpose of registering a reduction of pressure. In other words, they indicate the amount of vacuum being created by the vacuum pumps or venturi tube and assist in the proper setting of the relief valve in the vacuum system. A typical suction gage is illustrated in Fig. 12·19. The suction gage gives the pilot warning of impending failure of the system and informs him that he can no longer rely on the instruments which are operated by vacuum. It will be learned later that gyroscopes will operate for a short period of time even after the source of vacuum has been shut off or partially shut off, but the indications may be erroneous. Multiengine airplanes and some smaller ones are required to have an alternate source of vacuum available in the event of failure of the vacuum source being used. The suction gage indicates any fluctuation or impending failure of the system, thus giving the pilot warning so that he can switch over to the alternate vacuum source. For example, if an engine-driven vacuum pump on an inboard engine is being used, the alternate pump may be located on the opposite inboard engine. On the

Figure **12·19** *A suction gage.*

other hand, if the airplane has but one engine, the alternate source may be a **venturi tube.**

The venturi tube is dependent for its action on the forward motion of the airplane. A typical venturi tube, located on an airplane in the slipstream, causes a reduced pressure at the point where the line leads from it to the airplane. This is identical with the action and principle of the venturi in a float-type carburetor. The venturi tube is used only on some of the smaller aircraft and is not recommended for transport planes because of the following drawbacks. It is mounted on the slipstream of the airplane, thus causing additional drag; the amount of vacuum it creates is dependent on the speed of the airplane. In its location on the plane, it is subject to icing, and it renders gyroscope instruments ineffective until takeoff or until the airplane has sufficient forward speed to create the necessary vacuum. Therefore, on most transport planes you will find that two engine-driven vacuum pumps are used.

The suction gage is vented to the atmosphere or to the air filter if one is used in the system. The tube leading from the pressure-sensitive diaphragm in the instrument tees into the vacuum line as close to the instrument as possible. It is recommended by many manufacturers that it tee into the line leading directly to the gyro horizon in planes which include this instrument in the instrument panel. Theoretically, if sufficient vacuum is being created to operate the gyro horizon, all other instruments in the system will function satisfactorily. Whatever reduction of pressure is caused by the vacuum pump or venturi tube tends to collapse the diaphragm in the gage. This movement is transferred through the rocking shaft, sector, and pinion to give a continuous indication on the dial. The range of the dial is usually from 0 to 10 and represents inches of mercury below the surrounding atmospheric pressure.

If the suction gage is mounted on a shockproof panel and connected to another instrument on the same panel, it is not necessary to use rubber tubing for the connection. However, when the connecting tube is fastened to a rigid part of the airplane structure, flexible tubing must be used. The amount of vacuum which should be registered on the suction gage is dependent on the instruments which operate on that particular system and on the manufacturer's specifications. In instances where one instrument should have less vacuum than another but both operate from the same source of vacuum, a small restriction is placed in the line leading directly to the instrument requiring the least vacuum. Obviously the relief valve is set to furnish the maximum amount of vacuum required for any one instrument.

The suction gage is set to show 4 in. Hg for the artificial horizon and the directional gyro. The bank-and-turn instrument is set to 2 in. Hg by a suction gage connected temporarily to a fitting screwed into the bank-and-turn needle valve which is in the back of the indicator.

It must be pointed out that many airplanes are now equipped with electrically operated gyros, and it is not necessary for such airplanes to be equipped with vacuum systems. On the other hand, many of the most modern light planes still employ vacuum pumps driven by the engine to operate vacuum-driven gyroscope instruments such as the artificial horizon, the bank-and-turn indicator, and the directional gyro.

REVIEW QUESTIONS

1. What type of mechanism is generally used for high-pressure measuring instruments?
2. Describe a vapor-pressure instrument.
3. What pressure instruments are necessary for the operation of an aircraft engine?
4. Why is a restriction placed in the line leading to an oil-pressure gage?
5. What is the function of an instrument pressure transmitter?
6. Describe a diaphragm-type pressure instrument.
7. Explain the operation of an airspeed-indicator system.
8. What correction should be applied to the airspeed-indicator reading as altitude increases?
9. What compensating elements are included in a TAS indicator?
10. Compare a Machmeter with an airspeed indicator.
11. Why is the barometric setting important in the use of an altimeter?
12. What corrective elements are included in the Bendix compensated altimeter?
13. Describe a *pitot tube.*
14. Explain the operation of a rate-of-climb indicator.
15. What reading will be indicated on a manifold-pressure gage at sea level when the engine is not running?
16. What consideration should be given the location of the manifold-pressure gage on the instrument panel?
17. What is the value of a suction gage in an instrument system?
18. What is the purpose of a venturi tube in an instrument system?

CHAPTER 

Mechanical Instruments

TACHOMETER

Even though many of the tachometers in use today are of the electrical type, there are still light aircraft which employ the mechanical or magnetic types. Regardless of the type used, the tachometer measures one of the most important functions of the aircraft engine, that is, the number of times the engine crankshaft rotates every minute. In the early jet engines the tachometer often is used to indicate the percentage of power being delivered by the engine.

The tachometer is universally classified as one of the primary engine instruments because the rpm of the engine provides one of the principal indications of engine performance. In the discussion on manifold-pressure gages it was pointed out that the rpm developed by the engine combined with the manifold pressure gives an accurate indication of power output. On the ground, before takeoff, the pilot uses the tachometer to test the engine and to check the magnetos. In flight the tachometer is used to guide the pilot in proper throttle and propeller rpm settings, thus enabling him to choose the setting which will give the maximum performance or the most economical cruising speed. On a multiengine airplane the tachometer provides a means for synchronizing the engines. In flight it is essential that the pilot be able to sense impending engine failure, and one of the most reliable indicators is the tachometer. Much of the wear and tear on engines and much fuel waste can be avoided if the pilot of an airplane makes proper use of this important instrument.

The centrifugal tachometer is a widely used mechanical type because of its simplicity of construction, light weight, ease of calibrating, and reliability. If properly maintained, this instrument should have an accuracy of plus or minus 25 rpm. As its name implies, centrifugal force is the basic principle upon which the tachometer operates.

Some centrifugal tachometer mechanisms are equipped with two flyweights and others have three. The drive shaft from the engine connects to a gear assembly in the instrument and drives the rotating shaft carrying the flyweights. The flyweights tend to move outward from the center of rotation, and as they do this, they cause a collar to slide along the shaft. A schematic diagram of this arrangement is shown in Fig. 13·1. The movement of the collar is transmitted through a rocking shaft and sector gear to the pinion which moves the indicating needle. The needle is kept under tension against the mechanism by means of a hairspring.

A cutaway illustration of a typical centrifugal tachometer is shown in Fig. 13·2. A careful study of this illustration will provide an understanding of the operation of the instrument.

The tachometer is located in a prominent position with the engine instruments in the panel. The instrument end of the drive shaft should be higher than the engine end to prevent drainage of oil into the instrument case.

After each installation, the drive shaft should be tested for freedom of movement by disconnecting it at the engine end. If it can be turned freely with the fingers, it is a good indication that

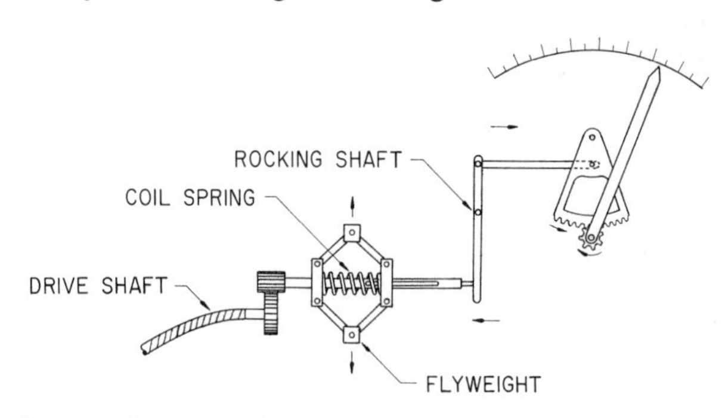

Figure **13·1** *Schematic diagram of centrifugal tachometer.*

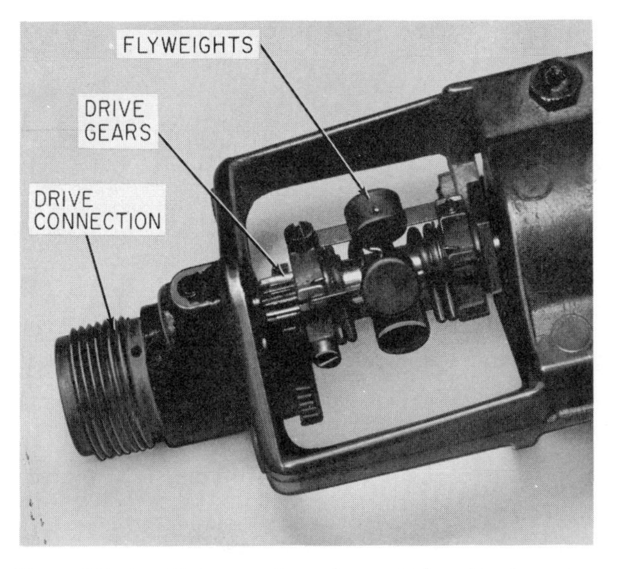

Figure 13·2 Cutaway view of a centrifugal tachometer.

the shaft is not binding in its housing. Whenever the shaft is removed for inspection or replacement, the technician should make certain that it is well covered with an approved grease before installing.

It can readily be seen that installations of the centrifugal tachometer can be made only on small aircraft because of the necessity for a short drive shaft. If the drive shaft is too long, it will cause a whipping motion which will in turn give erratic indications on the instrument. The drive shaft and housing should be installed so there is no pull on the drive or housing which may cause stress during operation.

One end of the drive shaft is connected to the engine crankshaft through a set of gears, and the other end is attached directly to the tachometer. The gear ratio is usually 2:1, engine to tachometer drive. That is, the tachometer drive rpm is one-half engine rpm. The drive shaft is enclosed in a semiflexible housing, which should be supported by clamps approximately 18 in. apart attached to available parts of the airplane structure. Care should be taken while installing the drive-shaft housing to see that there are no sharp bends. The radius of any curve should not be less than 6 in. and preferably not less than 12 in.

Magnetic tachometer

The magnetic tachometer may be classed as a mechanical instrument because it neither generates an electrical current nor requires an electrical current for operation. A simplified drawing of such an instrument is shown in Fig. 13·3. The drive shaft is connected to a cylindrical magnet which rotates in an aluminum drag cup. The rotation of the magnet induces eddy currents in

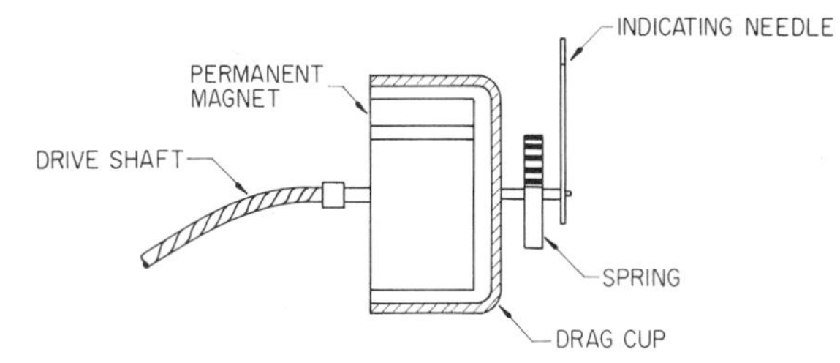

Figure 13·3 Schematic illustration of magnetic tachometer.

the metal of the drag cup, and these currents are in such a direction that they oppose the magnetism of the permanent magnet. Hence, the greater the speed of the rotation of the magnet, the greater will be the drag on the cup. The drag cup is connected to the indicating needle, thus causing it to rotate. The needle and the cup are held in the zero position by means of a hairspring when the tachometer shaft is not turning. The principle of the magnetic drag cup is also used for the transmitter of an electric tachometer and for automobile speedometers.

Accelerometer

The **accelerometer** is frequently used on new airplanes during test flights to measure the acceleration loads on the aircraft structure. It serves as a basis for stress analysis because it gives an accurate indication of stresses imposed on the airplane during flight. Its function is to measure in gravity units the accelerations of gravity being exerted on the airplane. It is also used as a service instrument on many fighter airplanes to indicate any excessive stress that might have occurred during flight. If an airplane is designed to withstand loads of 6 *g* and it is found after a particular flight that 8 *g* has been imposed on the airplane, it is necessary to subject the airplane to a very careful inspection to determine whether damage has been done as a result of the excessive loading. The most likely cause of excessive loads during flight is rough weather. Severe updrafts or downdrafts can cause very high loads on the aircraft, and the accelerometer will give an indication of the extent of the loads.

The accelerometer does not indicate any changes in velocity which take place in a line coinciding with the longitudinal axis of the airplane. If the airplane is in a dive, no vertical acceleration is registered by the accelerometer. When the airplane is pulling out of a dive, however, extremely high acceleration indications may be produced.

The accelerometer is usually graduated in gravity units up to plus 12 *g*, with minus 5 *g* as the lowest reading. Occasionally the instrument has a range from minus 1 to plus 8 *g*. Minus readings occur when the airplane is being nosed over into a dive or in level flight when a downward air current is encountered.

Vertical acceleration can be illustrated by carrying a heavy parcel in an elevator. When the elevator starts its downward motion, the parcel seems to lose weight. When the elevator assumes a steady rate of descent, the parcel again feels normal in weight. When the elevator slows down and just before it stops, the parcel seems to be excessively heavy. If these apparent changes in weight could actually be measured, the result would be the vertical acceleration of the parcel.

Some accelerometer instruments have two hands, but the more modern types are equipped with three hands. One hand measures the continuous acceleration, another measures the maximum acceleration reached at any time during the flight, and the third hand measures the minimum acceleration, or the largest minus reading, during the flight. The instrument is calibrated to read 1 *g* when the airplane is in normal flight or on the ground. This is the actual weight, or the vertical acceleration, of the airplane itself. This means that a load of 1 *g* is imposed upon the airplane as a result of its normal weight.

The principle of the accelerometer is illustrated in the diagram of Fig. 13·4. In this drawing, the mass weight is free to slide up and down on two mass shafts. As it moves up and down, it pulls on the cord which passes around three pulleys. The main pulley is attached to the shaft which carries the indicating needle. Thus, when the mass moves, it turns the main pulley and causes movement of the indicating needle. The mass is held in the 1-*g* position by the balance spring, which is of the flat coiled type such as a clock spring. The inside of this spring is attached to the shaft on which the main pulley and indicating needle are mounted, and the outer end is attached to a stationary part of the case.

A cutaway view of an accelerometer is shown in Fig. 13·5. In this instrument the main shaft is enclosed in a hollow shaft which is somewhat shorter than the main shaft. Attached to this hollow shaft is the maximum reading hand. Also fixed to the hollow shaft is a ratchet. As the main shaft rotates, a driver arm pushes a small tab which is a part of the ratchet, thus turning the hollow shaft along with the main shaft. This means that both the continuous reading hand and the maximum reading hand move simultaneously up to the point where the vertical acceleration on the weight is counterbalanced by the calibrat-

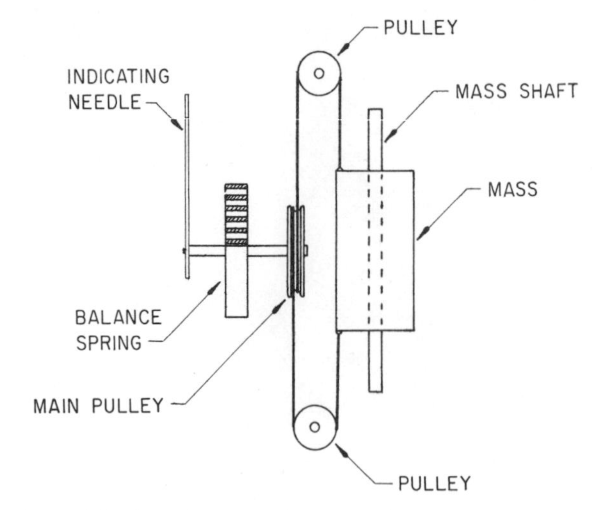

Figure **13·4** *Diagram of an accelerometer.*

ing spring. The maximum reading hand is stopped on the high point by means of the pawl, which engages one of the ratchet teeth. Obviously the ratchet and hand will stay in this position until such a time as a greater vertical acceleration is produced to move it farther around the scale. When the knob at the front of the instrument is turned, the pawl is disengaged and the maximum reading hand is free to return to its normal position.

The mechanism described in the foregoing section is only one of the many types of accelerometers, but in all cases the weight or pendulum weight works against a calibrated spring which determines the degree of travel of the mass weight. In inertial guidance systems for missiles and spacecraft small accelerometers are used to develop signals indicating what degree of acceleration is taking place. In a stable platform for an inertial guidance system there are usually three accelerometers: one for vertical acceleration, one for longitudinal acceleration, and one for lateral acceleration. These are arranged so the mass can move up and down, fore and aft, and from side to side, respectively. The accelerometer signals are sent to the computer section of the system, where correction signals are developed.

In the operation of missiles and spacecraft it is also a common practice to employ accelerometers to provide a constant signal showing the gravity loading on the vehicle. This is particularly important immediately after firing and upon reentry into the atmosphere. The indications provided by the accelerometers are used to show that loadings in excess of what a human being can stand are not developed in manned vehicles. Accelerometers are used in jet aircraft to limit the rate of rotation about the three axes.

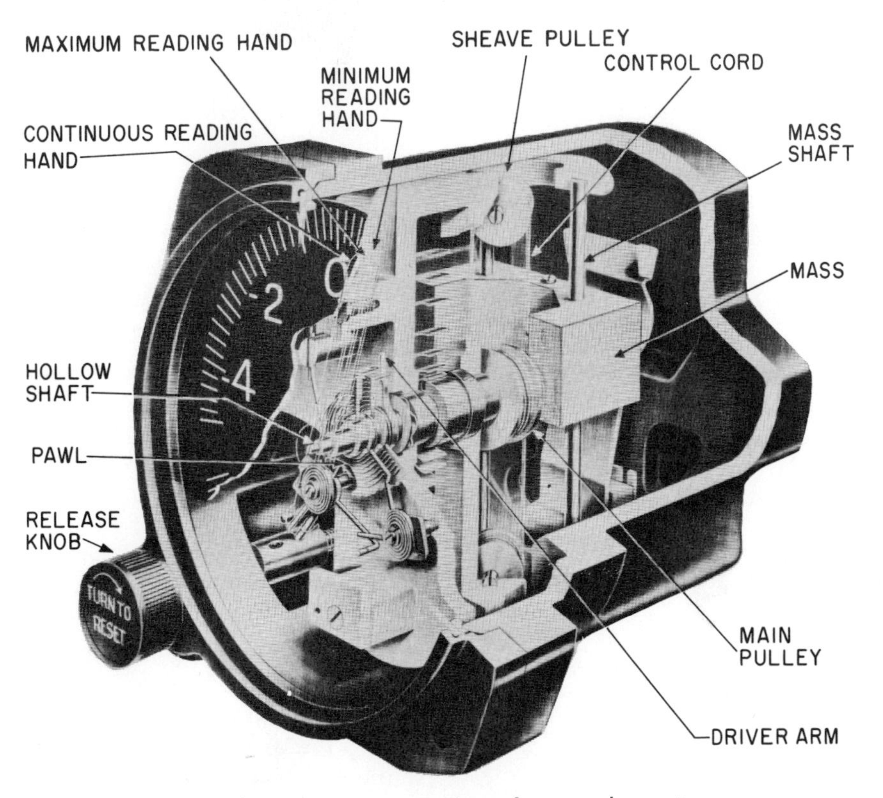

Figure **13·5** *Cutaway view of an accelerometer.*

FUEL FLOWMETER

On all transport aircraft, where economy of operation is paramount and where it is necessary to develop accurate cruise control, it is important that the operator of the engine or engines have an accurate indication of the amount of fuel being consumed. The fuel-flow rate indicates power developed and aids in planning the range of flight. To provide an indication of fuel-flow rate a fuel flowmeter is installed in the main fuel line to each engine. An indicator is installed on an instrument panel where it can be observed by either the pilot or the flight engineer. The fuel-flow indication is conveyed electrically from the transmitter to the indicator by means of a signal generator such as a synchro or magnetic pickoff. The electrical transmitter does not fall within the scope of this text, but the measuring assembly is described briefly.

One popular type of flowmeter is operated by the force of fuel flow against a vane which rotates in a spiral measuring chamber. With this arrangement the cross-sectional area of the space through which the fuel flows increases as the vane moves under the force of the fuel. The shape of the chamber is such that the vane can close it completely when no fuel is flowing. A schematic drawing of such an arrangement is shown in Fig. 13·6. As fuel starts to flow through the flowmeter, the vane moves against spring tension away from the closed position. As flow increases, the vane moves farther from the stop to provide a larger aperture through which the fuel can flow. The vane is connected by a small shaft to a transmitting element which generates a signal which is sent to the indicator on the instrument panel.

The indicator is calibrated in pounds or hundreds of pounds of fuel per hour, since the weight of the fuel consumed is the basis for computation of power output and range.

The flowmeter is a comparatively simple measuring device and has been found to be very accurate for all practical purposes. A relief valve is usually incorporated between the inlet and outlet ports so the instrument can be completely bypassed. This safety measure prevents the in-

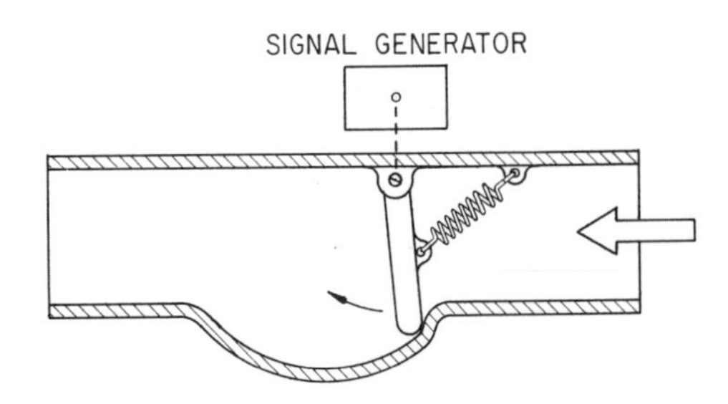

Figure **13·6** *Schematic drawing of a fuel flowmeter mechanism.*

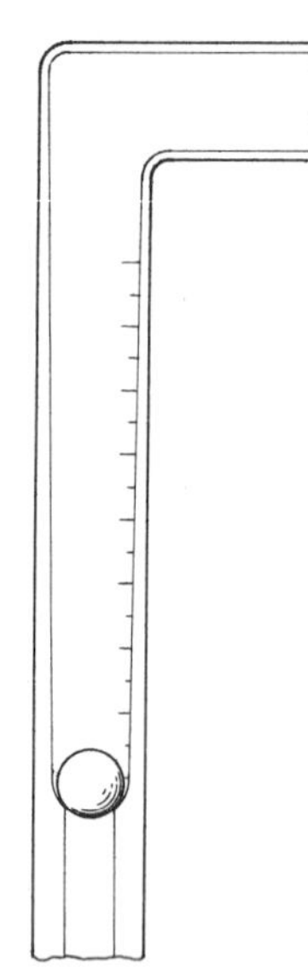

Figure 13·7 Tubular flowmeter.

strument from developing a high pressure drop and impeding the flow of fuel.

Flowmeters installed in aircraft should have the following proven characteristics:

1. They should be designed to cause the minimum of fuel-flow interference and be equipped with an easily opened bypass.
2. The instrument should be mounted on the instrument panel, but should not require fuel lines leading to the panel. Remote indicating devices allow the flowmeter to be installed on multiengine aircraft and also eliminate fire hazards to a large degree.
3. The flowmeter should not require frequent priming in order to eliminate air bubbles from the lines.

Another type of flowmeter is illustrated in Fig. 13·7. This flowmeter or flow gage is used on flow benches for checking the operation of carburetors and fuel-flow regulators. It can also be used in engine test cells to show the amount of fuel consumed by an engine under test.

In this flowmeter a ball or cone is installed in a glass tube which is tapered in the inside diameter. At the lower end of the tube the diameter is approximately the same as that of the ball. When fuel starts to flow, the ball rises in proportion to the rate of flow to allow a greater space through which the fuel can flow. The height of the ball in the tube indicates the rate of fuel flow.

FUEL-LEVEL GAGES

Float-type and direct-reading gages have been used on many light aircraft since the time that the first fuel gage was installed. These gages have many variations, depending upon the location of the fuel tanks. The inverted float gage is used on aircraft equipped with the gasoline tank located in the upper wing.

One gage of this type has a rod suspended from the float. The rod has a disk or a small piece of metal on the lower end, and this disk is visible through a glass tube. The glass tube is usually graduated in gallons to show the amount of fuel remaining in the tank and is protected by a metal frame which surrounds the tube. A slot in the frame wide enough to ensure good visibility of the tube allows the operator of the aircraft to obtain readings from his location in the cockpit. In the event the fuel tank is located in a lower wing, the same type of float gage can be used with the tube extending above the wing.

The **rotating dial gage** has a relatively simple mechanism. The indicator is a round drum-shaped device which has a revolving disk inside. The tank unit consists of a float on the end of a long arm, the other end of which transmits motion to the disk in the instrument by means of a semicircular gear. The semicircular gear is moved by the float rising and falling with the level of the fuel.

The **upright float gage** has the float arm directly connected to the pointer by a link arm. Thus, the pointer is moved up and down with the float and float arm. The tank must be located below the cockpit if this type of gage is used, thus placing the gage in clear view of the pilot.

The **sight-glass gage** is basically identical with the water-level gage on a water tank. It can be used only when the fuel tank is approximately at the same level as the cockpit. The indicator is simply a glass tube which runs from the top to the bottom of the fuel tank and is connected to the tank at both top and bottom. This allows the fuel to assume the same level in the tube that exists in the tank. Graduations are painted or inscribed on the tube, or they can be painted on a metal scale adjacent to it. As a safety factor, shutoff valves should be provided at each end of the tube to prevent leakage of fuel if the glass is broken.

TEMPERATURE GAGE

Temperature gages in modern aircraft are often operated electrically by means of the output of the thermocouple or Wheatstone bridge. These instruments are not within the scope of this text; however, we shall consider those instruments which utilize the expansion and contraction of various materials to provide a temperature indication.

Nearly all solid materials expand when heated and contract when cooled. Since the results of such expansions are more important than the causes, it is not necessary to describe the molecular activities which take place when heat is applied to a solid. The principal point to remember is that some metals expand more than others when subjected to heat. If the amount of expansion that takes place in various solids is measured for a given increase in temperature, a specific value can be assigned to each material. This value is called the **coefficient of expansion.** The coefficient of linear expansion is defined as **the change in length of each unit of length for a rise of temperature of one degree centigrade.**

As a result of extensive research on this subject in the past, tables have been prepared which show the coefficient of expansion for all the most common materials. These tables can be found in most physics textbooks.

Two metals commonly used in bimetallic thermometers are brass and iron. The coefficient of linear expansion of these two metals is, respectively, 0.0000105 and 0.0000067. Therefore if a strip of brass and a strip of iron of equal length at room temperature were securely brazed or otherwise bonded together, they could be used as a thermometer. As the temperature rises, both metals expand, but the length of the brass strip increases faster than the length of the iron strip. This causes the bimetallic combination to curve. Conversely, if the temperature drops lower than room temperature, the curve is in the opposite direction.

When one end of the bimetallic strip is attached to the instrument case and the other end is attached to a pointer which is free to rotate around a calibrated dial, the temperature changes can be converted to actual temperature measurements in centigrade or Fahrenheit scales on the instrument.

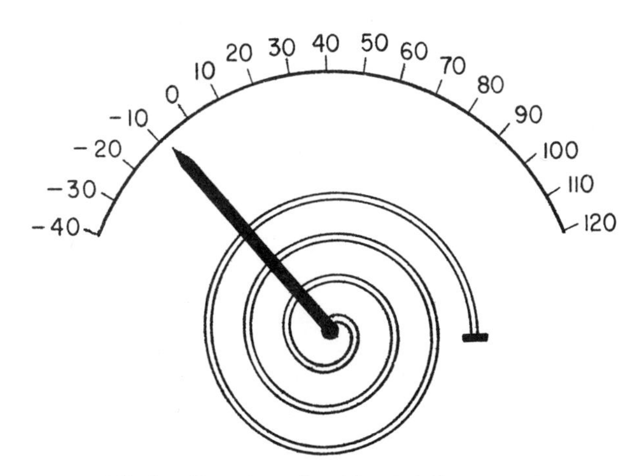

Figure **13·8** *Drawing of a bimetal thermometer.*

Some of these instruments have a range of minus 40 to plus 40°C. A diagram of a bimetal thermometer is shown in Fig. 13·8.

In all types of bimetallic thermometers, there will be some lag in registering rapid temperature changes because the thermal unit is enclosed. A few minutes must be allowed for the pointer to reach the correct position after a sudden temperature change takes place.

CLOCKS

Clocks or time indicators are considered necessary items for scientific flying and navigation. When the pilot is flying on instruments, the clock becomes an integral part of the basic flight group. Its main function is to aid navigation. Some of the specific uses of the clock are as follows:

1. Pilots must at all times be able to report their position and time accurately to their own station and to any control tower in the vicinity in order that the traffic on charted airways can be well regulated.
2. Operators familiar with their engines and rate of fuel consumption can estimate the fuel consumption by time if the fuel gage becomes inoperative. Hence, they can compute remaining fuel at any time.
3. Ground-speed checks cannot be made without knowing the elapsed time between two points.
4. The clock is necessary for maintaining schedules, complying with times for radio communications, and making checks against aircraft instruments, such as the rate-of-climb and turn-and-bank indicators.
5. All types of navigation require accurate knowledge of elapsed time, especially when flight is over unfamiliar territory; hence a good clock must be available for long-distance flying.

All standard instrument panels are equipped with at least one eight-day clock. These clocks must be carefully shock-mounted to ensure long life and accurate performance. Although the clocks being built today are ruggedly constructed and temperature compensated, vibration is one of the worst conditions to which a clock can be subjected. Variance on properly shock-mounted and properly calibrated clocks does not exceed 5 sec per day.

The normal maintenance of clocks by the technician consists only of winding, setting, and checking them for accuracy unless continued trouble has been experienced because of faulty installation. When a clock is wound, no great force should be exerted after the winding stem offers any appreciable resistance to further winding. In a check for accuracy, the second hand is checked against another clock of known accuracy for a period of not less than 1 hr.

Several different types and makes of clocks are being successfully used in airplanes. All are required to have the **hour, minute,** and **sweep second hands.** Others are equipped with five hands. In addition to the three hands already mentioned, these clocks include a **stopwatch** hand and an **elapsed-time** hand.

Under no condition should an aircraft maintenance technician open an aircraft clock for inspection or adjustment. This type of work should be done only in an instrument overhaul shop where conditions and equipment are suitable for the work.

REVIEW QUESTIONS

1. Explain the operation of a centrifugal tachometer.

2. Describe the construction of a magnetic tachometer.

3. What is the function of an accelerometer?

4. How is an accelerometer useful in the operation of missiles or spacecraft?

5. Describe the construction of a fuel flowmeter.

6. Why is a fuel flowmeter useful for the operation of long-range aircraft?

7. In what units is a fuel flowmeter usually calibrated?

8. Describe three types of fuel-level gages.

9. Explain the operation of a bimetallic temperature gage.

10. Why is an accurate clock essential in the navigation of an airplane?

11. What service should be regularly performed on a clock?

12. Who should perform disassembly and adjustment of a clock?

CHAPTER 14

Gyro Instruments

One of the most essential devices for the navigation of both aircraft and space vehicles is the **gyroscope.** The gyroscope is defined as **a device consisting of a wheel having much of its mass concentrated around the rim, mounted on a spinning axis which is free to rotate about one or both of two axes perpendicular to each other and to the spinning axis.** The characteristic of a gyroscope which makes it valuable as a navigation device is its ability to remain rigid in space, thus providing a directional reference.

Every boy is familiar with the spinning tops used as toys for children. These toys are made in many shapes and sizes, but they all operate on the principle of the gyroscope; that is, a spinning mass tends to stabilize with its axis fixed in space and will continue to spin in the same plane unless outside forces are applied to it.

A gyroscope mounted in rings so the mounting can be rotated in any direction without disturbing the gyro is called a **free gyro.** The rings in which the gyro is mounted and which permit it to move are called **gimbal rings.** Figure 14 · 1 is a drawing of a free gyro showing the three axes of rotation. The spinning axis of the gyro is the *X* axis and is horizontal in the illustration. The *Y* axis is also horizontal but is perpendicular to the spinning axis. The *Z* axis is vertical and is therefore perpendicular to the two other axes.

RIGIDITY IN A GYRO

The **rigidity** of a gyro is the force of the gyro which opposes any other force which tends to change its plane of rotation in space. The rigidity is increased as the mass at the rim of the gyro wheel is increased and as the speed of rotation is increased. A gyro built in the form of a heavy-rimmed wheel will have much more rigidity than a gyro shaped like a sphere or cylinder.

If a free gyro without friction or other outside influences were started running in a horizontal plane (vertical axis) at 12:00 noon at a particular point on the equator and then were observed for 24 hr, the plane of rotation would shift with respect to the earth's surface. At 3:00 P.M. the plane of rotation would have tilted up 45° toward the east and at 6:00 P.M. it would be vertical. At 12:00 midnight, the plane of rotation would be horizontal again, but it would appear to be inverted. As time continued for a total of 24 hr, the gyro would return to the original position. The foregoing action is the result of the rigidity of the gyro, and it is this characteristic which makes the device effective as a navigation reference.

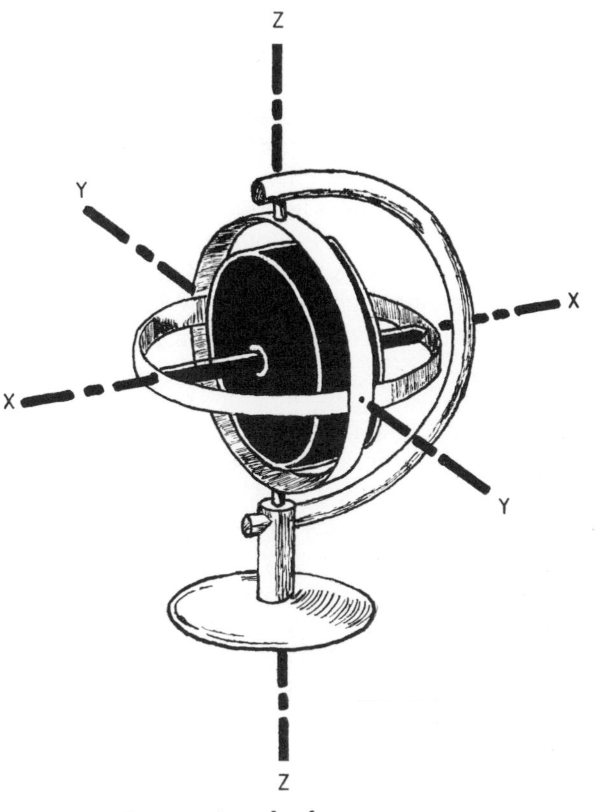

Figure **14 · 1** *Drawing of a free gyro.*

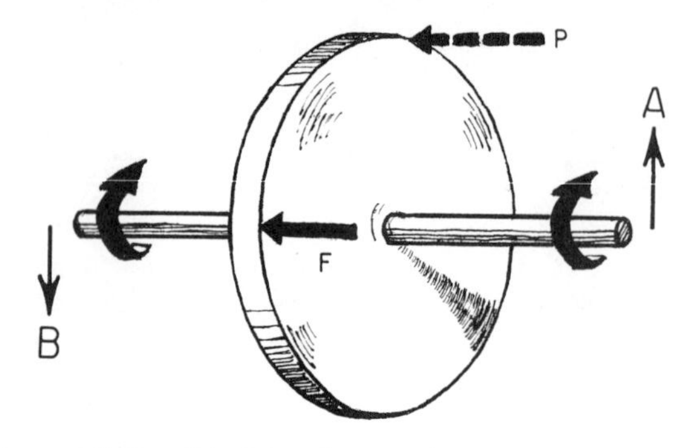

Figure **14·2** *Principle of precession.*

PRECESSION

Another important characteristic of the gyro is its tendency to **precess** if external forces are applied to it. **Precession** can be described briefly as the tendency of a gyro to shift its plane of rotation in a direction which is at an angle of 90° to the force applied to cause the shift. This is illustrated in Fig. 14·2. If a gyro is mounted on a shaft and spinning in the direction shown by the arrows and a force F is applied at the side of the wheel as shown, the precession force P will act at a point 90° in the direction of rotation from the applied force. This will tend to shift the axis of rotation as shown by the arrows A and B.

An analysis of the cause of precession is beyond the scope of this discussion. However, the precession force can be determined by the vector addition of two angular velocities, one being the angular velocity of the gyro and the other being the angular velocity of the applied force.

When we consider further the nature of precession, we observe the effect of an applied force when the gyro is **not** spinning.

In Fig. 14·3, a gyro is mounted with a spinning axis X. The axis of the inner gimbal is Y, and the axis of the outer gimbal is Z. When the rotor is not spinning, gyroscopic precession does not take place and the force F will cause the rotor to turn about the Y axis. We can say that the force F acting upon the nonspinning rotor causes each point on the upper half of the rotor to be accelerated in the direction of the applied force F. In the same way, because of the gimbal arrangement, every point on the lower half of the rotor is accelerated in the direction F'.

When the rotor is spinning, the force F must impart the same acceleration as before, but now each point on the rim is also moving about the spin axis. It is this spinning motion which contributes to the precessional motion. As each point moves around the spin axis from A to C, it is being accelerated in the direction F, and when it moves from C through D to A, it is accelerated in the direction F'. Since each point is continuously accelerated in the direction F during its travel through the upper portion of the circle, it must attain its maximum velocity in the F direction as it reaches position C. In the same way, as the point travels through the bottom portion of the circle, the acceleration in the F' direction results in the point attaining a maximum velocity in the F' direction at the end of this period of acceleration (at point A). Because of the gimbal system and the resulting velocity at A in the F' direction and at C in the F direction, the only compatible resulting motion of the rotor is a turning about the Z axis.

Thus we see that applying an accelerating force to a spinning gyroscope results in a motion in the direction of the applied force at a point on the rotor 90° along the rim in the direction of spin.

The rate at which the gyroscope precesses about the Z axis is directly proportional to the magnitude of the applied force and inversely proportional to the speed of the rotor. Rotors of different sizes, weights, and shapes will precess at different rates also. A large, heavy rotor will precess much more slowly than a small one as the result of the same applied force.

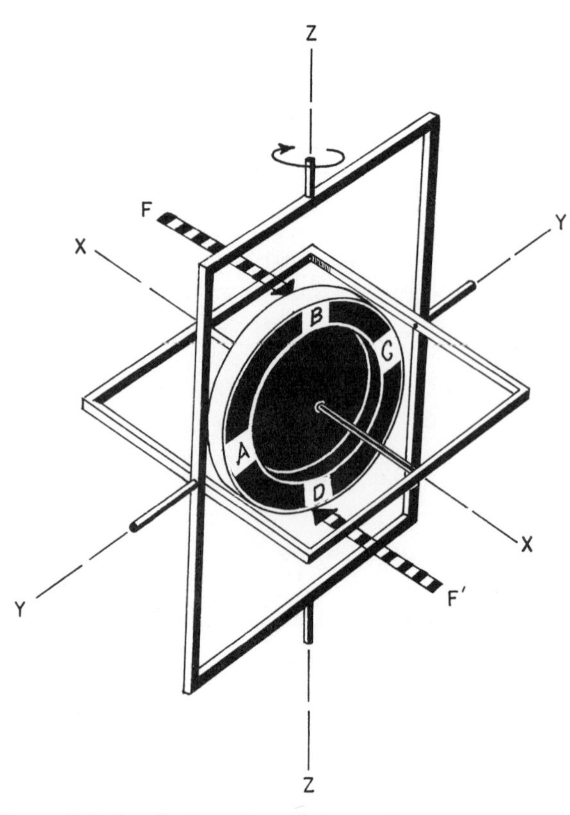

Figure **14·3** *Explanation of precession.*

EFFECTS OF BEARING FRICTION

In order to discuss the effect of bearing friction on the performance of a gyroscope, it is necessary to identify the axes of rotation as we have done previously. The spin axis of the rotor is axis *X*, and the rotor bearings will be called X bearings. The axis of rotation of the inner gimbal, which is horizontal, is the *Y* axis, and the axis of the outer gimbal is the *Z* axis. These are illustrated in Fig. 14 • 1. The *Z* axis is fixed to the case of the instrument, but the *Y* axis can move horizontally and the *X* axis can turn in azimuth with the *Y* axis and also can rotate vertically. Thus, it is said that the *X* axis of the gyroscope rotor has two degrees of freedom.

During this discussion, any motion of the spin axis (the gyro rotor axle) as a result of an applied torque while the rotor is spinning will be called **precession.**

The effect of friction in the *X*, *Y*, or *Z* axis makes it necessary to balance the gyroscope gimbals dynamically. If we balance the inner gimbal with the wheel stopped, there will be an unbalance remaining which is insufficient to overcome the static friction of the Y bearings. When the rotor is turning, there is a smaller amount of friction present in the bearings and the unbalance will be evident. The effects of unbalance are discussed later. In any event, final balancing tests must be performed with the rotor spinning.

Friction in the Z bearings can be detected by hanging a weight on the inner gimbal, at one end of the *X* axis, while the gyroscope is running. Theoretically this should cause only a precession of the spin axis in azimuth, but the motion in azimuth about the *Z* axis is retarded by the friction in the Z bearings. This friction is the equivalent of a torque about the *Z* axis which causes precession about the *Y* axis. As a result of the *Z*-axis friction, not only will the gyroscope be precessed in azimuth by the weight but its spin axis will drop on the end where the weight is hung. If the *Z*-axis friction is made extremely great, the weight causes the gyroscope rotor to fall rapidly. Actually the drop is the result of extreme stress within the *Z*-axis bearings. If, on the other hand, the frame were made to follow the motion of the outer gimbal perfectly, there would be no friction and no drop at all in the end of the *X* axis.

If the Z-bearing friction is very slight, another interesting gyroscopic action can be observed when the weight is placed on the inner gimbal. If the weight is placed on the gimbal suddenly, the *X* axis drops suddenly, then rises and oscillates until it settles out to a steady precessional motion in azimuth. The dip cannot now be caused by *Z*-axis friction, since we have assumed that it is negligible. The dip is caused by the inertia of the outer gimbal which prevents it from moving instantly. This inertia is equivalent to *Z*-axis friction at first and the dip occurs, but once the outer gimbal is moving, the *X* axis will cease to drop.

During the transient movement, the weight is decelerating in a downward direction and thus exerting a precessional torque in excess of that which exists when the weight has no downward movement. The outer gimbal, during the transient movement, achieves a precessional rate in excess of that called for from the static weight. When the weight ceases its downward motion, the outer gimbal is moving faster than it would otherwise. This excess of outer gimbal velocity will (through its inertia) exert a torque on the gyroscope spin axis, causing the weighted end to rise. This action slows the outer gimbal down. A continuation of the foregoing action occurs, and the outer gimbal slows down too much, thus permitting the weighted end of the spin axis to dip again. This oscillation, up and down, continues until the outer gimbal is moving exactly at the precession rate. The oscillation is called **nutation.** Nutation requires no external torque to sustain it, since energy is transferred back and forth from one element of the gimbal system to another. Nutation caused by the weight of the gimbals can be reduced by making the gimbal as light as possible in comparison with the mass of the rotor.

Friction in the X bearing, in addition to slowing down the rotor, is also apparent when the spin axis is precessed to the vertical so that the *X* and *Z* axes coincide. This friction then causes the inner and outer gimbals to be dragged around in the direction of spin.

If the gyroscope is driven electrically, the *X*-axis friction is overcome by the motor. The motor, running at synchronous speed, presses back on the inner gimbal with a force equal to that of the friction trying to drag the gimbal around. However, when the motor is accelerating, the force pressing back on the inner gimbal is appreciably greater than is necessary to overcome bearing friction. This force, although opposite in direction to the *X*-axis frictional torque, has an effect similar to that just described. If the inner and outer gimbals are not perpendicular, this force pushes not only on the Y bearings but also against the outer gimbal. This causes the gyro rotor to be precessed about the *Y* axis, and the gyro rotor axis becomes horizontal. Since the deceleration present when the unit is turned off is similar to an acceleration, the rotor axis is precessed towards the vertical. Thus it is desirable to provide braking action of some kind when an electrically driven gyro is turned off.

GYRO ROTOR DESIGN

The rotor of a gyro is basically a symmetrical mass capable of rotating at high speed. It has high angular momentum about its spin axis as a result of its speed and the way that its mass is distributed about the axis. Since the rigidity of a gyro is due to its angular momentum, it is desirable to obtain maximum angular momentum, with minimum weight and volume. The greatest angular momentum can be obtained by having most of the weight of the rotor at the rim of a large wheel rotating at high speed. However, the gimbals for such a rotor would have to be of a large diameter and the size of the instrument would be prohibitively large. A spherical rotor would have the most weight for a case of fixed volume, but then the distribution of weight about the gimbal axis would be identical with the distribution of weight about the spin axis. This would be equivalent to having heavy gimbals, which is one of the causes of nutation.

A rotor in the shape of a cylinder with its length equal to about 0.87 of its diameter ($\sqrt{3}/2$) has the inertial properties of a sphere of equal volume, while a rotor in the shape of a very thin disk has the best inertial properties. Therefore the cylindrical rotor of a useful instrument should have its length substantially less than 0.87 of its diameter. Actually, gyro rotors have been designed in a variety of shapes, since sometimes angular momentum is sacrificed in favor of other factors. The rotor should be made of a material of high mass. Most of the early rotors were made of brass, and this proved very satisfactory. Since the rotor of an electrically driven gyro serves as the rotor of the driving motor, it is of a laminated soft-iron squirrel-cage design inserted in a high-tensile-strength steel shell.

Many electric rotors are powered with three-phase 115-volt 400-cycle alternating current and have a running speed of slightly less than 24,000 rpm as compared with 8,000 rpm for some air-driven instruments. This high speed makes it possible to obtain high performance from relatively small airborne instruments, since the greater the speed of the rotor, the greater the rigidity of the gyro and the smaller will be the amplitude of any nutation that is present.

A gyro motor must be balanced about its spin axis and about each of its gimbal axes with its center of mass at the center of the gimbal system. Some gyroscopic rotors have a spring on the spin axle to maintain bearing loading under varying temperatures. As the raceways wear, the center of mass is shifted from the center of the gimbal system, causing an unbalance, and this results in a drift. Methods have been devised for assembling the rotor shaft without end play, thus overcoming the need for springs and eliminating most unbalance due to wear. The rotor bearings must be designed to exert as little frictional torque as possible, and for this reason sometimes cone pivots are used. However, when the contact area is small, the pressures exerted on the bearings are very high, and this often results in damage to the bearings. Any distortion of the bearings reduces the rigidity of the gimbal system and introduces high torques which further damage the bearings. For this reason, conventional double-race bearings are generally used even though they have higher friction factors. For the highly accurate sealed gyros used in missile-guidance systems, air bearings are sometimes employed, and this reduces friction to practically zero.

THE DIRECTIONAL GYRO

The **directional gyro** is a gyro-operated directional reference instrument designed to eliminate some of the problems associated with the magnetic compass. The gyro does not seek the North Pole; however, it will continue to tell the pilot of an airplane whether the airplane is holding a particular heading. The directional gyro must be reset to the magnetic compass from time to time to correct for precession or drift after a period of operation, usually after every 15 min.

The airborne directional gyro consists of a gyro rotor mounted in a set of gimbals so that the position of its spin axis can be maintained independent of the case of the instrument. The spin axis is normally horizontal. The axis of the inner gimbal is also horizontal and is perpendicular to the spin axis. The outer gimbal is pivoted on a vertical axis, so that all three axes are mutually perpendicular. It is the relative angle between the outer gimbal and a reference point on the case that is measured by the instrument and presented on the dial. Since the spin axis is horizontal and the case can be considered aligned with the directional axis of the aircraft, the angle presented on the dial is also the angle between the heading of the aircraft and the direction of the spin axis of the gyro. Any change in the heading of the aircraft is indicated on the dial, since the

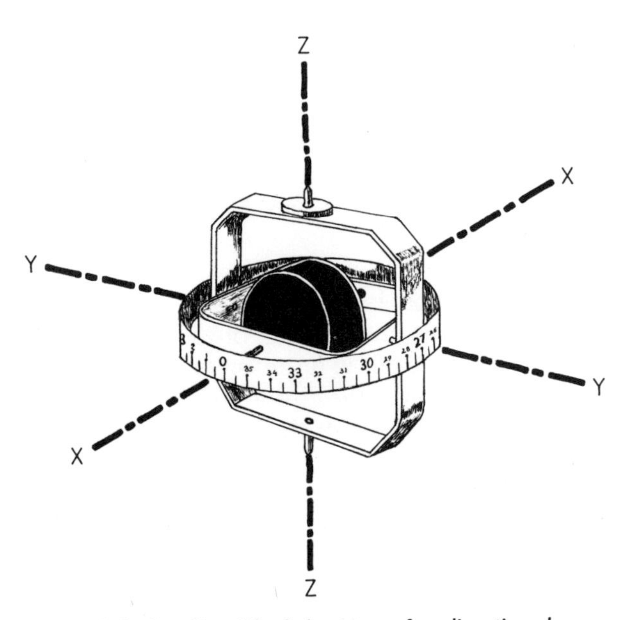

Figure **14·4** *Simplified drawing of a directional gyro.*

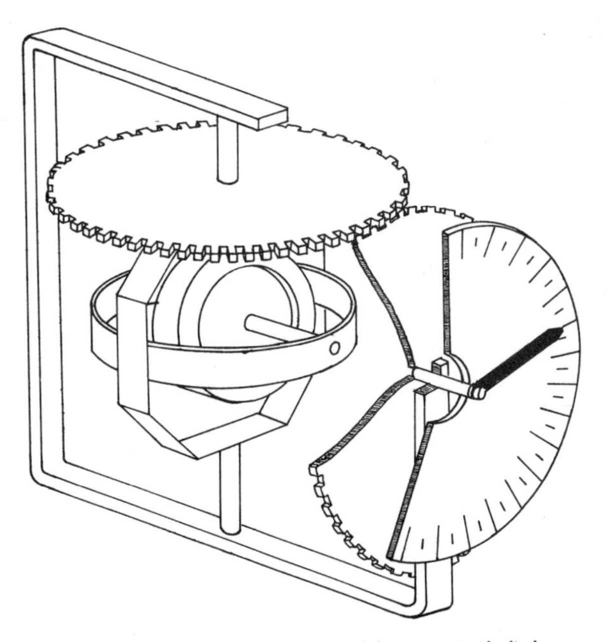

Figure **14·5** *Directional gyro with a vertical dial.*

position of the gyro is rigid in space and is not affected by the motion of the aircraft.

The principal parts of a directional gyro are illustrated in the drawing of Fig. 14·4. Observe the gyro with the X axis, the inner gimbal with the Y axis, and the outer gimbal with the Z axis. When the gyro is spinning, it will maintain its rigid position in space even though the case of the instrument is rotated about it in any direction. When the instrument is mounted in an airplane and in operation, it is easy to understand that, as the airplane turns to the right or left, there will be a relative movement between the dial mounted on the outer gimbal and the instrument case. The amount of this movement will indicate to the pilot the angular degrees through which the airplane has turned.

The designs of the dial faces for directional gyros vary widely, but they all indicate a value in degrees from 0 to 360°. A knob is provided on the instrument which permits the reading to be changed by the pilot. The reading is usually made to coincide with the average reading of a magnetic compass. The directional-gyro instrument is used as a reference during flight instead of the magnetic compass, since the magnetic compass fluctuates and oscillates considerably during airplane maneuvers. The directional gyro is a stable reference; hence the readings will be comparatively stable for normal flight maneuvers.

A directional gyro designed to provide a vertical dial indication is illustrated in the drawing of Fig. 14·5. This is accomplished merely by gearing the outer gimbal assembly to the gear which drives the indicating needle. The drawing does not indicate the actual construction of the instrument, but it is greatly simplified in order to illustrate the principle.

As mentioned previously, the gyros used in various instruments can be driven by air or by means of an electric current. If the gyro is electrically driven, the gyro itself is a part of the electric motor.

Figure 14·6 is a photograph of the rotor mechanism in an air-driven directional gyro. To drive this gyro, the case of the instrument is connected to a vacuum source. The partial vacuum created within the instrument draws air into the instrument through jets which direct the air into the "buckets" machined on the rim of the rotor. Within a short time after the vacuum system is turned on, the rotor is turning at a high rate of speed.

Figure **14·6** *Photograph of rotor mechanism in a directional gyro.*

Gyro instruments must necessarily be limited in the degree of movement through which the gimbals can travel except in the case of the directional gyro, where the Z axis can turn through a complete circle. If the degree of permitted movement is exceeded because of violent maneuvers of the airplane, the gyro rotor will be moved out of its normal position of rigidity, and it is then said to be "tumbled." In order to restore the gyro to its correct alignment, a "caging" mechanism is installed. When the gyro is caged, it is locked into its correct position mechanically. The caging mechanism must then be released to permit the gyro to function normally.

GIMBAL ERROR

During straight and level flight the gimbals of a directional gyro are perpendicular. Since the pointer and the compass card are positioned to represent the angle between the outer gimbal and the frame of the instrument, the position of the pointer indicates the heading of the aircraft. If the aircraft could be turned keeping the gimbals perpendicular, then the pointer would move around the card an amount equal to the amount of the turn and its position at any instant would be equal to the heading of the aircraft. However, when an aircraft turns, it must bank, and this banking causes the frame to move while the gyro rotor axis remains fixed in space. Unless the banking motion happens to be about the rotor spin axis, one or both of the gimbals will rotate about its axis to accommodate the motion of the frame. As a result the gimbals will no longer be perpendicular. Any rotation of the outer gimbal changes the relative positions of the compass card and the pointer, resulting in an erroneous reading. When the aircraft returns to level flight, the gimbals move again to perpendicular positions and the reading on the compass card becomes correct. This error is present in any gimbal system in which the indicator is controlled by the outer gimbal and the gyro spin axis serves as the actual reference direction. This error is called **gimbal error.**

The amount of gimbal error can be demonstrated by an example. Suppose that the present heading of the aircraft is 90° to the direction of the spin axis of the gyro. When the airplane banks for a turn, the outer gimbal does not rotate about its axis immediately, since the bank is about the axis of the inner gimbal, but as the aircraft turns in azimuth, both gimbals turn. If the aircraft turns 45° in azimuth, the base will turn 45°. However, to accommodate this motion the outer gimbal will rotate on its axis and the reading on the compass card will change more than 45°. The amount of error depends upon the bank angle. If the bank angle were 60°, the error would be 22°. That is, if the card originally read 90°, it would read 90° plus 45° plus 22° or 157° instead of 135°.

It should be understood that the error is an instantaneous error due to the relative direction of the spin axis and the heading of the aircraft and the amount of bank. The error is at maximum when the heading of the aircraft is approximately 45° from the position of the gyro spin axis, and its magnitude becomes greater for larger bank angles. When the bank angle becomes zero again as the aircraft levels off coming out of a turn, the error disappears.

LEVELING DEVICES

To be most effective as an indicator of azimuthal direction, a directional gyro should have its spin axis horizontal. In more complex equipment this would be accomplished by slaving the gyro gimbals to a gravity-detecting device. However, in order to keep the construction as simple as possible, most directional gyros are leveled so that the inner gimbal is perpendicular to the outer gimbal. This is usually satisfactory, since the instrument is installed in the aircraft with its outer gimbal approximately vertical. This means that in straight and level flight the spin axis is about horizontal. Furthermore, we have seen that gimbal error and X-axis frictional effects are at a minimum when the gimbals are perpendicular.

In the past several devices have been used to obtain perpendicularity or "level" position of the gyro. When gyros are air driven, the jets of air which spin the rotor are used to keep it level. In one model, there are two parallel jets which are directed at the buckets on the gyro. If one of the spin axes rises, the buckets move out of the jet stream until one of the jets is directing its stream of air at the side of the gyro. This jet then applies force about the vertical axis, thus causing the gyro to precess back to the horizontal position. One of the faults of this system is that the jet also tends to apply a force about the horizontal axis. This causes the gyro to precess in azimuth and causes an erroneous heading indication.

In a later design for an air-driven gyro, the airstream flows over the top of the rotor and around in the direction of spin toward the lower portion of the vertical gimbal. On this gimbal there is a "plow" in the form of a wedge which splits the airstream into two sections. This method

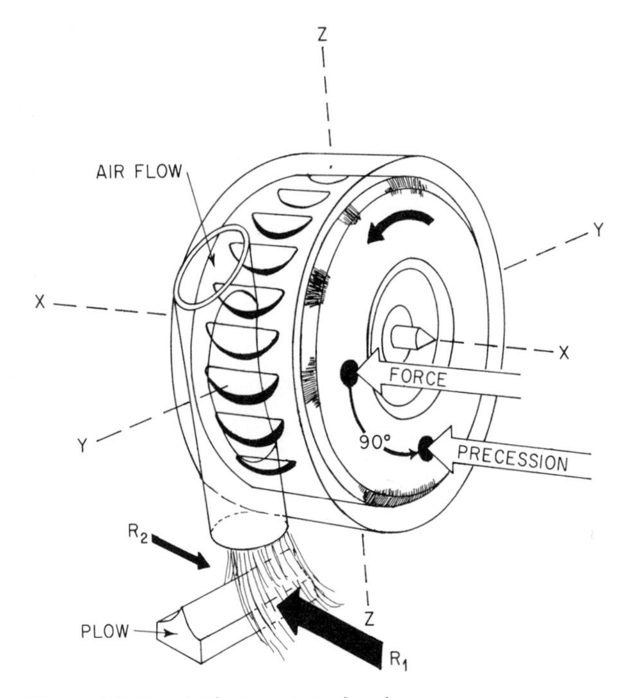

Figure **14·7** *Utilizing air to level a gyro.*

is shown in Fig. 14·7. If the gyroscope is level, the force on each face of the plow is equal, but if the gyro is tilted, then the airstream strikes only one side of the plow. The resulting unbalanced force attempts to rotate the outer gimbal about its vertical axis, but instead, the gyroscope is precessed back to its level position.

Another air-driven gyro instrument employs "pendulous vanes" which act as air valves to direct air for correction of position. As long as the gyro is level, the airstreams are balanced. If the gyro shifts position, the vanes move by gravity to a position which changes the airflow and applies a corrective force.

Electrically driven directional gyros are leveled by means of a torque motor located above the outer gimbal. This motor, by applying torque to the gimbal about its vertical axis, causes the gyro to be precessed to a level position. The motor is usually energized by a switch located between the inner and outer gimbals.

THE BANK-AND-TURN INDICATOR

The **bank-and-turn indicator** is an instrument designed to tell the pilot the rate at which the airplane is turning and whether the turn is coordinated, that is, the degree of bank is correct for the rate of turn. Turn-and-bank indicating instruments have also been adapted for use as signal-developing devices for the operation of autopilots.

The turn-indicating section of the turn-and-bank indicator is actually a **rate gyro,** and it produces an indication in proportion to the **rate of turn.** One needle width indicates a turn rate of 3° per sec. The diagram of Fig. 14·8 shows how a gyro serves to indicate a rate of turn. This diagram does not show the actual arrangement of a turn-and-bank indicator gyro, but it does demonstrate the principle of operation. In the illustration the gyro is set up to measure the rate at which its base is being turned about the *Z* axis. If the base is not turning, there is no force exerted on the gyro, since the springs attached to the *X* axis are adjusted so that under these conditions they are in balance.

If we turn the gyro assembly to the left as shown by the arrow on the base, a force will be applied to the left at *A* and to the right at *C*. As we remember the rule for precession, we find that the point *B* on the gyro will move to the left and the point *D* will move to the right, thus processing the gyro about the *Y* axis and causing the indicating needle to show a left turn. The rate of turn indicated will depend upon how rapidly the base of the unit is turned.

As the gyro precesses around the *Y* axis, the spring on the right end of the spin axle will be extended. The stretched spring will then apply a downward force on the end of the axle and, in effect, will be applying a force at *B* and *D*. This force at *B* and *D* results in a precessional motion about the *Z* axis in the direction in which the base is turning. When the gyro is precessing about the *Z* axis at the same rate of speed as the base is being turned externally, there is no longer

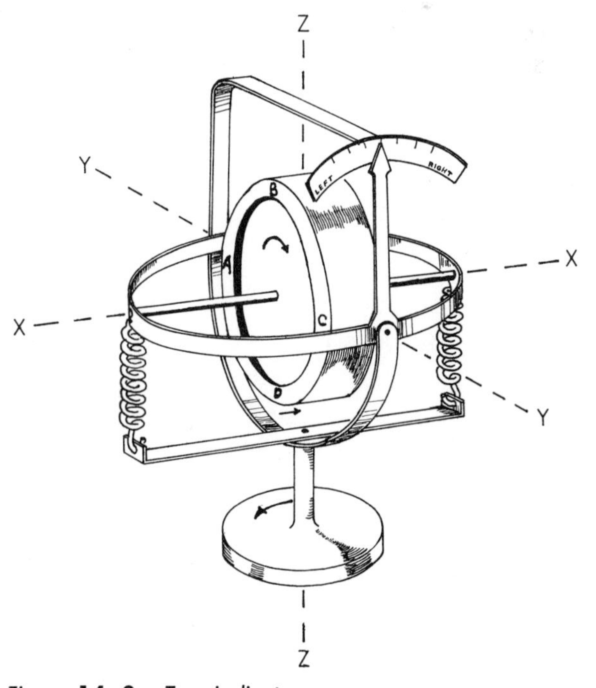

Figure **14·8** *Turn indicator.*

any force being exerted at points C and A. This means that the gyro will stop precessing about the Y axis and will hold its position. If, however, the rate at which the base is being turned is increased, there will once again be a force applied at C and D and the gyro will precess farther about the Y axis. Of course, the spring being stretched farther will cause a more rapid precession about the Z axis, and this will again match the external turning. Thus we see that, whenever the base is being turned, one of the springs is displaced enough to precess the gyro at a rate equal to the rate of turn. Whenever the base is stopped, the springs restore the gyro rotor to the neutral position.

A standard bank-and-turn indicator is shown in Fig. 14·9. This instrument is gyro operated and functions on a principle similar to that described in the previous paragraphs. During a turn the precession of the gyro causes the "needle" to swing to the right or left depending upon the direction of the turn. A turn of 3° per sec will cause the needle to move off center one needle width. This enables the pilot to determine his rate of turn by the instrument.

The bank indicator is purely a mechanical device consisting of a black ball in a curved tube filled with compass fluid or some similar liquid. As the airplane is tilted, the ball moves off center in the direction of the bank and the airplane will begin slipping. If the bank is too shallow, the ball will move away from the bank and the airplane will be skidding.

Figure 14·10 is a photograph of the gyro in an air-driven bank-and-turn indicator. It will be noted that this gyro is provided with buckets to catch the air and apply force to spin the gyro. The air is drawn through the instrument by means of a vacuum system which is operated either by an engine-driven vacuum pump or by a venturi tube mounted on the outside of the aircraft.

Figure 14·9 Bank-and-turn indicator.

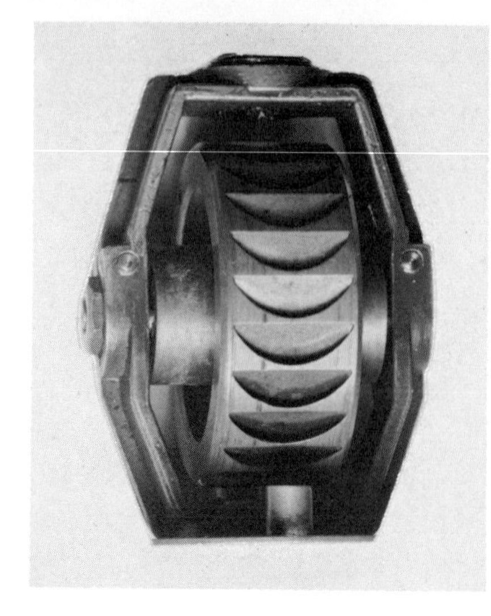

Figure 14·10 Gyro of an air-driven bank-and-turn indicator.

THE GYRO HORIZON INDICATOR

The **gyro horizon indicator,** also called the **artificial horizon** or **attitude gyro,** is designed to provide a visual reference horizon for an airplane which is flying "blind," that is, with no visible reference outside the airplane. This instrument provides a horizontal reference similar to the natural horizon, thus making it possible for the pilot of an airplane to see the position of the airplane with respect to the horizon. A white bar across the face of the instrument represents the horizon, and a small figure of an airplane in the center of the dial represents the airplane. The position of the airplane symbol relative to the horizon bar indicates the actual position of the airplane with respect to the natural horizon. The face of the gyro horizon indicator is shown in Fig. 14·11.

A properly installed gimbaled gyroscope can measure motion about any axis but its spin axis. For example, the directional gyro has its spin axis maintained in a horizontal position, so that any change in the heading of the aircraft (motion about the Z axis) can be detected, but this instrument cannot measure roll motion about the X axis. In order to detect pitch-and-roll motion of an aircraft, we use a gyro with a vertical spin axis and horizontal gimbal axes. The gyro horizon indicator is one of several instruments with such a vertical gyroscope. With the spin axis of the gyro maintained in a vertical direction, roll motion is detected by motion of the case about the outer gimbal (Z axis) and pitch motion is detected between the inner and outer gimbals (Y axis).

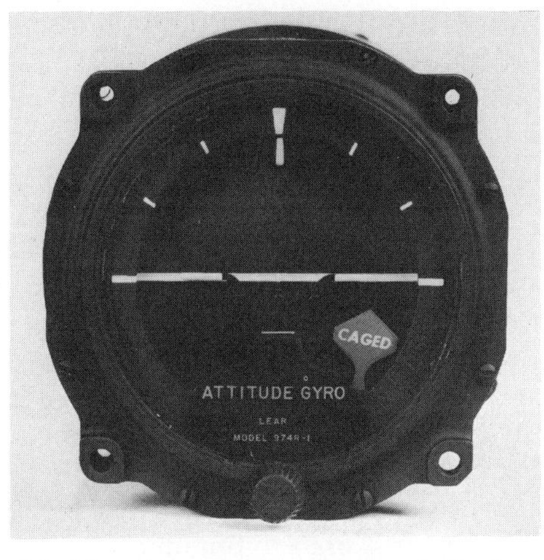

Figure **14·11** *Face of a gyrohorizon indicator.*

To maintain the spin axis in a vertical position, a vertical-seeking device of some sort is necessary. A plumb bob is such a device, and it would seem that a weight attached to the lower end of the spin axle of the gyro would act as a plumb bob and cause the spin axis to line up with the vertical. This will not work, however, because of gyroscopic precession, and any corrective force applied by the weight would result in a corrective force at 90° to the desired correction. If the gyro is not erect, such a weight exerts a force toward the vertical, but because of precession the weight will travel around in a small circle. A diagram of a vertical gyro is shown in Fig. 14·12. If we assume that the spin axis is off vertical so that position *B* is higher than position *D*, the weight at the base of the gyro would exert a downward force at *B*. The gyro would then start to precess around the *Z* axis, whereas what is actually needed is a precession about the *Y* axis. From our study of precession we find that a force applied downward at *B* would bring about a downward movement at *C* and the gyro would tilt to the right.

If the weight at the base of the gyro is replaced with a ball erector, such as that shown in the lower left portion of Fig. 14·12, the corrective forces will be applied at the proper point for erection of the gyro. When the gyro is tilted so that position *B* is higher than position *D*, the balls in the erector will run to the side of the erector at position D_1. The applied force is then approximately at A_1, so the precession force will be about the *Y* axis and position *B* will move downward to the point where it is again even with position *D*. The bottom of the ball erector is concave, so that when the gyro is erect, the balls remain in the center of the container. The ball erector prevents the gyro from drifting off the vertical, regardless of earth rate, normal bearing friction, or other influences.

The presence of the ball erector on the base of the inner gimbal does create another problem, however. Whenever the aircraft turns, a centrifugal force is present which, combined with gravitational force, changes the direction in which a weight aligns itself. The ball erector attempts to align the spin axis of the gyro to this direction during a turn. As the aircraft makes a turn to the right, the balls rolling to the left, because of centrifugal force, are carried by the pins to position B_1, where they exert a downward force at *B*. This causes precession about the *Z* axis with the top of the spin axis moving to the right, thus making the indicator produce an erroneous indication until the turn is completed.

To overcome this difficulty, the ball erector unit is mounted on the inner gimbal in such a way that, when the balls are in the center of the unit, the gyro spin axis is a few degrees off vertical in a forward direction and position *B* is a little lower than position *D*. At first this does not seem to solve the problem, since it is necessary to change the position of the spin axis as the aircraft turns so that the top of the spin axis remains slightly tilted in the direction of the heading of the aircraft. This requires a force to precess the spin axis at the same rate as the aircraft turns. By design, during a right turn, the force of the balls at *B* is just the correct force needed to keep the spin axis precessing to the right with the aircraft. In the same way, during a left turn, the balls exert a downward force at *D* and cause a precession of the spin axis about the vertical to the left, thus preserving the alignment of the spin axis and aircraft heading. In effect, then, the tilt of the spin

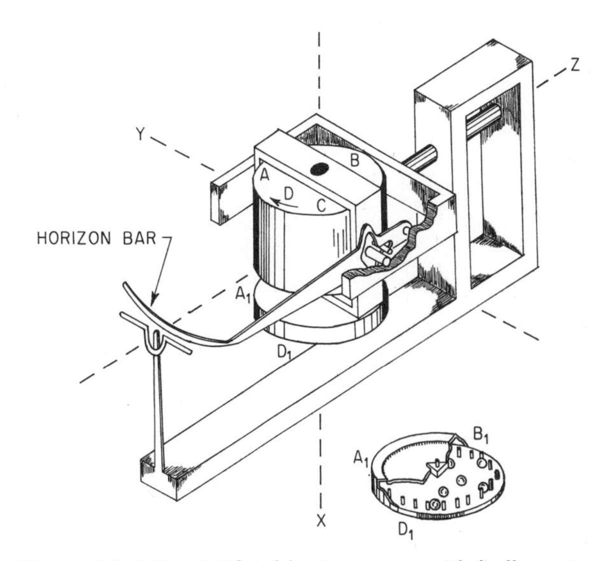

Figure **14·12** *Artificial horizon gyro with ball erector.*

axis is just enough to balance the centrifugal force developed during a turn.

The gyro mechanism is arranged with the gyro in a vertical position so it will respond to pitch-and-roll movements of the aircraft. The instrument is provided with a mechanical caging device which makes it possible to erect the gyro in case it is "tumbled" by violent maneuvers. The automatic erecting system consists of pendulous vanes which control the airflow in such a manner that a correcting force will be applied when the gyro spin axis moves out of the vertical position.

REVIEW QUESTIONS

1. Define a *gyroscope.*
2. What are *gimbal rings?*
3. What is meant by the *rigidity* of a gyroscope?
4. Explain *precession.*
5. In what direction does precession occur as the result of a force applied to a gyro?
6. What is the effect of bearing friction in the gimbal system?
7. Explain *nutation.*
8. What type of gyro rotor is most effective?
9. What means are used to cause rotation of a gyro?
10. How is the effectiveness of a gyro affected by the speed of the rotor?
11. How is the spin axis of a directional gyro placed?
12. Explain the operation of a directional gyro.
13. Why does gimbal error occur in the operation of a directional gyro?
14. Describe the construction of a turn indicator.
15. What means is used to obtain a *rate* indication with a gyro?
16. Describe the arrangement of the gyro in a gyro horizon instrument.
17. Explain the action of the *ball erector.*
18. Explain "tumbling" of a gyro and how a tumbled gyro can be erected.

CHAPTER 15

A Look into Outer Space

INTRODUCTION

In the study of aerospace vehicles an understanding of the environment in which a space vehicle must operate is desirable. The atmosphere around the earth is generally comfortable and "friendly," and man requires little effort to find suitable living conditions. The conditions on the surface of the earth are "made-to-order" for the benefit of man, and as long as man remains within the surface environment, he has no difficulty in adapting himself to the relatively small variations in temperature, humidity, and pressure which occur about him. When man leaves the surface of the earth and begins to move toward the outer atmosphere and beyond, he suddenly finds that he must make drastic changes in his normal mode of living. Conditions in space not only affect man himself but also affect the machines and equipment which man must use to place himself outside the lower atmosphere and on toward the reaches of space.

Still another factor which the space pioneer must consider is the vast difference in distance on earth and in space. On earth it may seem a long distance from Los Angeles to New York, but it takes about eighty times this distance to reach our nearest space neighbor, the moon. To travel the distance to the sun a man would have to go more than 30,000 times the distance from Los Angeles to New York. From this we see that, if man is to travel in space and expects to reach a comparatively close heavenly body, outside the solar system, within his lifetime, he must move at fantastic speeds. This, of course, requires new methods of propulsion and space ships which can maintain within themselves an environment in which man can live for long periods of time.

To meet the requirements of space travel, engineers and scientists are constantly at work to develop materials, devices, and systems which can function effectively in the space environment and can provide man with the special conditions which he needs for survival in space.

The purpose of this chapter is to provide the technician with a fundamental understanding of space, the bodies occupying space, the vast distances between the bodies in space, and the conditions which man will encounter in space. This understanding will provide him with a profound appreciation of the systems and devices upon which he may be required to work and will enable him to perform his duties in a manner consistent with the near perfection necessary to meet the reliability requirements for successful space flight.

HISTORY

Early recognition of astronomical phenomena

As far back as the time of the cavemen, cognizance was taken of the sun, moon, and other celestial bodies. This is proved by the drawings found on the walls of prehistoric caves wherein certain star patterns are shown which indicate that man of that early time was making careful observations of the celestial sphere. It is also indicated that the people of these early times observed that the movements of the sun, moon, and stars were in some way associated with the seasons. As civilization developed, times of planting, harvest, celebrations, and holy days were established in accordance with the movement of celestial bodies. The calendars found in the ruins of the ancient cities and buildings of the Mayans, Babylonians, Egyptians, and others show that these peoples had made very careful and accurate determinations concerning the movement of the sun with respect to the earth.

Astronomy in ancient Greece

Several centuries before Christ certain Greek philosophers became interested in the movements of the sun, planets, and stars. One of these,

Eudoxus, worked out a plan of the universe with the earth at the center. Somewhat later Aristarchus, another Greek, developed a system which indicated that the sun was at the center of the solar system and that the planets moved around the sun. This theory was not accepted at the time, however, and it was not until many centuries later that proof of the "heliocentric" theory became so strong that it was considered correct by a majority of astronomers. About 150 B.C., Hipparchus, an Egyptian philosopher, worked out many theories concerning the movements of the heavenly bodies, and later Ptolemy, also of Egypt, published a book called the "Almagest" which included the work of Hipparchus together with many observations and notes of his own. This book was known by the Arabs who preserved much scientific knowledge during the Dark Ages and made it available to others afterward.

Copernicus

Early in the sixteenth century one of the greatest of early astronomers, Nicolaus Copernicus of Poland, restated the theory that the sun was the center of the solar system and that the planets revolved about the sun. Copernicus' theories were published in the book "Concerning the Revolutions of the Celestial Spheres." He showed that the earth revolved on its axis and that the movements of the planets could be explained by the fact that they all moved in orbits around the sun.

Brahe and Kepler

Tycho Brahe, a Danish nobleman, was another of the great astronomers of the sixteenth century. Brahe built a large observatory on the island of Hven off the coast of Denmark and spent many years making careful observations of the stars and planets. He developed a vast store of accurate information. However, he did not come to the point of agreeing with Copernicus that the sun was the center of the solar system.

As a result of Brahe's observations, Johannes Kepler was able to evolve two of his fundamental laws. The first of these states that the planets have elliptical orbits and that the sun is located at one of the two foci of the ellipse. The other fundamental law states that a line drawn between the sun and a planet sweeps equal areas in equal intervals of time. These two laws are still in use today in the computation of orbits for satellites in orbit around the sun and around the earth.

Galileo

Galileo Galilei was a famous Italian scientist and mathematician who lived from 1564 to 1652. Through his use of the telescope Galileo discovered that the moon was not a smooth, round sphere, that Jupiter had several bright satellites, that Saturn was surrounded by rings, and that Venus and Mercury passed through phases similar to those of the moon. Galileo upheld the belief of Copernicus that the sun was the center of the solar system. Galileo also made studies in gravity, motion, and acceleration which were the basis for some of the later laws of motion stated by Sir Isaac Newton.

Sir Isaac Newton

Sir Isaac Newton is considered to be one of the greatest scientists and mathematicians who ever lived. He is particularly famous for his three "laws of motion," the universal law of gravitation, and his discoveries in mathematics. Newton lived from 1642 to 1727 and developed many of the scientific laws and principles which are the bases for modern science. He employed the discoveries of Galileo and Kepler to aid in developing the universal law of gravity and the laws of motion. He also invented the reflecting telescope and other instruments of great value to astronomers.

Recent discoveries

New discoveries are constantly being made concerning stars and their distances, sizes, velocities, etc. As long as man exists, however, he can hope to discover but a small part of what could be known about the universe. With the naked eye we can see very few stars, and with the 200-in. telescope of Mount Palomar we can find millions more. It cannot be known, however, how far into space the stars exist, and for all we can determine, they continue on indefinitely.

Since the time of Galileo and Newton, knowledge concerning the universe has increased rapidly. Old concepts have been discarded as new facts have been discovered. Among the discoveries in the last two centuries was the existence of the planets Uranus, Neptune, and Pluto. Neptune and Pluto were thought to exist before they were actually seen because of their effects on the movements of other planets.

Much of the new knowledge of the stars has been determined by spectrographic analysis of the light emitted by the stars. Analysis of the emitted light makes it possible to determine the chemical composition of stars, their temperatures, and, in some cases, their velocities. Since the 200-in. telescope came into use, astronomers have decided that many of the stars and galaxies are actually about twice as far from the earth as previously believed. Thus we see that exact knowledge of the distant members of the universe is most difficult to attain.

Astronomical distances

We can attain some degree of understanding of the distances within our own solar system by comparing the time required to reach the sun or a planet with a rocket ship traveling at a particular speed. For example, if we travel at the rate of 50 miles per sec we could cross the United States in 1 min. To reach the moon at this speed we would have to travel for 1 hr, 19 min, and 20 sec. To travel to the sun would require about 21 days, and a trip to Pluto would take about 20 months. These measurements are all within our own solar system. If we leave our solar system and wish to go to the nearest star, Alpha Centauri, still traveling at 50 miles per sec, it would take 16,750 years to make the trip. At the speed of light (about 186,300 miles per sec) it would take a little more than 4 years to reach this star. It is quite apparent then that a trip to the nearest star will not be attempted until man has devised vehicles capable of fantastic speeds, and even then he can expect to spend many years making the trip.

Because of the vast distances to the stars our computations of their sizes and distances cannot be accurate, especially for the more distant stars. In our solar system we can attain more accuracy; however, we still can determine the distance to the sun only within several thousand miles. The distance to the moon can be computed by observing its position simultaneously from two widely separated positions on the earth. This method is illustrated in Fig. 15 · 1. Two points on the earth's surface, A and C, are selected such that a straight line between them is exactly 7,500 miles in length. This distance is not measured on the curved surface of the earth but is computed as if the line were passing through the earth. If sightings of the moon are simultaneously taken from A and C at a time when the angle at C is exactly 90°, the angle at A will be approximately 88° 12′.

Using the method for solving a right triangle we can determine the distance BC by employing the tangent of angle A.

$$\tan A = \tan 88°12' = 31.8205$$

$$\tan A = \frac{BC}{AC} = \frac{BC}{7{,}500}$$

$$\frac{BC}{7{,}500} = 31.8205$$

$$BC = 31.8205 \times 7{,}500 = 238{,}650 \text{ miles}$$

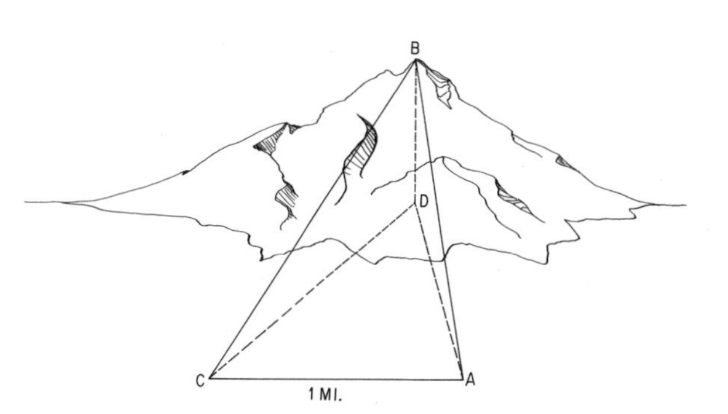

Figure **15 · 2** *Method for finding the height of a mountain.*

From the foregoing computation we have determined that the distance to the moon at the time of our observations was 238,650 miles. Of course, this distance would not be exact but would vary according to the accuracy of the instruments employed for measuring the angles.

It would not be necessary to use a right triangle for the problem we have just solved because any combination of angles will enable us to determine the distances BC or BA. The determining factor is the angle of **parallax** at B.

Parallax is the difference in the direction of an object when viewed from two positions not in alignment with the object. It is used in surveying as well as in astronomy. If a surveyor wishes to find the distance to the top of a peak, he lays out a precise distance on the ground as shown in Fig. 15 · 2 and then takes sightings from the ends of this measured line. With the angles C and A and the distance AC known, it is easy to find BC and AB by trigonometry. After the first computation the surveyor solves the triangle ABD to determine the altitude of the peak.

To measure the distance to the sun astronomers do not depend upon the parallax of the sun from the earth. The angle of parallax for the sun is only 8″ of arc when sightings are taken simultaneously from opposite sides of the earth, and this arc is too small for accurate computation. A better method for measuring the distance to the sun employs the position of the planetoid (small planetlike body) Eros as a reference. This planetoid comes within about 15,000,000 miles of the earth, and this is about one-sixth the distance to the sun. If angular measurements are taken at various times from different points on the earth, sufficient data are obtained to measure the dis-

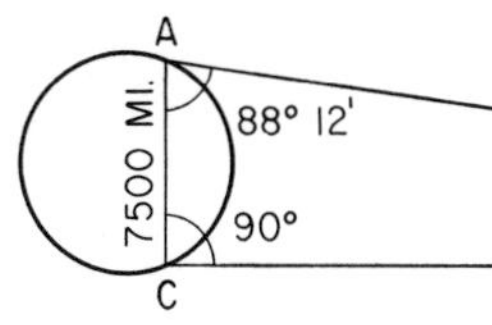

Figure **15 · 1** *Method for computing the distance to the moon.*

tance of the sun from the earth within a few thousand miles. This distance is approximately 93,000,000 miles, although at its greatest distance **(aphelion)** the sun is about 94,500,000 miles from the earth and at its nearest distance **(perihelion)** it is about 91,500,000 miles from the earth.

To measure the distance to the nearest stars the astronomers use the orbit of the earth around the sun as a base. The diameter of the earth's orbit is about 186,000,000 miles, and from this it is possible to obtain a very small parallax angle with the nearest stars. For example, the parallax of Alpha Centauri, the nearest star, is found to be 0.76″ of arc. From this it is determined that Alpha Centauri is about 25,000,000,000,000 miles from the earth.

To determine the distance of stars which are more remote, various methods are used including brilliance, color of the light from the star, and other measurements. At best the astronomers can arrive at only a rough approximation of the distance to the more remote stars.

Since the distances between stars in space are so great, astronomers do not use the mile as the unit of distance. One of the units used is the **astronomical unit,** which is the mean distance from the earth to the sun. A still larger unit of distance is the **parsec,** which is 206,265 astronomical units. This unit is used because it is the distance which would make the parallax of the star, subtended by the earth's orbit, equal to 1″ of arc. A more common unit of distance is the **light-year,** which is the distance light will travel in 1 year. One parsec is equal to approximately 19,182,645,000,000 miles, and one light-year is approximately 5,878,564,000,000 miles.

THE SOLAR SYSTEM

Figure 15·3 is a chart showing the relative positions of the planets in the solar system. Obviously the distances between the planets and the diameter of the sun cannot be in proportion. The planets, however, are shown in comparative sizes. It must also be pointed out that the orbits are not concentric circles; rather they are ellipses, generally near the plane of the **ecliptic** (the plane of the earth's orbit), with Pluto's orbit having an inclination of 17°, which is the greatest inclination of the planetary orbits.

Table 15·1 shows the distances of the planets from the sun, their periods of revolution about the sun, and their diameters in miles. The distances from the sun are given in astronomical units (93,000,000 miles), which are based upon the mean distance of the earth from the sun.

The sun

The **sun** is the center, or "nucleus," of our solar system. It is an ordinary star, many being smaller and many being larger. The diameter of the sun is approximately 865,000 miles, which gives it a diameter more than 100 times that of the earth and a volume about 1,300,000 times that of the earth. Since the sun is gaseous in nature, its mass per unit volume is about one-fourth that of the earth. Thus the total mass is only about 330,000 times that of the earth.

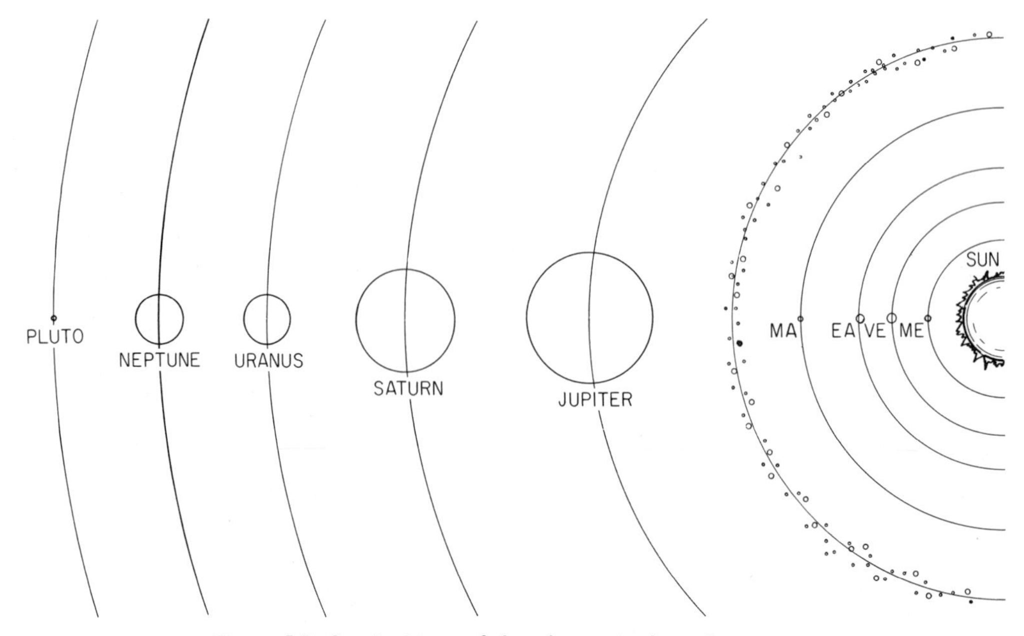

Figure **15·3** *Positions of the planets in the solar system.*

Table 15·1

Planet	Distance from sun	Period of revolution	Diameter, miles
Mercury	0.4	0.26 year	3,100
Venus	0.7	0.63 year	7,700
Earth	1.0	1 year	7,918
Mars	1.5	1.8 years	4,200
Asteroids	3.0	3 to 9 years	10 to 500
Jupiter	5.2	11.9 years	86,700
Saturn	9.5	29.5 years	71,500
Uranus	19.2	84 years	32,000
Neptune	30.1	164.8 years	31,000
Pluto	39.5	248.4 years	3,100–3,700

The temperature of the surface of the sun is about 6000°K, which is 5727°C or 10,340°F. The interior of the sun may reach a temperature as high as 20,000,000°C. This tremendous heat energy is generated as a result of a nuclear reaction which converts hydrogen atoms to helium atoms. This process goes on continuously and will apparently continue for several billions of years before the sun begins to "burn out."

The radiated energy of the sun presents one of the problems which must be solved by man in space flight. On the other hand, this energy provides the necessary environment, weather conditions, and power source which make it possible for man to live on the earth. The energy reaching the earth from the sun is approximately 7.15 Btu per sq ft per min.

The sun not only radiates heat and light energy but also emits electromagnetic energy in the lower wavelengths which greatly interferes with radio communication, contributes to the "radiation belts" around the earth, and causes the brilliant displays in the polar regions called the "aurora." Some of the most valuable information obtained from rockets and satellites has been concerned with the electromagnetic energy released by the sun.

The radiation of electromagnetic energy from the sun becomes particularly intense during sunspot activity. Sunspots are great gaseous storms, many thousands of miles in diameter, which rage across the surface of the sun. The illustration in Fig. 15·4 shows typical sunspots as they appear to the astronomer.

The composition of heavenly bodies is determined by means of a spectrographic analysis of the light emitted by the body. In the case of the sun it is found that about 70 of the elements found on the earth are detectable on the sun. The most common elements found in a study of the sun are hydrogen and helium. The fact that astronomers have not been able to detect certain elements does not mean that these elements do not exist on the sun, but it indicates that, if they do exist, they are not radiating light energy of sufficient strength to be measured at the earth.

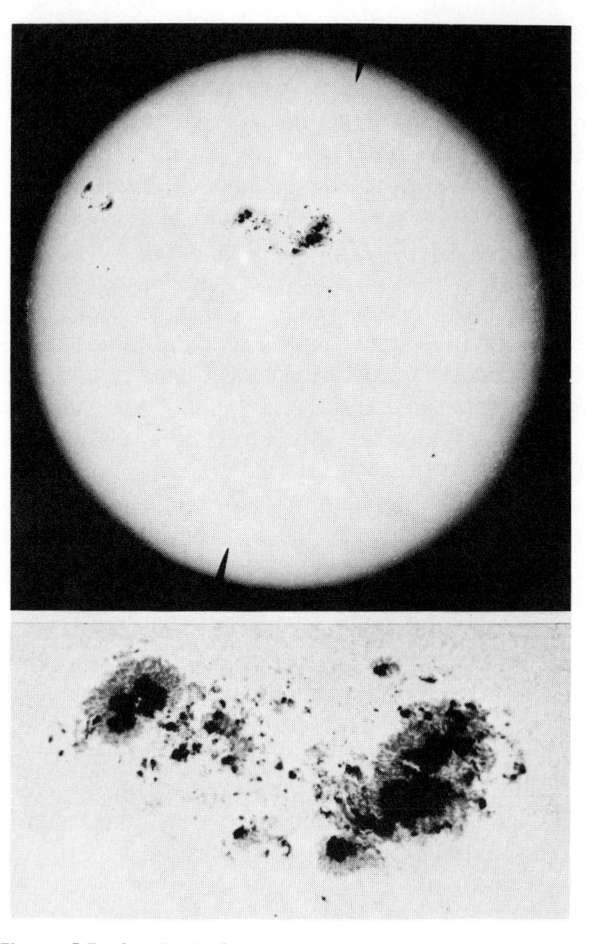

Figure **15·4** *Typical sunspots.*

The earth

The earth, of course, is the planet with which we are most familiar. However, our scientists are making new discoveries about it every day, and there is still an almost infinite amount of information to be learned. Geophysicists, geologists, astronomers, and other scientists work incessantly to discover new facts about the earth. For example, an expedition is now boring into the ocean floor at a depth of over 11,000 ft near the Galapagos Islands in an effort to find out what the earth's crust is like and what history can be learned from it.

The earth is essentially a sphere; however, it is not a perfect sphere. This fact makes it necessary for astronomers, navigators, and surveyors to make corrections for earth's slight oblateness. Recent discoveries made through the use of rockets and satellites show that the earth is not only oblate but that it is slightly pear-shaped; that is, the Southern Hemisphere is slightly more "filled out" than the Northern Hemisphere.

The best measurements of the earth's diameters at the present time are 7,899.98 miles measured from pole to pole and 7,926.68 miles measured through the center in the plane of the equator. Thus we see that the earth is apparently 26.70 miles "wider" than it is from pole to pole; that is, the equatorial diameter is 26.70 miles more than the polar diameter. This larger diameter at the equator is the result of the centrifugal force caused by the earth's rotation.

In order to relate other celestial bodies to a position with respect to the earth, it is necessary to establish a system of **coordinates** by which positions can be established. The most effective system is called the **equator system.** In this system certain references on the earth are projected to the **celestial sphere.** The celestial sphere may be considered a great, hollow ball with the earth at the center and with all the heavenly bodies mounted on the inside of the ball.

When the North and South Poles of the earth are projected to their intersection with the celestial sphere, they become the north and south **celestial poles.** Likewise, when the equator is projected outward to an intersection with the celestial sphere, the **celestial equator** is established.

The orbit of the earth around the sun produces a plane which is at approximately 23½° inclination to the equator. The projection of the plane of the earth's orbit to the celestial sphere is called the **ecliptic.** The ecliptic forms a plane of reference for establishing the positions of other bodies with respect to the earth and sun.

The intersection of the planes of the ecliptic and the plane of the equator forms a straight line passing through the center of the earth and extending to the celestial sphere in both directions. The two points where this line touches the celestial sphere are also where the ecliptic crosses the celestial equator and are called the **vernal** and the **autumnal equinoxes.** At the end of the intersection line where the sun crosses the celestial equator moving toward the north, the point is called the vernal equinox or the **First Point of Aries.** The meridian passing from the North Pole to the South Pole through this point is called the **zero hour circle.** This is the point used as a reference to determine the **azimuth** or the "east and west" position of a heavenly body.

Assume that there is a star at the point *B* in the illustration of Fig. 15·5. The elevation of the star above the celestial equator is called the **declination** and is indicated by the angle *BER* or

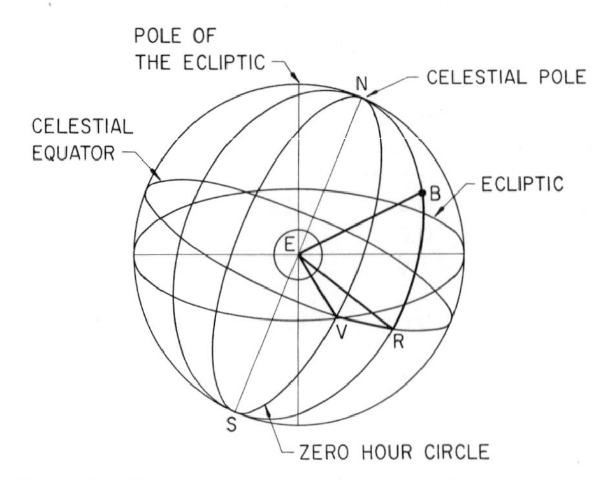

Figure **15·5** *Locating a star by celestial coordinates.*

the arc *BR* in the illustration. The "east-west" position of the star is called the **right ascension** and is measured from the vernal equinox to the meridian passing through the position of the star from north to south. This distance is shown as the angle *VER* or the arc *VR* in the illustration. We could say, for example, that the declination of the star is 50° and the right ascension is 25°, thus firmly fixing the position of the star in the celestial sphere. A position established in this manner is as accurate as a position on the surface of the earth established by longitude and latitude.

The earth orbits around the sun at a mean distance of about 93,000,000 miles. The orbit is actually an ellipse, being about 189,000,000 miles in diameter along the major axis and about 183,000,000 miles in diameter along the minor axis. The distance around the orbit is approximately 584,000,000 miles, and it requires one year for the earth to traverse this distance traveling at more than 66,000 mph or 18.5 miles per sec.

As previously stated, the plane of the earth's orbit is inclined to the earth's axis about 23.5°. As shown in Fig. 15·6 this inclination determines the seasons on the earth. In this diagram it will be noted that at the **summer solstice** the Northern Hemisphere of the earth receives more sunlight than the Southern Hemisphere. In like manner, at the **winter solstice** the Southern Hemisphere is receiving a greater amount of sunlight than the Northern Hemisphere. At the equinoxes the Northern and Southern Hemispheres receive equal shares of the sun's light.

The inclination of the earth's axis to the ecliptic is responsible for the change in the length of the days throughout the year. This can be explained by examining the drawing of Fig. 15·7 which shows **diurnal** (daily) paths of the sun at equinoxes and at solstices. Let us assume that

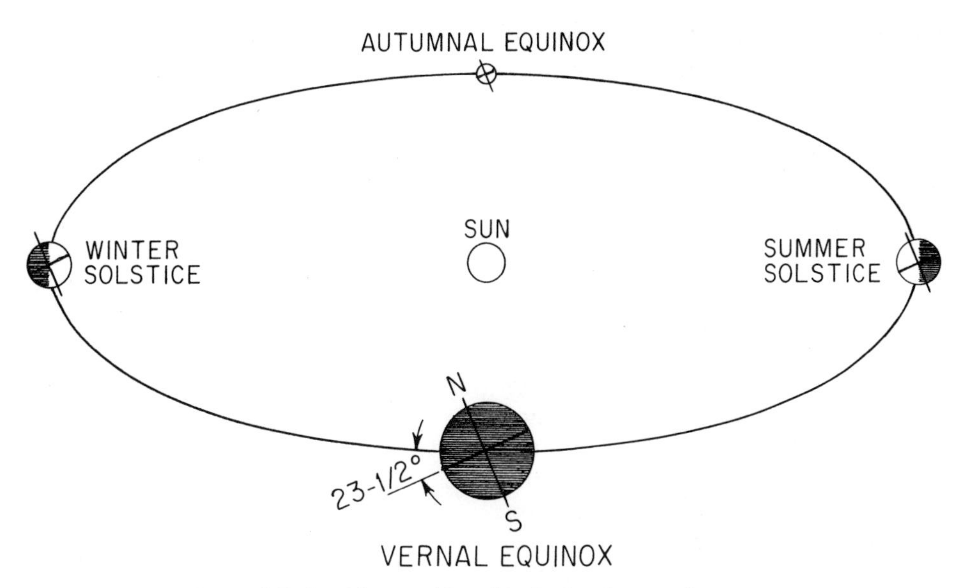

Figure **15·6** *The earth's orbit, inclination, and seasons.*

the ellipse *ENSW* represents the plane of the horizon to an observer at *A* where the latitude is 40°N. The point *NP* represents the position of the North Pole in the celestial sphere. At the winter solstice the sun will describe a path across the sky as shown by the partial circle *XX′* through the point 1. At the equinoxes the sun's path will be from *E* to *W* through the point 2, and at the summer solstice the sun's path will be from *Y* to *Y′* through the point 3. From this illustration it can be seen that the sun's path across the sky in the winter is much shorter than it is in the summer. This is one of the reasons that the temperature falls in the wintertime. The other cause of low temperatures is that the angle of the sun to the face of the earth at the observer's position is much less in winter than it is in the summer. This is also shown in the drawing. When the sun's rays strike the earth at an increased angle, a smaller amount of the sun's energy is received by a unit area of the surface. Also, the sun's rays must travel through a greater amount of atmosphere at the greater angle, and this also decreases the energy per unit of area.

The inclination of the earth's axis to the ecliptic establishes four parallel circles around the earth. These are the Arctic Circle, the Tropic of Cancer, the Tropic of Capricorn, and the Antarctic Circle (see Fig. 15·8). The **Arctic Circle** is established by the position of the sun at the winter solstice in the Northern Hemisphere. At this time the entire area of the earth north of the Arctic Circle is in shadow for the full day.

The **Tropic of Cancer** is established by the position of the sun at the summer solstice. At this time the sun will be directly overhead at noon; that is, it will be at 90° to the plane of the horizon on the Tropic of Cancer.

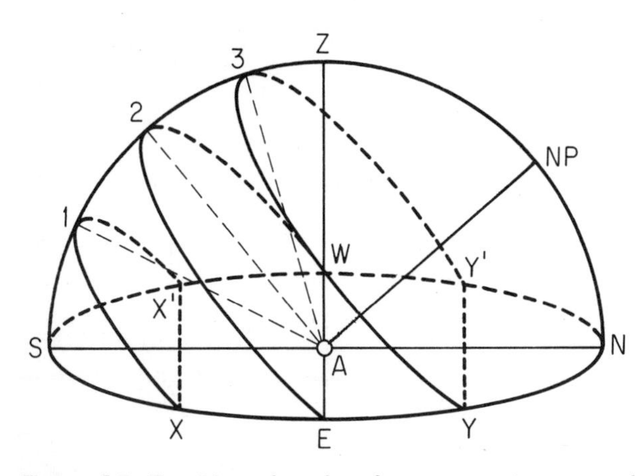

Figure **15·7** *Diurnal paths of sun at equinoxes and solstices.*

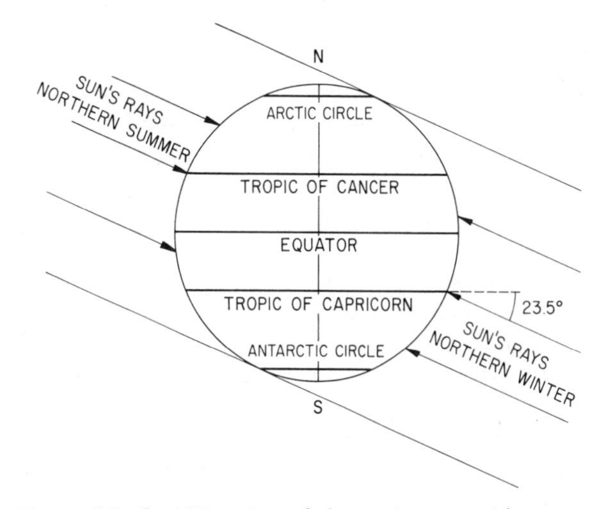

Figure **15·8** *Direction of the sun's rays with respect to the earth at the summer and winter solstices.*

The positions of the **Tropic of Capricorn** and the **Antarctic Circle** are established by the sun's positions at the summer solstice for the Southern Hemisphere and the winter solstice for the Southern Hemisphere, respectively.

The **seasons** on the earth are caused by the inclination of the earth's axis to the ecliptic. As mentioned previously, this inclination is approximately 23½°. At the vernal equinox (usually March 21) the night and day are equal in length all over the earth except at the poles, where a continuous sunrise or sunset exists for many hours. Three months later (June 21) the sun has reached its highest north position. This point is called the **summer solstice.** The elevation of the sun then declines through the **autumnal equinox** (September 21) and continues to its most southerly point, which is called the **winter solstice** (December 21).

Because of the orbiting of the earth around the sun, it appears that the sun is moving eastward among the stars slightly less than 1° per day. It could also be stated that the stars in the night sky appear to move westward almost 1° per day.

One of the most important quantities which must be measured in astronomy, as well as in other fields of science, is **time.** Time on earth is measured in seconds, minutes, hours, days, weeks, and years. For ordinary civil activities, the **standard** time with which we are familiar is adequate. However, for the determination of accurate time, for navigation, and for precise studies of the earth and its movements, we must establish exact references for time.

For general purposes we employ time based upon **mean solar time.** Mean solar time is based upon a uniform movement of the sun throughout the year. Actually the apparent movement of the sun varies because of the elliptical shape of the earth's orbit and the inclination of the earth's axis with respect to the ecliptic. To determine the movement of the **mean sun** the average apparent solar day is divided into 24 hr. In effect, then, the fictitious mean sun travels around the celestial equator in the same time that the real sun travels around the ecliptic. Thus the mean sun moves as though the earth's orbit were a circle. The **apparent solar day,** which is determined by the time that the sun crosses the meridian each day, varies considerably throughout the year. At the time of the winter solstice the day is about 24 hr plus 28 sec. At the vernal equinox, March 21, the day is about 18 sec less than 24 hr. Because of these variations in the length of the day it is necessary that we use the **mean solar day** of 24 hr to provide for uniformity.

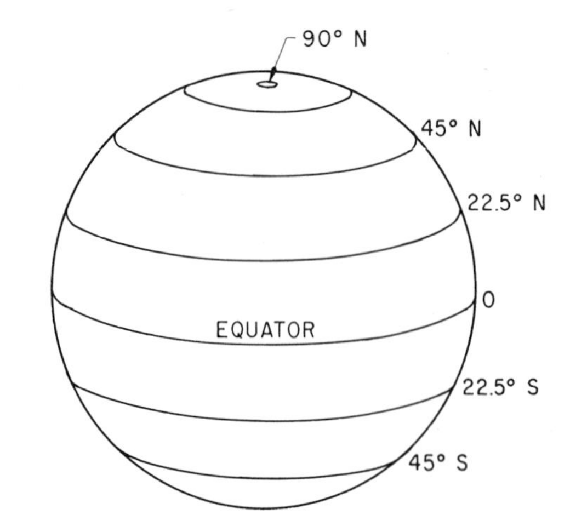

Figure **15·9** *Parallels of latitude.*

Sidereal time is established by the apparent movement of the stars caused by the rotation of the earth. The **sidereal day** is almost 4 min shorter than the mean solar day because of the movement of the earth in its orbit. Because of the accuracy of sidereal time and the fact that the movement (transit) of a star across the meridian can be very exactly determined, sidereal time is used as a reference to establish mean solar time. A sidereal day is the time required for the vernal equinox to move from the meridian around the earth and back to the meridian. Remember that the vernal equinox is a point on the celestial sphere where the ecliptic crosses the celestial equator. Sidereal time is commonly used in celestial navigation because the positions of the stars provide the most accurate references possible for the determination of a position on earth.

Positions on the earth are given in terms of **latitude and longitude.** The zero reference point for latitude is the equator. From the equator toward the north and toward the south, **parallels of**

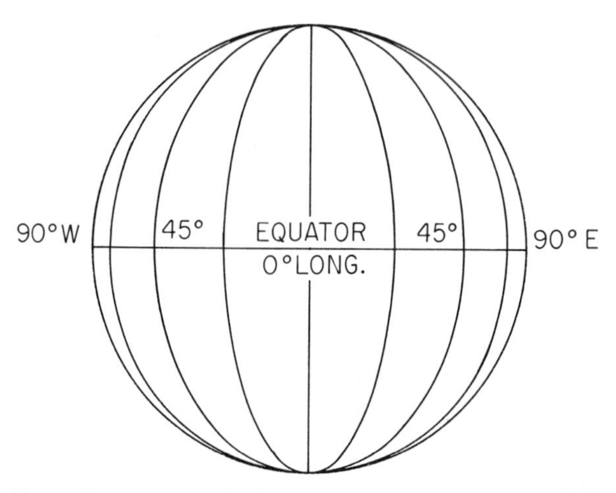

Figure **15·10** *Meridians of longitude.*

latitude are established as shown in Fig. 15 • 9. The measurement of latitude is made in degrees, minutes, and seconds. The North Pole is at lat. 90°N, and a point midway between the equator and the North Pole is lat. 45°N.

Longitude is the distance east or west of the prime meridian measured in degrees, minutes, and seconds. The prime or zero meridian has been established by international agreement as passing through the Greenwich Observatory in England. Figure 15 • 10 shows principal meridians of longitude.

To locate any spot on the earth it is merely necessary to determine the exact latitude and longitude of the place desired. For example, if we study a globe such as that shown in Fig. 15 • 11, we note that Sevilla, Spain, is located at long. 6°W and about lat. 41°24′ N.

Navigators use latitude and longitude to locate the position of a ship or airplane. This is particularly true when there are no land references by which they can be located. Since 1″ of longitude at the equator is approximately 100 ft, it is easy to see that, if a navigator plots his position within a few seconds of arc on the surface of the earth, his location is reasonably well established.

As previously mentioned, the earth is not a perfect sphere, being approximately 26.7 miles greater in diameter at the equator than if the diameter were taken in a direction from pole to pole. Also recent findings from a study of satellite orbits indicate that it is slightly pear-shaped. For this reason, the calculations of a surveyor or a navigator may not give very precise results unless suitable corrections are applied.

Another interesting fact to note is that the poles of the earth do not remain fixed but move about in an area equivalent to a rough circle approximately 1 mile in diameter.

Figure **15 • 11** *A terrestrial globe.*

The earth is a great magnet; however, its magnetic intensity is very small compared with a common magnet used in the laboratory or in electrical equipment. The magnetic poles are more than 1,000 miles from the geographical poles and are not diametrically opposite each other. The north magnetic pole is in the vicinity of 70°N and 100°W, and the south magnetic pole near 72°S and 155°E.

Because of the magnetic field around the earth, navigating instruments can utilize the magnetic lines of force as direction indicators. Charts have been prepared showing the direction of the lines of force over particular areas, so that proper corrections can be applied to a compass reading to give true direction. The difference between the indication of a magnetic compass and the true direction is called **compass variation.**

Although some of the planets exhibit atmospheres of various types, the earth appears to have the only atmosphere suitable for the support of life as we know it. As explained in another chapter of this text, the earth's atmosphere consists of 78 per cent nitrogen, 21 per cent oxygen, and 1 per cent other gases. The oxygen is the element which is most necessary for the use of living creatures.

The atmosphere forms a very thin layer on the surface of the earth, one-half of it being below 18,000-ft altitude. At 100,000-ft altitude only about 1 per cent of the atmosphere exists. Even though the atmosphere is comparatively shallow, it is a major barrier to the return of space ships to the earth. This is because of the great speeds developed from the force of the earth's gravity. A ship returning from space may have a speed of many thousands of feet per second, and when it encounters the atmosphere, the friction of the gas molecules against the surface of the ship generates heat. When the heat generated is greater than can be dissipated through radiation or conduction, the temperature of the ship rises, and eventually it may become so great that it melts or burns the surface of the ship. A freely falling body entering the atmosphere becomes white hot and is usually burned up. It has been necessary, therefore, for scientists and engineers to develop methods whereby the heat could be dissipated, the velocity of the body decreased so the heating effect of the atmosphere would not be too great, or the body could be cooled efficiently from within.

One of the methods employed to prevent the nose cones of rockets from burning up in the atmosphere is to apply a heavy coating of a heat-resistant material to the outside surface. This material will begin to melt at the surface when the temperature reaches a certain level. The melted material will flow away, or **ablate,** and as it does so, it will carry away a substantial amount of heat. This method of cooling is called **cooling by ablation.**

Another method used to prevent the burning of reentry vehicles is to install a very thick layer of heat-resistant metal on the nose of the vehicle. This layer of metal is called a **heat sink,** and it serves to absorb a large amount of heat before the melting point is reached. Deceleration of reentry vehicles is accomplished with drag devices such as parachutes. When the proper combination of heat resistance, heat absorption, and deceleration is accomplished, a reentry vehicle can be recovered successfully.

The pressure of the atmosphere varies from 29.92 in. Hg (14.7 psi) at sea level to 0.320 in. Hg at 100,000 ft. It is obvious then that the friction effects of the atmosphere will be almost negligible at altitudes of over 100 miles. For this reason satellites orbiting at more than 100 miles above the surface of the earth may stay aloft for many weeks or months before being decelerated to the point where they will fall back to earth.

It is of interest to note that human beings cannot usually exist without supplementary oxygen above 18,000-ft altitude. This is because the pressure and density of the air are such that the body organs cannot absorb sufficient oxygen from it to sustain life. At altitudes greater than 60,000 ft a human being must wear a pressurized suit to prevent his blood from boiling. These facts concerning the atmosphere and its importance to human life provide us with criteria for determining whether life exists on other planets. It must be noted, however, that there are living organisms which do not require the same conditions needed for human life as we know it.

Figure 15 · 12 is a chart illustrating the characteristics of the earth's atmosphere. It shows the temperature and the pressure of the air at all altitudes up to 100,000 ft above the surface of the earth.

Mercury

As previously shown, Mercury is the innermost known planet in the solar system. Its mean distance from the sun is approximately 36,000,000 miles. However, its orbit is so eccentric that it is nearly 15,000,000 miles closer to the sun at its perihelion than it is at aphelion. Thus, its closest approach to the sun is approximately 28,500,000 miles and its greatest distance from the sun is about 43,500,000 miles. The inclination of Mercury's orbit to the ecliptic is 7°. Mercury's sidereal period is about 88 days, and the synodic period is 116 days.

From years of observations it is apparent that Mercury always keeps the same side toward the sun. Because of its nearness to the sun and the fact that the same side always faces the sun, this one side of the planet is heated to a temperature of more than 300°C. For the same reason, the dark side of Mercury is almost at absolute zero.

Mercury has a diameter of about 3,100 miles and a mass of about one-eighteenth that of the earth. The density is therefore approximately the same as that of the earth. The gravity is about one-third of the earth's surface gravity.

It is difficult to observe Mercury from the earth because it is so close to the sun. Its greatest **elongation** (distance from the sun measured in degrees of arc) is 28°; hence it can be seen only during short periods of the year, soon after sundown or shortly before sunrise, provided the weather is clear.

It is unlikely that any atmosphere exists on Mercury because it would have been drawn away by the sun. Some astronomers have believed that an extremely light atmosphere may exist, but this is unlikely.

Venus

Venus is often called the earth's twin sister because of similarities which exist between the two planets. Its orbit lies between the orbit of Mercury and that of the earth, being approximately 67,200,000 miles from the sun. The diameter of Venus is approximately 7,580 miles as compared with about 7,926 miles for the earth. The mass of Venus is a little more than four-fifths that of the earth, its density about 5.2, and its surface gravity about 85 per cent of that of the earth. Venus has a sidereal period of about 225 days and a synodic period of 584 days. It is seen, therefore, that Venus and the earth are similar in a number of respects; however, there are many questions about the planet that are not yet answered.

Venus is the brightest heavenly body in the sky and is most often noticed as the evening or morning star. Since its greatest elongation from the sun is about 46°, it can be seen for as much as 2 or 3 hr after sunset for a part of the year and again for a similar time before sunrise during another part of the year. It is also of interest to note that Venus can be seen in broad daylight at certain times of the year if the sky is clear and a person knows where to look.

The brightness of Venus results from its nearness to the sun and earth and also its high **albedo**

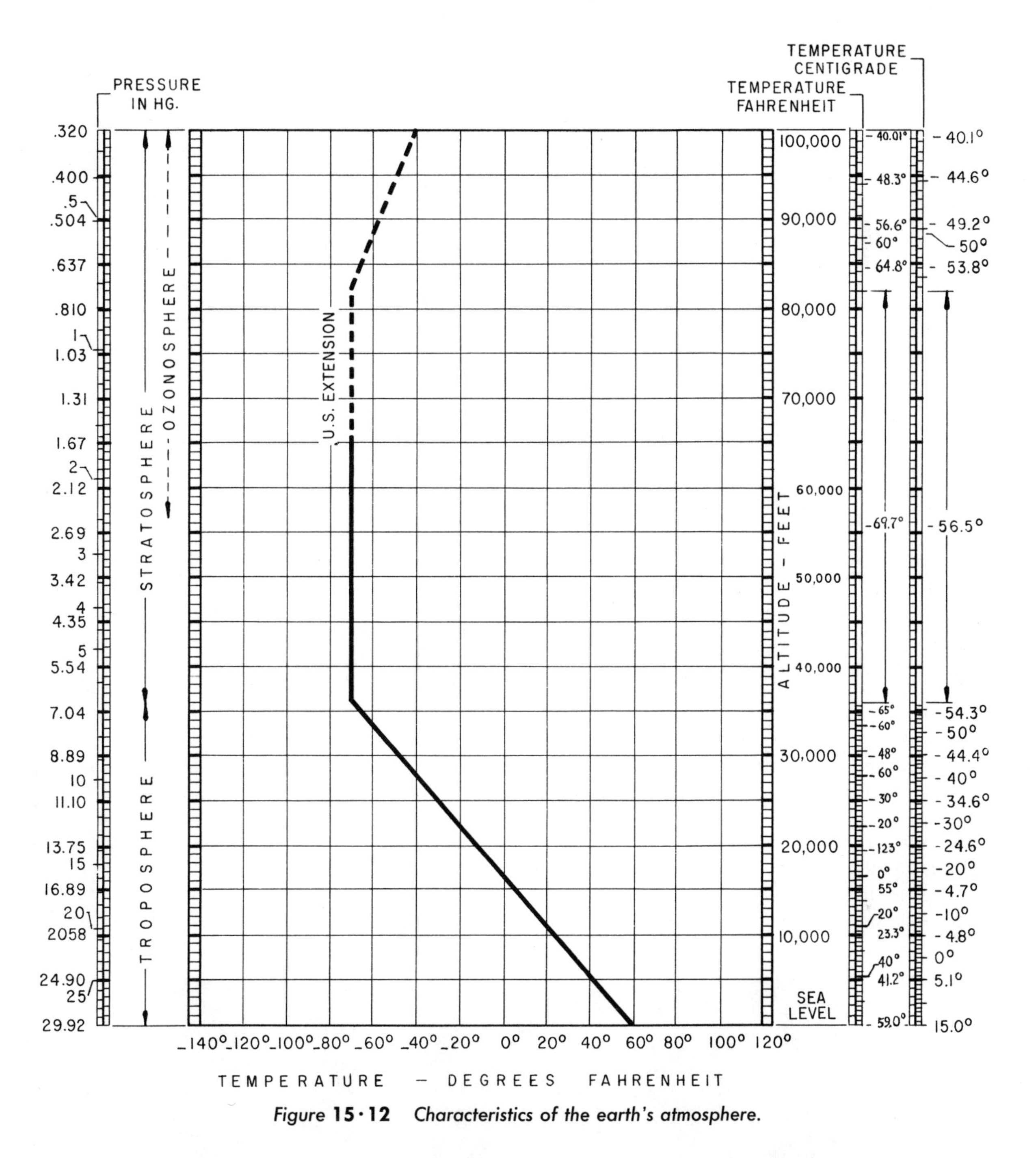

Figure **15·12** *Characteristics of the earth's atmosphere.*

(ratio of light reflected from the surface to the total light falling upon the surface). The high level of light reflection from Venus is probably due to the heavy layer of clouds which completely surrounds the planet. It is not known what elements are included in the atmosphere of Venus, although certain compounds and elements have been detected. It appears that one of the principal components of the atmosphere is carbon dioxide, being more than 200 times as strong as it is in the earth's atmosphere. The thickness of the atmosphere also appears to be much greater

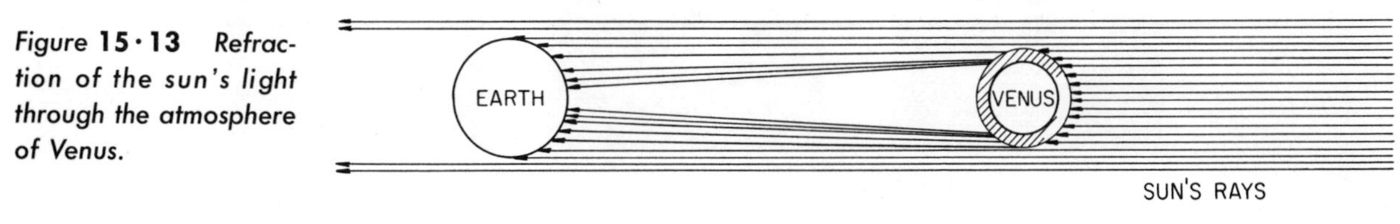

Figure **15·13** *Refraction of the sun's light through the atmosphere of Venus.*

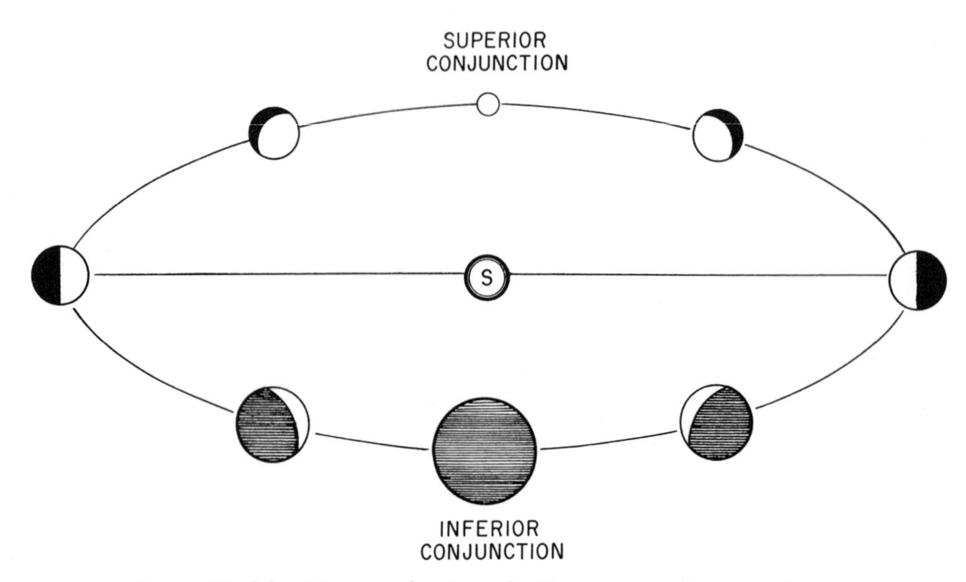

Figure **15 · 14** *Diagram showing why Venus passes through phases.*

than that of the earth and is reported as being approximately 300 miles.

One of the evidences of the atmosphere on Venus is that, during the time that Venus is between the earth and the sun (near inferior conjunction), a ring of light is seen almost all around the dark part of the planet's disk. This is caused by the sun's light shining into the atmosphere and being refracted and scattered sufficiently so that it can be seen on the earth. This is illustrated in Fig. 15 · 13.

The appearance of Venus through a telescope presents a picture somewhat like that of the moon. Venus goes through phases as illustrated in Fig. 15 · 14. At the point of **superior conjunction** (when the planet is in line with the sun and earth but is on the side of the sun away from the earth) Venus is in the "full" position. As it moves around the orbit, the percentage of the illuminated face decreases continuously until the point of **inferior conjunction,** when only the dark disk is facing the earth and visibility is most difficult. Photographs of Venus are shown in Fig. 15 · 15.

Since Venus is nearer the earth than any other planet, it presents one of the greatest challenges to scientists and space-age engineers. Plans are under way to conduct explorations of the surface eventually, although this event must be preceded by exploratory probes, which are now in preparation. It is hoped that a substantial amount of

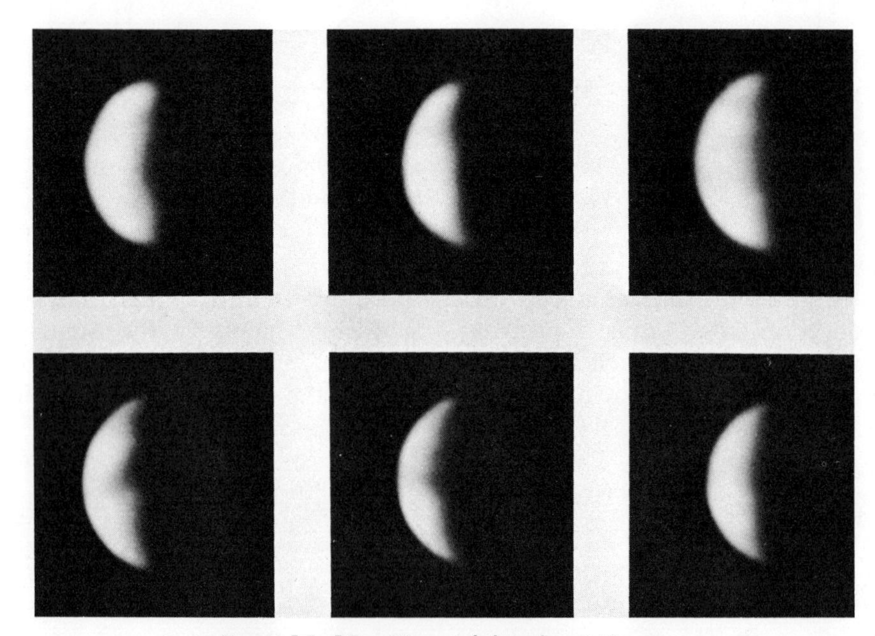

Figure **15 · 15** *Views of the planet Venus.*

information concerning the composition of the atmosphere, the temperatures, and the nature of the surface can be obtained by unmanned probes before man himself attempts to visit the planet. The matter of greatest interest, of course, is whether there is life on Venus and whether this life may be in the form of beings having intelligence. It is probable that the temperature on the surface of Venus is of a level that a human being could survive, but the presence of water and oxygen are in doubt, so we can only wait until someone lands on the surface to answer our questions.

The moon

Since the moon is the nearest heavenly body to the earth, we undoubtedly know more about it than we know about any planet, natural satellite, planetoid, asteroid, or star. The proximity of the moon is, of course, the principal reason we can know certain facts about it very accurately. Figure 15·16 is a photograph of the moon's surface. From this photograph we can learn much, particularly that there does not appear to be any atmosphere, which would be revealed by haze, clouds, vapor, etc. Also we can easily see that a substantial part of the surface of the moon is covered with craters and that the other parts are evidently expansive plains which are comparatively smooth.

Figure 15·16 A portion of the moon's surface.

The moon orbits the earth about once a month at an average distance from the earth of a little more than 238,000 miles. Since the orbit of the moon is an ellipse and is not symmetrical with respect to the earth, the nearest approach to the earth (**perigee**) is a distance of about 222,000 miles. The greatest distance from the earth (**apogee**) is approximately 253,000 miles. The moon's orbit is inclined an average of 5°9′ to the ecliptic with a variation of about 12′ each way from the mean value.

Because of the movement of the earth around the sun, there is a variation in the length of the moon's revolution around the earth with respect to the stars as compared with the revolution with respect to the sun. The **sidereal** month (revolution of the moon with respect to the stars) has a mean value of 27 days, 17 hr, 43 min, and 11.5 sec.

The **synodic** month (time that the moon completes the cycle from a particular phase back to the same phase) has a length of 29 days, 12 hr, 44 min, 2.8 sec. The reason for this is illustrated in Fig. 15·17. In the illustration, when the earth is in position 1 and the moon at position *A*, the sun, earth, moon, and a reference star are in alignment. Under these conditions the moon is at full phase. About 27.3 days later the earth, moon, and star are again in alignment, showing that the moon has made one revolution of the earth with respect to the stars and one sidereal month has passed. We note, however, that the moon has not reached the full-phase position because it is not in line with the sun and the earth. This position is not reached until more than 2 days later, when the earth is at position 3 in the diagram. At this time the moon is at *C* and is in full phase.

The diameter of the moon is about one-fourth that of the earth, being 2,160 miles. Its density is only 3.4 (density of water, 1), considerably less than that of the earth, which is about 5.5. For this reason the mass of the moon is only about one-eighth the density of the earth.

Since the moon is the captive of the earth, the two together must be considered as a unit when determining their effect on the sun and other planets. The CG for the moon and earth together is located at a point about 1,000 miles under the surface of the earth directly under the moon. This CG must be taken into account when making computations for the orbit of an artificial satellite or the path of a space vehicle.

The phases of the moon are caused in a manner similar to that explained for Venus. The diagram of Fig. 15·18 illustrates the reason for the moon's phases. Because the moon orbits the earth, the change in phases is much more rapid than simi-

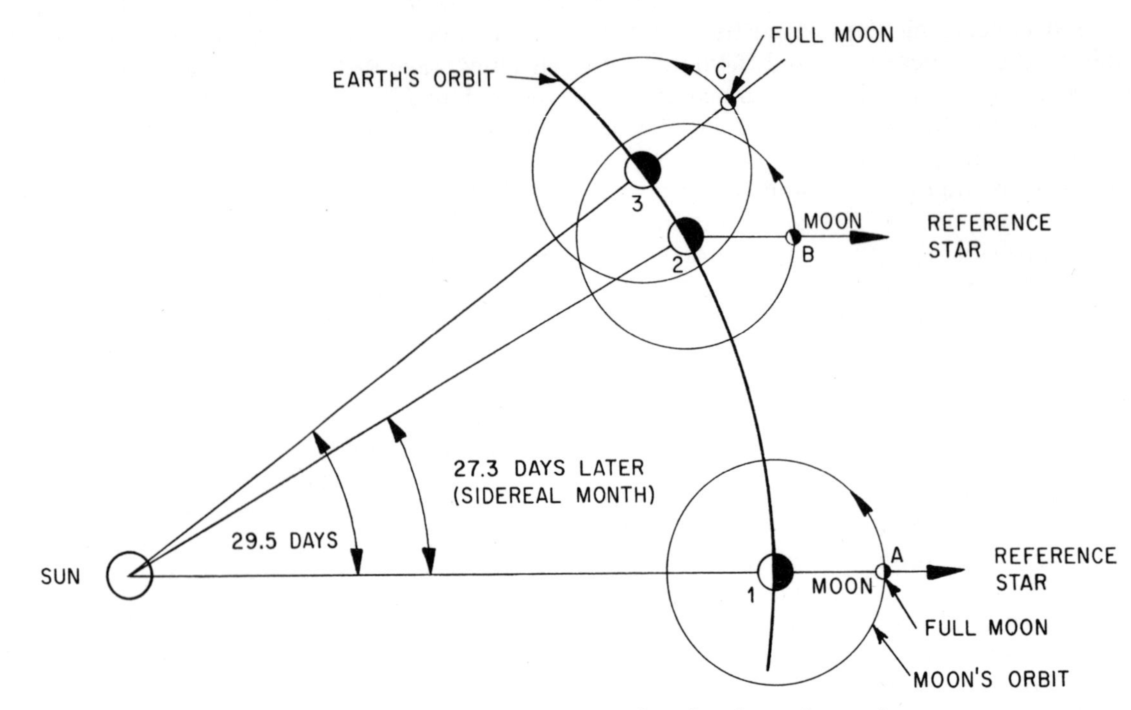

Figure **15 · 17** *Difference between sidereal and synodic months.*

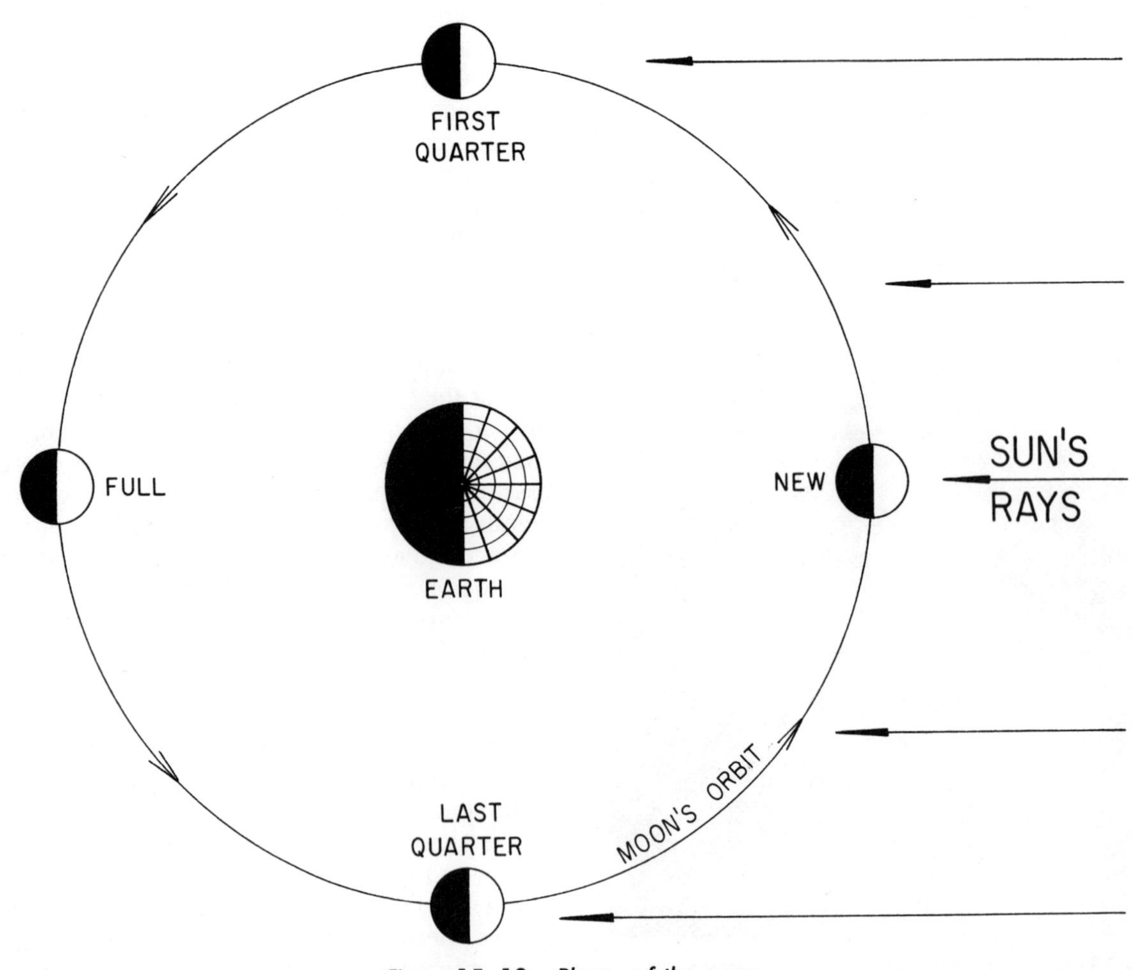

Figure **15 · 18** *Phases of the moon.*

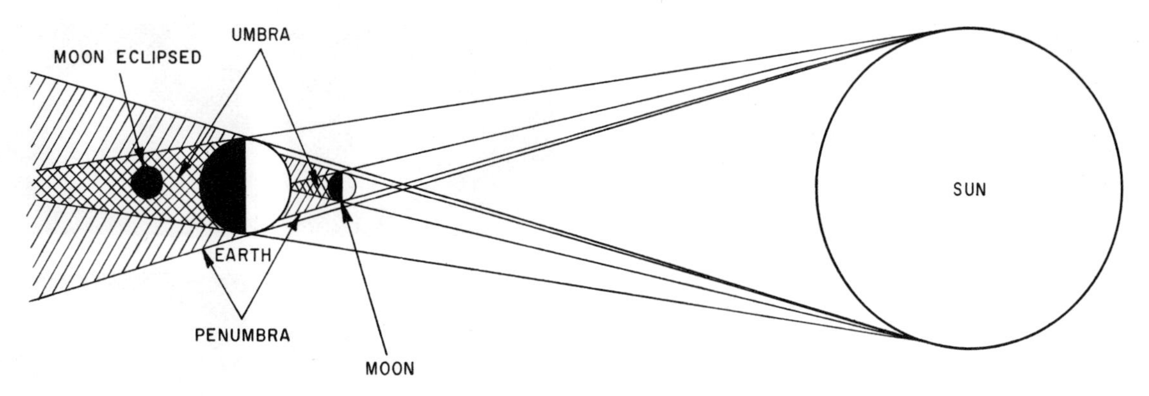

Figure **15 · 19** *The causes of eclipses.*

lar changes for Mercury or Venus or any of the other planets. As the moon moves from **last quarter** to **new,** it will appear to have the familiar crescent shape, with the crescent decreasing in thickness each day until it entirely disappears. A day or two after **new moon** the crescent again appears in the western sky shortly after sunset. It increases in width each day until it reaches the first quarter, when it has the appearance of a half moon.

In order to understand the movement of the moon with respect to the earth and the sun, it is well to remember certain facts. (1) At full moon the moon is in opposition to the sun; that is, its direction from the earth is 180° from that of the sun. (2) At new moon the moon is in conjunction with the sun. (3) At either first quarter or last quarter the moon is 90° to the sun.

The moon is the cause of an eclipse of the sun, and the earth is the cause of an eclipse of the moon. Figure 15 · 19 illustrates how eclipses occur. When the moon comes directly between the earth and the sun, an eclipse of the sun takes place. Actually a total eclipse of the sun can be seen only through a narrow band of area on the earth where the solid shadow (umbra) of the moon strikes. If an eclipse of the sun occurs when the moon is too far from the earth, the umbra will not strike the earth and a person in the proper position to observe the eclipse will see the sun as a ring of very bright light, the moon being in the center. An eclipse of this type is called an **annular** eclipse.

An eclipse of the moon occurs as the moon passes through the earth's shadow. Moon eclipses are quite common and can be seen over a wide area of the earth because, when the moon is eclipsed, it gives no appreciable light and anywhere it is visible on earth it will be in eclipse. During a total eclipse of the moon, it can usually be seen as a dull, reddish disk. The red light on the moon is caused by the red rays of light being bent around the earth by the atmosphere. If one could stand on the moon during a lunar eclipse, he would observe the earth as a dark disk with a red ring of light around it.

An important effect of the moon which must be considered is the gravitational pull which causes the tides. Actually the moon causes the tides to a certain degree, but the sun contributes almost half as much effect as does the moon. When the sun and the moon are both on the same side of the earth, the tides will be at a maximum. When the sun and moon are at 90° to each other, their effects tend to cancel and we experience lower tides. There are two high tides and two low tides on the earth constantly. The high tides are on the sides facing and opposite the moon, and the low tides are on the sides of the earth at 90° to the moon. The tide on the side of the earth facing the moon is caused by the fact that the water, being nearer the moon than the center of the earth, is attracted toward the moon more than the center of the earth is attracted. On the side of the earth away from the moon, the water is attracted less than is the center of the earth; hence the water tends to flow to the point most distant from the moon. Thus we have two high tides.

The tide which occurs when the moon and the sun are exerting the maximum effect on the same side of the earth is called a **spring** tide, and the tide which occurs when the sun and moon are at 90° to each other is called the **neap** tide. The highest tide, which occurs when the moon is nearest the earth, is called the **perigee** tide.

Mars

Mars is another planet of particular interest to man on earth because of the remote possibility that there may be some kind of life there. Mars has a thin atmosphere, a little water, and a temperature in which certain kinds of life could exist. It also has seasons and a day about the same length as the day on earth. These similarities to conditions on earth provide some basis for the thought that there may be life on Mars.

Mars has a diameter of about 4,140 miles and orbits at a mean distance of about 141,300,000 miles from the sun. The eccentricity of the orbit is comparatively large; hence the actual distance from the sun varies 13,000,000 miles in each direction, making a total difference between perihelion and aphelion of 26,000,000 miles. The orbit of Mars is inclined about 1°51′ to the ecliptic. The sidereal period is nearly 687 days, and the synodic period about 780 days.

Since the orbit of Mars is outside that of the earth, there is a large variation in the distance between Mars and the earth. When the perihelion of Mars occurs at the same time that Mars is in opposition to the sun, the planet is only about 35,000,000 miles from the earth, and this provides the best opportunity for observation of the surface. When Mars is in conjunction with the sun at aphelion, its distance from the earth is approximately 237,000,000 miles. At this time Mars is not visible from the earth.

The surface of Mars appears to be a red, sandy desert. Although it has been reported in the past that there appeared to be long, straight lines on the surface, which were called canals, recent observations do not reveal these. One of the outstanding features of the surface of Mars is the presence of polar ice caps during winter periods. These ice caps give infrared reflection spectra similar to frost or ice in the laboratory. It appears, then, that a certain amount of water exists on the planet, and this could help to support life. Another indication of some form of life is that portions of the surface of Mars become darker during the summer, thus indicating the growth of vegetation. Observations have shown clouds existing over large areas of the surface at certain times, and this would require an atmosphere for support of the clouds. Photographs of Mars are shown in Fig. 15·20.

The temperature of the surface of Mars is reasonably close to the temperatures on the earth, being well above the freezing point of water during the warm periods and below the freezing point of water during the cold periods. The temperature range is another factor which supports the contention that life exists on Mars.

An interesting feature of Mars is the presence of two small satellites, one with a radius of about 5,800 miles and the other with a radius of about 14,600 miles. The larger satellite, which is also the closest to the planet, is estimated to be about 10 miles in diameter and is named **Phobos,** meaning **fear.** The outer satellite, called **Deimos,** meaning

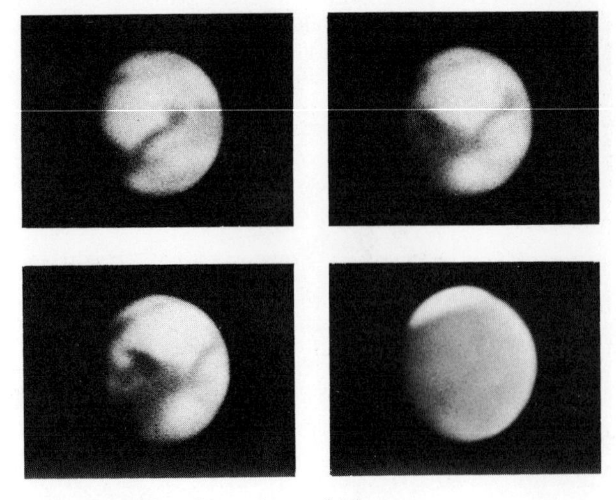

Figure **15·20** *Four views of Mars.*

panic, is estimated to be about 5 miles in diameter. Phobos rotates around Mars in 7 hr and 39 min while it requires about 132 hr for Deimos to travel around the planet. This is because Deimos has a sidereal period of 30.3 hr while the planet has a rotational period of 24.6 hr.

The asteroids

The **asteroids** are what may be termed "small planets" orbiting the sun generally in the space between Mars and Jupiter, although many of them swing inside the orbit of Venus and outside the orbit of Saturn. The first asteroid was discovered on January 1, 1801, by Piazzi in Palermo, Sicily. This was the asteroid which was later named Ceres. Three other asteroids were discovered within a few years after the discovery of Ceres. These were Pallas, Juno, and Vesta. Since that time more than 1,600 have been identified with numbers, and it seems apparent that there are many thousands of asteroids orbiting in the general area between Mars and Jupiter.

One of the most important asteroids to be discovered is Eros. This asteroid swings within 15,000,000 miles of the earth and has been used as a reference point for determining the distance to the sun.

Jupiter

Jupiter is the largest of the planets and is also one of the brightest. It orbits the sun at a mean distance of 484,000,000 miles. The eccentricity of the orbit is such that the distance from the sun varies each way by as much as 23,000,000 miles. The plane of the orbit is inclined 1°18′ to the plane of the ecliptic. Jupiter requires 11.86 years to travel around its orbit with respect to the stars (sidereal) and 399 days from one conjunction with the sun to the next (synodic period).

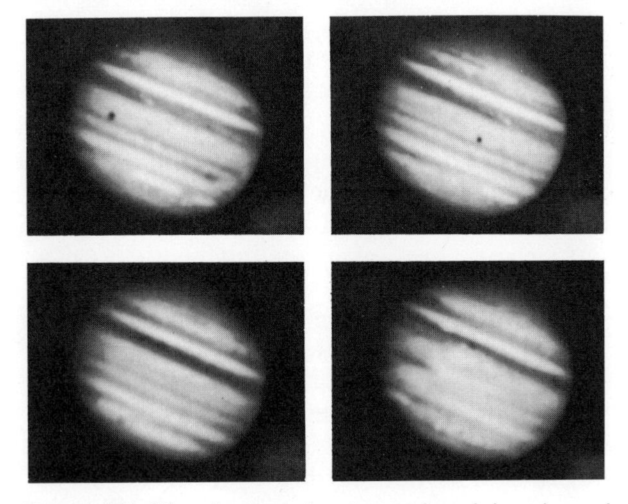

Figure **15·21** *Jupiter showing colored bands and two satellites.*

Jupiter has a mean diameter of 86,800 miles. However, because of its rapid rotation, 9 hr and 55 min, it is flattened at the poles so the polar diameter is 82,700 miles and the equatorial diameter is 88,700 miles. It has a density of only about 1.4, which is about one-fourth that of the earth. The volume is 1,300 times that of the earth, but its mass is only 318 times the earth's mass. From this it is believed that a layer of ice covers the surface to a depth of several thousand miles, which would account for the low density.

The telescopic appearance of Jupiter is shown by the photographs of Fig. 15·21. It will be noted from these that the atmosphere of Jupiter seems to form in parallel bands of different density. These bands continuously change in width and color, so it is difficult to determine what appearance the surface of the planet has.

The atmosphere of Jupiter consists largely of methane and ammonia, and because of the extremely low temperature, the ammonia is probably in frozen crystal form. It is also believed that substantial quantities of hydrogen exist in the upper atmosphere of the planet. Any water on Jupiter would be in the form of ice, and as mentioned previously, this probably forms a layer several thousand miles thick.

Because of its distance from the sun, the temperature on the surface of Jupiter is about −210°F. Because of the temperature and atmosphere it is probable that no form of life could exist on Jupiter.

Jupiter has a large family of satellites. Four of these are comparatively large and are named Io, Europa, Ganymede, and Callisto. These are 2,318, 1,967, 3,200, and 3,218 miles in diameter, respectively. All the other satellites, eight in number, are 100 miles or less in diameter, and the smaller ones can be seen only by means of photography. The large satellites are in the orbits nearer the planet, and all the others except one are in the more distant orbits. The distances of the satellites from the planet vary from 112,600 to 14,900,000 miles.

Saturn

Saturn is the second largest planet, being 75,000 miles in diameter through the equator and 67,000 miles in diameter through the poles. This difference of diameter, like that of Jupiter, is caused by the high rotational speed. The period of rotation is 10 hr and 38 min, which is almost as short as that of Jupiter.

The volume of Saturn is about three-fifths that of Jupiter, but its mass is only one-third as large. From this it is seen that the density of Saturn is only 75 per cent of the density of water. Thus, if Saturn were floated in a large ocean, only three-fourths of it would be submerged.

The most spectacular characteristic of Saturn is its three rings. These rings are concentric and are exactly in the equatorial plane of the planet. The inner ring starts at a distance of about 7,000 miles from the surface and continues outward for about 11,000 miles. Between the inner ring and the middle ring there is a gap of about 1,000 miles. The middle ring is 15,000 miles wide and is the brightest of the rings. Outside the middle ring is a gap of 2,500 miles, which is called Cassini's division. The outer ring is 10,000 miles across and has an outer diameter of 170,000 miles.

The rings of Saturn are exceedingly thin, and when they are edgewise to the earth, they cannot be seen. It is estimated that they are only about 7 to 10 miles in thickness. A photograph of Saturn and its rings is shown in Fig. 15·22.

The atmosphere of Saturn is very much like that of Jupiter, consisting principally of ammonia and methane. It is not possible to determine or estimate the nature of Saturn's surface with any degree of accuracy, although it has been

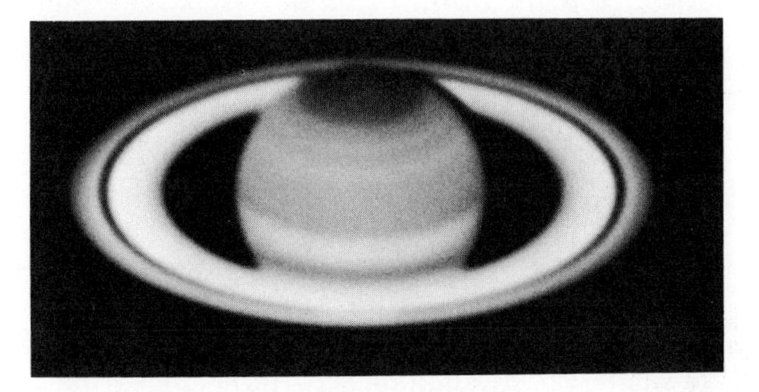

Figure **15·22** *Saturn and its rings.*

suggested by Wildt that the core may consist of dense material with a radius of about 10,000 miles. Over this is a layer of ice approximately 15,000 miles thick. This layer is then surrounded by an atmosphere of methane, ammonia, and hydrogen about 12,000 miles thick. With this combination of materials the density of the planet would equal that which has been measured.

Saturn orbits the sun at a mean distance of about 887,000,000 miles. The orbit is inclined 2°29′ to the ecliptic. It requires 29.5 years to travel the distance around the sun (sidereal period), and the synodic period is 378 days. The axis of Saturn is inclined about 27° to the plane of its orbit. This causes seasons on the planet, but because of its distance from the sun it is not likely that the seasonal changes have much effect on the surface conditions. The surface temperature is about −240°F, which is substantially colder than Jupiter.

Saturn has a large family of known satellites. These are, in order of their size from the largest to the smallest, Titan, Iapetus, Rhea, Tethys, Dione, Enceladus, Mimas, Hyperion, and Phoebe. The satellites are believed to range in size from 2,610 to 150 miles in diameter.

Uranus

Uranus was discovered in 1781, and prior to this time Saturn was thought to be the outermost planet. This is undoubtedly because Uranus is just barely visible to the naked eye, even under the most favorable conditions. Uranus is about 32,000 miles in diameter and has characteristics similar to Jupiter and Saturn as far as atmosphere, density, and temperature are concerned.

Uranus orbits the sun at a mean distance of about 1,784,000,000 miles in an orbit inclined about 0°46′ to the ecliptic. It requires 84 years to travel around its orbit and 369.7 days to complete the synodic period. The period of rotation is 10.7 hr. Uranus does not follow the pattern of other planets with respect to the inclination of its axis to its orbit. The axis is 82° from the perpendicular to the plane of the orbit, thus making it only 8° from parallel to the plane of the orbit. For this reason, at certain times, the poles of the planet are pointed almost directly toward the earth.

Uranus has a family of five known satellites, named in the order of their sizes Titania, Oberon, Ariel, Umbriel, and Miranda. The largest of these is 1,600 miles in diameter. The satellites orbit exactly in the plane of the equator; hence when the pole of the planet is facing toward the earth, the satellites describe almost perfect circles around the planet. When the equator of Uranus is toward the earth, the satellites appear to move up and down in a straight line.

Neptune

Neptune was discovered as the result of perturbations (seemingly erratic movements) of Uranus. Two astronomers, John C. Adams of England and Urbain Leverrier, made independent calculations of Uranus's perturbations and predicted where a planet should be to cause these unorthodox movements. The result was the discovery of Neptune by Johann Galle in 1846.

Neptune has a diameter of about 31,000 miles, thus making it an almost identical twin to Uranus. It is, of course, much farther from the sun, having a mean distance of about 2,796,000,000 miles from the sun. The orbit of Neptune is inclined 1°47′ to the ecliptic, and the planet has a sidereal period of 164.79 years, which is almost twice that of Uranus. The synodic period is 367.5 days.

Neptune also rotates at a comparatively high rate, that is, about 16 hr for a complete revolution. The axis is about 20° off the perpendicular to its orbit; hence it is in conformity with most of the other planets.

The atmosphere and composition of Neptune are similar to Jupiter, Saturn, and Uranus. The atmosphere is composed of ammonia, methane, and hydrogen, and the planet itself probably has a dense core covered with a thick layer of ice and a heavy atmosphere.

Neptune has two known satellites, Triton and Nereid. Triton is thought to be about 2,800 miles in diameter, and Nereid about 200 miles in diameter. Accurate measurements are not possible at such a great distance, so the diameters are considered just good estimates.

Pluto

Pluto is the outermost of the known planets, orbiting at the fantastic distance of 39.5 astronautical units (3,673,000,000 miles) from the sun. A beam of light leaving Pluto would require over 5 hr to reach the earth. The discovery of Pluto was announced in 1930, and it was found only as the result of a very careful search. The search was instituted because the planet Neptune appeared to have perturbations which were unexplainable without the presence of another planet.

Pluto is thought to be about 3,700 miles in diameter, although it is most difficult to measure because of its small size and great distance from the earth.

The orbit of Pluto is inclined about 17° to the ecliptic, its sidereal period is 248 years, and its synodic period is about 366.5 days. The den-

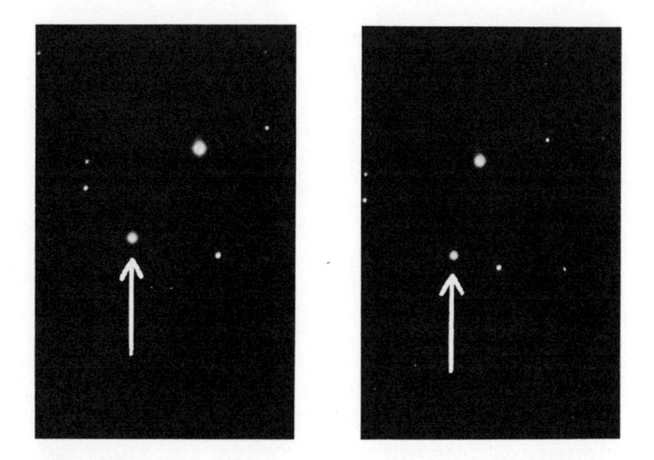

Figure **15·23** *Two views showing motion of Pluto in 24 hr.*

sity may be several times that of the earth; however, this is not certain. There is no evidence of an atmosphere.

Two interesting photographs are shown in Fig. 15·23. These photographs were taken with the 200-in. Hale telescope on Mt. Palomar and show the movement of Pluto during a 24-hr period.

The comets

Of all the bodies in the solar system, probably the **comets** are the least understood. Certain facts about them have been determined; however, it is not known precisely what they are made of or how they were created.

Figure 15·24 shows views of Halley's comet, and Fig. 15·25 is a photograph of Comet Cunningham. These illustrations show typical comet appearance.

A comet consists of a **nucleus** at the head surrounded by a less dense enveloping material called the **coma.** From the head of the comet the tail extends in a direction which is usually away from the sun. It is believed that the energy of the sun (pressure of photons) drives the tail material outward.

Diameters of the heads of comets vary from less than a mile to more than a million miles, and the nuclei have diameters up to 8,000 miles. The tails sometimes extend as much as 200,000,000 miles.

The density of the material in the head of a comet is so low that it has practically no effect on any other heavenly body which passes near it. It is believed that the average density of the head of a comet is less than a laboratory vacuum. It seems inconceivable that there would be any material to reflect light under these circumstances. However, when we observe the northern lights, we can begin to understand how the light may originate. Most of the light of a comet is thought to develop by fluorescence. The material in the

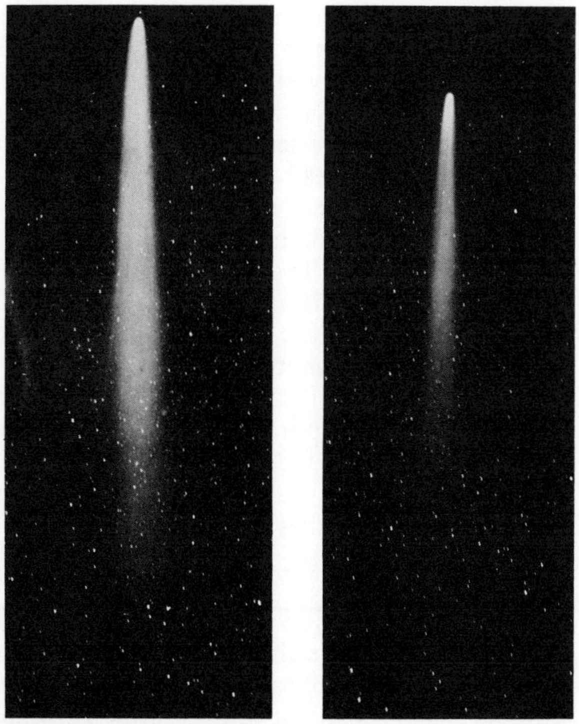

Figure **15·24** *Halley's comet.*

Figure **15·25** *Comet Cunningham.*

tail of a comet has a density so low that 1 oz would cover the entire earth with a depth of several hundred feet.

In general, comets orbit the sun in extremely elliptical orbits. Halley's comet, for example, approaches the sun inside the earth's orbit and then travels outward to a point well outside Neptune's orbit. Its period is approximately 75 years, although this can be changed by as much as 2 years by the gravitational effect of one of the planets. Some comets apparently come into our solar system from outer space and then leave it again in a hyperbolic orbit. Others are captured by our system and may remain in elliptical orbits about the sun.

Meteors and meteorites

It is a common sight on a clear dark night to see bright streaks of light flashing across the sky. These streaks are commonly said to be caused by "shooting stars." Actually, these streaks of light are the result of particles of "space debris" burning up in the earth's atmosphere. Any piece of material in space which is trapped by the earth's gravity will be drawn into the atmosphere. Since there is no friction in space, any body being drawn toward the earth will increase in velocity until it is moving at many thousands of feet per second. At such high velocity a body entering the earth's atmosphere will quickly be heated by friction to incandescense. Metallic elements in the body will melt and oxidize, while nonmetallic elements will oxidize or vaporize. The result is that the body will usually disappear before it reaches the surface of the earth. Bodies entering the earth's atmosphere and burning in this manner are called **meteors.**

When a meteor is of such size or composition that it survives the fiery dive to earth and actually strikes the surface, it is called a **meteorite.** It is estimated that thousands of meteorites strike the earth each day; however, most of these are so small that they are not noticed. The largest meteorite found on earth weighs approximately 66 tons. It is believed that a number of much larger meteorites have struck the earth and are probably buried deep beneath the surface. One of these is the meteorite which caused the crater near Canyon Diablo in Arizona. The crater is approximately 600 ft in depth and about 4/5 mile in diameter. Even though much drilling has been done in the crater, the meteorite has not been found. Many small meteorites ranging in size from less than an ounce to several hundred pounds have been found in the vicinity of the crater, so it is assumed that the meteorite either blew up or was shattered into many small pieces when it struck the ground. It is also believed that there is still a large mass of meteoric material under the surface of the earth in or near the crater.

Many fairly large meteorites have been found in various parts of the world, but most of these fell to earth hundreds or thousands of years ago. In recent years large meteorites have been known to fall in Siberia (1908) and in Kansas (1948). The Kansas meteorite is the largest actually seen to fall.

Meteorites are divided into three classes depending upon their composition. These are **iron meteorites, iron-stony meteorites,** and **stony meteorites.** Actually, these meteorites contain a fairly large number of elements; however, in the metallic meteorites the predominating material is iron. In the iron meteorites there is also a large percentage of nickel.

The exact source of meteors and meteorites is not known, but it is assumed that they are fragments of a disintegrated planet or asteroid. The age of the particles seems to be approximately the same as that of the earth, so it is assumed that meteorites are a part of the solar system.

THE STARS

The subject of stars, together with what is known about them and what is not known about them, is so vast that only elementary information can be given in a limited text. Certain facts and assumptions are of interest and provide a sound basis for appreciation of the endless space which we approach as we investigate the bodies occupying outer space. Particularly important is the beginning of an understanding of the sizes of the stars and the distances between them.

Using the diameter of the earth as a beginning, we first compare the diameter of this small planet with that of the sun. From this we find that the diameter of the sun is approximately 108 times that of the earth. Next we compare the diameter of the sun with the giant star ϵ Aurigae. Here we find a diameter ratio of 2,800:1. The giant star is then found to be approximately 2,400,000,000 miles in diameter. If the earth were the size of a common marble, the giant star would be a great ball more than 3½ miles in diameter.

The constellations

On a clear moonless night, preferably on a high mountain above the mists and haze found at lower altitudes, one can see thousands of stars with the naked eye. Some of these are very bright, while others are extremely faint. It will be noted that many of the brighter stars make various patterns, and with imagination, a person can visualize the possibility of likening some of the patterns to familiar objects, persons, or animals. It is these star patterns from which the ancient students of the heavens named the constellations.

In ancient times leaders of the people named the groups of stars after deities and heroes. From the time of Ptolemy (second century A.D.), 48 of the named constellations have been passed on to the present day. Today approximately 88 constellations are listed. One of the familiar constellations which we know as the Big Dipper is plainly seen as it circles the north polar region of the sky. The southernmost star of the Big Dipper is about 50° north of the celestial equator, and the northernmost star is about 62° north. The name given this constellation by the ancients is Ursa Major (Great Bear).

Another familiar constellation is Orion (named for a giant of mythology), which occupies a space from 10° south to 10° north of the celestial equator. Orion can be easily recognized by the three stars which form the "belt" of the giant and by bright stars in both the upper and lower parts of the "body." One of the brightest stars is Betelgeuse, a supergiant.

A group of 12 constellations was used by the ancient astrologers and soothsayers for the purpose of predicting the future and to determine when the time was right for planning important events. These constellations are called the **signs of the zodiac.** The sun occupies one of these signs for about one month each year. Even today fortune tellers and astrologers use the signs of the zodiac and the movements of the planets to prepare horoscopes which many people still consult in an effort to determine what their fortunes will be.

Table 15·2 lists the best known constellations; the first twelve are those in the zodiac.

Table 15·2

Aries (the Ram)	Boötes (the Plowman)
Taurus (the Bull)	Canis Major (the Great Dog)
Gemini (the Twins)	Canis Minor (the Lesser Dog)
Cancer (the Crab)	Cassiopeia
Leo (the Lion)	Cetus (the Whale)
Virgo (the Virgin)	Crux (the Cross)
Libra (the Scales)	Cygnus (the Swan)
Scorpio (the Scorpion)	Draco (the Dragon)
Sagittarius (the Archer)	Hercules
Capricorn (the Goat's Horn)	Hydra (the Serpent)
Aquarius (the Water Bearer)	Orion
Pisces (the Fishes)	Pegasus
Andromeda	Perseus
Aquila (the Eagle)	Ursa Major (the Great Bear)
Auriga (the Wagoner)	Ursa Minor (the Lesser Bear)

In order to become familiar with the stars and their locations in the sky it is important to become well acquainted with the constellations and their respective locations. The navigator of a ship or airplane who must use celestial navigation must be able to identify the star which he is using for a position fix so he can obtain the position of the star from a nautical almanac. Figure 15·26 is a star chart on which a number of the constellations are shown.

Types of stars

One of the methods for classifying the stars is by **spectral class.** The light radiated from a star is studied by means of a spectroscope, and the result determines to what class a star belongs. The stars with the highest temperatures produce a blue-white light and are classed as O-type stars. The surface temperatures of these stars are more than 25,000°K. Table 15·3 gives the spectral classifications for stars:

Table 15·3

Spectral class	*Color*	*Surface temperature, °K*
O	Blue-white	Over 25,000
B	Blue-white	21,000–25,000
A	White	7,500–11,000
F	Yellow-white	6000–7500
G	Yellow	5000–6000
K	Reddish	3500–5000
M	Red	2000–3500
N	Dull Red	Under 2,000

Most of the stars fall into the intermediate classes, and our sun is classed as a G-type star, or yellow dwarf. The supergiant stars are called red giants and fall into the K and M classifications. As explained previously, the supergiant stars are fantastic in size, being as much as several hundred times the diameter of our sun. One of the almost unbelievable facts to note about a supergiant star is that its density is extremely low and may be as low as that of a near vacuum. One cubic foot of such a star may weigh only 1/1,000 as much as 1 cu ft of our atmosphere at sea level.

The **main sequence** stars, into which our sun falls, include stars from one-tenth the size of our sun to about ten times its size. These stars, in general, have a mass proportional to luminosity and temperature.

Magnitude

In the second century A.D. the Egyptian astronomer Ptolemy gave values to the apparent

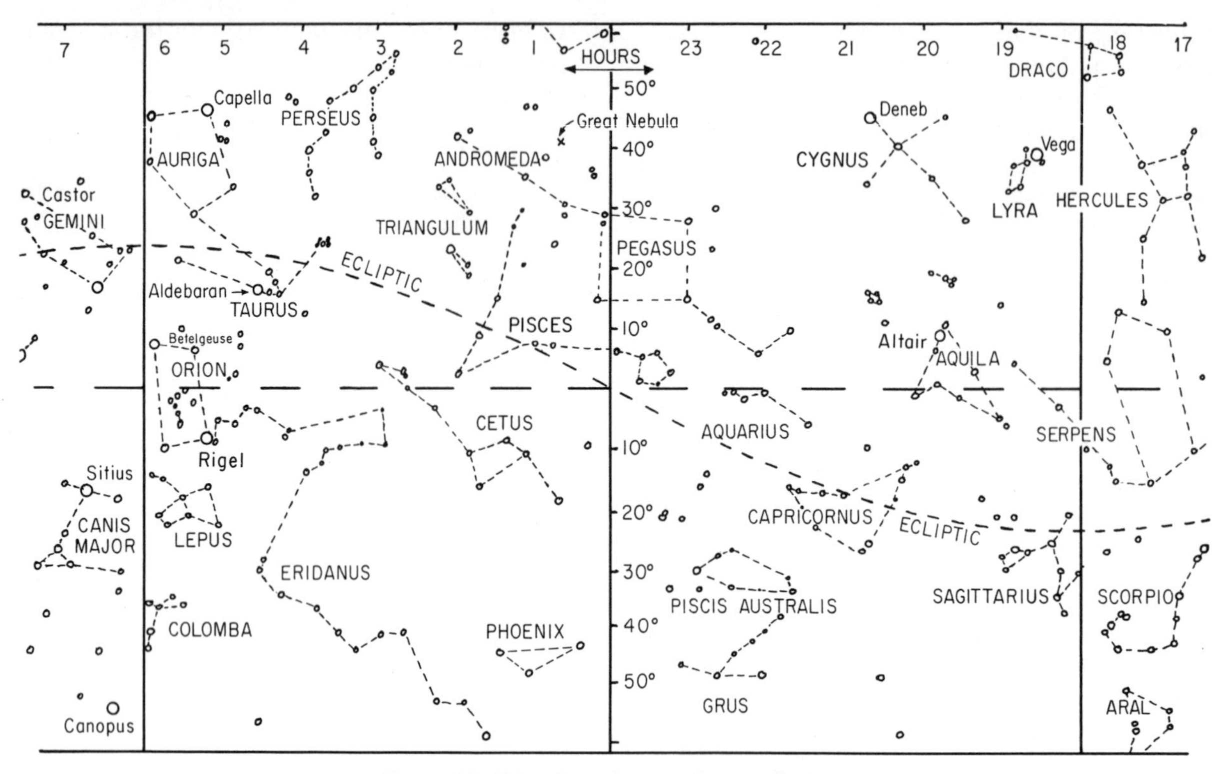

Figure **15·26** *Star chart and constellations.*

brilliance of the stars. He gave the brightest stars a magnitude of 1 and the faintest stars a magnitude of 6. All other visible stars were given values between 1 and 6. About the middle of the nineteenth century a ratio of 2.512 was established as the difference between magnitudes. Thus, when a star is said to be one magnitude brighter than another, it is 2.512 times as bright. A first-magnitude star is exactly 100 times as bright as a sixth-magnitude star.

Because most of the stars fall between the integral values on the magnitude scale, fractional magnitudes are also employed. If a star has a brightness exactly halfway between the third and the fourth magnitude, it is given a magnitude value of 3.5.

Some of the brightest stars are more brilliant than the first magnitude, and these are given fractional or negative magnitudes. Sirius, the brightest star in the sky, is given a magnitude value of -1.6, while the sun has a magnitude of -26.9.

The magnitudes we have discussed thus far are **apparent magnitudes;** that is, they represent the appearance of the star as we see it from the earth. This measure of brilliance cannot indicate the true brightness of a star because distance from the earth is also a factor. For example, one star could have a brightness four times as great as another. However, if it is twice as far away from the earth as the other, it would appear to have the same brightness. For this reason **absolute magnitudes** have been established.

The absolute magnitude of a star is equal to the apparent magnitude it would have if it were 10 parsecs (192,000,000,000,000 miles) from the earth. The absolute magnitude of our sun is $+4.86$ because, if it were 10 parsecs from the earth, it would appear to be a very tiny star. On the other hand, some of the distant stars have an absolute magnitude of -5, which means that their brightness is actually about 10,000 times as great as the sun.

As stated before, the faintest stars visible to the human eye have an apparent magnitude of 6. With the 200-in. Hale telescope, astronomers have photographed stars with apparent magnitudes of 23. These stars are so faint that they cannot be seen by means of the telescope, but they can be photographed with the telescope by using a very long exposure.

Binary stars

Many of the stars which we see as single points of light are actually pairs of stars orbiting around each other. These pairs are called **double stars** or **binary stars.** Some of these paired stars are very close to each other, while others are many light-years apart.

One of the greatest benefits obtained from the

study of binary stars is knowledge of the masses of stars. The distance between the primary star and its orbiting companion together with the period of revolution gives the astronomers the information which they need to determine the masses of the stars. Actually, a pair of binary stars rotates around a common center of gravity rather than one star orbiting the other. If the stars are of the same mass, the CG will be halfway between them. On the other hand, when there is a difference in the masses of the stars, the center of gravity will be nearer the star with the greatest mass. In any event, the stars will rotate around the CG.

When the plane of rotation of binary stars is edgewise to the earth, the stars will eclipse each other as they revolve. The point of this eclipse is easily determined by means of a spectroscope, even though the double nature of the star cannot actually be observed. When the eclipse occurs, there is a substantial reduction in the luminosity of the stars because one is cutting off the light of the other. When this occurs, the time can be recorded and the elapsed time to the next eclipse will be one-half the time of rotation.

Variable stars

In addition to the binary stars there are others whose luminosity changes periodically. One of the variable types is called the **Cepheid variable.** Stars of this type apparently expand and contract in a regular fashion according to what is known as the **pulsation theory.** According to this theory a Cepheid variable is a giant red star which becomes brighter as it expands and dimmer as it contracts. The Cepheid variables are named for the first one of the type discovered, δ Cephei. One of the most familiar stars in this class is Polaris, the polestar.

The Cepheid variables have proved to be useful to astronomers in determining distance. When the absolute magnitude is plotted against the velocity of expansion it is found that a definite relationship exists; that is, that luminosity increases with the velocity of expansion. From this study and others a period-luminosity curve has been developed, so that it is now possible to determine absolute magnitude directly from the curve. When absolute magnitude is known, it is a simple process to compute the distance to the star.

There are a number of other types of variable stars, all of which have certain similar characteristics. When we remember that the stars are actually composed largely of gaseous material at fairly high temperatures, we can understand how they might periodically contract and expand and thus produce a variation in light intensity.

Novae and supernovae

A rather unusual and spectacular type of star is the nova or supernova. Stars of this type seem to explode to a size and brilliancy thousands of times greater than their previous condition, and this happens in just a few days. It is believed that some kind of explosion occurs which greatly expands the surface gases of the stars and reveals the hot inner surface. After a time this inner surface cools and the star dims to its previous level or below its previous level. It is believed that **novation** occurs only once for most of the stars which experience the process and that it is a rare occurrence. In the history of astronomy less than 100 novae or supernovae have been observed.

The galaxy

When we speak of **the galaxy** we generally refer to the galaxy in which our own solar system is located. There are actually countless galaxies in the universe, many of which have been identified with names or numbers.

A galaxy is a grouping of stars, dust clouds, and gases, usually forming a disk somewhat like a convex lens. A diagram representing a cross section of our galaxy is shown in Fig. 15·27. Observe that the distance across the galaxy is approximately 100,000 light-years and our sun is about 30,000 light-years from the center.

To gain a slight awareness of the tremendous expanse of our galaxy we may consider its thickness at the location of our sun as being roughly 5,000 light-years. Since we cannot see individual stars for anywhere near 5,000 light-years, we may say that every star we can see with the naked eye would be included within the small dot we have used to indicate the position of our sun.

When we look into the plane of the galaxy on a dark clear night, we see it as the **Milky Way,** which appears as a light, cloudy trail across the sky. What we are actually seeing is the light from many billions of stars which are so distant that they cannot be discerned individually but their combined light is visible.

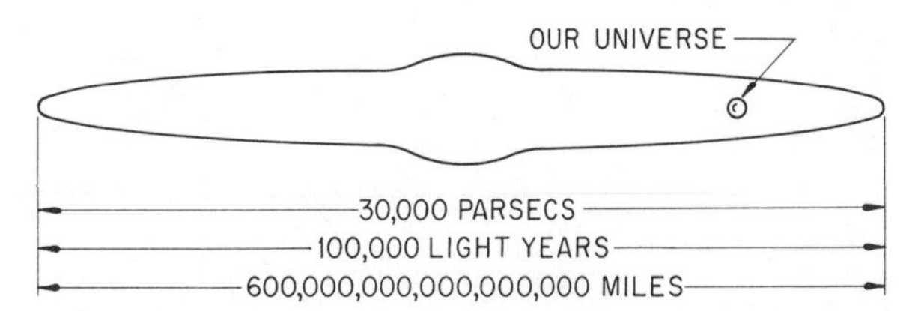

Figure 15·27 Diagram representing a cross section of our galaxy.

Figure **15 · 28** *Great Spiral Galaxy in Andromeda.*

Figure 15·28 is a photograph of the Great Spiral Galaxy in Andromeda. This galaxy can be seen in the constellation of Andromeda as a hazy object something like a light cloud. It appears to be somewhat smaller than the moon, and it can be seen only when the sky is dark and clear. The appearance of the galaxy in Andromeda is probably similar to what our own galaxy would look like to someone at a great distance outside it.

Figure **15 · 29** *Galaxy in Coma Berenices.*

Another galaxy which gives us an idea of our own is shown in Fig. 15·29. This is NGC 4565 in Coma Berenices as photographed with the 200-in. Hale telescope on Mt. Palomar. This galaxy is edgewise, so it gives us a good idea of the thickness of a typical galaxy relative to its diameter.

It must be pointed out that galaxies are composed of billions of stars but because of their great distance it is not possible to see the individual stars.

Nebulae

A **nebula** is a mass of gas, dust, or a combination of both which emits light as a result of ionization or by reflection from nearby stars. There are two general classes of nebulae, the **planetary,** which have fairly sharp definition, and the **diffuse,** which fade out at the edges like a misty cloud. Figure 15·30 shows the Ring nebula in Lyra, which is a planetary type. A diffuse type is the Great Nebula in Orion shown in Fig. 15·31. It is believed that many of the nebulae may be remains of supernovae which exploded thousands of years ago. This is because the outer areas are expanding at high velocities, and over a period of years, significant changes are seen in some of them. According to the best measurements possible, the nebulae observed and studied appear to be at a distance of 1,000 to 5,000 light-years from the earth. This means that they are within the area of our galaxy.

Computation of stellar distances

There are two principal methods for determining the distances and velocities of the stars, galaxies, and other celestial objects. These are by

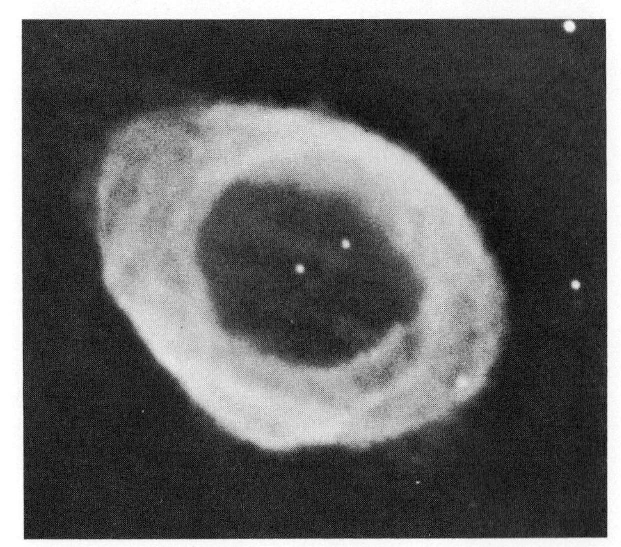

Figure **15 · 30** *Ring nebula in Lyra.*

Figure 15·31 Great Nebula in Orion.

trigonometric parallax (for only the nearest stars) and by spectrographic studies.

The parallax method is shown in Fig. 15·32. The relative positions of a near star and a distant star are noted at times 6 months apart. Since the earth is displaced by a distance of about 186,000,000 miles with respect to the solar system in a period of 6 months, there will be a change in the relative position of the star whose distance is to be computed and the distant star used as a reference. This change is represented by the angles x and y in the diagram of Fig. 15·32. By trigonometric methods the distance E_1S can be determined.

The method used for determining the distances to stars which are so far from the earth that the parallax method is ineffective is spectrographic analysis of the light emitted by the star combined with other known or probable factors. The distance is not determined directly from the spectrographic analysis; however, the velocities of stars can be determined by examining the spectrogram of the light which comes from them. When the velocity, direction of travel, luminosity, and color of the light are considered, it is possible to arrive at a reasonable estimate of the distance of the star.

The spectroscope

Since light travels in waves and each color of light has a certain wavelength, it is possible to separate white light into its component colors by means of a prism. When white light is passed through a prism, the red light, which has the longest wavelength, 7,594 Angstroms (A), is refracted least, while the other colors are refracted progressively more, up to violet, which has the shortest wavelength (3,968 A). Thus the light is spread out into a spectrum. The familiar rainbow is the spectrum of the sun's light.

A prism by itself produces a spectrum in which the colors overlap or fade into one another. In order to use the spectrum for analysis it is necessary that the different colors be sharply defined, and for this purpose a slit spectroscope is commonly used. The arrangement of the components of a spectroscope is shown in Fig. 15·33. Light passes through the slit at the right and then through the collimator, which makes the rays parallel. When the parallel rays enter the prism, the red component is refracted the least and therefore strikes the screen at the point R while the other colors are spread in sequence from R to V.

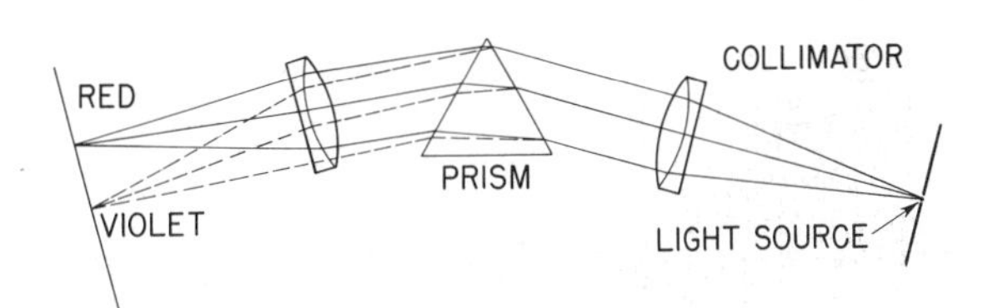

Figure 15·33 Diagram of a spectroscope.

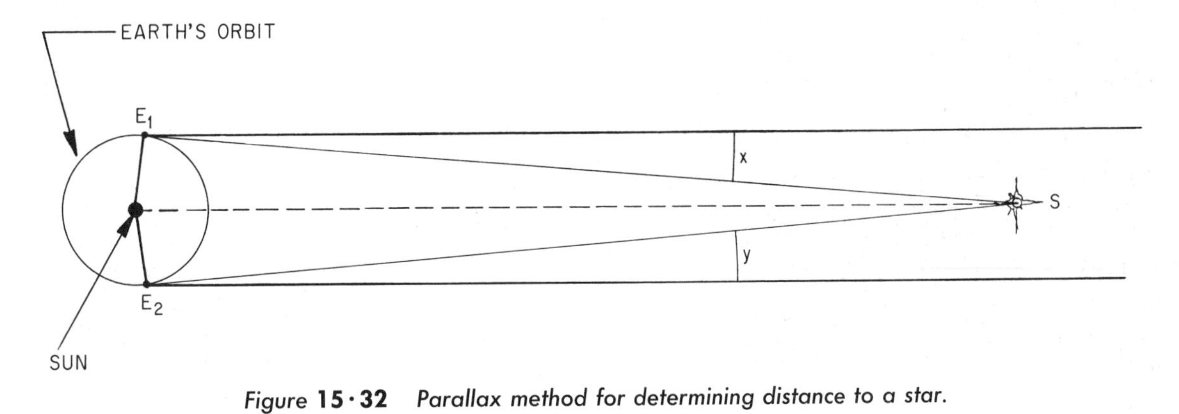

Figure 15·32 Parallax method for determining distance to a star.

Each chemical element when heated to the point where it will emit light produces a particular pattern of colored lines when the light is analyzed by means of the spectroscope. For this reason the spectroscope can be used to determine what elements are contained in a certain material if the material is heated sufficiently. It is apparent, then, that the light of a star can be analyzed with the spectroscope to determine what elements are involved in the emission of light from the star.

One of the great discoveries with respect to spectroscopy was made by a young German optician named Fraunhofer. When Fraunhofer was studying the spectrum of the light from the sun, he noted that there were dark lines across the colored bands at various points and that these lines seemed to form a definite pattern. Fraunhofer discovered that these lines actually were located at points in the spectrum where lines produced by particular elements were normally located. It has been found that the light from a particular gaseous element will be absorbed if it is passed through a layer of the gas at a lower temperature. For this reason the lines are called absorption lines. The absorption lines are named Fraunhofer lines in honor of their discoverer.

The origin of the Fraunhofer lines in the sun's spectrum is the layer of comparatively cool gases surrounding the sun. These gases absorb the light emitted from the sun in the particular frequency characteristic of the gas. In studying the light emitted by specific elements it is found that sodium emits a yellow light having a wavelength of 5,896 A. In the sun's spectrum a dark Fraunhofer line appears at this frequency; hence it is apparent that sodium exists in the gaseous envelope that surrounds the sun. In a similar manner, the other dark lines in the sun's spectrum can be compared with the spectra of different elements, and a pattern will be found for all the elements in the sun's outer atmosphere. The sun's spectrum is shown in Fig. 15·34.

One of the most important uses of the spectroscope in astronomy is to determine the velocities of various bodies. In an early section of this text it was explained that the frequency of sound waves appears to change if the source of the sound is moving toward or away from the listener. This is known as the Doppler effect. It is also true that the frequency of a light wave will be affected in the same manner by the velocity of the source of light. If a star is moving away from the earth,

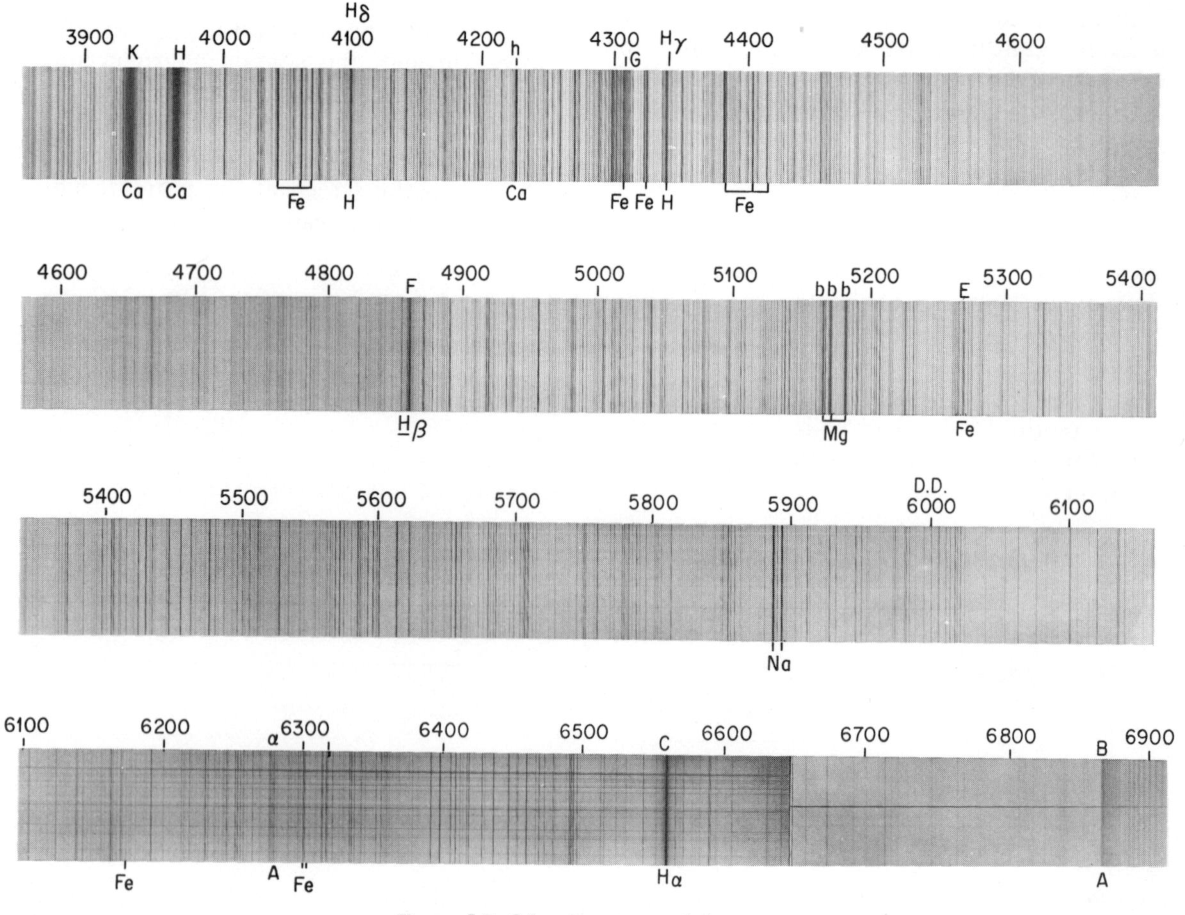

Figure **15·34** *Spectrum of the sun.*

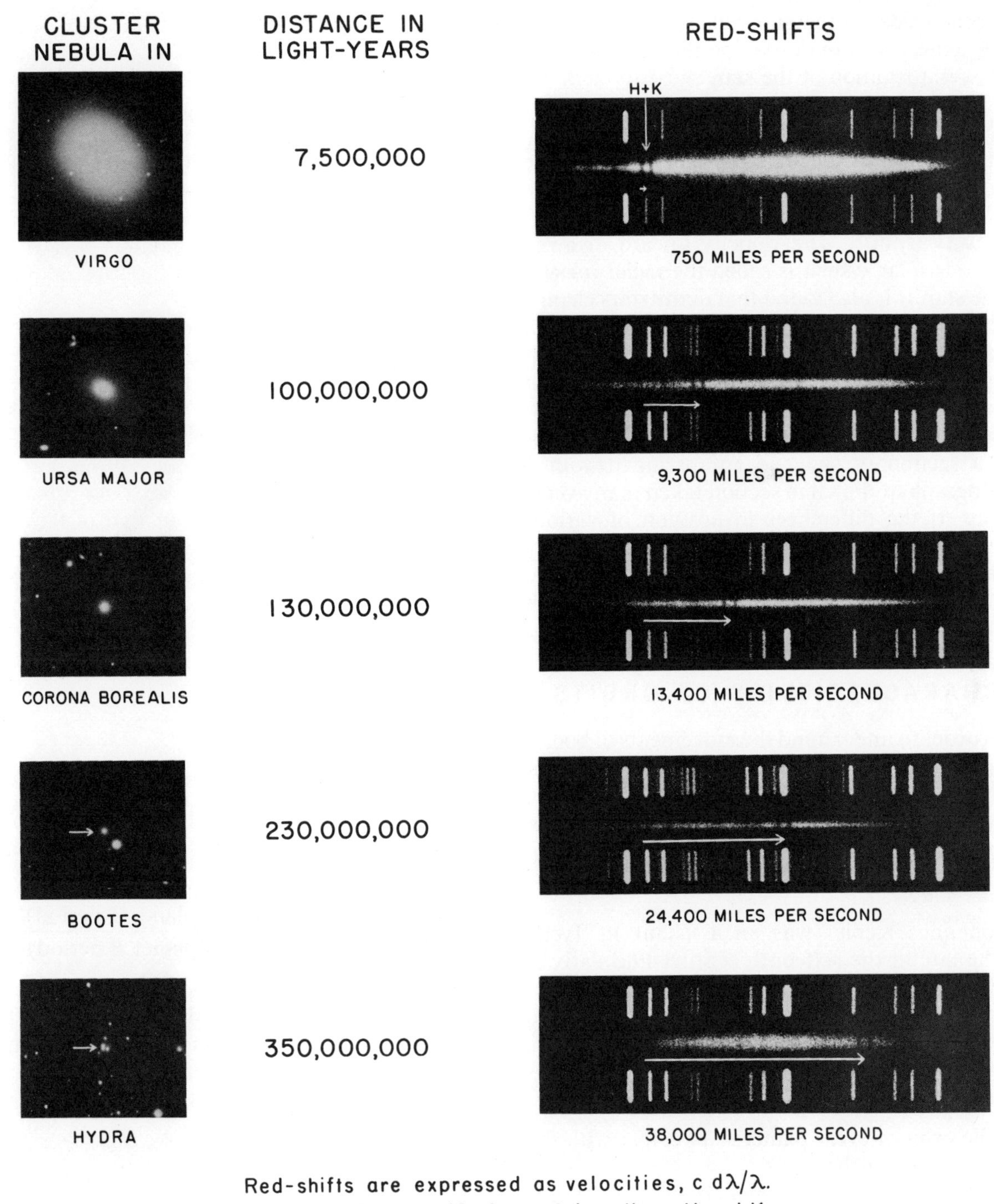

Figure **15 · 35** *Spectrographic analysis of light to indicate velocity, using the relation between red shift and distance for extragalactic nebulae.*

the normal frequency of its light will be reduced and the spectral lines will be shifted toward the red end of the spectrum. Also, if the star is moving toward the earth, the spectrum will be shifted toward the blue end. The amount of the shift in either case can be used to compute the velocity of the star. The use of spectra for determining velocity is shown in Fig. 15 · 35.

If a large star is rotating on an axis approximately at right angles to the line connecting the earth with the star, the light from one side of the star will shift toward the red and the light from the other side of the star will shift toward the blue; hence, we can determine the direction and velocity of rotation of the star.

Motions of stars

In the study of the stars with the spectroscope it is found that some stars are moving toward the earth (or our solar system) and others are moving away from it. The velocity toward or away from our solar system is called the **radial velocity** of the star. It is also found that many stars change their position with respect to the universe as a whole. This motion is called **proper motion.** It amounts to less than 10″ of arc per year in most cases and is usually less than 1″ of arc per year. Proper motion can be determined by photographing a section of sky and comparing it with a photograph of the same section taken many years before. If the differences in position of various stars with respect to one another are carefully measured and corrections for the movements of the earth applied, the proper motion of the stars can be determined.

CHARACTERISTICS OF ORBITS

In order to understand the movements of bodies in orbit, it is essential that certain laws and principles be considered. These principles govern the movements of planets as well as artificial satellites in orbit around the earth.

Kepler's laws

Johannes Kepler was an assistant to Tycho Brahe late in the sixteenth century and early in the seventeenth century. By using the measurements developed by Brahe, Kepler was able to discover three important laws of planetary motion. These are called Kepler's laws and are stated as follows:

1. The orbit of every planet is an ellipse with the sun at one of the foci.
2. A line joining any planet to the sun sweeps equal areas in equal periods of time.
3. The squares of the periods of revolution of any two planets are proportional to the cubes of their mean distances from the sun.

Kepler's first law is illustrated in Fig. 15·36. This drawing shows an exaggerated ellipse with the two foci shown as F_1 and F_2. The position of the sun is indicated by the letter S at F_2, and the position of a planet is indicated by the letter P.

The second law is illustrated by Fig. 15·37. The two shaded portions of the ellipse are of equal area, and the planet travels the distances indicated by arcs *ab* and *cd* in equal periods of time.

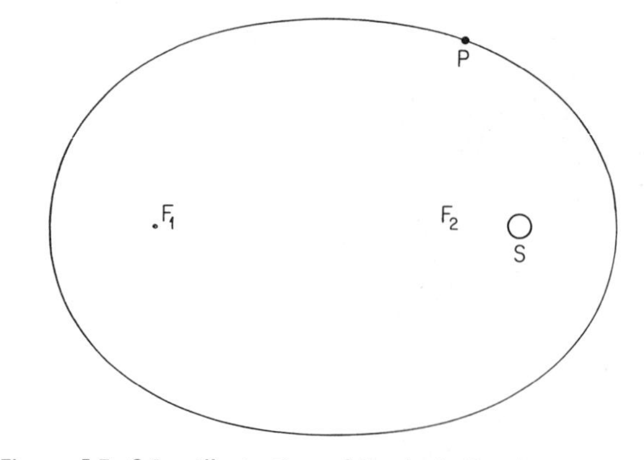

Figure **15·36** *Illustration of Kepler's first law.*

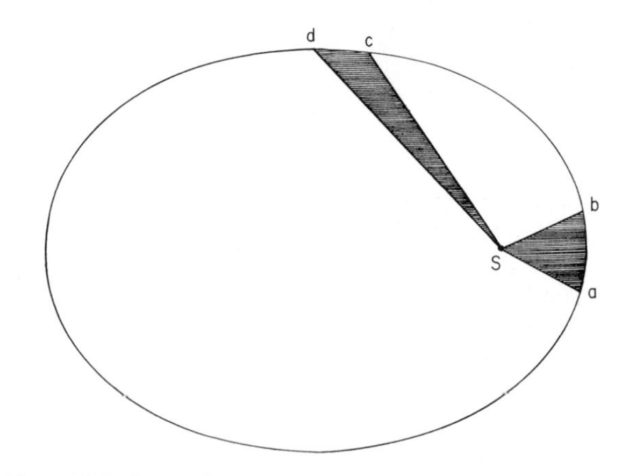

Figure **15·37** *Illustration of Kepler's second law.*

Kepler's third law can be illustrated by means of the equation

$$\frac{(\text{Planet } A \text{ distance})^3}{(\text{Planet } B \text{ distance})^3} = \frac{(\text{planet } A \text{ period})^2}{(\text{planet } B \text{ period})^2}$$

The laws stated apply to satellites orbiting the earth as well as to planets orbiting the sun. When speaking of satellites orbiting the earth, we must substitute the earth for the sun in the foregoing laws.

The elements of an orbit

In computing the nature of the orbit for any orbiting body, there are six elements which must be considered. These elements establish precisely the path of the body and can be used for predicting the position of the body at a future time.

It will be remembered that certain reference lines and points have been established for the celestial sphere. These were discussed in an earlier portion of this chapter and are illustrated in Fig. 15·5. The **ecliptic** is the plane of the earth's orbit around the sun and is a reference for the **inclination** of the planet's orbit. The **celestial equator** is the line established on the celestial sphere by the extension of the earth's equator into space. The line established by the intersection of the equator plane with the ecliptic is called the **line of nodes.** At the end of this line where the sun moves to the north of the celestial equator is the **vernal equinox** or **ascending node.** This point is indicated by the symbol (♈) for Aries because the point is also called the **First Point of Aries.** The plane of the ecliptic and the position of the vernal equinox are the two principal references by which the orbit of a planet is determined.

The elements of an orbit are given as follows:

1. Eccentricity of the orbit e
2. Length of the semimajor axis of the orbit a
3. Inclination of the orbit i
4. Longitude of the ascending node Ω
5. Direction of the perihelion from the ascending node ω
6. Time of perihelion passage T

The **eccentricity of the orbit** is the ratio of the distance of the sun from the center of the orbit to the semimajor axis. This is shown as AS/SB in Fig. 15·38. The **major axis** of an ellipse is the maximum distance across the ellipse, and the **semimajor axis** is one-half the major axis. The length of the semimajor axis is shown as AB in Fig. 15·38.

The **inclination of the orbit** i is illustrated in the drawing of Fig. 15·39. This inclination is represented by the angle ABC.

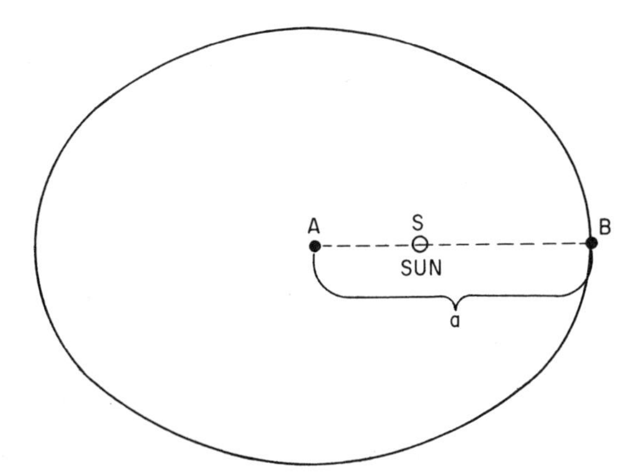

Figure **15·38** *Eccentricity of an orbit.*

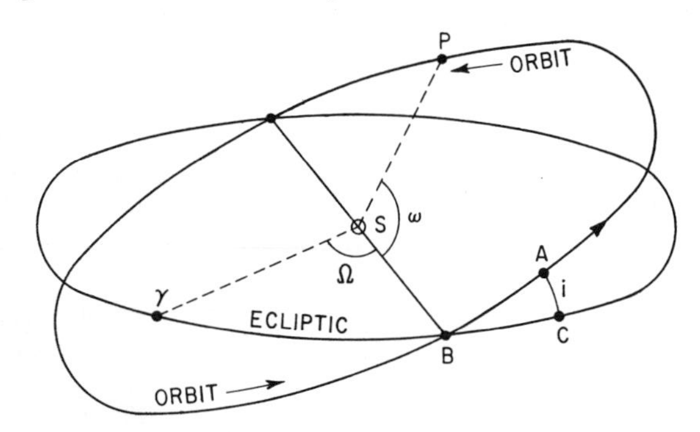

Figure **15·39** *Elements of an orbit.*

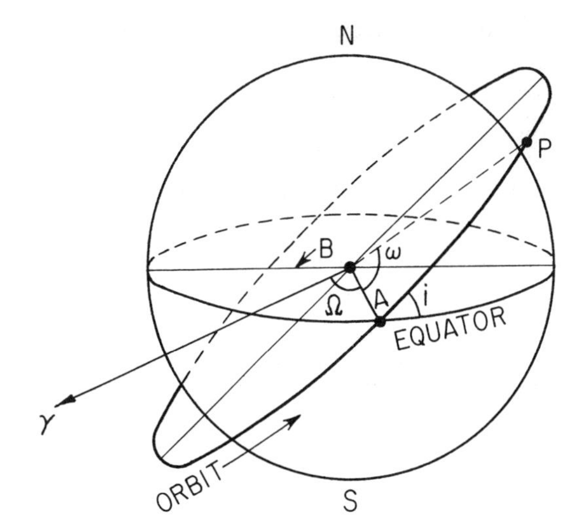

Figure **15·40** *Orbit of a satellite.*

The **longitude of the ascending node** Ω is the angle ♈SB in the illustration. The letter S represents the position of the sun and B is the ascending node. ♈ is the **equinox** or First Point of Aries.

The **direction of the perihelion from the ascending node** ω is represented by the angle PSB. P is the perihelion.

The epoch E is the time that the planet is at a particular position.

When a satellite is orbiting the earth, we employ six elements of the orbit as we do for a planet. In the case of an earth satellite, however, we employ the plane of the earth's equator as the reference plane for **inclination.** This is shown by the angle i in the illustration of Fig. 15·40. Point B in the illustration is the center of the earth. The ascending node is the point at which the satellite crosses the equator moving from south to north and is shown at A in Fig. 15·40. The point P is the **perigee** (the nearest point of the orbit to the earth). The line B♈ shows the direction of the vernal equinox from the center of the earth, and this line establishes the **right ascension** of the ascending node Ω. As noted previously, the ascending node is A. The symbol ω, called "argument perigee," represents the **angle** from the ascending node to perigee and is shown as PBA in Fig. 15·40. The **time** T is the time that the satellite passes through perigee.

The eccentricity is determined as shown in Fig. 15·38 except that the earth is at the position shown for the sun. The **semimajor axis** is one-half the major axis and is also the **mean distance** of the satellite from the center of the earth.

Transfer orbits

In our program to explore the planets by means of space ships we shall most likely utilize a **transfer orbit.** This will require the establishment of an

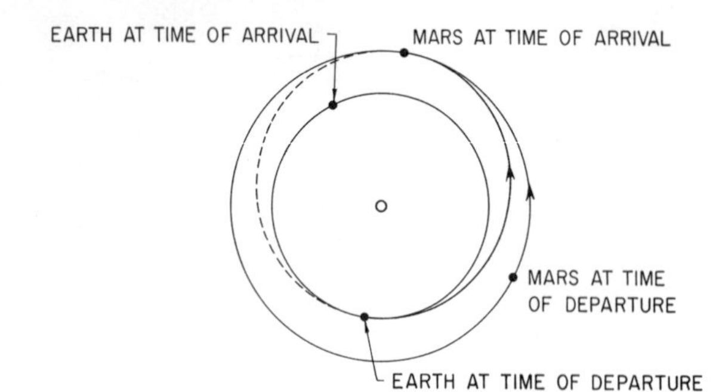

Figure **15·41** *Use of transfer orbit for flight to Mars.*

orbit for the space ship which will intersect both the orbit of the earth and the orbit of the planet which we wish to explore. This method is illustrated in Fig. 15·41 for a flight from earth to Mars.

In the transfer-orbit method we take advantage of the earth's orbital velocity and its surface velocity. This gives the space ship a speed of approximately 68,000 mph even before it is carried away from the earth by the rocket. The total velocity of the space ship must be such that it will establish an orbit around the sun as shown in the illustration. The eccentricity of the orbit must be such that it will intersect the orbit of the planet which we wish to visit at a time when the planet is in that position. On the return trip the ship must be timed and directed in a manner which will enable it to drop back into the orbit of the earth at a time and location which will enable it to reenter the earth's gravitational field.

REVIEW QUESTIONS

1. What peoples in ancient times were most active in the study of astronomy?
2. What early astronomer published the most nearly correct theory of the solar system?
3. Name other great astronomers who contributed to our present knowledge of the universe.
4. What phenomena led to the discoveries of the planets Uranus, Neptune, and Pluto?
5. Compare the distance to the sun with the distance to the nearest star.
6. How is the distance to the moon determined?
7. What is meant by *aphelion* and *perihelion?*
8. Explain the *parsec* and the *astronomical unit.*
9. How many miles are equal to one *light-year?*
10. Name the planets and give their distances from the sun in astronomical units.
11. Give a brief description of the sun.
12. How is the heat of the sun transmitted to earth?
13. How does the sun cause interference with radio signals?
14. Compare the polar diameter of the earth with the equatorial diameter.
15. Explain the following terms: *celestial equator, ecliptic, vernal equinox, zero hour circle, declination, right ascension.*
16. Describe the orbit of the earth.
17. What is meant by *summer solstice* and *winter solstice?*
18. Explain Arctic Circle, Tropic of Cancer, and Tropic of Capricorn.
19. Compare *sidereal* time and *solar* time.
20. Describe the atmosphere of the earth.
21. Give a brief description of the planet Mercury, and tell why it is doubtful that life exists there.
22. Compare the planet Venus with the earth.
23. Why do we believe that a substantial atmosphere exists on Venus?
24. Explain the phases of the moon.
25. Give the size and density of the moon.
26. In computing the orbit of a satellite around the earth, what consideration must be given the effect of the moon?
27. Explain the eclipses of the sun and the moon.
28. Why do we believe that life could exist on Mars?
29. What is the approximate distance to Mars at its nearest approach to the earth?
30. In what general area are the orbits of the asteroids located?
31. Give a brief description of the planet Jupiter.
32. Compare the planet Saturn with Jupiter.
33. In what ways are Uranus and Neptune similar?
34. What is unusual about the orbit of the planet Pluto?
35. Discuss the nature of the comets.
36. What is the difference between a meteor and a meteorite?
37. Compare the size of the earth with that of a giant star.
38. Discuss the constellations and how they acquired their names.
39. Give the approximate range of surface temperatures for the stars.
40. What have astronomers discovered concerning the density of the supergiant stars?
41. Explain *magnitude* with respect to the stars.
42. What is meant by *absolute magnitude?*
43. What are the *binary* stars?
44. Describe our *galaxy.*
45. What is the nature of a *nebula?*
46. How can astronomers determine interstellar distances?
47. Explain the operation of a spectroscope.
48. What is the significance of *Fraunhofer lines?*
49. State Kepler's three laws of planetary motion.
50. Name and explain the elements of an orbit.
51. What is the purpose of a transfer orbit?

Glossary

absolute altimeter: An altimeter designed to give accurate indications of absolute altitude.

absolute altitude: Actual altitude above the surface of the earth, either land or water. Also terrain clearance.

adiabatic: Denotes change in volume or pressure without gain or loss of heat.

aerodynamics: The science relating to the effects of air or other gases in motion.

aerostat: An aircraft that obtains all or most of its lift by virtue of a confined air or gas lighter than the surrounding air. A balloon or dirigible.

airscrew: A propeller.

airworthiness: The state or quality of an aircraft or of an aircraft component such that it will perform safely according to specifications.

alloy: A solid solution consisting of two or more metallic constituents. The alloy usually contains one predominant metal to which are added small amounts of other metals to improve strength and heat resistance.

alloy steel: A steel which contains metallic elements other than those found in carbon steels.

ambient: Surrounding. Ambient conditions are those conditions existing in the surrounding area.

amphibian: A fixed-wing or rotary-wing aircraft designed or equipped to take off from and alight upon both land and water.

aneroid: A thin, disk-shaped box or capsule, usually metallic, which is partially evacuated of air and sealed and which expands or contracts with changes in the pressure of the surrounding air or gas.

autogyro: A rotary-wing aircraft whose rotor is turned throughout its flight by air forces resulting from the motion of the craft through the air.

azimuth: Horizontal direction or bearing, measured in degrees from a zero reference point such as north.

balancing tab: A tab so linked that, when the control surface to which it is attached is deflected, the tab is deflected in an opposite direction, thus creating a force which aids in moving the larger surface.

bearing: The horizontal direction of an object or point, usually measured clockwise from a reference line or direction through 360°.

brake horsepower: The power produced by an engine and available for work through the propeller shaft. It is usually measured as a force on a brake drum or equivalent device and is abbreviated bhp.

bulkhead: A wall, partition, or similar member or structure in an airplane or missile fuselage at right angles to the longitudinal axis of the body and serving to strengthen, divide, or help give shape to the body.

cabane: A pyramidal arrangement of struts used to support a wing above the fuselage of an airplane or to provide a point of attachment for the inner ends of half axles in some types of landing gear.

calibrated airspeed: An airspeed value derived when corrections have been applied to an indicated airspeed to compensate for installation errors, instrument errors, errors in the pitot-static system, and aircraft attitude errors.

canard: An aircraft or aircraft configuration having its horizontal stabilizing and control surfaces in front of the wing or wings.

cantilever: A beam or member supported at or near one end only, without external bracing.

compressibility burble: A region of disturbed flow produced by and aft of a shock wave.

compression rib: A rib, more strongly built than others, designed to resist compression forces.

console: A control panel, pedestal, or stand in an airplane or test cell. It is so named because it has some resemblance to the console of an organ.

declination: The angular distance of a body from the celestial equator, measured along the hour circle passing through the body and named **north** or **south** according to the direction of the body from the celestial equator.

demand oxygen system: A system in which oxygen is supplied in proportion to demand during inhalation, the regulator being operated by pressure changes occurring during the breathing cycle.

density: The weight per unit volume of any substance.

density altitude: Pressure altitude corrected for free air temperature.

deviation: The deflection of a compass needle or indicator from magnetic north as a result of local magnetic conditions in the aircraft.

drift: The lateral divergence or movement of the flight path of a flying vehicle from the direction of its heading, measured between the heading and track, usually caused by a crosswind.

eddy: A region of undirected or swirling flow, as in the flow of air about or behind a body; a vortex.

effective span: The span of an airfoil less corrections for tip loss.

elevon: A control surface that functions both as an elevator and an aileron.

empennage: The assembly of stabilizing and control surfaces at the tail of an aircraft.

equivalent airspeed: A calibrated airspeed corrected for the effect of compression of air in the pitot system.

fairing: A part of structure having a smooth, streamlined outline, used to cover a nonstreamlined object or to smooth a junction.

fatigue strength: The measured resistance of a body to failure caused by repeated applications of stress.

ferrous: The term describing metal which is derived from an iron base.

flutter: A vibration or oscillation of definite period set up in an aileron, wing, or other surface by aerodynamic forces and maintained by the aerodynamic forces and by the elastic and inertial forces of the object itself.

gantry: A frame structure mounted on side supports to span a vehicle, usually traveling on rails, used for erecting and servicing large, vertically launched missiles or spacecraft.

g **force:** An accelerating force.

ground speed: The speed of an aircraft relative to the earth's surface.

gust: A sudden and brief change of wind speed or direction.

heading: The horizontal direction in which a craft points as it flies through the air, usually expressed as an angle measured clockwise from north to the longitudinal axis of the craft.

heat sink: In thermodynamic theory, a means by which heat is stored or dissipated in or transferred from the system under consideration. The thick metal shield on the nose cone of a rocket is often designed as a heat sink to absorb heat generated by air friction.

hypersonic flow: Flow at very high supersonic speed.

ideal angle of attack: The angle of attack of an airfoil at which the airflow meets the leading edge smoothly, resulting in a zero pressure differential across the leading edge.

IFR: The abbreviation of instrument flight rules. An airplane flying IFR is flying according to instrument flight rules.

ILS: The abbreviation for instrument landing system.

impact pressure: That pressure of a moving fluid brought to rest which is in excess of the pressure the fluid possesses when it does not flow. Also, it is the **dynamic pressure** at lower flow speeds.

impact tube: An open-ended tube pointing into a stream of fluid to sense the impact pressure. The pitot tube in an airspeed system is an impact tube.

indicated airspeed: The airspeed measurement shown by an airspeed indicator.

induced drag: That part of the drag of an airfoil caused by the lift, that is, the change in the direction of the airflow.

installation error: An error in a pitot-static system due to the location of the responsive element with respect to other aircraft components, thus affecting the measurements of the pitot-static instruments.

interference drag: Drag due to the interference of the airflow around aircraft components close to one another.

jet aircraft: Aircraft powered by one or more air-breathing jet engines.

jet engine: Any engine that ejects a jet or stream of gas or fluid, obtaining all or most of its thrust by reaction to the ejection.

jet stream: A strong, narrow band of wind or winds in the upper troposphere or stratosphere, moving in a general direction from west to east and often reaching velocities of hundreds of miles per hour.

keel: A longitudinal member or ridge along the center bottom of a seaplane float or hull.

knot: A rate of speed equivalent to 1 nautical mile (6,076.1033 ft) per hour.

lapse rate: The rate of change of temperature, pressure, or some other meteorological phenomenon with altitude, usually the rate of decrease of temperature with increased height.

lateral stability: The tendency of an aircraft to resist rolling.

load factor: A factor representing the ratio of some specified load to a basic load.

longitudinal stability: The stability of an aircraft with respect to pitching motions.

lox: A short term for liquid oxygen.

magnetic bearing: The bearing measured relative to magnetic north.

magnetic heading: The heading measured relative to magnetic north.

manometer: A gage for measuring the pressure of gases or vapors, having a sensing device consisting of a column of liquid in a glass tube.

mass: The quantity of matter in a body as measured in its relation to inertia.

mass ratio: The ratio of the mass of the propellant charge of a rocket to the total mass of the rocket charged with the propellant.

mesosphere: A sphere or layer of the atmosphere between the top of the stratosphere or the ionosphere and the exosphere (about 250 to 600 miles above the earth).

negative dihedral: A downward inclination of a wing or other surface.

negative *g:* A force acting upon a body undergoing negative acceleration. A reversal of gravitational force.

orbit: The path taken by a vehicle around a point or object, as by a satellite around the earth or a planet around the sun.

parasite drag: All the drag forces acting on an aircraft that are not generated in the production of lift.

positive *g:* A force acting on a body undergoing positive acceleration.

power loading: The ratio of the gross weight of an airplane to its power.

pressure altitude: Altitude above standard sea level (29.92 in. Hg) measured with a barometric altimeter.

ram: The action of air or other fluid shoving its way into an intake or open duct owing to the motion of the intake or duct through the fluid.

ram effect: The pressure resulting from ram.

rate gyroscope: A gyroscope sensitive to the rate of angular motion.

reaction propulsion: Propulsion by reaction to a jet or jets ejected from one or more reaction engines.

rotary-wing aircraft: A type of aircraft which is supported in the air wholly or in part by wings or blades rotating about a substantially vertical axis.

SAE number: Any of a series of numbers established as standard by the Society of Automotive Engineers for grading materials, components, and other products.

sandwich construction: A type of construction in which two sheets, sides, or plates are separated by a core of stiffening material, such as honeycomb or balsa wood.

stabilator: A horizontal all-movable tail surface.

stability: The property of an aircraft or other body to resist displacement and, if displaced, to develop forces which will tend to restore the original condition (straight and level flight).

stress raiser: A scratch, groove, rivet hole, forging defect, or other structural discontinuity causing concentration of stress.

tandem airplane: An airplane with two or more cockpits or seats, one behind the other.

thermal: A rising current of warm air.

torquemeter: A meter for measuring torque, as in the shaft of an aircraft engine.

torque nose: A mechanism or apparatus at the nose section of an engine that senses the engine torque and activates a torquemeter.

transonic speed: The speed of a body relative to the surrounding fluid at which the flow is in some places subsonic and in other places supersonic; usually from Mach 0.8 to 1.2.

troposphere: The lowest layer of the earth's atmosphere, characterized by relatively steady temperature lapse rate, varying humidity, and turbulence.

vertical-speed indicator: A rate-of-climb indicator.

vertical stabilizer: A vertical airfoil fixed approximately parallel to the plane of symmetry of an airplane; also called the fin.

VFR: Abbreviation for visual flight rules.

VTOL: Abbreviation for **vertical takeoff and landing.**

washin: A permanent warp or twist given a wing such that some specified angle of attack is greater at the tip than at the root.

washout: The opposite of washin, that is, tip angle less than root angle.

yaw: The movement of an aircraft about the vertical axis.

zero-lift angle of attack: The angle of attack at which no lift is created.

Appendix

Densities of Liquids

	Density, g per cu cm	Temp., °C
Alcohol	0.81	0
Benzine	0.90	0
Gasoline	0.68–0.72	0
Jet fuel	0.775–0.80	0
Lubricating oil	0.89–0.93	20
Mercury	13.596	0
Sulfuric acid	1.84	
Water (pure)	1.00	4

Densities of Metals

Aluminum	2.7
Brass	8.4
Copper	8.93
Gold	19.3
Iron	7.9
Lead	11.4
Mercury	13.596
Platinum	21.5
Titanium	4.4
Zinc	7.1

To determine the weight of a gallon of a liquid, multiply the density value by 8.35.

To determine the weight of a cubic foot of a metal, multiply the density value by 62.4.

Atmospheric standards

	English	Metric
Gravity	32.17405 ft/sec^2	9.80665 m/sec^2
Absolute zero	−459.688°F	−273.16°C
Standard values at sea level:		
Pressure	29.92 in. Hg	766 mm Hg
Pressure	2,116 lb/ft^2	10,332 kg/m^2
Temperature	59°F	15°C
Specific weight	0.07651 lb/ft^3	1.2255 kg/m^3
Density	0.0023769 slug/ft^3	

Greek alphabet

Name	Capital	Lower case	Use
Alpha	A	α	Angles
Beta	B	β	
Gamma	Γ	γ	Ratio of specific heats
Delta	Δ	δ	Relative absolute pressure
Epsilon	E	ϵ	Expansion ratio, surface emissivity
Zeta	Z	ζ	
Eta	H	η	Coefficient of kinematic viscosity, efficiency
Theta	Θ	θ	
Iota	I	ι	
Kappa	K	κ	
Lambda	Λ	λ	Capital, wing sweep angle; lower case, taper rate, wavelength
Mu	M	μ	Absolute viscosity
Nu	N	ν	
Xi	Ξ	ξ	
Omicron	O	o	
Pi	Π	π	Ratio of circumference to diameter (3.1416)
Rho	P	ρ	Mass density
Sigma	Σ	σ	Capital, sign of summation; lower case, relative density
Tau	T	τ	
Upsilon	Υ	υ	Kinematic viscosity
Phi	Φ	ϕ	Capital, relative viscosity; lower case, phase
Chi	X	χ	
Psi	Ψ	ψ	
Omega	Ω	ω	Capital, ohms; lower case, specific weight

Conversion table

Multiply	*By*	*To obtain*
atmospheres	76.0	centimeters Hg
atmospheres	29.9212	inches Hg
atmospheres	33.8985	feet H_2O
atmospheres	10,332.276	kilograms per square meter
atmospheres	14.69601	pounds per square inch
atmospheres	2,116.225	pounds per square foot
atmospheres	1.0133	bars
centimeters	0.393700	inches
centimeters	0.0328083	feet
centimeters Hg	5.352391	inches H_2O
centimeters Hg	0.4460326	feet H_2O
centimeters Hg	0.193368	pounds per square inch
centimeters Hg	27.84507	pounds per square foot
centimeters Hg	135.9510	kilograms per square meter
centimeters per second	0.0328083	feet per second
cubic centimeters	0.00099973	liters
cubic centimeters	0.06102338	cubic inches
cubic feet	1,728.00	cubic inches
cubic feet	7.480519	gallons
cubic feet	28,317.017	cubic centimeters
cubic feet	28.31625	liters
cubic feet	0.028317017	cubic meters
cubic feet per minute	0.471704	liters per second
cubic feet of water	62.42833	pounds
cubic inches	16.3871624	cubic centimeters
cubic inches	0.0163876	liters
cubic meters	61,023.3753	cubic inches
cubic meters	35.3144548	cubic feet
cubic meters	264.170	gallons
cubic yards	27.0	cubic feet
degrees arc	0.017453292	radians
feet	30.4800613	centimeters
feet H_2O	0.295	atmospheres
feet H_2O	0.433530	pounds per square inch
feet per minute	0.0113636	miles per hour
feet per second	0.681818	miles per hour
feet per second	0.5920858	knots
foot-pounds	0.138255	meter-kilograms
foot-pounds per minute	1/33,000	horsepower
foot-pounds per second	1/550	horsepower
gallons	231.0	cubic inches
gallons	0.13368	cubic feet
gallons	3.785332	liters
gallons	0.83268	imperial gallons
grams	15.43236	grains
grams	0.0352739	ounces
grams	0.002204623	pounds
grams	1,000.0	milligrams
grams	0.001	kilograms
grams	980.665	dynes
grams-calories	0.0039685	Btu
grams per centimeter	0.1	kilograms per meter
grams per centimeter	0.0055914	pounds per inch
grams per cubic centimeter	62.42833	pounds per cubic foot
horsepower	33,000.0	foot-pounds per minute
horsepower	1.013872	metric horsepower
horsepower, metric	75.0	kilogram-meters per second

Conversion table (Cont.)

Multiply	*By*	*To obtain*
horsepower-hour	2,545.06	Btu
horsepower-hour	1,980,000.0	foot-pounds
inches	2.54000508	centimeters
inches Hg	0.0334211	atmospheres
inches Hg	13.5951	inches H_2O
inches Hg	0.491157	pounds per square inch
inches H_2O	0.0735559	inches Hg
inches H_2O	0.1868324	centimeter Hg
inches H_2O	0.0361275	pounds per square inch
kilograms	2.20462234	pounds
kilograms	35.273957	ounces
kilograms	1,000.0	grams
kilogram-meters	7.2329983	foot-pounds
kilogram-meters	9.80665×10^7	ergs
kilograms per square meter	0.00142234	pounds per square inch
kilometers	0.62137	miles
kilometers	0.539553	nautical miles
kilometers per hour	0.9113426	feet per second
kilometers per hour	0.6213700	miles per hour
knots	1.0	nautical miles per hour
knots	1.151553	miles per hour
liters	1,000.027	cubic centimeters
liters	61.02503	cubic inches
liters	0.264178	gallons
meters	39.37	inches
meters	3.280833	feet
meters	1.093611	yards
meters per second	3.600	kilometers per hour
miles	5,280.0	feet
miles	1.609347	kilometers
miles	0.8683925	nautical miles
miles per hour	1.46666	feet per second
miles per hour	0.8683925	knots
ounces	1/16	pounds
ounces	28.349527	grams
ounces	437.5	grains
pounds	453.5924277	grams
pounds	16.0	ounces
pounds	42.174	poundals
pounds per cubic foot	16.018369	kilograms per cubic meter
pounds per cubic inch	1,728.0	pounds per cubic foot
pounds per square inch	2.036009	inches Hg
pounds per square inch	0.0680457	atmospheres
radians	57.29578	degrees arc
radians per second	0.159155	revolutions per second
radians per second	9.84930	revolutions per minute
revolutions	6.283185	radians
slugs	32.175	pounds
square centimeters	0.1549997	square inches
square feet	929.03412	square centimeters
square inches	645.162581	square millimeters
square meters	1.1959853	square yards
square yards	0.8361307	square meters

Index